AS
LEVEL

CHEMISTRY

FOR CCEA AS LEVEL

COLOURPOINT
EDUCATIONAL

Wingfield Glassey

© 2013 Wingfield Glassey and Colourpoint
   Creative Ltd

ISBN: 978-1-78073-015-8

First Edition
First Impression

Layout and design: April Sky Design
Printed by: W&G Baird Ltd, Antrim

Colourpoint Educational
An imprint of Colourpoint Creative Ltd
Colourpoint House
Jubilee Business Park
Jubilee Road
Newtownards
County Down
Northern Ireland
BT23 4YH

Tel: 028 9182 6339
Fax: 028 9182 1900
E-mail: info@colourpoint.co.uk
Web site: www.colourpoint.co.uk

The Author

Dr. Wingfield Glassey teaches Chemistry at Friends' School
Lisburn, and is an examiner for GCE AS and A2 Chemistry.
Dr. Glassey also maintains a professional interest in the
teaching and learning of science, and has published
scholarly articles in a number of peer-reviewed journals
including *The Journal of Chemical Education*.

Copyright

This material has been endorsed by CCEA.

CCEA endorsement does not mean that this material is essential to
achieve any CCEA qualification, nor does it mean that this is the only
suitable material available to support any CCEA qualification. While
this material has been through a CCEA quality assurance process, all
responsibility for the content remains with the publisher. Copies of
specifications for all CCEA qualifications may be found on the CCEA
website – www.ccea.org.uk

Approved/endorsed by CCEA on 1 November 2013. If in any doubt
about the continuing currency of CCEA endorsement, please contact
CCEA.

Publisher's Note: This book has been through a rigorous quality
assurance process by an independent person experienced in the
CCEA specification prior to publication. It has been written to help
students preparing for the AS Chemistry specification from CCEA.
While Colourpoint Educational, the author and the quality assurance
person have taken every care in its production, we are not able to
guarantee that the book is completely error-free. Additionally, while
the book has been written to closely match the CCEA specification,
it is the responsibility of each candidate to satisfy themselves that
they have fully met the requirements of the CCEA specification prior
to sitting an exam set by that body. For this reason, and because
specifications change with time, we strongly advise every candidate
to avail of a qualified teacher and to check the contents of the most
recent specification for themselves prior to the exam. Colourpoint
Creative Ltd therefore cannot be held responsible for any errors or
omissions in this book or any consequences thereof.

CONTENTS

Unit AS1: Basic Concepts in Physical and Inorganic Chemistry

Unit AS2: Further Physical and Inorganic Chemistry and Introduction to Organic Chemistry

Unit AS3: Practical Assessment

Unit AS 1:

Basic Concepts in Physical and Inorganic Chemistry

1.1 Formulas, Equations and Amounts of Substance

CONNECTIONS
- All matter is made from around 100 elements.
- Almost all life on earth is based on the element carbon.
- Hydrogen is the most abundant element in the universe.

Elements and Compounds

In this section we are learning to:

- Use the terms element and compound to classify pure substances.
- Recall examples of elements with metallic, molecular and giant structures.
- Distinguish between ionic compounds and nonmetal compounds.
- Recall examples of compounds with ionic, molecular and giant structures.
- Describe the structure of an ionic compound.
- Use the terms atom, molecule, monatomic and diatomic to describe the structure of molecular materials.
- Recall the effect of molecular size on the melting and boiling points of molecular materials.

Plastics, medicines and the other materials in the world around us are made of matter. The matter within any material is a combination of elements and compounds. An element is the simplest type of pure substance. A compound is also a pure substance and contains two or more elements bonded together. Water and carbon dioxide are examples of compounds. Water is a compound of the elements hydrogen and oxygen, and carbon dioxide is a compound of the elements carbon and oxygen.

A mixture contains a combination of compounds and elements. Crude oil, paint and air are all mixtures. Approximately 99% of air is made up of the elements nitrogen and oxygen. The remaining 1% is principally a mixture of water vapour, carbon dioxide and the element argon. The relationship between elements, compounds and mixtures is summarised in Figure 1.

Elements

There are approximately 100 elements. The properties of one element can be quite different to those of

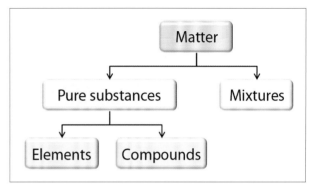

Figure 1: The relationship between elements, compounds and mixtures.

another. Relationships between the properties and behaviour of different elements are best understood by constructing a Periodic Table. The form of the modern Periodic Table is shown in Figure 2. In the modern Periodic Table each element is represented by a chemical symbol and is assigned an atomic number. The atomic number of the elements increases from left to right across each row and down each column. When arranged in this way the properties of the elements are similar within each group (column), and vary in a predictable way from left to right across each period (row). For example, the distribution of metals and nonmetals in Figure 2 suggests that the elements behave less like metals and more like nonmetals from left to right across a period, and towards the top of each group.

Metals and nonmetals have very different properties. This results from differences in the arrangement of matter within each element. If we start by defining an **atom** to be the smallest amount of an element, we can define an **element** to be a substance that contains only one type of atom. The atoms in a metal such as iron or silver are tightly packed together in an ordered arrangement. The resulting metallic structure is shown in Figure 3a. In contrast the atoms in nonmetals bond together to form molecules as in oxygen (Figure 3b), or to create

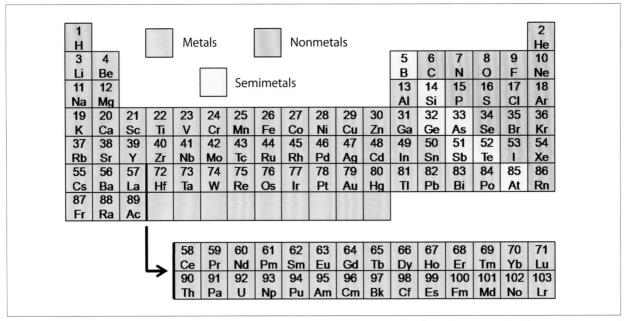

Figure 2: Classification of the elements as metals, nonmetals and semimetals. The term semimetal refers to elements that have properties in common with metals and nonmetals.

giant structures such as the network of carbon atoms in diamond (Figure 3c).

The term **molecule** is used when referring to two or more atoms bonded together to form a single uncharged particle. Substances that are made of molecules are referred to as **molecular materials**. The elements oxygen and nitrogen are both molecular materials. They are also examples of **diatomic elements** as the molecules in oxygen and nitrogen each contain two atoms. Molecules containing two atoms are referred to as **diatomic molecules**.

Substances with giant structures such as diamond (Figure 3c) are held together by strong bonds between the atoms. As a result, they have high melting points and are solids under normal conditions. Graphite – the major component in pencil 'lead' – is a different form of carbon that also contains a network of carbon

atoms. Like diamond, graphite has a high melting point and is a solid under normal conditions. Diamond and graphite are examples of allotropes where the term **allotrope** is used to refer to different physical forms of the same element.

In contrast, molecular materials may be solids, liquids or gases under normal laboratory conditions. Elements containing heavier atoms such as bromine and iodine are more likely to be liquids or solids. For example, under normal laboratory conditions oxygen is a gas, bromine is a liquid and iodine is a solid.

Oxygen, bromine and iodine are diatomic elements. Elements containing larger molecules are even more likely to be liquids or solids. Rhombic sulfur and white phosphorus are examples of allotropes containing large molecules. Both are solids. Molecules of rhombic sulfur and white phosphorus are shown in Figure 4.

(a) Atoms in iron
Formula: Fe

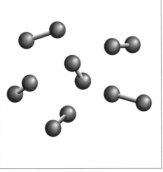

(b) Oxygen molecules
Formula: O_2

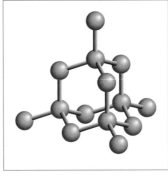

(c) Atoms in diamond
Formula: C

Figure 3: The arrangement of (a) atoms in iron, (b) molecules in oxygen gas and (c) carbon atoms in diamond.

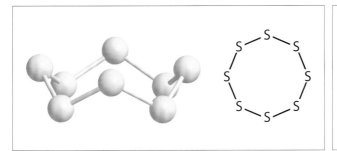

Figure 4: A molecule of (a) rhombic sulfur and (b) white phosphorus.

(a) Sulfur molecule
Formula: S_8

(b) Phosphorus molecule
Formula: P_4

The relationship between the size of the molecules in a substance and its melting point is further illustrated by the elements in Group VIII; a group of unreactive gases known as the noble gases. The noble gases are examples of **monatomic elements**. A substance is described as monatomic if the particles in the substance each contain a single atom. The fact that heavy noble gases such as krypton (Kr) and xenon (Xe) are gases, while much lighter elements such as sulfur are solids, demonstrates that the melting point of a molecular material is determined by the size of the molecules in the material.

Exercise 1.1A

Which of the following elements is (a) diatomic, (b) a gas and (c) a solid?

nitrogen, bromine, silver, sulfur, iodine

Before moving to the next section, check that you are able to:
• Use the terms atom, molecule, monatomic and diatomic to describe elements.
• Recall examples of elements with metallic, molecular and giant structures.
• Recall the effect of molecular size on melting and boiling point.

Compounds

The term **compound** refers to a pure substance that contains two or more elements bonded together. A compound cannot be easily separated into its constituent elements. Water, carbon dioxide and sodium chloride (table salt) are all examples of compounds.

The compounds formed when metals combine with nonmetals are known as **ionic compounds** and are very different to the compounds formed when nonmetals combine. For example, sodium chloride is an ionic compound formed by the reaction between sodium metal (Na) and the nonmetal chlorine (Cl). Ionic compounds such as sodium chloride contain ions packed tightly together in a regular pattern known as a lattice. The lattice in sodium chloride is held together by attractive forces between sodium (Na^+) ions and chloride (Cl^-) ions. The packing of the ions in the sodium chloride lattice is shown in Figure 5a.

Ionic compounds are solids. The ions in an ionic compound break apart when the solid dissolves or melts. In contrast, many nonmetal compounds such as water and carbon dioxide are made of molecules that remain intact when the compound dissolves or changes state. As was the case for elements, compounds containing small molecules such as hydrogen chloride,

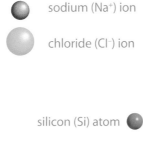

sodium (Na^+) ion

chloride (Cl^-) ion

silicon (Si) atom

oxygen (O) atom

(a) Sodium chloride

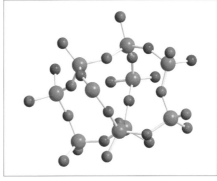

(b) Quartz

Figure 5: The structure of (a) sodium chloride and (b) quartz.

HCl and sulfur dioxide, SO_2 are gases. Compounds made of larger molecules such as phosphorus(III) chloride, PCl_3 and dichloromethane, CH_2Cl_2 are liquids, and compounds containing even larger molecules such as phosphorus(V) chloride, PCl_5 and phosphorus(V) oxide, P_4O_{10} are solids.

Many nonmetal compounds such as the mineral quartz – an allotrope of silicon dioxide, SiO_2 – have a giant structure held together by strong bonds between the atoms. The structure of quartz is shown in Figure 5b. The strong bonding between atoms in giant structures such as quartz does not break easily and explains why substances with a giant structure have very high melting points and tend to be insoluble in water and other solvents.

Exercise 1.1B

1. Which of the following (a) is an ionic compound, (b) is a molecular material, and (c) has a giant structure.

NO_2	$NaNO_3$	$MgBr_2$
CCl_4	SiO_2	

2. Which one of the following compounds is not molecular?

   a) carbon dioxide, c) hydrogen chloride,

   b) calcium chloride, d) phosphorus trichloride

   (Adapted from CCEA June 2011)

Before moving to the next section, check that you are able to:

• Recall the definition of a compound.

• Distinguish between ionic compounds and nonmetal compounds.

• Describe the structure of an ionic compound.

• Recall examples of compounds with ionic, molecular and giant structures.

Chemical Formulas

In this section we are learning to:

• Use the formula for a substance to deduce its composition and structure.

• Write the formula for ionic compounds and nonmetal compounds, including those containing an element with variable valency.

Interpreting Formulas

The **chemical formula** or 'formula' of a substance describes the amount of each element in the substance. The formula of a substance also represents the smallest amount of the substance that can participate in a chemical reaction. For example, the formula of sodium chloride is NaCl and indicates that there is one sodium (Na^+) ion for every chloride (Cl^-) ion in the compound. Similarly the formula for magnesium chloride, $MgCl_2$ indicates that there are two chloride (Cl^-) ions for every magnesium (Mg^{2+}) ion in the compound.

In molecular materials such as water and carbon dioxide, the formula of the compound describes the number of atoms in each molecule of the substance. For example, the formula of water, H_2O indicates that each molecule of water contains two hydrogen atoms and one oxygen atom. Similarly, the formula for carbon dioxide, CO_2 indicates that each molecule of carbon dioxide contains one carbon atom and two oxygen atoms.

The formula of an element is determined by how the atoms in the element are organised. In a metal such as iron, the atoms are closely packed in an ordered array (Figure 3a) and are indistinguishable from each other. A single metal atom is sufficient to represent any number of metal atoms in the structure. As a result the formula of a metal such as iron (formula: Fe) or gold (formula: Au) is simply the chemical symbol for the element, and represents one atom of the element. Similarly, a single atom is sufficient to represent any number of atoms in monatomic elements such as helium (formula: He) or neon (formula: Ne), and giant structures such as diamond (formula: C) in which the atoms are identical.

In elements with a molecular structure the formula of the element represents the atoms in one molecule of the element. For example, the formula of a diatomic element such as hydrogen (formula: H_2) or chlorine (formula: Cl_2) indicates that the element is made up of diatomic molecules. Similarly, formulas can be used to indicate that the molecules in white phosphorus contain four phosphorus atoms (formula: P_4), and the molecules in rhombic sulfur contain eight sulfur atoms (formula: S_8).

Writing Formulas

The formula of a compound is determined by the **valency** or 'combining power' of the elements in the compound. The valency of many elements can be determined from their location in the Periodic Table. This relationship is illustrated in Figure 6.

When a metal combines with one or more nonmetals to form an ionic compound such as NaCl, the metal loses electrons to form a positive ion and the nonmetal gains electrons to form a negative ion. From Figure 6 we see that sodium (Na) belongs to Group I and has a valency of 1. The valency of sodium tells us that when sodium combines with nonmetals each sodium atom will lose one electron to form a sodium ion (Na^+). Similarly, chlorine belongs to Group VII and has a valency of 1. The valency of chlorine tells us that when chlorine reacts with a metal such as sodium, each chlorine atom will gain one electron to form a chloride ion (Cl^-). In this way, the relationship between the location of an element in the Periodic Table and its valency can be used to deduce the charges on the ions in an ionic compound.

On noting that ionic compounds do not have a charge, we can infer that *the charges on the ions in one formula of an ionic compound must add to zero*. This idea can be used to construct the formula for any ionic compound. For example, magnesium (Mg) belongs to Group II and has a valency of 2. The valency of magnesium tells us that magnesium forms Mg^{2+} ions when it combines with nonmetals to form an ionic compound. We have already seen that chlorine (Group VII) has a valency of 1 and forms chloride (Cl^-) ions when it combines with metals. If the charges on the ions in magnesium chloride add to zero the compound must contain two chloride (Cl^-) ions for each magnesium (Mg^{2+}) ion.

The formula of magnesium chloride:

represents one Mg^{2+} ion and two Cl^- ions

....

Worked Example 1.1i

Write the formula for (a) magnesium oxide, (b) sodium oxide and (c) aluminium bromide.

Strategy

*   Use the valency of each element to calculate the charges on the ions.
*   Find the number of positive and negative ions needed to balance the charge in one formula.

Solution

(a) Magnesium (Group II) has a valency of 2 and forms Mg^{2+} ions. Oxygen (Group VI) has a valency of 2 and forms O^{2-} ions. Magnesium oxide contains one Mg^{2+} ion for every O^{2-} ion. The formula of magnesium oxide is MgO.

(b) Sodium (Group I) has a valency of 1 and forms Na^+ ions. Oxygen (Group VI) has a valency of 2 and forms O^{2-} ions. Sodium oxide contains two Na^+ ions for every O^{2-} ion. The formula of sodium oxide is Na_2O.

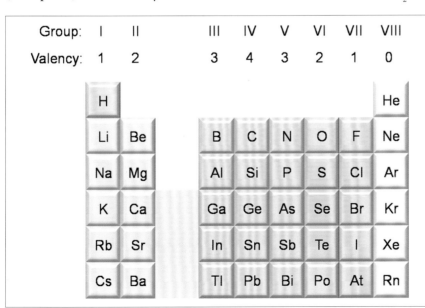

Figure 6: The relationship between the valency of an element and its location in the Periodic Table.

(c) Aluminium (Group III) has a valency of 3 and forms Al^{3+} ions. Bromine (Group VII) has a valency of 1 and forms Br^- ions. Aluminium bromide contains three Br^- ions for every Al^{3+} ion. The formula of aluminium bromide is $AlBr_3$.

Exercise 1.1C

Write the chemical formula for
(a) lithium fluoride, (b) potassium chloride,
(c) magnesium bromide, (d) magnesium sulfide,
and (e) aluminium oxide.

In nonmetal compounds such as carbon dioxide (formula: CO_2) and water (formula: H_2O), the atoms are held together by covalent bonds. The valency of an element tells us how many covalent bonds can be formed by an atom of the element when it combines with other elements to form a compound. For example, carbon belongs to Group IV and has a valency of 4. This tells us that a carbon atom can form up to four covalent bonds when bonding with other nonmetals. When carbon combines with oxygen (Group VI, valency 2) two oxygen atoms (total valency 2+2 = 4) are needed to equal the combining power of one carbon atom (valency 4). As a result, a molecule of carbon dioxide contains two oxygen atoms and one carbon atom.

The formula of carbon dioxide:

represents one carbon atom and two oxygen atoms

one molecule of carbon dioxide

Compounds of Hydrogen

Hydrogen, H is a nonmetal. It has a valency of 1 and combines with metals to form ionic compounds known as metal hydrides. Sodium hydride, NaH and calcium hydride, CaH_2 are examples of metal hydrides. Hydrogen also has a valency of 1 when it combines with nonmetals to form molecular compounds such as water, H_2O and ammonia, NH_3.

Worked Example 1.1ii

Find the formula of the compounds (a) H_xF, (b) H_xS, (c) NH_x and (d) CH_x.

Strategy

- Find the valency of each element.
- Find the value of x needed to balance the combining power of each element.

Solution

(a) Hydrogen (H) and fluorine (F) both have a valency of 1. One hydrogen atom is needed to combine with one fluorine atom. Formula: HF

(b) Hydrogen (H) has a valency of 1 and sulfur (S) has a valency of 2. Two hydrogen atoms are needed to combine with one sulfur atom. Formula: H_2S

(c) Hydrogen (H) has a valency of 1 and nitrogen (N) has a valency of 3. Three hydrogen atoms are needed to combine with one nitrogen atom. Formula: NH_3

(d) Hydrogen (H) has a valency of 1 and carbon (C) has a valency of 4. Four hydrogen atoms are needed to combine with one carbon atom. Formula: CH_4

Elements with Variable Valency

A number of metals and nonmetals have the ability to vary their valency when forming compounds. For example, carbon can combine with oxygen to form carbon monoxide, CO in which the valency of carbon is 2 and carbon dioxide, CO_2 in which carbon has a valency of 4. Similarly iron can combine with chlorine to form iron(II) chloride, $FeCl_2$ in which iron has a valency of 2, and iron(III) chloride, $FeCl_3$ in which the valency of iron is 3.

Worked Example 1.1iii

Write the formula for (a) tin(II) chloride, (b) tin(IV) chloride, (c) copper(II) oxide and (d) copper(I) oxide.

Strategy

- Tin is a 'poor metal' and will behave in a similar way to carbon and other non-metals in Group IV when bonding with other elements.
- The valency of tin and copper in each compound is indicated using roman numerals.

Solution

(a) Tin has a valency of 2 and chlorine has a valency of 1. Two chlorine atoms are needed to equal the combining power of tin. Formula: $SnCl_2$

(b) Tin has a valency of 4 and chlorine has a valency of 1. Four chlorine atoms are needed to equal the combining power of tin. Formula: $SnCl_4$

(c) The ions in copper(II) oxide are copper(II), Cu^{2+} and oxide, O^{2-}. One oxide ion is needed to balance the charge on one copper(II) ion. Formula: CuO

(d) The ions in copper (I) oxide are copper (I), Cu^+ and oxide, O^{2-}. Two copper (I) ions are needed to balance the charge on one oxide ion. Formula: Cu_2O

Exercise 1.1D

1. Write the chemical formula for
   (a) phosphorus(III) bromide, (b) nitrogen(IV) oxide, (c) sulfur(IV) fluoride and
   (d) mercury(II) chloride.

2. Write the chemical formula for (a) sulfur(IV) oxide, (b) phosphorus(V) chloride,
   (c) manganese(IV) oxide and (d) xenon(II) fluoride.

Before moving to the next section, check that you are able to:

- Use formulas to deduce the composition and structure of compounds.
- Determine the valency of an element from its location in the Periodic Table.
- Write the formula for ionic and nonmetal compounds, including those containing an element with variable valency.

Naming Compounds

In this section we are learning to:

- Name ionic compounds, including those containing polyatomic ions.
- Use prefixes to name nonmetal compounds.
- Name ionic and nonmetal compounds, including those containing an element with the ability to vary its valency.

Ionic Compounds

When a metal combines with a nonmetal to form an ionic compound the metal loses electrons to form positively charged ions (**cations**) and the nonmetal gains electrons to form negatively charged ions (**anions**). For example, when sodium reacts with oxygen to form sodium oxide, Na_2O each atom of sodium forms a sodium cation, Na^+ and each oxygen gains electrons to form an oxide anion, O^{2-}. Ionic compounds are named by following the name of the cation with the name of the anion. In the case of sodium oxide, Na_2O the name indicates that the compound contains sodium cations and oxide anions.

Sodium oxide, Na_2O contains

sodium cations and oxide anions

The names and formulas of common cations and anions are summarised in Table 1. Cations and anions such as ammonium (NH_4^+), carbonate (CO_3^{2-}) and sulfate (SO_4^{2-}) are listed separately as **polyatomic ions** as they contain more than one atom. The atoms in a polyatomic ion are held together by strong bonds between the atoms and will remain bonded together when the compound containing the polyatomic ion melts, reacts, or dissolves to form a solution.

Worked Example 1.1iv

Name the following ionic compounds.
a) Na_2S b) $MgBr_2$ c) Na_2CO_3 d) KNO_3
e) $(NH_4)_2CO_3$

Strategy

- Use the formula to identify the cations and anions in each compound.
- Use the names of the cation and anion to name the compound.

Solution

(a) Na_2S contains sodium cations (Na^+) and sulfide (S^{2-}) anions. Na_2S is the formula for sodium sulfide.

(b) $MgBr_2$ contains magnesium cations (Mg^{2+}) and bromide (Br^-) anions. $MgBr_2$ is the formula for magnesium bromide.

(c) Na_2CO_3 contains sodium cations (Na^+) and carbonate (CO_3^{2-}) anions. Na_2CO_3 is the formula for sodium carbonate.

(d) KNO_3 contains potassium cations (K^+) and nitrate (NO_3^-) anions. KNO_3 is the formula for potassium nitrate.

(e) $(NH_4)_2CO_3$ contains ammonium (NH_4^+) cations and carbonate (CO_3^{2-}) anions. $(NH_4)_2CO_3$ is the formula for ammonium carbonate.

Exercise 1.1E

1. Name the following ionic compounds.

   a) $CaCl_2$ b) Al_2O_3 c) $AgBr$ d) LiH e) ZnS

2. Name the following ionic compounds.

   a) $ZnCO_3$ b) $ZnSO_4$ c) $Mg(NO_3)_2$

   d) Mg_3N_2 e) $KMnO_4$

3. Name the following ionic compounds.

   a) $AgNO_3$ b) NH_4NO_3 c) $NaNO_2$

   d) $Al_2(SO_4)_3$ e) Na_2SO_3

4. Name the following ionic compounds.

   a) Na_2O b) Na_2O_2 c) $Ca(HCO_3)_2$ d) $NaClO$

   e) K_2CrO_4

Nonmetal Compounds

When naming nonmetal compounds the amount of each element in the compound can be described by using a prefix such as di- or tri-. For instance, the prefixes tri- and penta- could be used to distinguish phosphorus trichloride, PCl_3 from phosphorus pentachloride, PCl_5. Similarly the prefixes mon- di- and tri- could be used to distinguish carbon monoxide, CO from carbon dioxide, CO_2 and sulfur dioxide, SO_2 from sulfur trioxide, SO_3. The use of prefixes is further illustrated by the following examples.

Example	Element ratio	Prefix
carbon monoxide, CO	1:1	mon-
carbon dioxide, CO_2	1:2	di-
boron trifluoride, BF_3	1:3	tri-
carbon tetrachloride, CCl_4	1:4	tetra-
phosphorus pentachloride, PCl_5	1:5	penta-
sulfur hexafluoride, SF_6	1:6	hexa-

Worked Example 1.1v

Use prefixes to name the following compounds of nitrogen. a) NO b) NO_2 c) N_2O d) N_2O_4

Strategy

• If there is more than one atom of the first element, include a prefix for every element in the formula.

Solution

(a) NO contains one oxygen atom (prefix: mon-) for every nitrogen atom. The compound NO is called nitrogen monoxide.

(b) NO_2 contains two oxygen atoms (prefix: di-) for every nitrogen atom. The compound NO_2 is called nitrogen dioxide.

(c) N_2O contains two nitrogen atoms (prefix: di-) for

Table 1: Common cations and anions

Cations	Anions	Polyatomic Ions
Hydrogen, H^+	Hydride, H^-	*Cations:*
Group I:	*Group V:*	Ammonium, NH_4^+
Lithium, Li^+	Nitride, N^{3-}	*Anions:*
Sodium, Na^+		Peroxide, O_2^{2-}
Potassium, K^+	*Group VI:*	Nitrate, NO_3^-
Group II:	Oxide, O^{2-}	Nitrite, NO_2^-
Magnesium, Mg^{2+}	Sulfide, S^{2-}	Sulfate, SO_4^{2-}
Calcium, Ca^{2+}		Sulfite, SO_3^{2-}
Barium, Ba^{2+}	*Group VII:*	Carbonate, CO_3^{2-}
Other metals:	Fluoride, F^-	Hydrogencarbonate, HCO_3^-
Aluminium, Al^{3+}	Chloride, Cl^-	Phosphate, PO_4^{3-}
Copper(II), Cu^{2+}	Bromide, Br^-	Hypochlorite, ClO^-
Iron(II), Fe^{2+}	Iodide, I^-	*Anions containing metals:*
Iron(III), Fe^{3+}		Chromate, CrO_4^{2-}
Zinc, Zn^{2+}		Dichromate, $Cr_2O_7^{2-}$
Silver, Ag^+		Permanganate, MnO_4^-

every oxygen (prefix: mon-). The compound N_2O is called dinitrogen monoxide.

(d) N_2O_4 contains four oxygen atoms (prefix: tetra-) for every two nitrogen atoms (prefix: di-). The compound N_2O_4 is called dinitrogen tetroxide.

Note: The 'a' at the end of the prefix is removed to avoid the combination of vowels 'ao' in tetraoxide.

Exercise 1.1F

1. Use prefixes to name the following compounds.

   a) SF_4 b) SO_3 c) $SiCl_4$ d) PBr_3 e) XeF_4

> **Before moving to the next section, check that you are able to:**
>
> • Identify the ions in an ionic compound, including those containing polyatomic ions, and use the names of the ions to name the compound.
> • Use prefixes to name nonmetal compounds.

Elements with Variable Valency

When naming an ionic compound containing an element that has the ability to vary its valency, the valency of the element is included in the name. For example, the name iron chloride is not sufficient to distinguish between the compounds iron(II) chloride, $FeCl_2$ and iron(III) chloride, $FeCl_3$. A number of cations formed by metals with the ability to vary their valency are included in Table 1.

Worked Example 1.1vi

Name the following compounds of iron.
a) FeS   b) $FeSO_4$ c) $Fe(NO_3)_3$ d) Fe_2O_3

Strategy

• Identify the anion.
• Use the charge on the anion to calculate the valency of iron.

Solution

(a) The compound FeS contains one sulfide (S^{2-}) anion for every iron cation. The cation must have a valency of two (Fe^{2+}) if the charges on the ions in the formula are to add to zero. The compound FeS is iron(II) sulfide.

(b) The compound $FeSO_4$ contains one iron cation for every sulfate (SO_4^{2-}) anion. The iron cation must

have a valency of two (Fe^{2+}) if the charge on the ions is to add to zero. The compound $FeSO_4$ is iron(II) sulfate.

(c) The compound $Fe(NO_3)_3$ contains three nitrate (NO_3^-) anions for every iron cation. The cation must have a valency of three (Fe^{3+}) if the charges on the ions are to add to zero. The compound $Fe(NO_3)_3$ is iron(III) nitrate.

(d) The compound Fe_2O_3 contains three oxide (O^{2-}) anions for every two iron cations. The cations must each have a valency of three (Fe^{3+}) if the charges on the ions are to add to zero. The compound Fe_2O_3 is iron(III) oxide.

Exercise 1.1G

Name the following ionic compounds.

   a) CuO   b) $CuSO_4$ c) Cu_2O d) $CuCl_2$
   e) $HgCl_2$ f) Hg_2Cl_2

A similar approach can be used when naming nonmetal compounds containing elements with the ability to vary their valency. For example, the name phosphorus chloride does not distinguish between phosphorus(III) chloride, PCl_3 and phosphorus(V) chloride, PCl_5 and it becomes necessary to specify the valency of phosphorus, or alternatively use a naming prefix, when naming the compounds.

Worked Example 1.1vii

The elements sulfur and nitrogen have the ability to vary their valency when forming compounds. Name the following compounds by specifying the valency of nitrogen and sulfur.

   a) NO   b) NO_2 c) N_2O d) SO_3 e) SF_6

Strategy

• Determine the combined valency of the oxygen/fluorine atoms.
• The combined valency of the nitrogen/sulfur atoms is equal to the combined valency of the oxygen/fluorine atoms.

Solution

(a) The nitrogen atom in NO has the same valency as the oxygen atom (2). The compound NO is nitrogen(II) oxide.

(b) The valency of the nitrogen atom in NO_2 is the same as the combined valency of the two oxygen atoms $(2 + 2 = 4)$. The compound NO_2 is nitrogen(IV) oxide.

(c) The combined valency of the nitrogen atoms in N_2O $(1 + 1 = 2)$ is the same as the valency of the oxygen atom (2). The compound N_2O is nitrogen (I) oxide.

(d) The valency of the sulfur atom in SO_3 is equal to the combined valency of the oxygen atoms $(2 + 2 + 2 = 6)$. The compound SO_3 is sulfur(VI) oxide.

(e) The valency of the sulfur atom in SF_6 is equal to the combined valency of the fluorine atoms $(6 \times 1 = 6)$. The compound SF_6 is sulfur(VI) fluoride.

. . . .

Exercise 1.1H

Name the following compounds.

a) SF_4 b) $SnCl_2$ c) $SiCl_4$ d) PBr_3

e) XeF_4 f) PbO_2

Before moving to the next section, check that you are able to:

- Name ionic and nonmetal compounds using prefixes, and by specifying the valency of an element with the ability to vary its valency.

Chemical Equations

In this section we are learning to:

- Use the chemical equation for a reaction to relate the amount of reactants used and the amount of products formed by the reaction.
- Write chemical equations for reactions, including the use of state symbols to describe the physical state of the reactants and products.

Interpreting Chemical Equations

A **chemical equation** is used to summarise the change that occurs when a chemical reaction takes place. For example, when hydrogen burns in air it reacts with the oxygen in air to form water. The chemical change that occurs in the reaction is described by the chemical equation:

$$2H_2 + O_2 \rightarrow 2H_2O$$

The equation reads: two formulas of hydrogen ($2H_2$) react with one formula of oxygen (O_2) to form two formulas of water ($2H_2O$). In this example the reactants (to the left of the arrow) and the products (to the right of the arrow) are all molecular materials. This allows for the equation to be read as: two molecules of hydrogen ($2H_2$) react with one molecule of oxygen (O_2) to form two molecules of water ($2H_2O$).

A slightly different approach is needed when interpreting the chemical equation for a reaction involving non–molecular materials. For example, magnesium burns in air to form magnesium oxide. The equation for the reaction is:

$$2Mg + O_2 \rightarrow 2MgO$$

The equation reads: two formulas of magnesium ($2Mg$) react with one formula of oxygen (O_2) to produce two formulas of magnesium oxide ($2MgO$). Magnesium and magnesium oxide are not molecular materials. At this point it is helpful to recall that the formula Mg represents one atom of the metal, and the formula MgO represents the ions in one formula of magnesium oxide. In this way the equation for the reaction can also be read: two atoms of magnesium ($2Mg$) react with one molecule of oxygen (O_2) to produce two formulas of magnesium oxide ($2MgO$), each containing one magnesium (Mg^{2+}) ion and one oxide (O^{2-}) ion.

Writing Chemical Equations

When learning to write chemical equations it is often helpful to begin by writing the chemical equation in words. For example, sodium chloride is formed when sodium metal reacts with chlorine gas. The so-called word equation for the reaction is:

$$\text{sodium} + \text{chlorine} \rightarrow \text{sodium chloride}$$

The names of the reactants (to the left of the arrow) and products (to the right of the arrow) can then be replaced with a formula to produce the unbalanced chemical equation for the reaction.

$$\text{Unbalanced equation:} \quad Na + Cl_2 \rightarrow NaCl$$

In any chemical reaction *the number of atoms of an element in the reactants must be the same as the number of atoms of the element in the products*. This is equivalent to stating that atoms cannot be formed or destroyed in the reaction. As a result, the number of sodium ions in the sodium chloride formed by the reaction must be same as the number of sodium atoms that reacted. Similarly, the number of chloride ions in the sodium chloride formed by the reaction must be the same as the number of atoms of chlorine gas that reacted. This balance is achieved by reacting two atoms of sodium (2Na) with one molecule of chlorine (Cl_2) to form two formulas of sodium chloride (2NaCl), each containing one sodium (Na^+) ion and one chloride (Cl^-) ion.

Balanced equation: $2Na + Cl_2 \rightarrow 2NaCl$

Worked Example 1.1viii

Write the chemical equation for the reaction that occurs when aluminium powder reacts with bromine to form aluminium bromide, $AlBr_3$.

Solution

Aluminium is a metal (formula: Al) and bromine is diatomic (formula: Br_2).

Unbalanced equation: $Al + Br_2 \rightarrow AlBr_3$

Balanced equation: $2Al + 3Br_2 \rightarrow 2AlBr_3$

Exercise 1.1I

1. Coal (mostly carbon) forms carbon dioxide when it burns in air. If the supply of oxygen is limited carbon monoxide is formed instead of carbon dioxide. Write an equation for the reaction that occurs when coal burns in air to form (a) carbon dioxide and (b) carbon monoxide.

2. Magnesium burns in air to form magnesium oxide. A small amount of magnesium nitride is also formed as a result of the reaction between magnesium and nitrogen in the air. Write a balanced equation for the formation of magnesium nitride.

3. Phosphorus reacts with an excess of chlorine to form phosphorus(V) chloride. If the amount of chlorine is limited phosphorus(III) chloride is formed. Write a chemical equation for the reaction of phosphorus with (a) an excess of chlorine, and (b) a limited amount of chlorine.

State Symbols

The chemical equation for a reaction relates the amount of each reactant used, and the amount of products formed in the reaction. It can also be used to describe the physical states of the reactants and products by including a **state symbol** after the formula for each reactant and product. For example, if hydrogen reacts with oxygen at room temperature, the water formed in the reaction is formed as droplets of liquid water. This information is included in the chemical equation by adding the state symbol (l) or (g) after each formula to identify the individual reactants and products as liquids or gases.

$$2H_{2\ (g)} + O_{2\ (g)} \rightarrow 2H_2O_{\ (l)}$$

If the reaction occurred at temperatures above 100 °C the reaction would instead produce steam and the equation would be written:

$$2H_{2\ (g)} + O_{2\ (g)} \rightarrow 2H_2O_{\ (g)}$$

Clearly these two quite different outcomes could not be distinguished without the use of state symbols.

Worked Example 1.1ix

Write a chemical equation for the reaction that occurs when sulfur burns in air to form sulfur dioxide. Include state symbols.

Solution

The chemical equation for the reaction is:

$$S + O_2 \rightarrow SO_2$$

Note that sulfur can be represented by the formula S or S_8 when writing equations.

Sulfur is a solid. The state symbol for a solid is (s). Oxygen and sulfur dioxide are gases. The state symbol for a gas is (g). Including state symbols gives the equation:

$$S_{\ (s)} + O_{2\ (g)} \rightarrow SO_{2\ (g)}$$

Exercise 1.1J

1. Write the chemical equation for the following reactions. Include state symbols.

a) sodium + chlorine $\rightarrow$ sodium chloride

c) hydrogen + chlorine $\rightarrow$ hydrogen chloride

b) calcium + oxygen $\rightarrow$ calcium oxide

d) magnesium + bromine $\rightarrow$ magnesium bromide

2. Write the chemical equation for the following reactions. Include state symbols.

   a) iron + sulfur → iron(II) sulfide

   b) calcium carbonate → calcium oxide + carbon dioxide

   c) iron + bromine → iron(III) bromide

   d) aluminium + iodine → aluminium iodide

Before moving to the next section, check that you are able to:

- Interpret the chemical equation for a reaction in terms of the number of formulas reacting or formed in the reaction.
- Write balanced chemical equations that include state symbols.

Aqueous Solutions

In this section we are learning to:

- Use the term aqueous to describe a solution made by dissolving one or more substances in water.
- Identify the ions present in acids, alkalis and solutions of metal salts.
- Recall the solubility rules for compounds and use solubility to distinguish bases from alkalis.

The term **aqueous solution** is used when referring to the compounds or ions in a solution formed by dissolving one or more substances in water. When writing chemical equations the compounds or ions in aqueous solution are identified by the state symbol (aq). For example, the formula for hydrochloric acid is written $HCl_{(aq)}$ to distinguish it from hydrogen chloride gas, $HCl_{(g)}$. Similarly, the formula for sodium hydroxide solution is written $NaOH_{(aq)}$ to distinguish it from solid sodium hydroxide, $NaOH_{(s)}$.

Solutions Containing Salts

Ionic compounds such as metal chlorides, nitrates and sulfates are collectively referred to as 'salts'. When a salt dissolves in water it breaks apart into its constituent ions. The ions then become surrounded by water molecules and move freely throughout the solution. For example, dissolving magnesium chloride produces an aqueous solution of magnesium chloride, $MgCl_{2\,(aq)}$ that contains aqueous magnesium ions, $Mg^{2+}_{(aq)}$ and aqueous chloride ions, $Cl^{-}_{(aq)}$.

$$MgCl_{2\,(s)} \rightarrow \underbrace{Mg^{2+}_{(aq)} + 2Cl^{-}_{(aq)}}_{MgCl_{2\,(aq)}}$$

Similarly, sodium sulfate dissolves in water to form an aqueous solution of sodium sulfate, $Na_2SO_{4\,(aq)}$ that contains aqueous sodium ions, $Na^+_{(aq)}$ and aqueous sulfate ions, $SO_4^{2-}_{(aq)}$.

$$Na_2SO_{4\,(s)} \rightarrow \underbrace{2Na^+_{(aq)} + SO_4^{2-}_{(aq)}}_{Na_2SO_{4\,(aq)}}$$

It is possible to make some general statements about the solubility of salts and other compounds in water. The rules used to determine the solubility of compounds in water are summarised in Table 2.

Table 2

The solubility of compounds in water
• All nitrate salts are soluble.
• Group I salts and ammonium salts are soluble.
• Chloride, bromide, and iodide salts are soluble. *Exceptions: Silver and lead salts are insoluble.*
• Carbonates, oxides, and hydroxides are insoluble. *Exceptions: Barium hydroxide is soluble.*
• Hydrogencarbonates are soluble.
• Sulfate salts are soluble. *Exceptions: Silver, lead and barium salts are insoluble.*
• Sulfide salts are insoluble. *Exceptions: Group II sulfides are soluble.*

Worked Example 1.1x

Which of the following compounds is soluble in water? Explain your reasoning.

a) Na_2O b) $FeCl_3$ c) $PbSO_4$ d) Al_2O_3
e) FeS f) $Ba(NO_3)_2$ g) $Cu(OH)_2$

Strategy

- Apply the solubility rules in Table 2.

Solution

(a) Sodium oxide, Na_2O is soluble because all Group I salts are soluble.

(b) Iron(III) chloride, $FeCl_3$ is soluble because all chlorides (except silver and lead) are soluble.

(c) Lead sulfate, $PbSO_4$ is NOT soluble because all sulfates (except silver, lead and barium) are soluble.

(d) Aluminium oxide, Al_2O_3 is NOT soluble because oxides (except Group I and ammonium) are insoluble.

(e) Iron(II) sulfide, FeS is NOT soluble because sulfides (except Group I, Group II and ammonium) are insoluble.

(f) Barium nitrate, $Ba(NO_3)_2$ is soluble because all nitrates are soluble.

(g) Copper(II) hydroxide, $Cu(OH)_2$ is NOT soluble because hydroxides (except Group I, ammonium and barium) are insoluble.

Exercise 1.1K

1. Which of the following compounds are soluble in water?

   a) $MgBr_2$ b) $AgBr$ c) $CuCl_2$ d) $PbCl_2$

2. Which of the following compounds are soluble in water?

   a) Na_2S b) KOH c) Na_2CO_3 d) $(NH_4)_2CO_3$

3. Which of the following compounds are soluble in water?

   a) $BaSO_4$ b) $BaCl_2$ c) $MgCO_3$ d) $CuSO_4$

4. Which of the following compounds are soluble in water?

   a) $Mg(OH)_2$ b) CaO c) $Ba(OH)_2$
   d) $Ca(HCO_3)_2$

Before moving to the next section, check that you are able to:

- Identify the ions present in solutions of metal salts.
- Recall the solubility rules and use the rules to determine the solubility of compounds in water.

Acids and Alkalis

Many compounds dissolve in water to form aqueous solutions that behave as acids or alkalis. An **acid** is a substance that contains hydrogen (H^+) ions. For example, hydrochloric acid $HCl_{(aq)}$ is an aqueous solution containing hydrogen ions, $H^+_{(aq)}$ and chloride ions, $Cl^-_{(aq)}$. Hydrochloric acid is formed when hydrogen chloride, $HCl_{(g)}$ dissolves in water.

$$HCl_{(g)} \rightarrow \underbrace{H^+_{(aq)} + Cl^-_{(aq)}}$$

hydrochloric acid, $HCl_{(aq)}$

Similarly sulfuric acid, $H_2SO_{4\,(aq)}$ is an aqueous solution containing hydrogen ions, $H^+_{(aq)}$ and hydrogensulfate ions, $HSO_4^-_{(aq)}$. It is formed when sulfur trioxide, $SO_{3\,(g)}$ dissolves in water.

$$SO_{3\,(g)} + H_2O_{(l)} \rightarrow \underbrace{H^+_{(aq)} + HSO_4^-_{(aq)}}$$

sulfuric acid, $H_2SO_{4\,(aq)}$

An **alkali** is an aqueous solution containing hydroxide (OH^-) ions and is formed when a base dissolves in water. Aqueous sodium hydroxide, $NaOH_{(aq)}$ and aqueous ammonia, $NH_{3\,(aq)}$ are alkalis.

$$NaOH_{(s)} \rightarrow \underbrace{Na^+_{(aq)} + OH^-_{(aq)}}$$

$NaOH_{(aq)}$

$$NH_{3\,(g)} + H_2O_{(l)} \rightarrow \underbrace{NH_4^+_{(aq)} + OH^-_{(aq)}}$$

aqueous ammonia, $NH_{3\,(aq)}$

Aqueous ammonia, $NH_{3\,(aq)}$ is commonly referred to as 'ammonia solution'. A small fraction of the molecules in aqueous ammonia react with water to form ammonium ions, $NH_4^+_{(aq)}$ and hydroxide ions, $OH^-_{(aq)}$.

When we describe an alkali as a soluble base, we are using the term base to refer to any compound that reacts with an acid to produce a salt, water, and possibly carbon dioxide. Metal oxides, hydroxides, carbonates and hydrogencarbonates are all bases. We have also seen that nonmetal compounds such as ammonia, NH_3 are bases and are able to generate hydroxide ions by reacting with water. Similarly, insoluble bases such as calcium oxide, CaO form hydroxide ions by reacting with water.

$$CaO_{(s)} + H_2O_{(l)} \rightarrow Ca^{2+}_{(aq)} + 2OH^-_{(aq)}$$

Soluble carbonates such as sodium carbonate, $Na_2CO_{3\,(s)}$ generate hydroxide ions when the carbonate ions in an aqueous solution of the carbonate react with water.

$$CO_3^{2-}_{(sq)} + H_2O_{(l)} \rightarrow HCO_3^-_{(aq)} + OH^-_{(aq)}$$

Exercise 1.1L

1. Vinegar is an aqueous solution of ethanoic acid, $C_2H_4O_2$. Explain, with the help of an equation, why vinegar is an acid.

2. Phosphoric acid, H_3PO_4 is a weak acid found in fizzy drinks. (a) Explain, with the help of an equation, why phosphoric acid is an acid. (b) Suggest why phosphoric acid is a weak acid.

3. Explain how the reaction between zinc oxide and sulfuric acid can be used to demonstrate that zinc oxide is a base.

$$ZnO_{(s)} + H_2SO_{4\,(aq)} \rightarrow ZnSO_{4\,(aq)} + H_2O_{(l)}$$

4. Suggest, with the help of a chemical equation, why aqueous ammonium carbonate is an alkali.

Before moving to the next section, check that you are able to:

- Identify the ions present in common acids such as hydrochloric acid and sulfuric acid.
- Use the solubility of metal salts to distinguish alkalis from bases.
- Account for the presence of hydroxide ions in common alkalis such as aqueous sodium hydroxide and aqueous ammonia.

Ionic Equations

In this section we are learning to:

- Use the solubility rules for metal salts to account for the formation of a precipitate in aqueous solution.
- Recall that neutralisation occurs when hydrogen ions combine with hydroxide ions to form water.
- Write ionic equations for chemical reactions including neutralisation and precipitation.

In many chemical reactions, particularly those that take place in aqueous solution, some of the molecules and ions in the reaction mixture are not involved in the reaction. An **ionic equation** contains only those compounds and ions that react, or are formed, by the reaction. Ionic equations do not include compounds and ions that are unchanged by the reaction. As a result, the ionic equation for a reaction gives a clear picture of the chemical change that occurs during the reaction.

Precipitation Reactions

The term **precipitate** refers to an insoluble solid formed in a chemical reaction. For example, adding a few drops of aqueous barium chloride, $BaCl_{2\,(aq)}$ to an aqueous solution containing sulfate ions, $SO_4^{2-}{}_{(aq)}$ produces a white precipitate of barium sulfate, $BaSO_{4\,(s)}$.

Chemical equation:

$$BaCl_{2\,(aq)} + SO_4^{2-}{}_{(aq)} \rightarrow BaSO_{4\,(s)} + 2Cl^-{}_{(aq)}$$

The precipitate is formed when barium (Ba^{2+}) ions from the barium chloride solution combine with the sulfate ions already in the solution.

Ionic equation:

$$Ba^{2+}{}_{(aq)} + SO_4^{2-}{}_{(aq)} \rightarrow BaSO_{4\,(s)}$$

The ionic equation reminds us that the chloride ions from the barium chloride solution do not get involved in the reaction and, for this reason, are known as **spectator ions**.

Precipitates formed by the addition of acidified silver nitrate solution to solutions containing (from L to R) chloride, bromide and iodide ions.

....

Worked Example 1.1xi

Write an ionic equation for any reactions that occur when a few drops of aqueous barium chloride are added to the following solutions.

a) $Na_2SO_{4\,(aq)}$ b) $NaCl_{(aq)}$ c) $KOH_{(aq)}$ d) $Na_2CO_{3\,(aq)}$

Strategy

- Make a list of the cations and anions in the reaction mixture.
- Use the solubility rules in Table 2 to determine if the cations and anions in the reaction mixture can combine to form an insoluble salt.

Solution

(a) The reaction mixture contains Na^+ (aq), SO_4^{2-} (aq), Ba^{2+} (aq) and Cl^- (aq) ions. Barium (Ba^{2+}) ion forms a precipitate when it combines with sulfate (SO_4^{2-}).

Ionic equation: Ba^{2+} (aq) $+ SO_4^{2-}$ (aq) $\rightarrow BaSO_4$ (s)

(b) The reaction mixture contains Na^+ (aq), Cl^- (aq) and Ba^{2+} (aq) ions. All sodium salts are soluble and barium (Ba^{2+}) ion does not form a precipitate with chloride (Cl^-). A precipitate will not form.

(c) The mixture contains K^+ (aq), OH^- (aq), Ba^{2+} (aq) and Cl^- (aq) ions. All potassium salts are soluble and barium (Ba^{2+}) ion will not form a precipitate with chloride (Cl^-) or hydroxide (OH^-). A precipitate will not form.

(d) The mixture contains Na^+ (aq), CO_3^{2-} (aq), Ba^{2+} (aq) and Cl^- (aq) ions. Barium (Ba^{2+}) ion forms a precipitate with carbonate (CO_3^{2-}).

Ionic equation: Ba^{2+} (aq) $+ CO_3^{2-}$ (aq) $\rightarrow BaCO_3$ (s)

Exercise 1.1M

1. Write the ionic equation for the reaction that occurs when silver nitrate solution is added to aqueous sodium iodide. Include state symbols.

2. Write the ionic equation for the reaction that occurs when aqueous calcium chloride is added to dilute sodium carbonate solution. Include state symbols.

Before moving to the next section, check that you are able to:

- Use the solubility rules for metal salts to account for the formation of a precipitate in aqueous solution.
- Write an ionic equation to describe the formation of a precipitate.

Neutralisation Reactions

An acid will react with a base to form a salt, water and possibly carbon dioxide. This type of reaction is referred to as a **neutralisation reaction**. For example, adding sodium hydroxide solution to dilute hydrochloric acid produces a solution of sodium chloride in water.

Chemical equation:

HCl (aq) $+$ NaOH (aq) $\rightarrow$ NaCl (aq) $+ H_2O$ (l)

The acid is neutralised when hydrogen (H^+) ions from the acid react with hydroxide (OH^-) ions from the alkali to form water. The sodium ions and chloride ions in the reaction mixture are spectator ions and are not included when writing the ionic equation.

Ionic equation: H^+ (aq) $+ OH^-$ (aq) $\rightarrow H_2O$ (l)

Worked Example 1.1xii

Write the chemical equation and ionic equation for the reaction that occurs when aqueous potassium hydroxide is added to dilute sulfuric acid.

Strategy

- Write a balanced chemical equation for the reaction.
- Re-write the chemical equation showing all of the ions in solution.
- Identify and remove spectator ions to form the ionic equation.

Solution

Chemical equation:

H_2SO_4 (aq) $+ 2KOH$ (aq) $\rightarrow K_2SO_4$ (aq) $+ 2H_2O$ (l)

Ions in solution:

H^+ (aq) $+ HSO_4^-$ (aq) $+ 2K^+$ (aq) $+ 2OH^-$ (aq)

$\rightarrow 2K^+$ (aq) $+ SO_4^{2-}$ (aq) $+ 2H_2O$ (l)

The potassium (K^+) ions are spectator ions. They are not involved in the reaction and do not appear in the ionic equation.

Ionic equation:

H^+ (aq) $+ HSO_4^-$ (aq) $+ 2OH^-$ (aq) $\rightarrow SO_4^{2-}$ (aq) $+ 2H_2O$ (l)

The ionic equation clearly shows that two hydrogen (H^+) ions are neutralised for every formula of sulfuric acid that reacts.

If an acid reacts with an insoluble base the ionic equation more closely resembles the chemical equation for the reaction but is still helpful. Consider, for example, the neutralisation reaction that occurs when dilute hydrochloric acid is added to calcium carbonate.

Chemical equation:

$$CaCO_{3\,(s)} + 2HCl_{(aq)} \rightarrow CaCl_{2\,(aq)} + H_2O_{(l)} + CO_{2\,(g)}$$

The chloride (Cl^-) ions in the hydrochloric acid are the only spectator ions as they remain in solution and are unchanged by the reaction. Removing the spectator ions gives the ionic equation for the reaction.

Ionic equation:

$$CaCO_{3\,(s)} + 2H^+_{(aq)} \rightarrow Ca^{2+}_{(aq)} + H_2O_{(l)} + CO_{2\,(g)}$$

Exercise 1.1N

1. Write the (a) chemical equation and (b) ionic equation for the reaction that occurs when copper(II) oxide is added to dilute hydrochloric acid.

2. Write the (a) chemical equation and (b) ionic equation for the reaction that occurs when aqueous sodium carbonate is added to dilute hydrochloric acid.

Before moving to the next section, check that you are able to:

- Recall that neutralisation occurs when hydrogen ions combine with hydroxide ions to form water.
- Identify spectator ions and write ionic equations for reactions involving solids, liquids and gases.

Amounts of Substance

In this section we are learning to:

- Define one mole of substance in terms of Avogadro's number.
- Use Avogadro's number to calculate the number of particles in a given amount of substance.
- Calculate the molar mass of a substance and use molar mass to relate amounts of a substance in grams and moles.

Previously we had begun to interpret chemical equations in terms of the amount of reactants used and the amount of products formed, for example:

$$2Na_{(s)} + Cl_{2\,(g)} \rightarrow 2NaCl_{(s)}$$

2 formulas   1 formula   2 formulas

This interpretation becomes inconvenient if we are

working with amounts of substance measured in grams and we must develop alternative measures for the amount of substance that allow us to easily relate quantities with masses that range from grams to tonnes (1 tonne = 1000 kg).

Avogadro's number and The Mole

One gram of a substance contains approximately 10^{23} atoms. As a result it becomes convenient to define an amount of substance that contains approximately 10^{23} atoms when working with amounts of substance measured in grams. For this reason amounts of substance are measured in units known as moles (unit: mol). One **mole** of any substance contains 6.02×10^{23} formulas of the substance where the number 6.02×10^{23} is known as Avogadro's number (symbol: L). Having defined a mole to be a number of formulas, chemical equations can be interpreted in terms of the moles of substance reacting and the moles of products formed. For example, the reaction between sodium and chlorine can be interpreted as the reaction between two moles of sodium (2Na) and one mole of chlorine (Cl_2) to form two moles of sodium chloride (2NaCl).

$$2Na_{(s)} + Cl_{2\,(g)} \rightarrow 2NaCl_{(s)}$$

2L formulas   L formulas   2L formulas
2 moles   1 mole   2 moles

Molar Mass

The **molar mass** of a substance is defined to be the mass of one mole of the substance in grams (unit: $g\,mol^{-1}$). For example, the molar mass of oxygen (O_2) is $32\,g\,mol^{-1}$. This means that one mole of oxygen gas (O_2) has a mass of 32 g, two moles have a mass of $2 \times 32 = 64$ g, three moles have a mass of $3 \times 32 = 96$ g and so on.

The molar mass of an element or compound can be obtained from the Periodic Table by adding the relative atomic mass (RAM) for each atom in the formula of the substance. The sum of the RAMs for the atoms in one formula is known as the **relative formula mass (RFM)** of the substance. In this way the molar mass of a substance simply becomes the RFM of the substance in units of $g\,mol^{-1}$.

....

Worked Example 1.1xiii

Calculate the molar mass of a) oxygen and b) sodium chloride.

Strategy

- Calculate the RFM of the substance by adding the RAMs for the atoms in one formula of the substance.
- The molar mass is the RFM in units of $g\ mol^{-1}$.

Solution

(a) The formula of oxygen (gas) is O_2

The RAM of O is 16

RFM of oxygen $(O_2) = 16 + 16 = 32$

Molar mass of oxygen $(O_2) = 32\ g\ mol^{-1}$

(b) The formula of sodium chloride is NaCl

The RAM of Na is 23 and the RAM of Cl is 35.5

RFM of NaCl $= 23 + 35.5 = 58.5$

Molar mass of sodium chloride $= 58.5\ g\ mol^{-1}$

The relationship between the amount of substance in moles and its equivalent mass in grams is summarised by the equation:

$$Moles = \frac{Mass}{Molar\ Mass}$$

Worked Example 1.1xiv

Calculate the number of moles in 20 g of the following substances.

a) iron   b) gold   c) water   d) sodium carbonate

Strategy

- Calculate the molar mass.
- Use the molar mass to calculate the number of moles in 20 g.

Solution

(a) Molar mass of iron (Fe) $= 56\ g\ mol^{-1}$

Moles of iron $=$

$$\frac{Mass}{Molar\ Mass} = \frac{20\ g}{56\ g\ mol^{-1}} = 0.36\ mol$$

(b) Molar mass of gold (Au) $= 197\ g\ mol^{-1}$

Moles of gold $=$

$$\frac{Mass}{Molar\ Mass} = \frac{20\ g}{197\ g\ mol^{-1}} = 0.10\ mol$$

(c) Molar mass of water $(H_2O) = 1 + 1 + 16 = 18\ g\ mol^{-1}$

Moles of water $=$

$$\frac{Mass}{Molar\ Mass} = \frac{20\ g}{18\ g\ mol^{-1}} = 1.11\ mol$$

(d) Molar mass of $Na_2CO_3 = (2 \times 23) + 12 + (3 \times 16)$

$= 106\ g\ mol^{-1}$

Moles of $Na_2CO_3 =$

$$\frac{Mass}{Molar\ Mass} = \frac{20\ g}{106\ g\ mol^{-1}} = 0.19\ mol$$

Before moving to the next section, check that you are able to:

- Define one mole of substance in terms of Avogadro's number.
- Calculate the molar mass of a substance and use molar mass to relate amounts of a substance in grams and moles.

Using Avogadro's number

Avogadro's number can be used to calculate the number of particles in a given amount of substance, or to calculate the amount of substance that contains a specified number of particles.

By definition, one mole of any substance contains Avogadro's number (L) of formulas of the substance. In the case of a molecular material such as carbon dioxide (formula: CO_2), each formula represents one molecule. As a result, one mole of carbon dioxide contains L molecules, two moles contains 2L molecules, and so on. This relationship is summarised by the equation:

$$Number\ of\ molecules = Moles \times L$$

If the substance is a metal (formula: Fe, Au, ...), a monatomic gas (formula: He, Ne, ...), or an element with a giant structure such as diamond (formula: C), one formula represents one atom. The relationship between the number of atoms in the substance and the amount of substance in moles is summarised by the equation:

$$Number\ of\ atoms = Moles \times L$$

In the case of an ionic compound such as NaCl or $MgCl_2$, each formula contains the ions needed to describe the composition of the substance. If one formula contains N ions, one mole of formulas contains N moles of ions, and the total number of ions in a given number of moles of the compound is given by the equation:

$$Number\ of\ ions = Moles \times N \times L$$

Worked Example 1.1xv

How many particles (ions, atoms or molecules) are in the following. Leave your answers in terms of Avogadro's number (L).

  a) 3 mol of nitrogen
  b) 2 mol of iron
  c) 2 mol of magnesium sulfate

Strategy

- Identify the particles in one formula.
- Multiply the number of particles in one formula by the number of moles.

Solution

(a) Nitrogen is a molecular material (formula: N_2). Each formula represents one molecule, therefore 1 mol contains L molecules and 3 mol contains $3 \times L = 3L$ molecules.

(b) Iron is a metal (formula: Fe). Each formula represents one atom therefore 1 mol (L formulas) contains L atoms and 2 mol contains $2 \times L = 2L$ atoms.

(c) Magnesium sulfate is an ionic compound (formula: $MgSO_4$). Each formula represents one magnesium (Mg^{2+}) ion and one sulfate (SO_4^{2-}) ion. As a result 1 mol (L formulas) contains 2L ions and 2 mol contains $2 \times 2L = 4L$ ions.

Having demonstrated the use of Avogadro's number to calculate the number of particles in a mole of substance, and the use of molar mass to relate the amount of substance in moles and grams, we can now combine these methods and use moles to determine the number of particles in a given mass of substance.

Worked Example 1.1xvi

Carbon, in the form of graphite, is a major component of the 'lead' in pencils. A single dot made by a pencil contains approximately 0.00010 g of carbon. How many atoms of carbon are in the dot?

Strategy

- Calculate the moles of carbon in the dot.
- Use Avogadro's number to convert moles to atoms.

Solution

Moles of carbon in the dot =

$$\frac{\text{Mass}}{\text{Molar Mass}} = \frac{1.0 \times 10^{-4}\,\text{g}}{12\,\text{g mol}^{-1}} = 8.3 \times 10^{-6}\,\text{mol}$$

Carbon atoms in the dot =
Moles $\times$ L = $(8.3 \times 10^{-6})(6.02 \times 10^{23}) = 5.0 \times 10^{18}$

Exercise 1.10

1. A 1 penny coin contains approximately 1 g of copper. How many atoms are in a 1p coin?

2. What mass of sodium contains the same number of atoms as 1.00 g of lithium? *(CCEA January 2003)*

3. A female cockroach secretes a chemical with the formula $C_{11}H_{18}O_2$. It is reported that the male of the species will respond to as little as 60 molecules of the chemical. Calculate (a) the relative formula mass, (b) the mass of one mole, (c) the mass of one molecule, and (d) the mass of 60 molecules of the chemical. *(CCEA June 2001)*

> Before moving to the next section, check that you are able to:
>
> - Use Avogadro's number to calculate the number of particles in a given amount of substance.

Calculating Reacting Amounts

> **In this section we are learning to:**
>
> - Use chemical equations to relate the amounts of substances that react and the amounts of products formed in a chemical reaction.
> - Identify a reactant as *limiting* if the amount of reactant present in the reaction mixture determines the amount of products formed.
> - Calculate the amount of product formed in the presence of a limiting reactant.

The chemical equation for a reaction can be used to calculate the amount of products formed in a reaction and the amount of reactants needed to form a specified amount of product. Both are common problems faced by chemists and can be tackled by applying the following scheme:

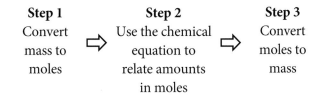

Step 1		Step 2		Step 3
Convert mass to moles	⇨	Use the chemical equation to relate amounts in moles	⇨	Convert moles to mass

Worked Example 1.1xvii

Calculate the mass of magnesium oxide formed when 10 g of magnesium is completely burnt in oxygen. The chemical equation for the reaction is:

$$2Mg_{(s)} + O_{2(g)} \rightarrow 2MgO_{(s)}$$

Strategy

Apply the 3-step approach.
1. Calculate the number of moles in 10 g of magnesium.
2. Use the answer from step 1 to calculate the moles of MgO formed.
3. Use the answer from step 2 to calculate the mass of MgO formed.

Solution

1. Moles of Mg =

$$\frac{Mass}{Molar\ Mass} = \frac{10\ g}{24\ g\ mol^{-1}} = 0.42\ mol$$

2. The chemical equation shows that 1 mol of MgO is formed for every mole of magnesium that reacts. Moles of MgO formed = Moles of Mg reacted = 0.42 mol

3. Mass of MgO formed = Moles × Molar mass = 0.42 mol × 40 g mol⁻¹ = 17 g

- -

Exercise 1.1P

1. Aspirin, $C_9H_8O_4$ is prepared by reacting salicylic acid, $C_7H_6O_3$ with acetic anhydride, $C_4H_6O_3$. Calculate (a) the mass of anhydride needed to react with 500 g of salicylic acid, and (b) the mass of aspirin formed in the reaction.

$$C_7H_6O_3 + C_4H_6O_3 \rightarrow C_9H_8O_4 + C_2H_4O_2$$

2. Lithium oxide, Li_2O is used in spacecraft to remove water from the air supply. Calculate the mass of water that can be removed by an 'air scrubber' containing 500 g of lithium oxide.

$$Li_2O_{(s)} + H_2O_{(g)} \rightarrow 2LiOH_{(s)}$$

3. Mercury(II) oxide, HgO decomposes on heating. (a) Calculate the mass of mercury formed when 10 g of mercury(II) oxide decomposes. (b) Calculate the mass of mercury(II) oxide needed to produce 0.5 mol of oxygen.

$$2HgO_{(s)} \rightarrow 2Hg_{(l)} + O_{2(g)}$$

4. Potassium chlorate, $KClO_3$ decomposes on heating. Calculate the mass of potassium chlorate needed to produce 0.5 mol of oxygen.

$$2KClO_{3(s)} \rightarrow 2KCl_{(s)} + 3O_{2(g)}$$

5. Photosynthesis converts carbon dioxide into glucose, $C_6H_{12}O_6$ and oxygen. A fully grown tree will consume 300 kg of carbon dioxide each year and convert it to oxygen. Calculate the mass of oxygen produced by the tree each year.

$$6CO_{2(g)} + 6H_2O_{(l)} \rightarrow C_6H_{12}O_{6(s)} + 6O_{2(g)}$$

(CCEA June 2005)

6. In industry, iron is produced by the reduction of iron(III) oxide, Fe_2O_3. Calculate the mass of carbon dioxide in kg released into the atmosphere for every 0.100 tonne of iron produced (1 tonne = 1000 kg).

$$Fe_2O_3 + 3CO \rightarrow 2Fe + 3CO_2$$

The 3-step approach to calculating reacting amounts can also be used to determine the amount of an element in a given amount of a substance.

- -

Worked Example 1.1xviii

In industry iron is obtained from iron(III) oxide, Fe_2O_3 using a blast furnace. How much iron can be obtained from 1 tonne (1 tonne = 1000 kg) of iron(III) oxide?

Strategy

Apply the 3-step approach.
1. Calculate the moles of iron(III) oxide in 1 tonne of iron(III) oxide.
2. Use the answer from step 1 to calculate the number of moles of iron in 1 tonne of iron(III) oxide.
3. Use the answer to step 2 to calculate the mass of iron in 1 tonne of iron(III) oxide.

Solution

1. Moles of Fe_2O_3 in 1 tonne =

$$\frac{Mass}{Molar\ Mass} = \frac{1.0 \times 10^6\ g}{160\ g\ mol^{-1}} = 6.25 \times 10^3\ mol$$

2. Moles of Fe in 6.25×10^3 mol of Fe_2O_3 = $2 \times 6.25 \times 10^3 = 1.25 \times 10^4$ mol

3. Mass of Fe in 1 tonne = $(1.25 \times 10^4\ mol)(56\ g\ mol^{-1})$ = $7.00 \times 10^5\ g = 700\ kg$

- -

Exercise 1.1Q

One tonne (1000 kg) of sulfur costs £160. What is the cost (to the nearest £) of the sulfur needed to make 1 tonne of sulfuric acid, H_2SO_4?

(CCEA June 2006)

Before moving to the next section, check that you are able to:

- Use chemical equations to calculate the amount of reactants used and the amount of products formed in a chemical reaction.

Limiting Reactants

The compound iron(II) sulfide, FeS is formed by heating a mixture of iron and sulfur. If the amount of sulfur in the mixture is increased until the mixture contains just enough sulfur to react with the iron, the entire reaction mixture will be converted into iron(II) sulfide. If the amount of sulfur in the mixture is increased further, all of the iron will be converted to iron(II) sulfide and some sulfur will remain in the reaction mixture. The amount of iron(II) sulfide formed is limited by the amount of iron in the reaction mixture. In this way iron has become the **limiting reactant** and sulfur is described as being **in excess**.

The method used previously to calculate reacting amounts must be modified slightly to allow for the possibility of a limiting reactant:

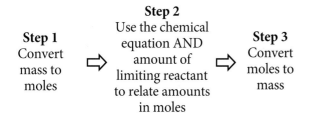

Step 1 Convert mass to moles ⇨ **Step 2** Use the chemical equation AND amount of limiting reactant to relate amounts in moles ⇨ **Step 3** Convert moles to mass

---

Worked Example 1.1ixx

How many moles of iron(II) sulfide are formed when a mixture containing 3.0 g of iron and 3.0 g of sulfur is heated?

$$Fe_{(s)} + S_{(s)} \rightarrow FeS_{(s)}$$

Strategy

Apply the 3-step approach.

1. Calculate the moles of each reactant.

2. Use the moles of limiting reactant to calculate the moles of product formed.

3. Use the answer from step 2 to calculate the mass of product formed.

Solution

1. Moles of Fe $= \dfrac{\text{Mass of Fe}}{\text{Molar Mass of Fe}} = \dfrac{3.0 \text{ g}}{56 \text{ g mol}^{-1}}$

   $= 0.054$ mol

   Moles of S $= \dfrac{\text{Mass of S}}{\text{Molar Mass of S}} = \dfrac{3.0 \text{ g}}{32 \text{ g mol}^{-1}}$

   $= 0.094$ mol

2. The chemical equation shows that 1 mol of iron reacts with 1 mol of sulfur. Moles of S reacted = Moles of Fe reacted = 0.054 mol

   Not all of the sulfur reacts. Sulfur is in excess and iron is the limiting reactant.

   One mole of FeS is formed for every mole of iron that reacts. Moles of FeS formed = Moles of Fe reacted = 0.054 mol

3. Mass of FeS = Moles of FeS × Molar mass
   $= (0.054 \text{ mol})(88 \text{ g mol}^{-1}) = 4.8 \text{ g}$

Exercise 1.1R

1. Calculate the amount of copper obtained by adding 0.42 g of iron to an excess of copper(II) sulfate solution.

   $$Fe + CuSO_4 \rightarrow FeSO_4 + Cu$$

   (CCEA June 2002)

2. Iron(III) oxide can be reduced by carbon to form iron. Calculate the maximum mass of iron that can be produced by reacting 3.20 kg of iron(III) oxide with 0.72 kg of carbon.

   $$2Fe_2O_3 + 3C \rightarrow 4Fe + 3CO_2$$

   (CCEA January 2010)

3. The extraction and purification of uranium from its ore involves the following reaction between uranium(IV) fluoride and magnesium. Calculate the mass of uranium extracted by reacting 500 tonnes of uranium(IV) fluoride with 50 tonnes of magnesium.

   $$2Mg + UF_4 \rightarrow U + 2MgF_2$$

   (CCEA June 2009)

4. Phosphoric acid, H_3PO_4 is manufactured by the reaction of sulfuric acid with calcium phosphate.

Calculate the mass of phosphoric acid that would be obtained by reacting 60 kg of sulfuric acid with 60 kg of calcium phosphate.

$$3H_2SO_4 + Ca_3(PO_4)_2 \rightarrow 2H_3PO_4 + 3CaSO_4$$

(CCEA January 2009)

5. Titanium is extracted in a two-stage process. The first stage involves the conversion of titanium(IV) oxide to titanium(IV) chloride. In the second stage, the titanium(IV) chloride is reduced using magnesium. How much titanium would be obtained when 8.0 kg of titanium(IV) oxide is converted to titanium(IV) chloride and then reduced using 7.2 kg of magnesium?

$$TiO_2 + C + 2Cl_2 \rightarrow TiCl_4 + CO_2$$

$$TiCl_4 + 2Mg \rightarrow Ti + 2MgCl_2$$

(CCEA June 2010)

Before moving to the next section, check that you are able to:

- Identify a limiting reactant as any reactant that limits the amount of product formed in a chemical reaction.
- Calculate the amount of reactants used and the amount of products formed in the presence of a limiting reactant.

Salts Containing Water

In this section we are learning to:

- Use the term water of crystallisation to refer to water that is chemically bonded within a salt.
- Refer to salts containing water of crystallisation as hydrated salts or 'hydrates'.
- Use the term anhydrous to refer to salts that do not contain water of crystallisation.
- Calculate the % water by mass in hydrated salts.
- Determine the formula of a hydrated salt by the technique of heating to constant mass.

Water of Crystallisation

Hydrated copper(II) sulfate, $CuSO_4.5H_2O$ is an example of a salt that contains water. Like other ionic compounds hydrated copper(II) sulfate is a solid. The water contained within the salt is known as **water of**

crystallisation and gives crystals of hydrated copper(II) sulfate their characteristic blue colour.

Hydrated copper(II) sulfate.

Salts containing water of crystallisation are referred to as **hydrated** or 'hydrates'. The formula of hydrated copper(II) sulfate indicates that the salt contains 5 moles of water of crystallisation (5 H_2O) for every mole of copper(II) sulfate in the crystal. The amount of water of crystallisation in a hydrate is included when naming the salt.

Examples of naming hydrates:

Formula	Name
$CoCl_2.2H_2O$	cobalt(II) chloride-2-water
$CuSO_4.5H_2O$	copper(II) sulfate-5-water
$Na_2CO_3.10H_2O$	sodium carbonate-10-water

The water of crystallisation in a salt can be removed by heating. When blue crystals of hydrated copper(II) sulfate are heated the water of crystallisation evaporates leaving anhydrous copper(II) sulfate, $CuSO_4$. Anhydrous copper(II) sulfate is a white powder. The term **anhydrous** is used to refer to salts that do not contain water of crystallisation.

Anhydrous copper(II) sulfate.

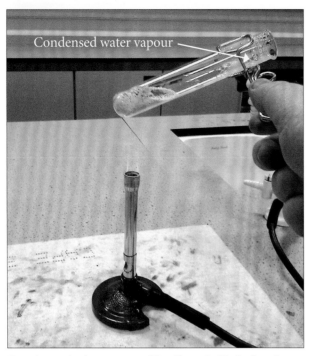

Forming anhydrous copper(II) sulfate, CuSO₄ by heating hydrated copper(II) sulfate, CuSO₄.5H₂O. The water removed from the salt condenses on the sides of the test tube.

Worked Example 1.1 xx

Calculate the percentage water by mass in copper(II) sulfate-5-water.

Solution

Molar mass of $CuSO_4.5H_2O$ = 250 g mol^{-1}

Molar mass of H_2O = 18 g mol^{-1}

Mass of H_2O in 1 mol of hydrate = 5 × 18 = 90 g

% water by mass = $\dfrac{90 \text{ g}}{250 \text{ g}}$ × 100 = 36%

Exercise 1.1S

Calculate the percent water by mass in crystals of washing soda, $Na_2CO_3.10H_2O$.

Before moving to the next section, check that you are able to:

- Use the terms hydrated and anhydrous to describe the amount of water of crystallisation in a salt.
- Name salts containing water of crystallisation.
- Calculate the percentage water by mass in a hydrated salt.

Determining the Formula of a Hydrate

The amount of water of crystallisation in a salt is determined by a technique known as **heating to constant mass**.

Method

- Weigh a sample of the hydrate in a pre-weighed crucible.
- Heat the sample in the crucible using a blue Bunsen flame.
- Allow the crucible to cool to room temperature before weighing the crucible.
- Repeat the process of heating and weighing until the mass remains constant.
- Calculate the mass of anhydrous salt formed.

Heating a solid compound to constant mass.

Worked Example 1.1xxi

Use the following information to determine the chemical formula for hydrated iron(II) sulfate, $FeSO_4.xH_2O$.

Mass of crucible	= 19.38 g
Mass of hydrate + crucible	= 22.32 g
Mass after heating (constant)	= 20.99 g

Strategy

Calculate:

1. The moles of water removed by heating.

2. The moles of anhydrous salt remaining after heating.
3. The number of moles of water per mole of anhydrous salt.

Solution

$$FeSO_4.xH_2O_{(s)} \rightarrow FeSO_{4(s)} + x\ H_2O_{(l)}$$

1. Mass of water removed from hydrate = 22.32 − 20.99 = 1.33 g

   Moles of water in hydrate

   $$= \frac{Mass}{Molar\ Mass} = \frac{1.33\ g}{18\ g\ mol^{-1}} = 0.0739\ mol$$

2. Mass of anhydrous salt = 20.99 − 19.38 = 1.61 g

   Moles of anhydrous salt ($FeSO_4$)

   $$= \frac{Mass}{Molar\ Mass} = \frac{1.61\ g}{152\ g\ mol^{-1}} = 0.0106\ mol$$

3. $x = \dfrac{Moles\ of\ water}{Moles\ of\ anhydrous\ FeSO_4} = \dfrac{0.0739}{0.0106} = 6.97$

   Rounding to the nearest whole-number gives
   x = 7

   The chemical formula of hydrated iron(II) sulfate is $FeSO_4.7H_2O$

Exercise 1.1T

1. A sample of hydrated cobalt(II) chloride weighing 2.38 g was heated to constant mass. The sample weighed 1.20 g after heating. Calculate the formula of the hydrate.

2. The hydrated form of barium chloride has the formula, $BaCl_2.xH_2O$. Use the following information to find x.

Mass of hydrate + crucible	= 43.44 g
Mass after heating	= 43.26 g
Mass of crucible	= 42.22 g

Before moving to the next section, check that you are able to:

- Recall the procedure to determine the amount of water of crystallisation in a salt by heating to constant mass.
- Calculate the formula of a hydrated salt using data obtained by heating a sample of the hydrate to constant mass.

1.2 Atomic Structure

Atoms Ions and Isotopes

In this section we are learning to:

- Describe the modern picture of the atom and recall the properties of the subatomic particles within an atom.
- Recall that elements are organised in order of increasing atomic number in the modern Periodic Table.
- Describe the formation of ions from atoms.
- Explain the existence of isotopes and use the mass number of an isotope to calculate the number of protons, electrons and neutrons in the isotope.
- Recall the definition of relative isotopic mass (RIM) and relative atomic mass (RAM) in terms of the carbon-12 mass standard.
- Calculate the relative atomic mass (RAM) of an element and the relative molecular mass (RMM) of a molecule from a mass spectrum.

The Modern Atom

The modern picture of the atom is based on the model proposed by Ernest Rutherford in 1911. In Rutherford's model, an atom is made up of negatively charged electrons orbiting a positively charged nucleus. We now know that the nucleus contains two types of particle: protons and neutrons. Protons and neutrons have approximately the same mass and are about 1840 times heavier than an electron. As a result, the nucleus of an atom contains almost all of the atom's mass but occupies only a tiny fraction of the space inside the atom. The remainder of the space is occupied by electrons orbiting the nucleus as shown in Figure 1a.

The particles that make up atoms are known as subatomic particles. The charges on subatomic particles such as protons and electrons are measured in units of electron charge (symbol: e). In these units each proton has a charge of 1+ and each electron has a charge of 1–. Neutrons do not have a charge. The properties of electrons, protons and neutrons are summarised in Figure 1b.

There are approximately 100 elements in the modern Periodic Table, each made from one type of atom. The elements are represented by their chemical symbols and are arranged in order of increasing atomic number as shown in Figure 2. The **atomic number** of an element is defined to be the number of protons in each atom of the element. For example, the element carbon

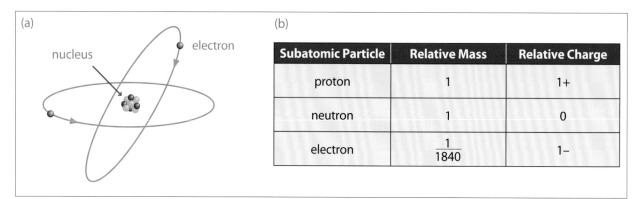

Subatomic Particle	Relative Mass	Relative Charge
proton	1	1+
neutron	1	0
electron	$\frac{1}{1840}$	1–

Figure 1: (a) The modern picture of the atom. (b) Properties of subatomic particles

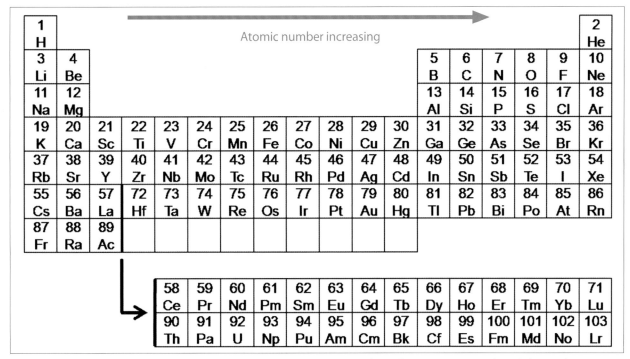

Figure 2: The form of the modern Periodic Table. The atomic number of the elements increases from left to right across each row.

(symbol: C) is element 6 in the Periodic Table. This tells us that the atomic number of carbon is 6, and that every carbon atom has 6 protons in its nucleus.

Atoms and Ions

The atoms of an element do not have a charge; they contain equal numbers of protons (1+ charge) and electrons (1– charge). When an atom loses or gains electrons it becomes charged and is known as an **ion**.

If an ion is formed by removing electrons from an atom, the total positive charge on the protons is greater than the total negative charge on the remaining electrons and the ion has an overall (net) positive charge. For example, when a copper atom loses 2 electrons it becomes a copper(II) ion, Cu^{2+}.

Conversely, when an atom gains electrons the total charge on the protons is less than the total charge on the electrons and the ion has a negative charge. For example, when a chlorine atom gains an electron it becomes a chloride ion, Cl^-.

The relationship between the charge on an ion and the numbers of protons (p) and electrons (e) in the ion can be summarised in the form of an equation.

Charge on ion =
number of protons (p) – number of electrons (e)

Worked Example 1.2i

Identify the atoms or ions shown in (a), (b) and (c).

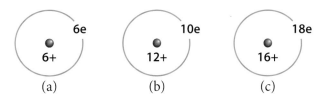

Strategy

- Use the charge on the nucleus to determine the atomic number.
- Calculate the charge on the ion (p – e).
- Recall that the charge on an atom (p – e) is zero.

Solution

(a) Atomic number = 6 (6+ charge on nucleus)

　Charge on (a) = p – e = 6 – 6 = 0

　Species (a) is a carbon atom

(b) Atomic number = 12

　Charge on (b) = p – e = 12 – 10 = 2+

　Species (b) is a magnesium ion, Mg^{2+}

(c) Atomic number = 16

　Charge on (c) = p – e = 16 – 18 = 2–

　Species (c) is a sulfide ion, S^{2-}

Exercise 1.2A

Which one of the following elements contains the same number of electrons as a Mg^{2+} ion: calcium, fluorine, neon or sodium? *(CCEA June 2011)*

Isotopes

Not all atoms of an element are identical. Atoms with the same number of protons but different numbers of neutrons are known as **isotopes**. For example, the element carbon has three isotopes: carbon-12 (^{12}C), carbon-13 (^{13}C) and carbon-14 (^{14}C). All three isotopes are present in materials containing the element carbon. The numbers 12, 13 and 14 are the mass numbers of the isotopes where the **mass number** of an isotope is the total number of protons and neutrons in an atom of the isotope. The numbers of protons, neutrons and electrons in each carbon isotope are summarised in Table 1.

Table 1: The number of protons, neutrons and electrons in the isotopes of carbon

Isotope	Symbol	Protons (p)	Neutrons (n)	Electrons (e)
carbon-12	^{12}C	6	6	6
carbon-13	^{13}C	6	7	6
carbon-14	^{14}C	6	8	6

Worked Example 1.2ii

Calculate the number of neutrons in an atom of the following isotopes.

a) ^{31}P b) ^{56}Fe c) ^{197}Au d) ^{238}U

Solution

a) Phosphorus-31, ^{31}P is an isotope of phosphorus (p = 15)
   Mass number = p + n = 31
   therefore n = 31 − p = 16

b) Iron-56, ^{56}Fe is an isotope of iron (p = 26)
   Mass number = p + n = 56
   therefore n = 56 − 26 = 30

c) Gold-197, ^{197}Au is an isotope of gold (p = 79)
   Mass number = p + n = 197
   therefore n = 197 − 79 = 118

d) Uranium-238, ^{238}U is an isotope of uranium (p = 92)
   Mass number = p + n = 238
   therefore n = 238 − 92 = 146

Exercise 1.2B

1. State the number of protons, electrons and neutrons in an atom of ^{23}Na.

2. Explain why ^{23}Na and ^{24}Na are regarded as isotopes. *(CCEA June 2006)*

The **relative isotopic mass (RIM)** of an isotope is the mass of one atom of the isotope relative to one-twelfth of the mass of one atom of carbon-12. On this scale protons and neutrons have a mass of one and the RIM of an isotope is equal to the mass number of the isotope. For example, the RIM of an atom of carbon-12 (6 protons + 6 neutrons) is 12 and the RIM of an atom of carbon-13 (6 protons + 7 neutrons) is 13. Relative masses do not have units.

Worked Example 1.2iii

Which one of the following statements about the isotope carbon-14 is incorrect? *(CCEA June 2002)*

A   It is used as a standard for measuring mass
B   It has a relative isotopic mass of 14
C   It has a mass number of 14
D   It has eight neutrons

Solution

The standard for measuring mass is carbon-12. Statement A is incorrect.

Atomic Mass

The **relative atomic mass (RAM)** of an element is the average mass of one atom of the element relative to one-twelfth of the mass of an atom of carbon-12. The RAM of an element is obtained directly from the Periodic Table. For example, the RAM of nitrogen (N) is 14 and the RAM of silicon (Si) is 28.

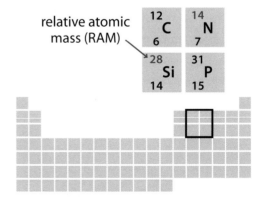

Before moving to the next section, check that you are able to:

- Describe the modern picture of the atom and recall the properties of the subatomic particles within an atom.
- Recall that elements are organised in order of increasing atomic number in the Periodic Table.
- Describe the formation of ions from atoms.
- Explain the existence of isotopes and use the mass number of an isotope to calculate the number of protons, electrons and neutrons in the isotope.
- Recall the definition of relative isotopic mass (RIM) and relative atomic mass (RAM) in terms of the mass of carbon-12.

Mass Spectrometry

Many elements contain significant amounts of two or more isotopes and, as a result, the atomic mass of the element can only be determined if the relative amount of each isotope in the element is known. This information is obtained using an experimental technique called mass spectrometry.

In a mass spectrometry experiment a small sample of the element is injected into a machine known as a mass spectrometer. Once in the spectrometer (Figure 3) the sample is vaporised and then bombarded with a beam of high energy electrons. The electrons in the beam knock electrons from the particles in the vapour to form positively charged ions; a process known as ionisation. For instance, when a sample of neon gas is injected into a mass spectrometer the neon atoms are converted to neon ions: $Ne_{(g)} + e^- \rightarrow Ne^+_{(g)} + 2e^-$. The Neon ions ($Ne^+$) are then accelerated and passed through a magnetic field. When a charged particle such as an ion passes through a magnetic field it experiences a force and is deflected from its path. The size of the deflection depends on the mass of the ion, making it possible to calculate the mass of the ion by measuring the size of the deflection. The number of ions detected is also recorded and used to construct the **mass spectrum** for the sample; a plot that shows the relative number of ions detected with each mass. The mass spectrum for neon gas is shown in Figure 4.

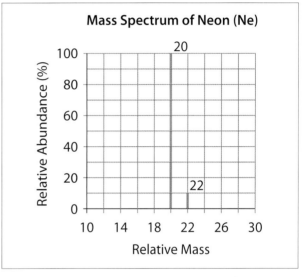

Figure 4: Mass spectrum for neon gas.

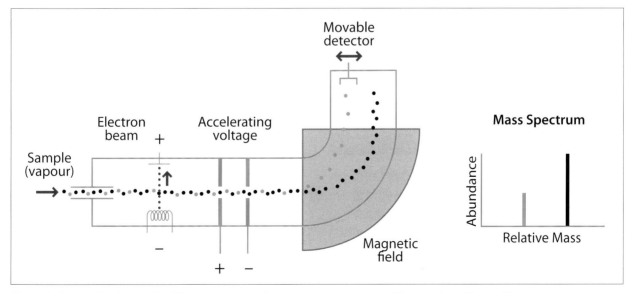

Figure 3: Separating ions with different masses using a mass spectrometer. The number of ions with each mass is recorded in the form of a mass spectrum.

In reality a mass spectrometer detects the mass-to-charge ratio (m/e) of each ion and it is common to see the horizontal axis of a mass spectrum labelled m/e. In routine mass spectrometry experiments the charge on the ions (e) is 1+ and the ratio m/e simply becomes the mass of the ion (m/1 = m). As a result, an axis labelled 'm/e' can be simply interpreted as the relative mass of the ions detected.

Calculating Atomic Mass

The mass spectrum for Neon in Figure 4 reveals that 91% of the neon atoms in a sample of neon gas are neon-20 and the remaining 9% are neon-22. In this way the mass spectrum for neon can be used to determine that every 100 neon atoms in a sample of neon gas is made up of 91 neon-20 atoms (RIM = 20) and 9 neon-22 atoms (RIM = 22).

If we recall that the relative atomic mass (RAM) of an element is defined to be the average mass of one atom of the element, the RAM for neon can be calculated from the relative abundance of each isotope as follows.

RAM of Ne =

$$\frac{\text{Mass of } ^{20}\text{Ne atoms} + \text{Mass of } ^{22}\text{Ne atoms}}{\text{Total number of atoms}} =$$

$$\frac{(91 \times 20) + (9 \times 22)}{100} = 20.2$$

If we compare the calculated RAM for neon with the value given on the Periodic Table, we are reminded that the RAMs on the Periodic Table are often rounded to the nearest whole number. This is a reasonable approximation when most of the atoms in an element are the same isotope. Chlorine is an exception. Chlorine contains two isotopes: ^{35}Cl (RIM = 35) and ^{37}Cl (RIM = 37). The RAM of chlorine is approximately half-way between 35 and 36 as chlorine contains significant amounts of both isotopes and the RAM of chlorine is usually rounded to 35.5 (1 decimal place).

Worked Example 1.2iv

Chlorine contains two isotopes: ^{35}Cl and ^{37}Cl. The relative abundance of the ^{35}Cl isotope is 76%. Calculate the atomic mass (RAM) of chlorine.

Solution

For every 100 atoms of chlorine in a sample of chlorine gas:

76 atoms (76%) are ^{35}Cl atoms and (100 – 76) = 24 atoms are ^{37}Cl atoms.

RAM of Cl =

$$\frac{\text{Mass of } ^{35}\text{Cl atoms} + \text{Mass of } ^{37}\text{Cl atoms}}{\text{Total number of atoms}} =$$

$$\frac{(35 \times 76) + (37 \times 24)}{100} = 35.5$$

Exercise 1.2C

Calculate the relative atomic mass of sodium in a sample containing 2.00% ^{24}Na and 98.00% ^{23}Na by mass to two decimal places. *(CCEA June 2006)*

The following example demonstrates how to calculate the RAM for an element containing more than two isotopes.

Worked Example 1.2v

A sample of carbon was found to have the following composition. Calculate the relative atomic mass of the carbon sample to two decimal places.

Isotope:	^{12}C	^{13}C	^{14}C
% abundance:	98.50	1.25	0.25

(CCEA June 2005)

Solution

For every 100 atoms of carbon: 98.50 atoms (98.50%) are ^{12}C atoms, 1.25 atoms (1.25%) are ^{13}C atoms and 0.25 (0.25%) are ^{14}C atoms.

RAM of C =

$$\frac{\text{Mass of } ^{12}\text{C atoms} + \text{Mass of } ^{13}\text{C atoms} + \text{Mass of } ^{14}\text{C atoms}}{\text{Total number of atoms}}$$

$$= \frac{(98.50 \times 12) + (1.25 \times 13) + (0.25 \times 14)}{100} = 12.02$$

Exercise 1.2D

1. Several isotopes of iodine are produced in nuclear reactions. The percentage abundance of each isotope in a sample of radioactive dust is given in the table. Calculate the relative atomic mass of iodine to one decimal place.

Isotope:	^{127}I	^{129}I	^{131}I
% abundance:	95.91	2.49	1.60

(CCEA June 2004)

2. Xenon has a number of naturally occurring isotopes. The percent abundance of each isotope is given in the table. Calculate the relative atomic mass of Xenon.

Relative Mass:	129	131	132	134	136
% abundance:	27	23	28	12	10

(CCEA January 2009)

Determining Molecular Mass

The technique of mass spectrometry can also be used to accurately determine the mass of individual molecules. The mass of a molecule is referred to as the **relative molecular mass (RMM)** of the molecule and is defined to be the mass of the molecule relative to one-twelfth of the mass of an atom of carbon-12.

When a molecule (M) enters the mass spectrometer it is vaporised before being ionised by collisions with a beam of high energy electrons.

$$M_{(g)} + e^-_{(g)} \rightarrow M^+_{(g)} + 2e^-_{(g)}$$

The molecular ions (M^+) formed by this process pass into the mass spectrometer and are detected. The **molecular ion** (M^+) has the same RMM as the molecule (M). As a result, the molecular ion (M^+) signal on a mass spectrum can be used to determine the RMM of the molecule (M). For example, the mass spectrum of naphthalene, $C_{10}H_8$ (Figure 5) contains a large molecular ion signal corresponding to an RMM of 128 and a significantly smaller signal corresponding to an RMM of 129. An RMM of 128 results from the ionisation and detection of molecules with the formula $^{12}C_{10}{}^1H_8$. The signal corresponding to an RMM of 129 reminds us that approximately 1 in every 100 carbon atoms is carbon-13 and, as a result, approximately 1 in every 10 molecules has the formula $^{12}C_9{}^{13}C_1H_8$. In this way we see that the RMM describes the mass of individual molecules and, by so doing, reflects the isotopes present in individual molecules.

Figure 5: Mass spectrum for naphthalene, $C_{10}H_8$.

Worked Example 1.2vi

The mass spectrum of molecular chlorine, Cl_2 is shown below. Which peak should not be present?

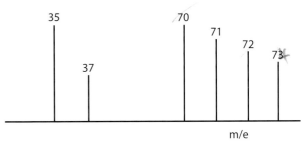

(CCEA January 2011)

Solution

The mass spectrum would be expected to contain a signal corresponding to each of the following RMMs.

Species:	^{35}Cl	^{37}Cl	$^{35}Cl^{35}Cl$	$^{35}Cl^{37}Cl$	$^{37}Cl^{37}Cl$
RMM:	35	37	70	72	74

The signal corresponding to an RMM of 71 does not correspond to an atom or molecule of chlorine and should not appear in the mass spectrum.

Exercise 1.2E

Chlorine exists as the isotopes, ^{35}Cl and ^{37}Cl with the result that the relative atomic mass of chlorine is 35.5. Which one of the following is correct?

a) The isotopes have different chemical properties.

b) The ^{37}Cl isotope has a natural abundance of 75%.

c) The mass spectrum of chlorine, Cl_2 includes peaks at 70, 72 and 74.

d) The nuclei of the isotopes have the same number of neutrons. *(CCEA June 2008)*

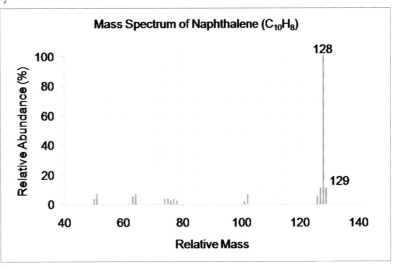

Before moving to the next section, check that you are able to:

- Calculate the relative atomic mass (RAM) of an element given the percent abundance of each isotope in the element.
- Explain the terms relative molecular mass (RMM) and molecular ion.
- Calculate the RMM of a molecule from its mass spectrum.

Atomic Structure

In this section we are learning to:

- Describe the arrangement of electrons in atoms in terms of atomic orbitals.
- Use spd-notation to write electron configurations for atoms and ions.
- Explain how ionisation energies can be used to provide evidence for electron shells and subshells in atoms.

Atoms are much too small to be seen with instruments such as a light microscope. They must, instead, be visualised with much more sensitive instruments such as a Scanning Tunnelling Microscope (STM). STM images of atoms on the surface of pieces of gold and silicon are shown in Figure 6. In an STM image each atom appears as a cloud of electrons that results from electrons moving within regions of space known as **atomic orbitals**.

Figure 6: STM images of atoms on the surface of (a) gold and (b) silicon.

Atomic Orbitals

The electrons in an atom are arranged in atomic orbitals. There are four types of atomic orbital: s, p, d and f. Each type of atomic orbital has a characteristic shape. An s-orbital is a sphere (ball) centred on the nucleus of the atom. In contrast, a p-orbital has 2 lobes and is shaped like a 'dumb-bell' with the nucleus between the lobes.

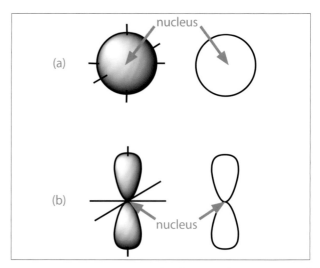

Figure 7: The shape and cross-section of (a) an s-orbital and (b) a p-orbital.

The shapes of the d and f orbitals are more complex. When drawing orbitals it is only necessary to draw the cross-section; the shape obtained by cutting through the orbital. The shapes and cross-sections of s and p-type atomic orbitals are shown in Figure 7.

In an atom the atomic orbitals are arranged in **shells**. Each shell is assigned a number (n) that is then used to identify the s, p, d and f orbitals belonging to the shell. For example, the first shell (n=1) contains one s-type atomic orbital. This orbital is referred to as the 1s orbital to indicate that it is an s-orbital belonging to the first shell (n=1). The second shell (n=2) contains one s-type orbital and a set of three p-type atomic orbitals. The s-orbital is referred to as the 2s orbital and the set of p-orbitals is referred to as the 2p orbitals to indicate that they belong to the second shell.

The sets of s, p, d and f orbitals belonging to each shell are known as **subshells**. We have already seen that the first shell contains the 1s subshell while the second shell contains the 2s and 2p subshells. The third shell (n=3) is bigger and consists of the 3s, 3p and 3d subshells. As with other s and p subshells, the 3s subshell contains a single s-type orbital and the 3p subshell contains a set of three p-type atomic orbitals. The 3d subshell consists of a set of five d-type atomic orbitals. Other d-type subshells such as the 4d and 5d subshells also contain a set of five d-type atomic orbitals. The fourth and fifth shells are larger still and contain sets of f-type atomic orbitals. The 4f and 5f subshells each contain seven f-type atomic orbitals.

Each atomic orbital holds a maximum of two electrons. As a result, the single s-orbital in an s-subshell holds a maximum of two electrons, the set

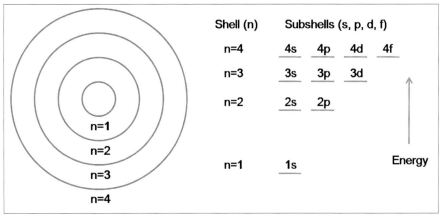

Figure 8: Energies of the subshells in a hydrogen atom.

of three p-orbitals in a p-subshell holds a maximum of 3 × 2 = 6 electrons, and the set of five d-orbitals in a d-subshell holds up to 5 × 2 = 10 electrons. The sets of seven f-orbitals in the 4f and 5f subshells each hold up to 7 × 2 = 14 electrons.

The energies of the subshells belonging to the first four shells in a hydrogen atom (n=1–4) are shown in Figure 8. In a hydrogen atom the atomic orbitals in the subshells associated with a shell have the same energy. As a result the electron in a hydrogen atom has the same energy when it occupies any of the atomic orbitals in the 3s, 3p and 3d subshells. This situation is unique to hydrogen and ions containing one electron such as He^+, Li^{2+} and Be^{3+}. In atoms and ions with two or more electrons, the atomic orbitals in different subshells have different energies.

Electron Configuration

Atoms with more than one electron are referred to as **multielectron atoms**. The distribution of the electrons amongst the subshells in a multielectron atom is referred to as the **electron configuration** of the atom. For example, the electron configuration of a nitrogen atom is: $(1s)^2 (2s)^2 (2p)^3$. The electron configuration for nitrogen indicates that the 1s subshell holds two electrons, the 2s subshell holds two electrons and the remaining three electrons are in the 2p subshell.

When writing the electron configuration for an atom the subshells are written in the order in which they fill with electrons. In a multielectron atom the lowest energy subshell fills first. The subshells then fill in order of increasing energy until all of the electrons have been placed in subshells. This procedure is known as the **Aufbau principle** or 'building-up' principle.

The energies of the subshells in a multielectron atom are illustrated in Figure 9. According to the Aufbau principle the subshells in a multielectron atom fill in the order: 1s (lowest energy), 2s, 2p, 3s, 3p, 4s, 3d, 4p ... The subshell filling order in a multielectron atom can be remembered by 'following the arrows' in the construction shown in Figure 9b.

The electron configuration obtained using the Aufbau principle is the lowest energy configuration for the electrons and is referred to as the **ground state** of the atom.

Worked Example 1.2vii

Write the ground state electron configuration for an atom of: (a) helium, (b) lithium, (c) oxygen, (d) aluminium and (e) iron.

Strategy

- Recall that subshells fill in the order: 1s 2s 2p 3s 3p 4s 3d ...
- Recall that an s-subshell holds up to 2 electrons, a p-subshell holds up to 6 electrons and a d-subshell holds up to 10 electrons.

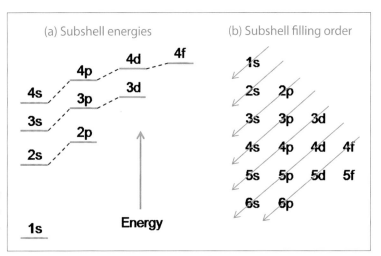

Figure 9: The (a) energies of the subshells and (b) filling order of the subshells in a multielectron atom. The filling order is given by 'following the arrows'.

Solution

(a) Helium has two electrons. Both electrons occupy the 1s subshell. The electron configuration is $(1s)^2$.

(b) Lithium has three electrons. Two electrons occupy the 1s subshell. The third goes in the 2s subshell. The electron configuration is $(1s)^2 (2s)^1$.

(c) Oxygen has eight electrons. The first four electrons occupy the 1s and 2s subshells. The remaining four electrons occupy the 2p subshell. The electron configuration is $(1s)^2 (2s)^2 (2p)^4$.

(d) Aluminium has 13 electrons. The 1s, 2s, 2p and 3s subshells hold 12 electrons. The remaining electron occupies the 3p subshell. The electron configuration is $(1s)^2 (2s)^2 (2p)^6 (3s)^2 (3p)^1$.

(e) Iron has 26 electrons. The 1s, 2s, 2p, 3s and 3p subshells hold 18 electrons. The remaining eight electrons occupy the 4s and 3d subshells. The electron configuration is $(1s)^2 (2s)^2 (2p)^6 (3s)^2 (3p)^6 (4s)^2 (3d)^6$.

....

Electron Configurations for Ions

The Aufbau principle can also be used to determine the ground state electron configuration for ions. In the case of a negative ion the electron configuration is obtained by adding electrons to the electron configuration for the corresponding atom. For example, the electron configuration for a chloride (Cl^-) ion is obtained by adding one electron to the electron configuration for a chlorine atom.

$(1s)^2(2s)^2(2p)^6(3s)^2(3p)^5$ ➡ $(1s)^2(2s)^2(2p)^6(3s)^2(3p)^6$
chlorine atom: Cl   chloride ion: Cl^-

The electron configuration for a positive ion is obtained by removing electrons from the electron configuration for the corresponding atom. For example, the electron configuration for a sodium (Na^+) ion is obtained by removing one electron from the electron configuration for a sodium atom. The electrons in the highest energy orbitals are the easiest to remove and are removed first. As a result, when removing electrons, the Aufbau principle is followed but in reverse.

$(1s)^2(2s)^2(2p)^6(3s)^1$ ➡ $(1s)^2(2s)^2(2p)^6$
sodium atom: Na   sodium ion: Na^+

....

Worked Example 1.2viii

Use spd-notation to write the ground state electron configuration for (a) Mg^{2+} (b) F^- and c) S^{2-}.

Strategy

- Write the electron configuration for the atom.
- Add or remove electrons to form the electron configuration for the ion.

Solution

(a) The electron configuration for a magnesium atom is $(1s)^2 (2s)^2 (2p)^6 (3s)^2$. The electron configuration for a magnesium ion (Mg^{2+}) is obtained by removing two electrons. The electron configuration for a Mg^{2+} ion is $(1s)^2 (2s)^2 (2p)^6$.

(b) The electron configuration for a fluorine atom is $(1s)^2 (2s)^2 (2p)^5$. The electron configuration for a fluoride ion (F^-) is obtained by adding one electron. The electron configuration for a F^- ion is $(1s)^2 (2s)^2 (2p)^6$.

(c) The electron configuration for a sulfur atom is $(1s)^2 (2s)^2 (2p)^6 (3s)^2 (3p)^4$. The electron configuration for a sulfide ion (S^{2-}) is obtained by adding two electrons. The electron configuration for a S^{2-} ion is $(1s)^2 (2s)^2 (2p)^6 (3s)^2 (3p)^6$.

....

Exercise 1.2F

1. Calcium oxide is an ionic substance. Use spd-notation to show the formation of a calcium ion and an oxide ion from a calcium atom and an oxygen atom and state the charge on each ion. *(CCEA January 2006)*

2. Write the ground state electron configuration for (a) neon and (b) argon. Which of the following ions have the same ground state electron configuration as (c) neon and (d) argon?

Li^+ Al^{3+} F^- Cl^- K^+

The situation is slightly different when removing electrons from the group of metals known as the d-block elements. The d-block is located between groups II and III on the Periodic Table and contains the elements Sc-Zn, Y-Cd and La-Hg. In a d-block element the outermost electrons occupy a d-subshell. For example, the ground state electron configuration of an iron atom (Fe) is ... $(3s)^2 (3p)^6 (4s)^2 (3d)^6$. When a d-block element forms a positive ion electrons are first removed from the outermost s-subshell, and then from the d-subshell until the required number of electrons has been removed. In the case of iron $(4s^2 3d^6)$, an iron(II) ion, Fe^{2+} is formed by removing two electrons from the 4s subshell. An iron(III) ion, Fe^{3+} can then be formed by removing a further electron from the 3d subshell.

$$\ldots (3s)^2 (3p)^6 (4s)^2 (3d)^6 \implies \ldots (3s)^2 (3p)^6 (3d)^6$$
$$\text{iron atom: Fe} \qquad \text{iron(II) ion: Fe}^{2+}$$

$$\implies \ldots (3s)^2 (3p)^6 (3d)^5$$
$$\text{iron(III) ion: Fe}^{3+}$$

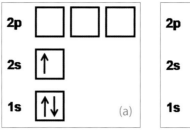
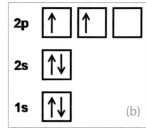
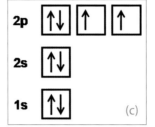

Figure 10: Electrons-in-boxes representation of the electrons in an atom of (a) lithium, (b) carbon and (c) oxygen.

Worked Example 1.2ix

Use spd-notation to write the electron configuration for the ground state of a V^{2+} ion. *(CCEA June 2008)*

Strategy

* Write the ground state electron configuration for a vanadium atom.
* Remove two electrons from the outermost s-subshell.

Solution

Ground state for V atom:
$(1s)^2 (2s)^2 (2p)^6 (3s)^2 (3p)^6 (4s)^2 (3d)^3$

Ground state for V^{2+} ion:
$(1s)^2 (2s)^2 (2p)^6 (3s)^2 (3p)^6 (3d)^3$

Exercise 1.2G

1. Use spd-notation to write the ground state electron configuration for the following atoms and ions.

   a) Mn   b) Mn^{2+} c) Zn^{2+} d) Ni

2. Use spd-notation to write the ground state electron configuration for the following atoms and ions.

   a) Sc   b) V   c) V^{3+} d) Ca

Electron Spin

Electrons have a property called **spin**. Each atomic orbital holds a maximum of two electrons: one 'spin-up' ($\uparrow$) the other 'spin-down' ($\downarrow$). The spin of the electrons in each atomic orbital can be shown by drawing the electron configuration of an atom or ion in the form of 'electrons-in-boxes'. The electrons-in-boxes representations for the electrons in atoms of lithium, carbon and oxygen are shown in Figure 10.

In an electrons-in-boxes representation each atomic orbital is represented by a box. The subshells are drawn in energy order with the orbitals in each subshell arranged side-by-side. The electrons-in-boxes configurations are obtained by applying the Aufbau principle while remembering to add one electron to each orbital in a subshell ($\uparrow$) before pairing the electrons ($\uparrow\downarrow$). For example, in lithium (Figure 10a) two electrons pair up in the 1s orbital: one spin-up ($\uparrow$), the other spin-down ($\downarrow$). The third electron then occupies the 2s orbital. In carbon (Figure 10b) the first four electrons pair up in the 1s and 2s orbitals. The remaining electrons each occupy a p-type orbital in the 2p subshell. And finally, in oxygen (Figure 10c), the 2p subshell contains additional electrons that begin to pair up once each orbital in the subshell contains a single electron ($\uparrow$).

Exercise 1.2H

1. Which one of the following electron configurations contains two unpaired electrons?

   a) $1s^2 2s^1$ b) $1s^2 2s^2 2p^3$ c) $1s^2 2s^2 2p^4$
   d) $1s^2 2s^2 2p^6 3s^2 3p^5$

   (CCEA June 2006)

2. Which of the following atoms contains one unpaired electron in its ground state?

   sulfur   fluorine   potassium   argon

   (Adapted from CCEA June 2011)

Exceptions to the Aufbau Principle

The Aufbau principle can be used to reliably predict the ground state electron configuration for most elements and ions. The ground state electron configurations for chromium and copper are amongst the few configurations not predicted correctly by the Aufbau principle. According to the Aufbau principle, the electron configurations for chromium and copper should be:

Cr $[Ar] (4s)^2 (3d)^4$ and Cu $[Ar] (4s)^2 (3d)^9$

where we have used the shorthand [Ar] to represent the electron configuration of an argon atom. The electron configurations are instead found to be:

Cr $[Ar] (4s)^1 (3d)^5$ and Cu $[Ar] (4s)^1 (3d)^{10}$

These exceptions demonstrate that an electron configuration with a half-filled or completely filled d-subshell such as s^1d^5 or s^1d^{10} is more stable than a configuration with a part-filled d-subshell such as s^2d^4 or s^2d^9.

> Before moving to the next section, check that you are able to:
>
> - Describe the shape of s and p orbitals and draw their cross-section.
> - Use the Aufbau principle to construct the ground state electron configuration for atoms and ions of the elements in the first four periods (up to Kr).
> - Use electrons-in-boxes notation to describe the filling of subshells.
> - Explain exceptions to the Aufbau principle in terms of the stability of filled and half-filled subshells.

Evidence for Shells and Subshells

The **first ionisation energy (IE1)** of an element is defined as the energy needed to remove one mole of electrons from one mole of gaseous atoms to form one mole of gaseous ions with a single positive charge.

First ionisation energy (IE1): $E_{(g)} \rightarrow E^+_{(g)} + e^-_{(g)}$

The plot of IE1 against atomic number in Figure 11 reveals that IE1 generally increases from left to right across a period. Smaller fluctuations in IE1 across a period can be explained in terms of the arrangement of electrons in subshells and provide direct evidence for the existence of subshells in atoms. The plot of IE1 against atomic number in Figure 11 also reveals that IE1 decreases down a group. This is particularly evident for the noble gases (Group VIII) and the Alkali Metals (Group I).

Trend in IE1 within a Group

The orbitals in a subshell get bigger as the energy of the subshell increases.

Subshell energy increasing

$1s < 2s < 2p < 3s < 3p < 4s < 3d < 4p < ...$

Orbital size increasing

In a multielectron atom the electrons in the outermost (biggest) subshell are attracted to the nucleus and, at the same time, repelled by electrons in the smaller subshells closer to the nucleus. This

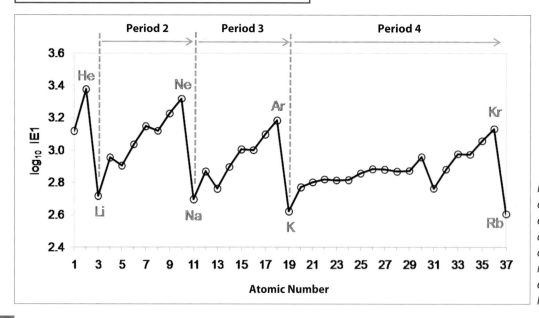

Figure 11: Graph of first ionisation energy (plotted as $\log_{10}$ IE1) against atomic number for the elements in Periods 1–4.

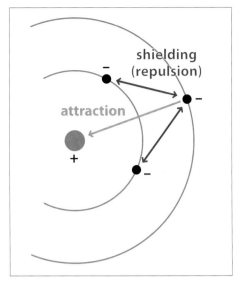

Figure 12: Shielding of the outer electrons in a multielectron atom.

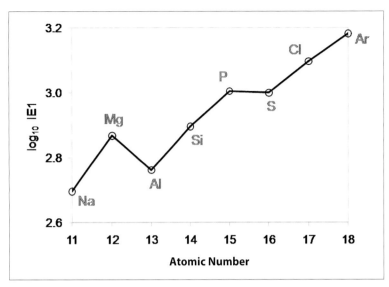

Figure 13: Graph of first ionisation energy (plotted as $\log_{10}$ IE1) against atomic number for the elements belonging to the third period.

repulsion between electrons has the effect of reducing the attraction felt by the electrons in the outermost subshell and is referred to as **shielding**. The shielding of outer electrons from the nucleus is illustrated in Figure 12. As the number of filled subshells increases, electrons in the outermost subshell are further from the nucleus and better shielded by electrons in the subshells closer to the nucleus. This allows the electrons in the outermost subshell to be more easily removed from the atom and explains why IE1 decreases down a group in the Periodic Table.

Exercise 1.2I

State two reasons why the first ionisation energy of calcium is less than that of magnesium.

(CCEA January 2009)

Trend in IE1 Across a Period

The plot of IE1 against atomic number in Figure 11 demonstrates that IE1 generally increases on going from left to right across a period. Increasing the atomic number of an atom by one is equivalent to adding a proton to the nucleus and an electron to the outermost subshell of an atom. Adding an electron to the outermost subshell does not increase shielding of the electrons already in the outermost subshell. As a result the electrons in the outermost subshell are more strongly attracted to the nucleus and become harder to remove. This explains why, in general, IE1 increases as the atomic number of the elements increases from left to right across a period.

The plot of IE1 against atomic number in Figure 11 also reveals similar variations in IE1 across period 2, period 3, and those groups in period 4 in common with periods 2 and 3. The variations in IE1 across a period can be explained by the order in which the electrons occupy the outermost subshells. In this way, the variations in IE1 across a period can be used as evidence to support the existence of subshells, and the subshell filling order as defined by the Aufbau principle.

Consider, for example, the variations in IE1 across Period 3 (Figure 13). The electron configuration for a sodium atom is: $(1s)^2(2s)^2(2p)^6(3s)^1$. The single 3s electron is the only electron in the n=3 shell and is effectively shielded by the electrons in the smaller 1s, 2s and 2p subshells that lie between the 3s electron and the nucleus. As a result the 3s electron experiences a relatively small attraction to the nucleus, and is easy to remove.

Magnesium has an additional electron in the 3s subshell. The electron configuration for a magnesium atom is: $(1s)^2(2s)^2(2p)^6(3s)^2$. Shielding of the 3s electrons in magnesium is similar to the shielding experienced by the 3s electron in sodium. As a result, the 3s electrons in magnesium experience a greater attraction to the nucleus and are harder to remove than the single 3s electron in sodium. This explains why IE1 for magnesium is greater than IE1 for sodium.

The electron configuration for an aluminium atom is: $(1s)^2(2s)^2(2p)^6(3s)^2(3p)^1$. The electron in the 3p subshell has a higher energy than the electrons in the

3s subshell and is therefore easier to remove from the atom. This explains why IE1 for aluminium is less than IE1 for magnesium.

IE1 then increases steadily from aluminium ($3p^1$) to phosphorus ($3p^3$) as electrons are added to the 3p subshell. Adding electrons to the 3p subshell does not increase the shielding of the electrons already in the 3p subshell with the result that the electrons in the 3p subshell are more strongly attracted to the nucleus and become harder to remove as the charge on the nucleus increases from aluminium to phosphorus.

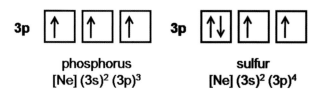

phosphorus
[Ne] $(3s)^2 (3p)^3$

sulfur
[Ne] $(3s)^2 (3p)^4$

The electrons-in-boxes description of the 3p electrons in phosphorus ($3p^3$) and sulfur ($3p^4$) reveals that while the 3p electrons in phosphorus are equivalent, the 3p electrons in sulfur are not equivalent. In sulfur some of the electrons in the 3p subshell are paired while others remain unpaired. Electrons that have become paired repel (both are negatively charged) and are therefore easier to remove than electrons in the same subshell that remain unpaired. In this way we can explain why IE1 for sulfur is less than might otherwise be expected.

The unexpectedly low IE1 for sulfur can also be explained by noting that IE1 for phosphorus ($3p^3$) is, in fact, higher than might be expected on account of the stability associated with a half-filled subshell (p^3). The stability associated with a half-filled subshell has previously been used in a similar way to explain why an $s^1 d^5$ electron configuration is preferred over an $s^2 d^4$ configuration in chromium.

IE1 then increases from sulfur ($3p^4$) to argon ($3p^6$) as the atomic number increases and the electrons in the outermost 3p subshell become more strongly attracted to the nucleus. The increase in IE1 towards the right of the period can also be attributed to the stability associated with a full subshell of electrons ($3p^6$) in the same way as the stability associated with a full d-subshell was used to explain the preference for an $s^1 d^{10}$ configuration over an $s^2 d^9$ configuration in copper.

When taken together, these explanations provide considerable evidence for the existence of subshells, and the subshell filling order defined by the Aufbau principle.

Worked Example 1.2x

The graph below shows the first ionisation energy (IE1) for the first twelve elements:

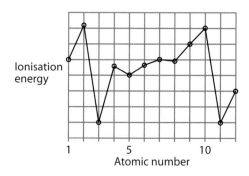

a) Explain why oxygen has a lower IE1 than nitrogen.

b) Explain why lithium and sodium have a low IE1.

c) Explain why helium and neon have a high IE1.

d) Write the equation defining IE1 for beryllium. Include state symbols. *(CCEA June 2007)*

Solution

a) The electron configuration for oxygen is $(1s)^2 (2s)^2 (2p)^4$. The electron removed from the 2p subshell in oxygen is paired and is therefore easier to remove than an unpaired electron from the 2p subshell in nitrogen.

Alternative answer:

The electron configuration for nitrogen is $(1s)^2 (2s)^2 (2p)^3$. The electron removed from the 2p subshell in nitrogen belongs to a half-filled subshell and is therefore more difficult to remove than an electron from the 2p subshell in oxygen.

b) Lithium and sodium have one electron in their outermost shell. The electron in the outermost shell is well shielded from the nucleus and is therefore easily removed from the atom.

Alternative answer:

Lithium and sodium have one electron in their outermost shell. The electron in the outermost shell is easily removed to form a stable ion with a full outer shell of electrons.

c) Helium and neon have full outer shells and are stable.

d) Be $_{(g)}$ → Be$^+$ $_{(g)}$ + e$^-$ $_{(g)}$

Exercise 1.2J

1. (a) What is meant by the term ground state?

   (b) Use electrons-in-boxes notation to represent the ground state of a phosphorus atom.

   (c) Explain why phosphorus has an unusually high first ionisation energy.

   (CCEA January 2003)

2. Which one of the following lists the first ionisation energies (in kJ mol^{-1}) for magnesium, aluminium, silicon, phosphorus and sulfur in this order?

   (a) 496   736   577   786   1060

   (b) 577   786   1060   1000   1260

   (c) 736   577   786   1060   1000

   (d) 786   1060   1000   1260   1520

   (CCEA January 2011)

3. The graph represents the first ionisation energies of the elements sodium to argon.

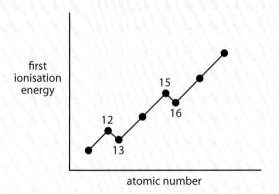

   (a) Explain the general rise in the first ionisation energy across the period.

   (b) Explain the decrease in ionisation energy from atomic number 12 to 13.

   (c) Explain the decrease in ionisation energy from atomic number 15 to 16.

   (CCEA January 2008)

Successive Ionisation

Some of the most direct evidence for the existence of shells in atoms is revealed by plotting successive ionisation energies (IE1, IE2, IE3, ...) for an atom.

Second ionisation energy (IE2): $E^+_{(g)} \rightarrow E^{2+}_{(g)} + e^-_{(g)}$

Third ionisation energy (IE3): $E^{2+}_{(g)} \rightarrow E^{3+}_{(g)} + e^-_{(g)}$

Fourth ionisation energy (IE4): $E^{3+}_{(g)} \rightarrow E^{4+}_{(g)} + e^-_{(g)}$

etc

Consider, for example, successive ionisation of a magnesium atom. The electron configuration for magnesium is: $(1s)^2(2s)^2(2p)^6(3s)^2$. The first and second ionisation energies (IE1 and IE2) are the energies needed to remove the first and then the second electron from the outermost 3s subshell. The next six ionisation energies (IE3 to IE8) detail the energy needed to successively remove electrons from the 2p subshell. The ionisation energies IE9 to IE12 then detail the energy needed to remove electrons from the 2s subshell (IE9 and IE10) and the 1s subshell (IE11 and IE12).

The successive ionisation energies for magnesium are plotted in Figure 14. Electrons in the 3s subshell (n=3 shell) have low IE's as they are furthest from the nucleus and experience the greatest shielding. Electrons in the 2s and 2p subshells (n=2 shell) are closer to the nucleus and are less shielded than the electrons in the 3s subshell (n=3 shell). As a result, electrons in the second (n=2) shell are more strongly attracted to the nucleus and are harder to remove than electrons in the third (n=3) shell. This explains why the IE's for the electrons in the second shell (IE3 to IE10) are significantly greater than the ionisation energies for the electrons in the third shell (IE1 and IE2). The electrons in the 1s subshell (n=1) are even more difficult to remove as they are closest to the nucleus and are less shielded than the electrons in the second shell. As a result, the IE's for the 1s electrons

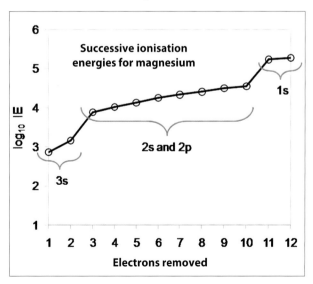

Figure 14: Successive ionisation energies for magnesium (plotted as $\log_{10}$ IE).

(IE11 and IE12) are significantly greater than the IE's for the electrons in the second shell (IE3 to IE10). In this way the successive ionisation energies for an atom can be used as evidence for the existence of electron shells in atoms.

Worked Example 1.2xi

The first four ionisation energies of aluminium are 578, 1817, 2745 and 11578 kJ mol^{-1}. Label the subshells in the following diagram and use the electrons-in-boxes notation to show how the electrons are arranged in an Al^{2+} ion.

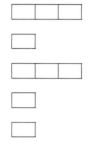

a) Write the equation used to define the fourth ionisation energy of aluminium. Include state symbols.

b) Explain why the third ionisation energy of aluminium is much smaller than the fourth ionisation energy.

(CCEA January 2010)

Solution

3p ☐☐☐   a) Al^{3+} (g) → Al^{4+} (g) + e$^-$ (g)

3s ↑   b) The outermost (3s) electron in Al^{2+} is further from the nucleus
2p ↑↓↑↓↑↓   and better shielded than the
2s ↑↓   outermost (2p) electrons in Al^{3+}.
1s ↑↓

Exercise 1.2K

1. (a) Give two reasons why potassium has a lower first ionisation energy than sodium.

   (b) Why is the second ionisation energy for a Group I metal much higher than the first ionisation energy? *(CCEA June 2011)*

2. The first six ionisation energies of an element Z are: 590, 1100, 4900, 6500, 8100 and 10500 kJ mol^{-1}. Which ion is formed when Z reacts with chlorine?

   (a) Z^+ (b) Z^{2+} (c) Z^- (d) Z^{2-}

   (CCEA January 2004)

3. The first six ionisation energies of an element M are: 578, 1817, 2745, 11578, 14831 and 18378 kJ mol^{-1}. What is the formula of the oxide of M?

   (a) MO   (b) MO_2 (c) M_2O (d) M_2O_3

   (CCEA January 2006)

4. Plot the successive ionisation energies of aluminium. *(CCEA June 2010)*

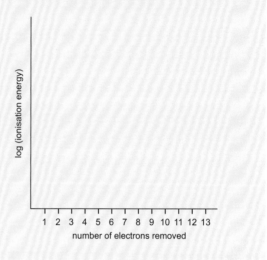

Before moving to the next section, check that you are able to:

- Explain trends in IE1 within a group in terms of orbital size and the shielding of electrons.

- Explain trends in IE1 across a period in terms of the filling of subshells and the stability associated with filled and half-filled subshells.

- Define the successive ionisation energies of an atom and account for the size of successive ionisation energies in terms of the filling of subshells.

Atomic Spectroscopy

In this section we are learning to:

- Explain the emission of radiation from atoms in terms of electrons moving between shells.
- Calculate the frequency, wavelength and energy of radiation emitted from atoms.
- Relate the convergence of wavelengths in the hydrogen emission spectrum to the spacing of energy levels in a hydrogen atom.
- Calculate the first ionisation energy for hydrogen from the hydrogen emission spectrum.

When an electric current is passed through a gas, the atoms in the gas emit visible light. Often the colour of light emitted makes the element suitable for a particular use. For instance, the intense yellow colour emitted by sodium vapour makes it ideal for use in fog lamps. The study of the absorption and emission of light and other non-visible frequencies by atoms is referred to as atomic spectroscopy.

Electromagnetic Radiation

The term visible light refers to one type of electromagnetic (EM) radiation. Other non-visible types of EM radiation include: infra-red radiation, ultra-violet radiation, microwaves and X-rays. All types of EM radiation behave as a wave; a series of evenly spaced peaks and troughs similar to water waves. The distance between adjacent crests (or troughs) is known as the **wavelength** of the wave and is given the Greek symbol lambda, λ (pronounced 'lamb-da'). The wavelengths corresponding to several different colours of visible light are compared in Figure 15. The wavelength of visible light is conveniently measured in nanometres (symbol: nm) where $1 \text{ nm} = 1 \times 10^{-9}$ m.

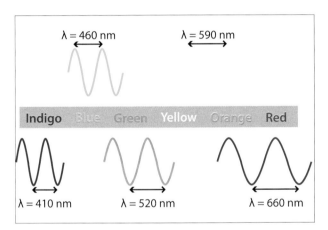

Figure 15: Wavelengths for several different colours of visible light.

All EM radiation travels at the speed of light (symbol: c) where $c = 3.00 \times 10^8$ m s^{-1}. The speed of light can be used to relate the wavelength of EM radiation to its **frequency** (symbol: f) as shown in equation 1. Frequency is measured in units of 'per second' (unit: s^{-1}) and refers to the number of wave crests passing a point every second. Frequency may also be reported in units of Hertz (symbol: Hz) where $1 \text{ Hz} = 1 \text{ s}^{-1}$.

$$c = f\,\lambda \quad \textbf{(Equation 1)}$$

Worked Example 1.2xii

Calculate the frequency of (a) red light with a wavelength of 650 nm and (b) blue light with a wavelength of 460 nm.

Solution

a) frequency of red light, $f = \dfrac{c}{\lambda} =$

$$\frac{3.00 \times 10^8 \text{ ms}^{-1}}{650 \times 10^{-9} \text{ m}} = 4.62 \times 10^{14} \text{ s}^{-1}$$

b) frequency of blue light, $f = \dfrac{c}{\lambda} =$

$$\frac{3.00 \times 10^8 \text{ ms}^{-1}}{460 \times 10^{-9} \text{ m}} = 6.52 \times 10^{14} \text{ s}^{-1}$$

The worked example clearly demonstrates that frequency and wavelength are inversely related; as one increases the other decreases.

The Hydrogen Emission Spectrum

When an electric current is passed through a sample of hydrogen gas the hydrogen molecules (H_2) dissociate into atoms. If a hydrogen atom gains sufficient energy the electron in the hydrogen atom can move from the 1s orbital in the n=1 shell to an orbital associated with a higher energy shell (n=2,3,...). The electron can then lose its energy by emitting EM radiation and returning to a lower energy shell as illustrated in Figure 16.

The frequency of the radiation emitted (f) when the electron moves from a shell with energy (E_2) to a shell with a lower energy (E_1) can be calculated using equation 2. The constant, $h = 6.63 \times 10^{-34}$ Js is known as Planck's constant.

$$E_2 - E_1 = h\,f \quad \textbf{(Equation 2)}$$

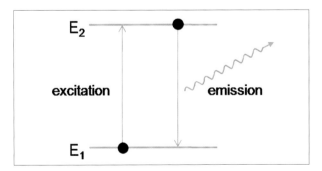

Figure 16: The emission of radiation after the electron in a hydrogen atom has been excited to a higher energy shell.

Worked Example 1.2xiii

Hydrogen atoms emit red light with a wavelength of 656 nm when the electron returns to the n=2 shell from the n=3 shell. Calculate the energy difference between the n=2 and n=3 shells in units of kJ mol⁻¹.

Strategy

The energy difference between the shells ($E_3 - E_2$) is equal to the energy of the light emitted (hf).

- Use the wavelength to calculate the energy of the red light.
- Multiply by Avogadro's number to convert to J mol⁻¹.
- Divide by 1000 to convert to kJ mol⁻¹.

Solution

a) Frequency of red light, $f = \dfrac{c}{\lambda}$

$$= \frac{3.00 \times 10^8 \text{ ms}^{-1}}{656 \times 10^{-9} \text{ m}} = 4.57 \times 10^{14} \text{ s}^{-1}$$

Energy of red light $= h\,f$

$$= (6.63 \times 10^{-34})(4.57 \times 10^{14}) = 3.03 \times 10^{-19} \text{ J}$$

Energy difference between n=2 and n=3:

$$E_3 - E_2 = h\,f = 3.03 \times 10^{-19} \text{ J}$$

Convert to J mol⁻¹ and then kJ mol⁻¹:

$$E_3 - E_2 = (3.03 \times 10^{-19})(6.02 \times 10^{23})$$

$$= 1.82 \times 10^5 \text{ J mol}^{-1} = 182 \text{ kJ mol}^{-1}$$

The set of wavelengths produced when atoms of an element are excited and emit radiation is known as the emission spectrum of the element. The wavelengths in the visible portion of the hydrogen emission spectrum are summarised in Figure 17.

The emission spectrum reveals that the spacing between wavelengths decreases as the wavelength of the light decreases. This suggests that the difference between successive wavelengths will continue to decrease, and the series will eventually converge, when the difference between successive wavelengths becomes zero. This type of behaviour also indicates that the wavelengths in the visible portion of the hydrogen emission spectrum are related.

The electron transitions giving rise to wavelengths in

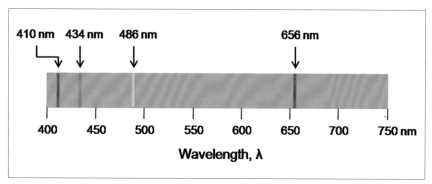

Figure 17: Wavelengths in the visible portion of the hydrogen emission spectrum.

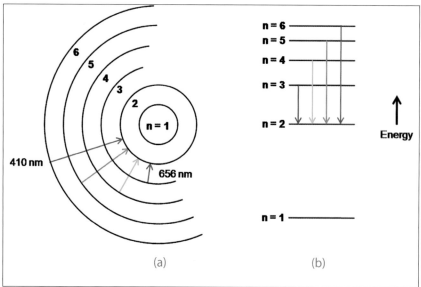

Figure 18: (a) Electron transitions giving rise to wavelengths in the visible portion of the hydrogen emission spectrum. (b) The corresponding energy changes.

the visible part of the hydrogen emission spectrum are drawn in Figure 18a. The transitions in Figure 18a reveal that wavelengths in the visible part of the hydrogen emission spectrum are produced when the electron in a hydrogen atom returns to the n=2 shell from a higher energy shell (n=3,4,5...). The corresponding energy changes in Figure 18b reveal that the smallest frequency (longest wavelength) is produced when the electron returns to the n=2 shell from the n=3 shell. Higher frequencies (shorter wavelengths) are produced when the electron returns to the n=2 shell from higher energy shells (n=3,4,5...).

Exercise 1.2L

1. Which one of the following electron transitions is responsible for the lowest frequency line in the visible region of the emission spectrum of atomic hydrogen. *(CCEA June 2010)*

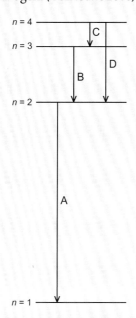

2. Which one of the following is a correct description of electronic transitions in a given series in the atomic emission spectrum of hydrogen?

   a) They all start from the ground state.
   b) They all end in the ground state.
   c) They all start from one particular energy level.
   d) They all end at one particular energy level.
   (CCEA January 2011)

3. The emission line spectrum of atomic hydrogen arises when

   a) hydrogen atoms lose electrons to form ions.

b) hydrogen atoms combine together to form molecules.
c) electrons move to energy levels further away from the nuclei.
d) electrons move to energy levels closer to the nuclei. *(CCEA June 2002)*

4. Which one of the following statements about the line emission spectrum for atomic hydrogen is incorrect?

   a) Electromagnetic radiation is emitted when the electron is promoted to a higher energy level.
   b) The electron can only move between fixed energy levels.
   c) In the visible region of the spectrum the electron returns to the n=2 energy level.
   d) The lines in the spectrum converge as frequency increases. *(CCEA June 2003)*

The series of visible wavelengths produced by transitions to the n=2 shell (Figure 18) is known as the **Balmer series**. Transitions to the n=1 shell give rise to a similar series of wavelengths known as the **Lyman series** in the ultra-violet region of the emission spectrum (below 400 nm). Several wavelengths belonging to the Lyman series are shown in Figure 19. As in the Balmer series, the wavelengths in the Lyman series converge. The transitions to the n=2 shell in Figure 18 demonstrate that the wavelengths in the Balmer series converge as the energies of the shells get closer together. The wavelength at which the series converges is known as the **convergence limit** and corresponds to the point at which *the energy spacing between the electron shells has become zero.*

In the Lyman series (Figure 19) the convergence limit corresponds to the wavelength emitted when the electron returns to the n=1 shell from the shell with the highest possible energy (very large n). The energy lost by the electron in this process is equivalent to the energy needed to ionise hydrogen.

Ionising hydrogen:

$$H_{(g)} \rightarrow H^+_{(g)} + e^-_{(g)}$$

electron in   very large n
n=1 shell

As a result, the wavelength at the convergence limit can be used to calculate the ionisation energy for

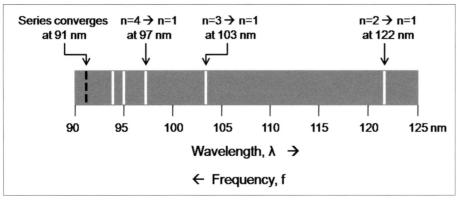

Figure 19: Wavelengths belonging to the Lyman series in the ultra-violet portion of the hydrogen emission spectrum.

hydrogen. The relationship between the wavelength at the convergence limit, λ_{limit} the corresponding frequency, f_{limit} and the ionisation energy (IE) is given in equation 3.

$$\text{IE} = \text{h } f_{limit} \quad \text{where} \quad f_{limit} = \frac{c}{\lambda_{limit}} \quad \text{(Equation 3)}$$

Worked Example 1.2xiv

The ultra-violet portion of the hydrogen emission spectrum is shown in the diagram.

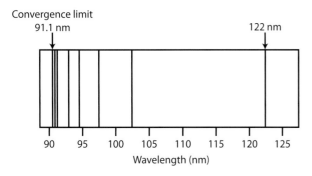

a) Which transition is responsible for the line at 122 nm?

b) Explain what is meant by the convergence limit.

c) Write an equation, including state symbols, for the ionisation of atomic hydrogen.

d) Use the information in the spectrum to calculate the frequency of the line at the convergence limit.

e) Use this frequency to calculate the energy needed to ionise (i) one hydrogen atom and (ii) one mole of hydrogen atoms in units of kJ mol⁻¹.

(CCEA June 2009)

Solution

a) The transition from n=2 to n=1.

b) The convergence limit is the frequency that provides just enough energy to remove an electron from the atom.

c) $H_{(g)} \rightarrow H^+_{(g)} + e^-_{(g)}$

d) Frequency, $f_{limit} = \dfrac{c}{\lambda_{limit}} = \dfrac{3.00 \times 10^8 \text{ ms}^{-1}}{91.1 \times 10^{-9} \text{ m}}$

$= 3.29 \times 10^{15} \text{ s}^{-1}$

e) i) IE = h f_{limit} = $(6.63 \times 10^{-34})(3.29 \times 10^{15})$

$= 2.18 \times 10^{-18}$ J

ii) IE = $(2.18 \times 10^{-18})(6.02 \times 10^{23})$

$= 1.32 \times 10^6$ J mol⁻¹ = 1320 kJ mol⁻¹

Exercise 1.2M

1. The ionisation energy of hydrogen is 1312 kJ mol⁻¹. Use this value to calculate the frequency at convergence in the hydrogen emission spectrum. *(CCEA June 2010)*

2. (a) Write the equation, using state symbols, for the first ionisation energy of sodium.
   (b) The frequency of the radiation needed to remove the outermost electron from a sodium atom is 1.25×10^{15} s⁻¹. Calculate the first ionisation energy of sodium in kJ per mole. *(CCEA June 2011)*

3. Which one of the following represents the emission spectrum of atomic hydrogen in the ultraviolet region? *(CCEA January 2010)*

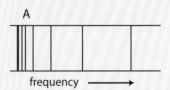

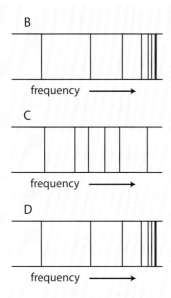

4. Explain how the emission spectrum of an element can be used to calculate the first ionisation energy of the element. *(CCEA January 2009)*

Before moving to the next section, check that you are able to:

- Explain the convergence of wavelengths in the hydrogen emission spectrum in terms of the spacing between energy levels.
- Explain the origin of the Lyman and Balmer series in the hydrogen emission spectrum.
- Calculate the ionisation energy of hydrogen from the hydrogen emission spectrum.

Flame Tests

The spectrum of wavelengths emitted by the atoms of an element can be used to confirm the presence of the element in a compound or mixture. For example, when a few crystals of sodium chloride are placed in a flame, the flame turns a characteristic yellow/orange colour indicating that sodium ions are present in the compound. This type of experiment is known as a **flame test**. The characteristic flame colours produced by metal compounds are summarised in Figure 20.

Method

- Make a small loop at the end of a nichrome wire.
- Dip the loop in concentrated hydrochloric acid and then into the sample.
- Place the loop in a blue Bunsen flame and record the flame colour.

Worked Example 1.2xv

(a) Complete the table by stating the flame colour for each of the ions listed.

(b) Explain, with the help of an energy level diagram, how flame colours arise.

Metal ion	Flame colour
Ba^{2+}	
Ca^{2+}	
Cu^{2+}	

(CCEA January 2009)

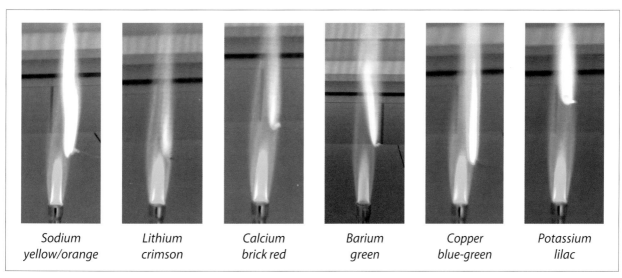

Sodium	Lithium	Calcium	Barium	Copper	Potassium
yellow/orange	crimson	brick red	green	blue-green	lilac

Figure 20: Characteristic flame colours for compounds containing metal ions.

Solution

(a)

Metal ion	Flame colour
Ba^{2+}	Green
Ca^{2+}	Brick red
Cu^{2+}	Blue-green

(b)

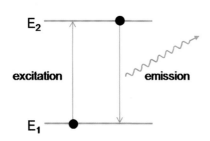

The electron is excited to a higher energy level. The electron then returns to a lower energy level, releasing energy in the form of light.

....

Exercise 1.2N

Lithium sulfate can be used in a flame test. Explain how a flame test could be carried out and state the expected colour of the flame.

(CCEA January 2011)

Before moving to the next section, check that you are able to:

• Recall the procedure used to conduct a flame test.

• Recall the characteristic flame colours for common metal ions.

• Explain, with the aid of a diagram, how the flame colour arises in a flame test.

1.3 Bonding and Structure

Ionic Compounds

In this section we are learning to:

- Explain the characteristic properties of ionic compounds in terms of their structure and the formation of ionic bonds in the compound.
- Use dot-and-cross diagrams to explain the formation of ionic bonds.

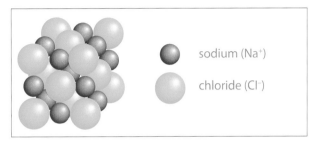

Figure 1: The ionic lattice in sodium chloride.

An ionic compound is formed when a metal combines with one or more nonmetals. Ionic compounds contain an ordered array of tightly packed ions known as an **ionic lattice**. Many ionic compounds form crystals with well-defined edges and shapes that reflect the order within the lattice. The ionic lattice in sodium chloride is illustrated in Figure 1.

In sodium chloride, NaCl the lattice consists of sodium ions (Na^+) surrounded by chloride ions (Cl^-) and vice versa. The ions are held or 'bonded' together by strong attractive forces between neighbouring positive and negative ions; a type of bonding known as **ionic bonding**. Compounds held together by ionic bonds are referred to as ionic compounds.

A great deal of energy is needed to break the strong ionic bonds between ions in the lattice. As a result ionic compounds have high melting and boiling points. For instance, the melting point of sodium chloride is 801 °C.

The strength of the ionic bonds between neighbouring ions, and a lack of space due to the tight-packing of ions, prevents the ions from moving within the lattice. As a result there are no charged particles able to move within the lattice and the solid is unable to conduct electricity. The inability of the ions to move past each other in the lattice also explains why most ionic solids are hard materials.

The filling of electron shells in sodium, chlorine and their ions is shown in Figure 2. The sodium ion (Na^+) has the same electron configuration as the noble gas

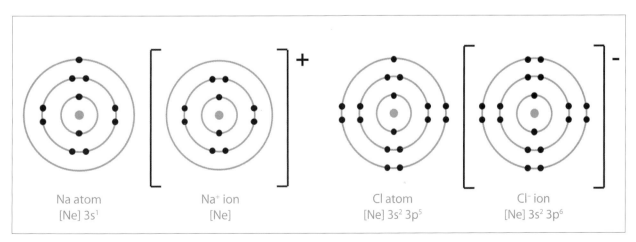

Figure 2: The filling of electron shells in sodium, chlorine and their ions. The shorthand [Ne] is used to represent the electron configuration of neon.

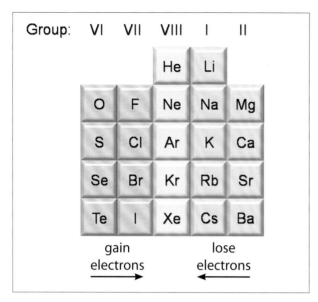

Figure 3: Achieving a noble gas configuration by losing or gaining electrons.

neon (Ne). Similarly the chloride ion (Cl^-) has the same electron configuration as the noble gas argon (Ar). The noble gases (Group VIII) are very unreactive and form few compounds. Their stability is due to a full outer shell of electrons. As a result, when forming compounds, the elements towards the left and right sides of the Periodic Table will try to achieve a noble gas configuration. This trend is illustrated in Figure 3.

We can use the idea that elements form ions with full outer shells to determine the formula of an ionic compound. For example, when magnesium (Group II) combines with chlorine (Group VII) to form magnesium chloride, magnesium achieves a noble gas configuration by losing two electrons to form a magnesium (Mg^{2+}) ion. Similarly, chlorine (Group VII) achieves a noble gas configuration by gaining one electron to form a chloride (Cl^-) ion. The formation of ions in an ionic compound can be illustrated by

drawing a 'dot-and-cross' diagram in which dots and crosses are used to distinguish outer shell electrons belonging to different atoms. A dot-and-cross diagram describing the formation of ions in magnesium chloride is shown in Figure 4.

An ionic compound such as magnesium chloride does not have a charge. The positive charge on the magnesium (Mg^{2+}) ions in the lattice balances the negative charge on the chloride (Cl^-) ions in the lattice. As a result, the formula for magnesium chloride must represent an ionic lattice in which there are two chloride (Cl^-) ions for every magnesium ion (Mg^{2+}). This explains why the formula for magnesium chloride is $MgCl_2$.

The formula of magnesium chloride:

$$MgCl_2$$

represents one Mg^{2+} ion and two Cl^- ions

Worked Example 1.3i

Use dot-and-cross diagrams to explain how strontium atoms combine with fluorine atoms to form strontium fluoride. Show only outer shell electrons.
(CCEA June 2010)

Strategy

The diagram must clearly show:

- A strontium atom achieving a full outer shell by donating two electrons to form a strontium (Sr^{2+}) ion.
- Two fluorine atoms each gaining one of the electrons donated by the strontium atom to form two fluoride (F^-) ions.

Figure 4: A dot-and-cross diagram showing the formation of ions when magnesium and chlorine combine to form magnesium chloride, $MgCl_2$. Only outer shell electrons are shown.

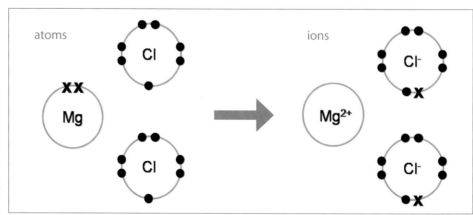

Solution

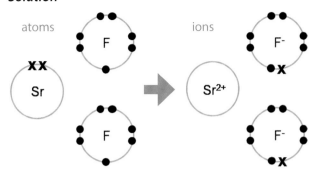

atoms   ions

Exercise 1.3A

1. (a) Write an equation, including state symbols, for the formation of sodium fluoride from sodium and fluorine.
   (b) Draw dot-and-cross diagrams, using outer electrons only, to show the formation of sodium fluoride from sodium and fluorine atoms. *(CCEA January 2008)*

2. (a) Using outer electrons only draw diagrams to explain the formation of calcium bromide from calcium atoms and bromine atoms.
   (b) Use spd-notation to write the electron configuration for the calcium ions and bromide ions in calcium bromide.

Before moving to the next section, check that you are able to:

- Describe the ionic lattice and the nature of the bonding in an ionic compound.
- Explain the high melting point and lack of conductivity of ionic compounds in terms of the formation of strong ionic bonds.
- Use dot-and-cross diagrams to explain the formation of ions when an ionic compound is formed from its elements.

Covalent Bonding

In this section we are learning to:

- Describe the formation of covalent bonds in molecules in terms of the sharing of electrons between atoms and the octet rule.
- Use structural formulas to represent covalent bonding in molecules and ions.
- Describe the formation and properties of coordinate bonds.
- Identify and explain exceptions to the octet rule.
- Describe the formation of bond dipoles in terms of the sharing of electrons between atoms with different electronegativities.
- Construct the permanent dipole for a molecule from bond dipoles and relate the size of the permanent dipole to the shape of the molecule.

The Octet Rule

As in ionic compounds, the atoms in nonmetal compounds such as water (H_2O) and carbon dioxide (CO_2) bond with each other in an attempt to achieve a full outer shell of electrons. The bonding between atoms in ionic compounds and nonmetal compounds is governed by the **octet rule** which asserts that *atoms will attempt to gain, lose or share electrons when forming compounds in order to achieve a full outer shell containing eight electrons.*

For example, a molecule of chlorine (Cl_2) is formed when two chlorine atoms achieve a full outer shell by sharing a pair of electrons as illustrated in Figure 5. The shared electrons are attracted by the nucleus of both atoms and, as such, 'glue' the atoms together. The bond that results when two atoms each use one electron to form a shared pair of electrons is known as a **covalent bond**.

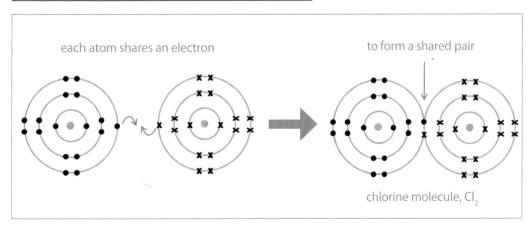

each atom shares an electron   to form a shared pair

chlorine molecule, Cl_2

Figure 5: The formation of a covalent bond between two chlorine atoms to form a chlorine molecule, Cl_2.

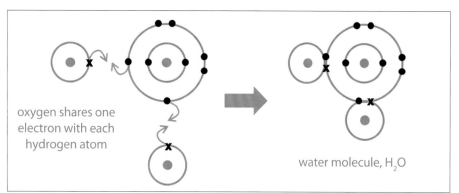

Figure 6: Covalent bonding in a water molecule, H₂O.

oxygen shares one
electron with each
hydrogen atom

water molecule, H₂O

The atoms in water are also held together by covalent bonds. A molecule of water (H_2O) contains two hydrogen atoms and one oxygen atom. Each hydrogen atom shares a pair of electrons with the oxygen atom to form a covalent bond as illustrated in Figure 6. In this way all three atoms in the molecule attain a full outer shell (Noble Gas configuration) and become stable.

Exercise 1.3B

1. (a) Write an equation for the formation of phosphorus trifluoride, PF_3 by the reaction of fluorine with phosphorus, P_4.

   (b) Draw a dot-and-cross diagram, using outer electrons only, to show the bonding in PF_3.

   (c) With reference to PF_3 explain the octet rule.
   (CCEA June 2007)

Multiple Bonding

When two oxygen atoms combine to form a molecule of oxygen (O_2), the oxygen atoms achieve a full outer shell by using two electrons to create two shared pairs of electrons as illustrated in Figure 7. Each shared pair of electrons results in a covalent bond between the oxygen atoms and the pair of covalent bonds between the oxygen atoms is referred to as a **double bond**. Similarly, a **triple bond** is formed when two atoms

each use three electrons to create three shared pairs of electrons. Molecules of nitrogen (N_2) and ethyne (C_2H_2) contain triple bonds.

The formation of two or more covalent bonds between a pair of atoms is known as **multiple bonding**. The double bond in a molecule of oxygen (O_2) and the triple bond in a nitrogen molecule (N_2) are examples of multiple bonds. Most covalent bonds are strong and a lot of energy is needed to break the bond. The additional shared pairs in a double or triple bond make the bond even stronger and more difficult to break than a single covalent bond.

Exercise 1.3C

1. Which one of the following molecules has two double bonds?

   C_2H_4 N_2 CO_2 $BeCl_2$

   (Adapted from CCEA June 2009)

Structural Formula

The **structural formula** of a molecule shows how the atoms are connected as a result of forming covalent bonds between atoms. A line between two atoms represents a single covalent bond formed by sharing a pair of electrons. Unshared or 'lone' pairs of electrons in the outer shell of an atom are represented by a pair of dots.

each oxygen atom shares
two electrons

double bond
(2 shared pairs)

The Figure 7: The formation of a double bond (2 shared pairs) between two oxygen atoms to form a molecule of oxygen, O₂.

oxygen molecule, o₂

Molecular formula	Structural formula
Cl_2	:C̈l—C̈l:
H_2O	H—Ö—H
O_2	:Ö=Ö:
N_2	:N≡N:

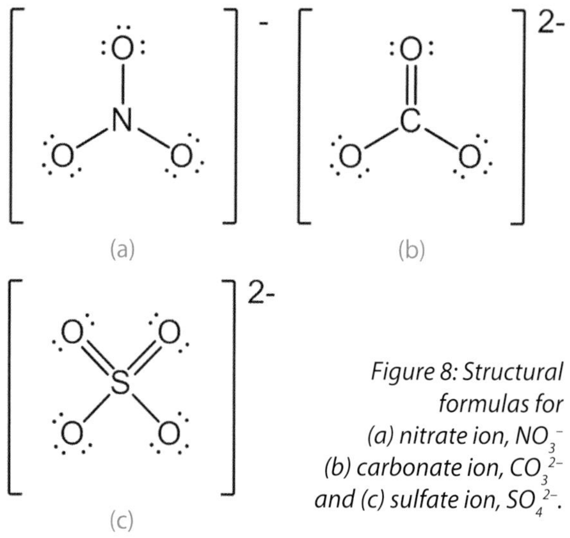

Exercise 1.3D

Draw structural formulas for ethane, C_2H_6 ethene, C_2H_4 and ethyne, C_2H_2.

Polyatomic Ions

Ions containing more than one atom are known as **polyatomic ions**. Sulfate (SO_4^{2-}), carbonate (CO_3^{2-}) and nitrate (NO_3^-) are all examples of polyatomic ions.

The polyatomic ions in compounds such as calcium carbonate, $CaCO_3$ behave in exactly the same way as the ions in ionic compounds such as sodium chloride, $NaCl$. The Ca^{2+} and CO_3^{2-} ions in $CaCO_3$ are tightly packed in an ionic lattice held together by ionic bonds. In contrast, the atoms within a polyatomic ion are held together by covalent bonds. The structural formulas for several common polyatomic ions are shown in Figure 8. The strong covalent bonding within a polyatomic ion such as nitrate, NO_3^- or sulfate, SO_4^{2-} does not break when the salt containing the polyatomic ion melts or dissolves.

Figure 8: Structural formulas for (a) nitrate ion, NO_3^-, (b) carbonate ion, CO_3^{2-} and (c) sulfate ion, SO_4^{2-}.

Melting magnesium sulfate:

$MgSO_{4\ (s)}$ → $Mg^{2+}_{\ (l)}$ + $SO_4^{2-}_{\ (l)}$

Dissolving magnesium sulfate:

$MgSO_{4\ (s)}$ → $Mg^{2+}_{\ (aq)}$ + $SO_4^{2-}_{\ (aq)}$

Coordinate Bonding

Most covalent bonds are formed when two atoms each use one electron to form a shared pair of electrons. For example, in a molecule of ammonia, NH_3 each hydrogen atom uses its electron to form a covalent bond with the nitrogen atom as shown in Figure 9.

Alternatively, a covalent bond can be formed by two atoms sharing a pair of electrons that have been donated by one of the atoms forming the bond. This type of bond is referred to as a **coordinate bond**. Ammonium ion, NH_4^+ contains a coordinate bond. The coordinate bond in an ammonium ion is formed when the nitrogen atom in a molecule of

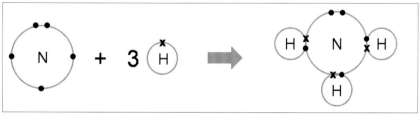

Figure 9: Covalent bonding in a molecule of ammonia, NH_3. Only outer shell electrons are shown.

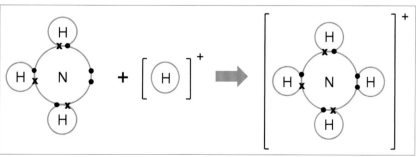

Figure 10: Formation of a coordinate bond in an ammonium ion, NH_4^+.

ammonia shares its lone pair with a hydrogen ion (H^+) as shown in Figure 10. The coordinate bond in an ammonium ion is identical to the other N-H bonds in the ion. The only difference between the coordinate bond and the other covalent bonds in the ion is the way in which the coordinate bond was formed.

Formation of a coordinate bond in a molecule or ion is indicated by drawing an arrow between the atoms forming the bond. The direction of the arrow indicates the direction of electron donation in the bond. The use of an arrow to indicate the formation of a coordinate bond in an ammonium ion, NH_4^+ is shown in Figure 11.

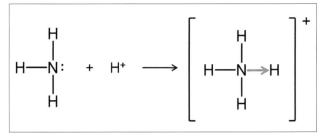

Figure 11: Using an arrow to indicate the formation of a coordinate bond in an ammonium ion, NH_4^+.

Exercise 1.3E

Boron trifluoride can combine with ammonia to form the following molecule.

(a) Name the type of bond formed between the boron and nitrogen atoms.

(b) Explain how this bond is formed.

(CCEA June 2010)

Exceptions to the Octet Rule

As a rule, atoms will try to satisfy the octet rule when they combine to form compounds. However, in some cases a stable compound can still form when there are not enough electrons to form an octet of (eight) electrons around one or more of the atoms. For example, the dot-and-cross diagram for beryllium chloride, $BeCl_2$ (Figure 12) reveals that while each chlorine atom has satisfied the octet rule, beryllium has not achieved a full outer shell and has not satisfied the octet rule. Molecules in which one or more atoms have not satisfied the octet rule are described as **exceptions to the octet rule**.

Boron trifluoride, BF_3 is also an exception to the octet rule. The dot-and-cross diagram for boron trifluoride (Figure 13) reveals that while each fluorine atom has attained a full outer shell and satisfied the octet rule, the boron atom has only six electrons in its outer shell and has not satisfied the octet rule.

It is also possible to form a stable compound that contains atoms with more than eight electrons in their outer shell. In the case of PCl_5 (Figure 14), each chlorine atom achieves a full outer shell by sharing an electron pair with phosphorus. As a result, phosphorus has ten electrons in its outer shell. An outer shell that contains more than eight electrons is known as an **expanded octet**. Atoms with an expanded octet do not obey the octet rule and are considered exceptions to the octet rule.

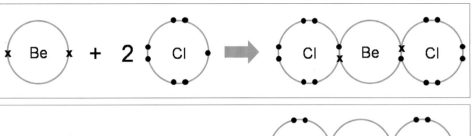

Figure 12: Covalent bonding in a molecule of beryllium chloride, $BeCl_2$.

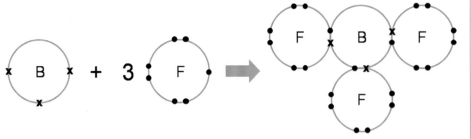

Figure 13: Covalent bonding in a molecule of boron trifluoride, BF_3.

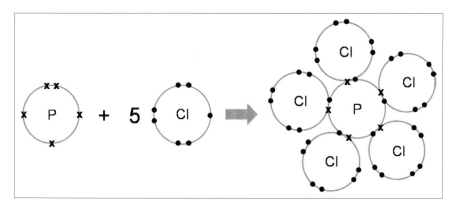

Figure 14: Covalent bonding in a molecule of phosphorus pentachloride, PCl_5.

The sulfur atom in sulfur hexafluoride, SF_6 is another example of an atom with an expanded octet. In SF_6 each fluorine atom forms a single covalent bond with the sulfur atom. As a result, the outer shell of the sulfur atom contains 12 electrons; two from each of the six S-F bonds.

Exercise 1.3F

1. In which of the following molecules does the underlined element (a) form two covalent bonds and (b) satisfy the octet rule?

   $\underline{Be}Cl_2$ $\underline{C}H_4$ $\underline{N}H_3$ $H_2\underline{O}$

   (Adapted from CCEA June 2009)

2. (a) Draw a dot-and-cross diagram, using outer shell electrons only, to show the bonding in SF6.

   (b) Explain whether SF_6 obeys the octet rule.

   (CCEA June 2010)

Before moving to the next section, check that you are able to:

- Explain the formation of covalent bonds in molecules and ions in terms of the sharing of electrons between atoms and the octet rule.
- Draw structural formulas to represent covalent bonding in molecules and ions.
- Describe the formation and properties of coordinate bonds.
- Identify and explain exceptions to the octet rule.

Polar Covalent Bonds

In molecules such as chlorine (Cl_2) covalent bonds are formed by the sharing of electrons between identical atoms. The electrons are shared equally by the atoms and the bond is described as a **nonpolar covalent bond**. In contrast, the electrons in a covalent bond between atoms of different elements are not shared equally. For example, in a molecule of hydrogen chloride (HCl), the chlorine atom is more able to attract the shared electrons in the covalent bond. As a result, the chlorine atom acquires a small negative charge ($\delta-$) and the hydrogen atom becomes slightly positive ($\delta+$). The covalent bond in HCl is an example of a **polar covalent bond** where we are using the term 'polar' to describe a bond in which the electrons forming the bond are not shared equally by the atoms. The use of partial charges ($\delta+$ and $\delta-$) to describe the unequal sharing of electrons in polar covalent bonds is illustrated in Figure 15.

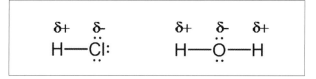

Figure 15: The use of partial charges to describe the unequal sharing of electrons in polar covalent bonds.

The ability of an atom to attract the shared electrons in a covalent bond to itself is referred to as the **electronegativity** of the element. In a polar covalent bond the more electronegative element acquires a small negative charge ($\delta-$) and the less electronegative element acquires a small positive charge ($\delta+$). The separation of charge ($\delta+$ $\delta-$) that develops between the atoms in a polar covalent bond is known as a **bond dipole**. The size of the dipole associated with a polar covalent bond becomes larger as the difference between the electronegativity values of the atoms forming the bond increases.

The periodic trends in Figure 16 reveal that the electronegativity of the elements increases from left to right across a period and towards the top of each group. As a result metals on the far left of the Periodic

Figure 16: Periodic trends in electronegativity.

H 2.1									He
Li 1.0	Be 1.5			B 2.0	C 2.5	N 3.0	O 3.5	F 4.0	Ne
Na 0.9	Mg 1.2			Al 1.5	Si 1.8	P 2.1	S 2.5	Cl 3.0	Ar
K 0.8	Ca 1.0			Ga 1.6	Ge 1.8	As 2.0	Se 2.4	Br 2.8	Kr
Rb 0.8	Sr 1.0			In 1.7	Sn 1.8	Sb 1.9	Te 2.1	I 2.5	Xe
Cs 0.7	Ba 0.9			Tl 1.8	Pb 1.9	Bi 1.9	Po 2.0	At 2.1	Rn

Electronegativity increasing (→)

Electronegativity increasing (↑)

Table have the lowest electronegativity values and nonmetals have the highest electronegativity values. This suggests that big differences in electronegativity between the metals and nonmetals in compounds such as $NaCl$ and $MgCl_2$ give rise to ionic bonding, while smaller differences in compounds such as H_2O and CO_2 result in polar covalent bonding. In this way polar covalent bonding can be viewed as the link between ionic bonding and 'pure' (nonpolar) covalent bonding.

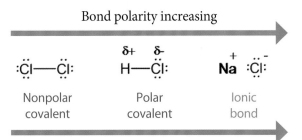

Bond polarity increasing →

Electronegativity difference increasing →

Exercise 1.3G

1. (a) Explain the meaning of the term electronegativity. (b) Using electronegativity suggest why beryllium chloride is a covalent molecule and barium chloride is an ionic compound. *(CCEA January 2011)*

2. Which one of the following molecules contains the most polar bond?

   CH_4 NH_3 H_2O HF

   (CCEA January 2009)

Permanent Dipoles

The presence of one or more polar covalent bonds in a molecule may result in the molecule having a positive end and a negative end. In the case of chloromethane, CH_3Cl the C-Cl bond dipole results in the chlorine end of the molecule having a small negative charge ($\delta-$) and the methyl (CH_3) end of the molecule having a small positive charge ($\delta+$). The direction of a bond dipole is indicated by a 'dipole arrow' which, by convention, points from the positive end of the dipole to the negative end of the dipole. The use of a dipole arrow to describe the C-Cl bond dipole in chloromethane, CH_3Cl is shown in Figure 17.

The separation of charge that gives rise to positive and negative ends in a molecule such as chloromethane is described as a **permanent (molecular) dipole**. Molecules with a permanent dipole are referred to as **polar molecules**. The use of dipole arrows to describe individual bond dipoles makes it easier to visualise how the individual bond dipoles combine to produce a permanent dipole in the molecule. In the case of

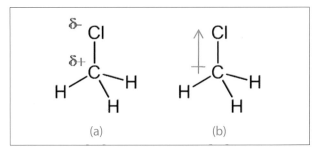

Figure 17: The use of (a) partial charges and (b) a dipole arrow to indicate the nature of the C-Cl bond dipole in chloromethane, CH_3Cl.

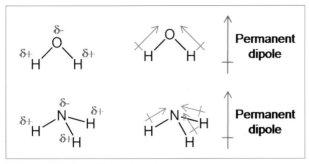

Figure 18: Combining bond dipoles to form a permanent dipole in (a) water and (b) ammonia.

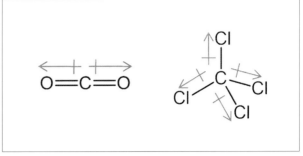

Figure 19: Combining bond dipoles in (a) carbon dioxide and (b) carbon tetrachloride to produce molecules with no permanent dipole.

chloromethane (CH_3Cl) the C-H bond dipoles are very small and the permanent dipole for chloromethane is almost entirely due to the C-Cl bond dipole. In contrast, in water (H_2O) and ammonia (NH_3) several bond dipoles combine to produce a much larger permanent dipole. The process of combining bond dipoles to produce a molecular dipole is illustrated in Figure 18. The examples in Figure 18 demonstrate that the permanent dipole for a molecule is obtained by adding the bond dipoles in a way that takes account of their size and direction.

The presence of bond dipoles in a molecule is, however, not always sufficient to produce a permanent dipole in the molecule. For instance, the bond dipoles in carbon dioxide (CO_2) and carbon tetrachloride (CCl_4) combine to produce molecules with no permanent dipole. The shapes of CO_2 and CCl_4 (Figure 19) are similar in that they represent the most symmetric way to arrange two and four identical atoms around a central atom. In contrast, the shapes of water and ammonia (Figure 18) are much less symmetric and give rise to permanent dipoles. Together these examples demonstrate that highly symmetric molecules are less likely to have a permanent dipole than those with much less symmetry.

Before moving to the next section, check that you are able to:

- Define electronegativity in terms of the sharing of electrons in covalent bonds.
- Explain the origin of bond dipoles in terms of electronegativity.
- Construct the permanent dipole for a molecule from bond dipoles.
- Relate the size of the permanent dipole for a molecule to its shape.

Covalently Bonded Materials

In this section we are learning to:

- Account for the physical properties of molecular materials in terms of their molecular structure and the weak attractive forces between the molecules.
- Recall that diamond and graphite are allotropes of carbon and have a giant covalent structure.
- Explain how the properties of diamond and graphite arise from the bonding within their giant structures.

Molecular Materials

Gases such as nitrogen (N_2), carbon dioxide (CO_2), and methane (CH_4) are molecular materials and are described as having a **molecular covalent structure**. The properties of a molecular material are determined by the nature of the covalent bonds in the molecules, and the much weaker forces of attraction between the molecules. The attractive forces between molecules in materials containing larger molecules such as sulfur (S_8) and phosphorus (P_4), or heavier atoms such as iodine (I_2), are significantly greater than the attractive forces between the molecules in gases such as nitrogen and carbon dioxide. As a result substances such as sulfur and iodine have higher melting points, and are more likely to be liquids or solids under normal laboratory conditions.

Molecular solids such as iodine, sulfur and ice are soft and brittle where a material is considered brittle if it powders easily when struck. The soft, brittle nature of molecular solids is due to the weak attractive forces between the molecules in the solid.

The solubility of a molecular material in a particular solvent is largely determined by the nature of the attractive forces between molecules in the solid and the nature of the attractive forces between molecules in the solvent. Molecular materials containing polar molecules

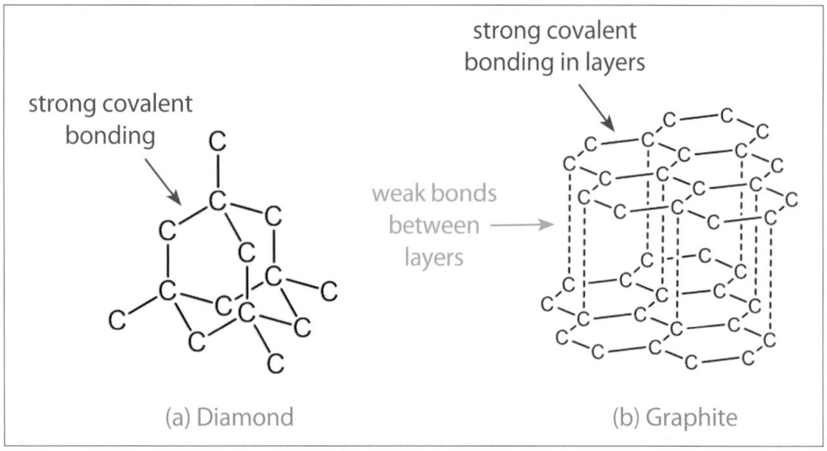

Figure 20: The giant covalent structures formed by carbon atoms in (a) diamond and (b) graphite.

such as ammonia (NH_3) will dissolve in polar solvents such as water. Conversely materials containing less polar molecules such as sulfur (S_8) and iodine (I_2) will dissolve in less polar solvents such as hexane.

The electrons in a molecular material are associated with individual molecules and are not free to move and carry a charge through the material. As a result molecular materials such as iodine and sulfur do not conduct electricity. Further, molecular materials do not contain ions and therefore cannot conduct an electric current when molten or dissolved in a solution.

Giant Covalent Materials

Many nonmetals have molecular covalent structures. Others prefer to form 'giant' structures and do not contain molecules. Diamond and graphite are different physical forms (allotropes) of the element carbon. In diamond each carbon atom forms a covalent bond with four neighbouring carbon atoms to form a three-dimensional network of atoms known as a **giant covalent structure**. The structure of diamond is shown in Figure 20a.

The network of carbon atoms in diamond is extremely strong with each atom held tightly in place by four strong covalent bonds in a tetrahedral arrangement. The strength of the bonding between neighbouring carbon atoms can be used to explain why diamond is one of the hardest naturally occurring substances, has a very high melting point, and does not dissolve in water. The rigidity and organisation of the atoms in the giant structure also makes it possible to cut diamond into shapes with smooth faces and well-defined edges. This property helps make diamond ideal for use in jewellery and in drills for the mining and oil industries.

The carbon atoms in diamond use all four of their outer shell electrons to form covalent bonds with neighbouring carbon atoms. As a result, all of the outer shell electrons are held tightly in covalent bonds and there are no electrons free to move and carry a charge through the solid. This explains why diamond is unable to conduct electricity and is an electrical insulator.

In contrast, graphite is a soft powdery solid that conducts electricity. It has a slippery feel and is used as a solid lubricant. The carbon atoms in graphite form two-dimensional layers that are stacked as shown in Figure 20b. Within each layer the carbon atoms use three of their four outer shell electrons to form covalent bonds with neighbouring carbon atoms. The strength of the covalent bonding between the carbon atoms in each layer can be used to explain why graphite has a very high melting point. The fourth outer shell electron on each atom is shared with atoms from neighbouring layers to form weak bonds between the layers. The electrons shared between the layers are **delocalised** as they are no longer associated with an atom and are able to move freely. The delocalised electrons in graphite can carry a charge through the solid making graphite an electrical conductor.

The weak bonds between layers can be easily overcome with the result that the layers can slide over each other and can be readily pulled apart. The weak bonding between layers explains why graphite is soft and the ability of the layers to slide over each other explains why graphite feels slippery; a property that makes graphite ideal for use in pencil 'lead' and graphite grease – a solid lubricant.

Exercise 1.3H

1. With reference to structure and bonding explain why graphite conducts electricity and why it may be used as a lubricant. *(CCEA June 2003)*

2. (a) Explain what is meant by the term *covalent*.
   (b) Describe the structures of diamond and graphite.
   (c) Explain why graphite conducts electricity.
   (d) Explain why diamond is exceptionally hard.
   (CCEA June 2009)

3. All of the atoms in the giant covalent structure shown below are atoms of the same element.

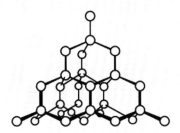

   (a) Name the substance. (b) Explain whether the substance is hard or soft. (c) Explain whether the substance conducts electricity or not.
   (CCEA June 2011)

4. A solid melts sharply at 100–101 °C, does not conduct electricity when molten, and dissolves in hydrocarbon solvents. The structure of the solid is:
   (a) atomic   (b) giant covalent   (c) ionic
   (d) molecular covalent   *(CCEA January 2011)*

Before moving to the next section, check that you are able to:

- Account for the low melting point, solubility, and poor electrical conductivity of molecular covalent materials in terms of weak attractive forces between molecules and the absence of charged particles that can move and carry charge.
- Describe the giant covalent structures of diamond and graphite.
- Explain the high melting point, hardness and poor electrical conductivity of diamond in terms of the formation of strong covalent bonds.
- Use a combination of strong bonding within layers and weak bonding between layers to explain the high melting point, electrical conductivity and lubricating properties of graphite.

Metals

In this section we are learning to:

- Explain the physical properties of metals in terms of the formation of metallic bonds between the metal atoms.
- Use the model of metallic bonding in a metal to explain trends in the strength of metallic bonding within groups and periods.

In a metal the outer shell electrons of each metal atom become detached from the atom and are able to move freely through the metal. As a result, metals contain an array of positively charged metal ions in a 'sea' of delocalised electrons as shown in Figure 21. The metal ions are bonded together by forces of attraction between the metal ions and the delocalised electrons; a type of bonding referred to as **metallic bonding**.

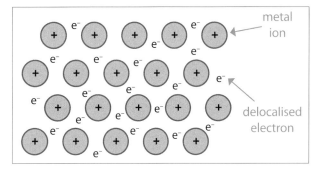

Figure 21: The model of metallic bonding in a Group I metal (one delocalised electron per ion).

The atoms in a Group I metal such as sodium have a single electron in their outer shell. As a result, the atoms in a Group I metal each lose one electron to form an ion with a 1+ charge surrounded by delocalised electrons. As the metal ions get bigger down the group the delocalised electrons are further from the positive nucleus of each metal ion and are therefore less attracted to the metal ions. This explains why the strength of metallic bonding in the Group I metals decreases down the group.

In a Group II metal such as magnesium, each metal atom loses two electrons to form an ion with a 2+ charge. The attraction between the ions and the delocalised electrons in a Group II metal is significantly greater than in a Group I metal and, as a result, the bonding in a Group II metal is significantly stronger than the bonding in a Group I metal. This explains why Group I metals are soft and can be cut with a knife while Group II metals are much harder and have higher melting points than Group I metals.

Metallic bonds are similar to covalent bonds. Both types of bonding involve the sharing of electrons and can result in very strong bonds. The metallic bonding in most metals is strong and can be used to explain why the metal ions in a metal are tightly packed to produce a hard, dense solid with a high melting point. In contrast, the relatively weak metallic bonding in Group 1 metals such as sodium can be used to explain why the metal ions are less tightly packed to produce soft metals with low densities.

The ability of the outer shell electrons to move freely allows the metal ions to move without disturbing the bonding in the metal. The ability of metal ions to move past each other without disturbing the metallic bonding in the metal explains why metals can be deformed when struck with a harder object (metals are **malleable**) and why metals can be drawn into wires (metals are **ductile**).

The ability of the outer shell electrons to move freely through the metal can also be used to explain why metals are good **electrical conductors**. When a power supply (battery) is attached to a metal the mobile electrons move towards the positive terminal of the power supply resulting in an electrical current within the metal.

> Before moving to the next section, check that you are able to:
>
> - Describe the nature of metallic bonding within a metal and explain periodic trends in the strength of metallic bonding.
> - Explain the high melting point, malleability, ductility and electrical conductivity of metals in terms of the nature of the metallic bonding within the metal.

Exercise 1.3I

1. Explain why sodium (a) is malleable and (b) conducts electricity. *(CCEA January 2008)*

2. Describe the bonding in a metal and use this to explain the ductility and electrical conductivity of a typical metal. *(CCEA January 2006)*

3. Compare the electrical conductivity of solid strontium metal with that of solid strontium fluoride. Explain your answer. *(CCEA June 2010)*

4. (a) Explain, with the help of a labelled diagram, what is meant by the term metallic bonding.

   (b) Suggest why the melting points of the Group I metals decrease from sodium to caesium.

   (c) Use the concept of metallic bonding to suggest why calcium should be a better electrical conductor than potassium. *(CCEA June 2011)*

1.4 Shapes of Molecules and Ions

CONNECTIONS
- The characteristic shapes formed when atoms bond with each other make it possible for scientists to design materials with specific properties, including medicines to treat specific diseases.

VSEPR Theory

In this section we are learning to:

- Explain the shape of molecules and ions in terms of the repulsion between outer shell electrons.
- Recall the possible shapes for molecules and ions with up to six atoms bonded to a central atom.
- Explain the size of the permanent dipole for a molecule or ion in terms of the formation of polar bonds and their arrangement in the molecule.

The shape of a molecule or ion is determined by the arrangement of the outer shell electrons about each atom in the molecule. For example, the structural formulas in Figure 1 reveal that methane (CH_4), ammonia (NH_3) and water (H_2O), each have four pairs of electrons around their central atom. If we refer to a pair of electrons involved in covalent bonding as a **bonding pair** the carbon atom in methane can be said to have four bonding pairs in its outer shell. Of the four electron pairs in the outer shell of the nitrogen atom in ammonia only three are bonding pairs. The fourth pair of electrons is not involved in bonding and is referred to as a **lone pair** of electrons. In this way the oxygen atom in water can be said to have two bonding pairs and two lone pairs in its outer shell.

Valence Shell Electron Pair Repulsion (**VSEPR**) **theory** asserts that a molecule or ion will always try to minimise the repulsion between outer shell electrons by arranging the outer shell electrons as far away from each other as possible. In a molecule or ion with four pairs of electrons around the central atom, the repulsion between the electron pairs is minimised when the electron pairs point towards the corners of a tetrahedron. The tetrahedral arrangement of hydrogen atoms in methane (CH_4) is shown in Figure 2a. The angle between adjacent hydrogen atoms in methane is 109.5°.

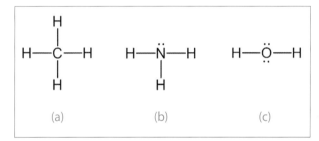

Figure 1: Structural formulas for (a) methane, (b) ammonia and (c) water.

The arrangement of the bonding pairs and lone pairs about the central atom in ammonia and water is also shown in Figure 2. Comparing the angle between adjacent hydrogen atoms in methane, ammonia and water (Figure 2) reveals that the angle between adjacent hydrogen atoms decreases as the number of lone pairs on the central atom increases. This occurs because the repulsion between bonding pairs and lone pairs is greater than the repulsion between bonding pairs,

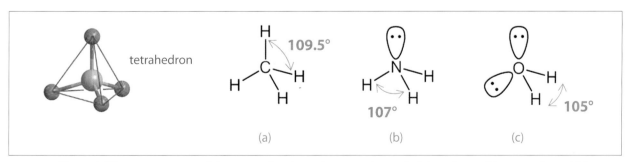

Figure 2: The arrangement of electron pairs about the central atom in (a) methane, (b) ammonia and (c) water.

forcing the bonding pairs further from the lone pairs.

bond pair – bond pair < bond pair – lone pair < lone pair – lone pair

→

Repulsion increasing

The molecular shapes resulting from the arrangement of electron pairs in Figure 2 are shown in Figure 3. The structural formulas and names used to describe the shapes of methane, ammonia and water are also given in Figure 3 and demonstrate that while all three molecules have a tetrahedral arrangement of electron pairs about the central atom, only methane has a tetrahedral shape.

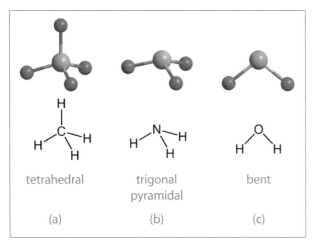

| tetrahedral | trigonal pyramidal | bent |
| (a) | (b) | (c) |

Figure 3: Structural formulas and names used to describe the molecular shapes of (a) methane, (b) ammonia and (c) water.

Exercise 1.4A

1. Draw and explain the shape of an ammonia molecule. (CCEA June 2009)

2. (a) Draw a dot-and-cross diagram to show the bonding in phosphine, PH_3.
   (b) Draw and name the shape of a phosphine molecule. (CCEA January 2010)

3. Draw and name the shape of an ammonium ion. (CCEA January 2005)

4. (a) Draw the structure of chloroform, $CHCl_3$ showing all the bonds present.
   (b) Draw a dot-and-cross diagram using outer shell electrons only, to show the bonding in chloroform.
   (c) State and explain the shape of the chloroform molecule. (CCEA January 2006)

5. (a) Draw a dot-and-cross diagram, using outer shell electrons only, to show the bonding in oxygen difluoride, OF_2.
   (b) Suggest and explain the shape of the oxygen difluoride molecule. (CCEA June 2005)

6. The structural formula for hydrogen peroxide is H-O-O-H.
   (a) Draw a dot-and-cross diagram for a molecule of hydrogen peroxide showing outer shell electrons only.
   (b) Suggest why a hydrogen peroxide molecule is not linear. (Adapted from CCEA June 2004)

Before moving to the next section, check that you are able to:

- Recall examples of molecules with tetrahedral, trigonal pyramidal and bent shapes.

- Explain how the repulsion between bonding pairs and lone pairs can be used to explain the shapes of molecules and ions with four pairs of electrons around a central atom.

- Recall the bond angles in CH_4, NH_3 and H_2O and use these angles to predict the bond angles around atoms with four electron pairs in their outermost shell.

Shapes Based on Two or Three Repulsions

In carbon dioxide, CO_2 the central carbon atom forms a double bond with each oxygen atom (O=C=O). The repulsion between the electrons in one double bond and the electrons in the other double bond is minimised when the bonds are 180° apart and all three atoms lie in a straight line. This arrangement of atoms is described as linear. Similarly, in hydrogen cyanide, HCN the central carbon atom forms a single covalent bond with hydrogen and a triple bond with the nitrogen atom (H-C≡N). The repulsion between the electrons in the single bond and the electrons in the triple bond is minimised when the bonds are 180° apart and the arrangement of the atoms about the carbon atom is linear. The linear arrangement of the atoms about the central atom in CO_2 and HCN gives both molecules a linear shape as illustrated in Figure 4. In this way both molecules demonstrate that a linear arrangement of atoms results from the repulsion between two groups of electrons around a central atom.

The atoms in a molecule of beryllium chloride, $BeCl_2$

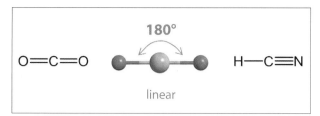

Figure 4: The linear shape of CO_2 and HCN resulting from the linear arrangement of two groups of electrons about the central atom.

also have a linear arrangement. Unlike the central carbon atom in CO_2 and HCN, the central beryllium atom in $BeCl_2$ does not have a full outer shell. The beryllium atom uses the two electrons in its outer shell to form a covalent bond with each chlorine atom. The repulsion between the electrons in one Be-Cl bond and the electrons in the other Be-Cl bond is minimised when the Be-Cl bonds are 180° apart giving the molecule a linear shape.

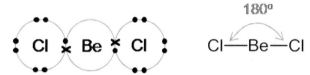

Boron trifluoride, BF_3 is an example of a molecule with three groups of electrons around a central atom. In BF_3 the central boron atom forms a single covalent bond with each fluorine atom. The repulsion between the electrons in each B-F bond is minimised when the bonds are directed towards the corners of a triangle as shown in Figure 5. The shape of boron trifluoride is described as trigonal planar to reflect the trigonal arrangement of fluorine atoms with all four atoms in the same plane.

Formaldehyde, H_2CO also has a trigonal planar shape (Figure 5) in which the central carbon atom forms a covalent bond with each hydrogen atom, and a double bond with the oxygen atom. The angle between the C=O bond and each of the C-H bonds is slightly greater than 120° on account of greater repulsion

between the two pairs of electrons in the C=O double bond and the pair of electrons in a C-H bond.

Exercise 1.4B

1. (a) Using outer electrons only, draw the dot-and-cross diagram for boron trifluoride.
   (b) State the octet rule and explain why boron trifluoride does not obey the octet rule.
   (c) Draw and explain the shape of boron trifluoride. *(CCEA January 2004)*

2. Beryllium chloride can be prepared by the action of chlorine or hydrogen chloride on the metal.
   (a) Write the equation for the reaction of beryllium with hydrogen chloride.
   (b) Draw a dot-and-cross diagram to show the formation of beryllium chloride from beryllium and chlorine atoms showing only outer shell electrons.
   (c) Beryllium chloride can be said to obey and at the same time not obey the octet rule. Explain this contradiction.
   (d) Draw and name the shape of a beryllium chloride molecule.
   (e) Explain the shape of a beryllium chloride molecule. *(CCEA January 2011)*

Before moving to the next section, check that you are able to:

- Recall examples of molecules with linear and trigonal planar arrangements of electrons about a central atom.
- Explain the shape of molecules containing multiple bonds in terms of the repulsion between groups of electrons around a central atom.

Shapes Based on Five or Six Repulsions

The shape of molecules such as PCl_5 and SF_4 is determined by the repulsion between five pairs of

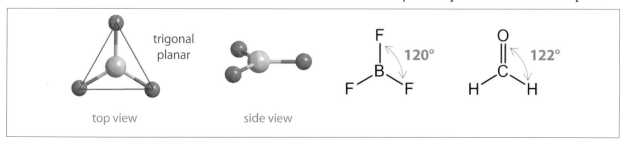

Figure 5: The trigonal planar arrangement of atoms in boron trifluoride, BF_3 and formaldehyde, H_2CO resulting from the trigonal planar arrangement of three groups of electrons about the central atom.

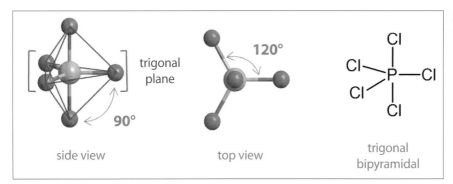

Figure 6: The trigonal bipyramidal arrangement of chlorine atoms in PCl_5 resulting from the trigonal bipyramidal arrangement of five electron pairs about the central phosphorus atom.

side view   trigonal plane   top view   90°   120°   trigonal bipyramidal

electrons on the central atom. In PCl_5 the central phosphorus atom forms a single covalent bond with each chlorine atom. The repulsion between the bonding pairs of electrons in the P-Cl bonds is minimised when the chlorine atoms are located at the corners of a shape known as a trigonal bipyramid. The arrangement of the chlorine atoms in PCl_5 is shown in Figure 6.

In PCl_5 three of the chlorine atoms are arranged in trigonal planar arrangement about the central phosphorus atom. The remaining two chlorine atoms lie above and below the trigonal plane (Figure 6). The angle between an atom in the trigonal place and the atoms above and below the trigonal plane is 90°. This angle is significantly smaller than the bond angles in molecules based on a tetrahedral shape (105–109°) and results in much greater repulsion. As a result, when one of the electron pairs around the central atom is a lone pair, as in SF_4, the repulsion between electron pairs is greatly reduced if the lone pair occupies one of the three sites in the trigonal plane. The preference for lone pairs to occupy sites in the trigonal plane can also be used to explain the shapes of molecules and ions such as ClF_3 and I_3^-, both of which have five pairs of electrons arranged in the shape of a trigonal bipyramid around a central atom. The structural formulas and names used to describe the shapes of molecules and ions such as SF_4, ClF_3 and I_3^- are shown in Figure 7.

Molecules such as SF_6 and XeF_4 have six electron pairs around a central atom. In sulfur hexafluoride, SF_6 the central sulfur atom is surrounded by six pairs of electrons; one from each of the six S-F bonds. In

xenon(IV) fluoride, XeF_4 two of the six electron pairs around xenon are lone pairs. In each case the six electron pairs around the central atom are directed towards the corners of an octahedron as illustrated in Figure 8. In an octahedron the six pairs of electrons are arranged at 90° to each other. In a molecule such as XeF_4 the lone pairs are placed 180° apart to avoid the very great repulsion that would result from placing the lone pairs at 90° to each other.

Exercise 1.4C

1. Explain why a molecule of silicon tetrachloride, $SiCl_4$ has a tetrahedral shape and a molecule of sulfur tetrafluoride, SF_4 has a see-saw shape.

2. Explain why a molecule of BF_3 is trigonal planar, a molecule of PF_3 is trigonal pyramidal and a molecule of ClF_3 is T-shaped.

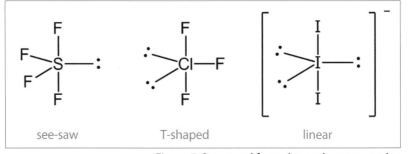

see-saw   T-shaped   linear

Figure 7: Structural formulas and names used to describe the shapes of SF_4, ClF_3 and I_3^-.

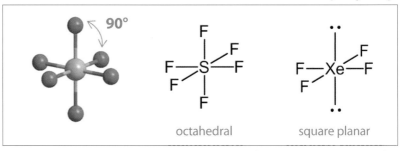

90°   octahedral   square planar

Figure 8: Structural formulas and names used to describe the shapes of SF_6 and XeF_4.

Before moving to the next section, check that you are able to:

- Recall examples of molecules with trigonal bipyramidal, see-saw, T-shaped and linear shapes and explain how these arise from the repulsion between five pairs of electrons on a central atom.
- Recall examples of molecules with octahedral and square planar shapes and explain how these result from the repulsion between six pairs of electrons on a central atom.

Nonpolar Molecules

Molecules and ions containing polar bonds do not always have a permanent dipole. The dipoles within individual covalent bonds result from a separation of charge ($\delta+$ and $\delta-$) between the atoms forming the bond. If the average position of the positive charges due to the bond dipoles (the $\delta+$ charges) coincides with the average position of the negative charges (the $\delta-$ charges) the molecule will not have a permanent dipole. A molecule that does not have a permanent dipole is referred to as a **nonpolar molecule**.

Conversely, molecules with a permanent dipole are referred to as polar molecules. The size of the permanent dipole largely depends on the shape of the molecule. Molecules in which the bond dipoles are arranged more symmetrically about the central atoms will have smaller permanent dipoles than molecules in which the bond dipoles are less symmetrically arranged. The molecular shapes shown in Figure 9 are highly symmetric and will always give rise to nonpolar molecules.

(c) Explain why carbon dioxide has this shape.

(d) Explain why a carbon dioxide molecule does not have a permanent dipole.

(CCEA June 2011)

3. Explain why (a) hydrogen fluoride is polar and (b) boron trifluoride is nonpolar.

(CCEA June 2007)

4. Which one of the following molecules is polar?

(a) BF_3 (b) CF_4 (c) OF_2 (d) F_2

(CCEA January 2010)

5. (a) Draw, name and explain the shape of the SF_6 molecule.

(b) Suggest why SF_6 is a nonpolar molecule even though it contains polar bonds.

(CCEA June 2010)

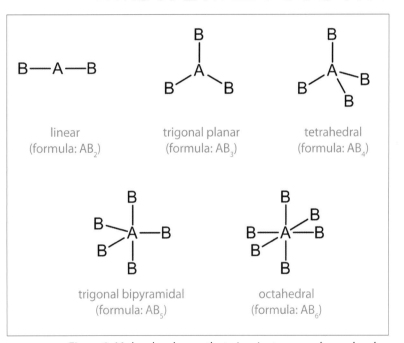

Figure 9: Molecular shapes that give rise to nonpolar molecules.

Exercise 1.4D

1. Which one of the following compounds is nonpolar?

(a) HCl (b) CCl_4 (c) CH_3Cl (d) $CHCl_3$

(CCEA June 2006)

2. (a) Using outer shell electrons only, draw the dot-and-cross structure of carbon dioxide.

(b) Draw and name the shape of a carbon dioxide molecule.

Before moving to the next section, check that you are able to:

- Recall that a permanent (molecular) dipole results from combining individual bond dipoles.
- Identify molecular shapes that give rise to nonpolar molecules.

1.5 Intermolecular Forces

The term **intermolecular force** refers to any type of bonding interaction between molecules. The physical properties of many substances are determined by the nature of the intermolecular forces between molecules in the substance. For example, intermolecular forces can be used to explain why ice floats on water, and why some liquids mix while others do not. Variations in the strength of the intermolecular forces between molecules can also be used to explain why heavier elements such as iodine tend to be solids, while lighter elements such as hydrogen and oxygen have lower melting and boiling points and are gases.

Van der Waals Forces

In this section we are learning to:

- Explain the nature of van der Waals forces of attraction between molecules.
- Recall the factors that affect the size of the van der Waals attraction between molecules and their effect on the melting and boiling point of a substance.

Van der Waals forces of attraction exist between all molecules. A van der Waals force results when the electrons in a molecule are repelled by the electrons on neighbouring molecules. The repulsion between electrons on neighbouring molecules gives rise to temporary dipoles known as **induced dipoles** as shown in Figure 1. The attraction between the induced dipoles on neighbouring molecules is known as a **van der Waals force**.

The size of the attraction between the induced dipoles on neighbouring molecules increases as the size of the induced dipole increases. Molecules with more electrons will generate larger induced dipoles and will experience greater van der Waals attraction. For instance, the melting and boiling points of the Noble Gases (Group VIII) increase down the group as the number of electrons in each Noble Gas atom increases. Similarly, an increase in van der Waals attraction between halogen molecules can be used to explain why the lighter halogens (F_2 and Cl_2) are gases with relatively low melting and boiling points, while the heavier halogens (Br_2 and I_2) are liquids and solids.

The size of the van der Waals attraction between molecules is also affected by the shape of the molecules. Increasing the surface area of a molecule increases the strength of the van der Waals attraction between molecules by increasing the amount of contact between the electrons in neighbouring molecules. For example, pentane (C_5H_{12}) and 2,2-dimethylpropane (C_5H_{12}) have the same formula and contain similar types of bonds. The boiling point of pentane is, however, higher as it has a larger surface area that allows for more attraction between induced dipoles and, as a result, stronger van der Waals attraction between molecules. The induced dipoles in pentane and 2,2-dimethylpentane are illustrated in Figure 2.

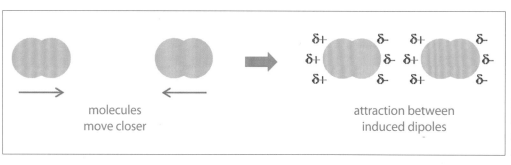

molecules move closer

attraction between induced dipoles

Figure 1: Generating induced dipoles on neighbouring molecules.

Figure 2: Induced dipoles in (a) pentane, C_5H_{12} and (b) 2,2-dimethylpropane, C_5H_{12}.

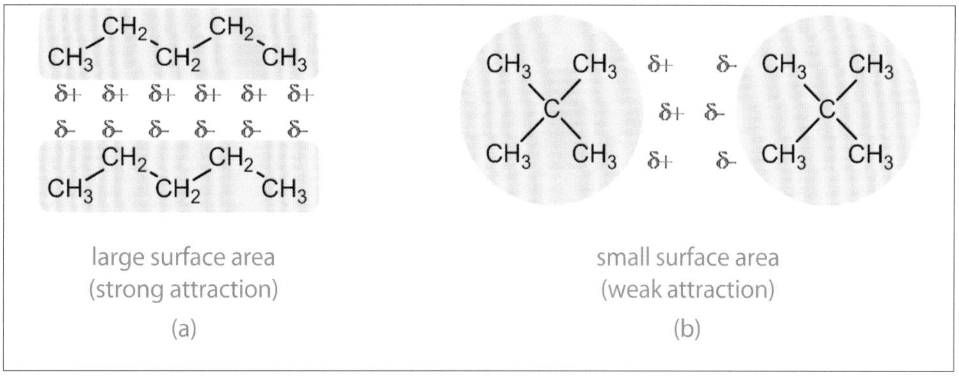

large surface area
(strong attraction)

(a)

small surface area
(weak attraction)

(b)

Before moving to the next section, check that you are able to:

- Explain the existence of van der Waals attractions between molecules.
- Recall the effect of adding electrons and increasing surface area on the strength of van der Waals attractions.
- Explain the effect of increasing van der Waals attraction on the melting and boiling point of a substance.

Dipole Forces

In this section we are learning to:

- Explain the existence of dipole forces between molecules.
- Describe the organisation of dipoles in solids and liquids.
- Recall the effect of dipole forces on the boiling point of a liquid.

Molecules with a permanent dipole can also experience attraction resulting from the attractive force between the positive end of the permanent dipole ($\delta+$) on one molecule and the negative end of the permanent dipole ($\delta-$) on neighbouring molecules. The attractive forces between permanent dipoles on neighbouring molecules are referred to as **dipole forces**. The interactions between permanent dipoles in solids and liquids are illustrated in Figure 3.

The extent to which van der Waals forces and dipole forces influence the physical properties of materials can be demonstrated by comparing the boiling points of the molecules in Figure 4. Butane (C_4H_{10}) and 2-methylpropane (C_4H_{10}) have the same formula and contain the same types of bonds. The molecules in both compounds experience only van der Waals attraction as neither molecule has a significant permanent dipole. The boiling point of butane is, however, greater as the larger surface area of butane gives rise to more attraction between induced dipoles and stronger van der Waals attraction between molecules.

The structures in Figure 4 reveal that a molecule of acetone (C_3H_6O) is similar in size and shape to a molecule of 2-methylpropane. As a result, the van der Waals attraction between molecules of acetone is expected to be similar to the van der Waals attraction between molecules of 2-methylpropane. However, unlike butane and 2-methylpropane, an acetone molecule has a permanent dipole. The presence of dipole forces in acetone is evidenced by the much higher boiling point of acetone and demonstrates the extent to which dipole forces can affect the properties of molecular materials.

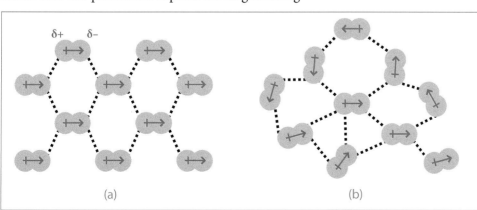

(a)

(b)

Figure 3: The interaction of permanent dipoles in (a) a liquid and (b) a solid.

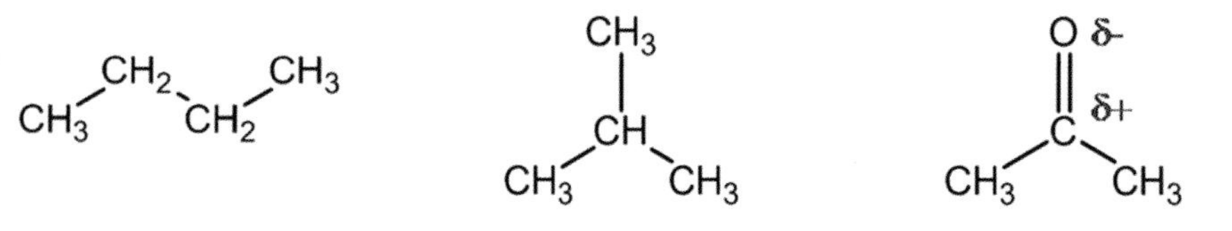

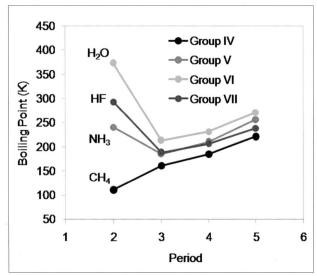

Figure 4: The effect of surface area and dipole forces on the boiling point of liquids.

butane, C_4H_{10}
boiling point 0 °C

2-methylpropane, C_4H_{10}
boiling point -11 °C

acetone, C_3H_6O
boiling point 56 °C

Before moving to the next section, check that you are able to:

- Recall that substances containing molecules with a permanent dipole experience dipole forces.
- Use dipole arrows to represent permanent dipoles in molecules and describe the organisation of permanent dipoles in solids and liquids.
- Explain the effect of dipole forces on the boiling point of liquids.

Hydrogen Bonding

In this section we are learning to:

- Recall the molecular features required for the formation of hydrogen bonds between molecules.
- Recall the effect of hydrogen bonding on melting and boiling point, and its effect on the density of water as it freezes to form ice.

The boiling points of the hydrides formed by the elements in Groups IV, V, VI and VII (Figure 5) reveal the presence of very strong intermolecular forces in the hydrides of nitrogen (NH_3), oxygen (H_2O) and fluorine (HF).

Figure 5: Boiling points for the hydrides of the Group IV, V, VI and VII elements.

The Group IV hydrides (CH_4, SiH_4, GeH_4, SnH_4) have a tetrahedral shape. As a result, the bond dipoles cancel and the hydrides do not have a permanent dipole. In the absence of dipole forces the increase in the boiling points of the Group IV hydrides results from an increase in van der Waals attraction as the number of electrons in the Group IV element increases down the group.

With the exception of NH_3, H_2O and HF, the boiling points of the Group V, VI and VII hydrides also increase steadily down the group. This again reflects an increase in van der Waals attraction between molecules as the number of electrons in the hydride increases down the group.

Unlike the Group IV hydrides, the Group V, VI and VII hydrides have a permanent dipole. The additional dipole force between the molecules increases the boiling point of the hydrides with the result that the boiling points of the Group V, VI and VII hydrides in Periods 3, 4 and 5 are higher than the boiling points of the corresponding Group IV hydrides.

Dipole forces cannot, however, account for the unexpectedly high boiling points of NH_3, H_2O, and HF. The unexpectedly high boiling points of NH_3, H_2O and HF are, instead, due to the formation of **hydrogen bonds** between molecules. A hydrogen bond is a strong dipole-like force of attraction between a lone pair on a very electronegative atom (N, O or F) and a hydrogen atom attached to a very electronegative atom (N, O or F) on a neighbouring molecule. The increase in the boiling points of NH_3, H_2O and HF resulting from hydrogen bonding (Figure 5) is much greater than the increase resulting from dipole forces and indicates that hydrogen bonds are significantly stronger than dipole forces. The formation of hydrogen bonds in NH_3, H_2O and HF is illustrated in Figure 6.

The formation of hydrogen bonds between neighbouring molecules can be used to explain a number of physical properties. In liquid water the hydrogen bonds between neighbouring molecules are constantly breaking and forming. When water freezes

Figure 6: Formation of a hydrogen bond between (a) NH_3 molecules, (b) H_2O molecules and (c) HF molecules.

hydrogen bond

(a) (b) (c)

the hydrogen bonds hold the molecules in fixed positions. This generates a highly ordered structure in which the molecules are more widely spaced, and results in the density of ice being lower than the density of liquid water. In this way the presence of hydrogen bonding between water molecules can be used to explain why ice floats on water.

Intermolecular forces arising from the interaction between hydrogen and other electronegative elements such as chlorine and bromine on a neighbouring molecule do not involve hydrogen bonding. The bonding between molecules in compounds such as hydrogen chloride (HCl) and hydrogen bromide (HBr) instead results from a combination of van der Waals attraction and dipole forces. In this way the forces between molecules can either be a combination of van der Waals attraction and hydrogen bonding as in water, or a combination of van der Waals attraction and dipole forces as in HCl and HBr.

Exercise 1.5A

1. Which one of the following would not form hydrogen bonds? (CCEA June 2004)
   a) $CH_3CH_2CH_2Cl$ b) $CH_3CH_2CH_2OH$
   c) $CH_3CH_2CH_2NH_2$ d) $CH_3CH(OH)CH_3$

2. There are three accepted types of intermolecular force: van der Waals forces, permanent dipole attractions and hydrogen bonding. Complete the following table where ✓ = present and ✗ = not present.

liquid	van der Waals	permanent dipole	hydrogen bonding
water	✓	✗	✓
ammonia			
xenon			
hydrogen chloride			

(CCEA June 2006)

3. What is the strongest intermolecular force in (a) ammonia, NH_3 (l) (b) hydrogen chloride, HCl (l) and (c) methane, CH_4 (l)? (CCEA June 2009)

4. The variation in the boiling point of the Group V hydrides is shown below.
   (a) Explain why ammonia, NH_3 has a much higher boiling point than phosphine, PH_3.
   (b) Explain why antimony hydride, SbH_3 has a higher boiling point than arsenic hydride, AsH_3.

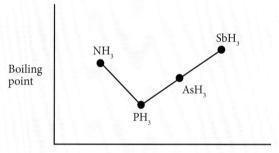

(CCEA June 2005)

5. The structure of ice is shown below. The water molecules are held together by hydrogen bonds which are a type of intermolecular force.

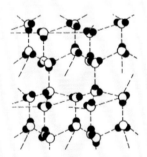

   (a) Name two other types of intermolecular force.
   (b) Explain how hydrogen bonding takes place between water molecules in ice.
   (c) Explain, using the structure, why ice is less dense than water. (CCEA January 2011)

6. Water forms hydrogen bonds between neighbouring molecules but is not capable of forming long chains of 'polywater' at room temperature. In contrast, in the liquid state, molecules such as hydrogen fluoride do form short chains. Suggest why water does not form chains and liquid hydrogen fluoride does. (CCEA January 2011)

7. Ammonia has a pyramidal structure and can form hydrogen bonds. (a) Draw two molecules of ammonia and show the hydrogen bond between the molecules. (b) Explain why ammonia loses the ability to form hydrogen bonds when it reacts with a hydrogen ion. (CCEA January 2011)

8. Explain why boron trifluoride is a gas despite having a molecular mass which is much greater than that of water. (CCEA January 2004)

Before moving to the next section, check that you are able to:

- Identify molecules capable of forming hydrogen bonds and use structural formulas to illustrate the formation of hydrogen bonds between molecules.
- Identify and describe the effect of hydrogen bonding on the melting and boiling point of a substance.
- Account for the decrease in the density of water as it freezes in terms of the formation of hydrogen bonds between water molecules.

Properties of Liquids

In this section we are learning to:

- Identify the types of intermolecular force between the molecules in a liquid.
- Explain the ability of liquids to mix in terms of the types of intermolecular forces between the molecules in each liquid.

Many properties of liquids can be explained in terms of the type of intermolecular forces experienced by the molecules in the liquid. For example, the presence of strong hydrogen bonds can be used to explain the high boiling points of alcohols such as ethanol, CH_3CH_2OH, and the ability of ethanol and water to mix. The formation of hydrogen bonds between molecules of

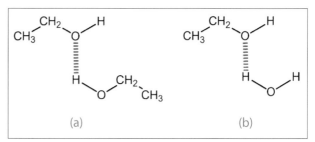

Figure 7: The formation of hydrogen bonds (a) in ethanol and (b) between ethanol and water.

ethanol, and between ethanol and water, is illustrated in Figure 7. This example illustrates the general principle that if liquids are to mix, the intermolecular forces between the molecules in each liquid should be of a similar type. The principle is often referred to as **the principle that 'like dissolves like'**.

Liquids that mix are described as **miscible**. Alcohols such as ethanol, CH_3CH_2OH are able to form hydrogen bonds and are, as a result, miscible in water and other liquids capable of forming hydrogen bonds. In contrast, liquids such as dichloromethane, CH_2Cl_2 are unable to form hydrogen bonds and do not mix with water and other liquids that form hydrogen bonds. Liquids that do not mix are described as **immiscible**.

Liquids such as dichloromethane, CH_2Cl_2 instead mix with solvents such as acetone, CH_3COCH_3. The intermolecular forces in acetone and dichloromethane are very similar. Both compounds have a permanent dipole and are unable to form hydrogen bonds. As a result the molecules in acetone, dichloromethane, and a mixture of acetone and dichloromethane, experience a combination of van der Waals attraction and dipole forces.

The principle of like-dissolves-like can also be extended to molecules that do not have permanent dipoles. For example, the halogens (F_2, Cl_2, ...) do not have a permanent dipole and cannot form hydrogen bonds. The intermolecular forces between halogen molecules consist solely of van der Waals attraction. As a result, the halogens mix with liquids containing nonpolar molecules such as hexane, C_6H_{14}.

In this way we see that in order to operate the principle of like-dissolves-like, we must first classify liquids based on the types of intermolecular force operating between molecules in the liquid. The classification used to operate the principle of like-dissolves-like is illustrated in Figure 8.

Nonpolar liquids
• van der Waals forces

Examples:
Bromine, Br_2
Hexane, C_6H_{14}

Polar liquids
• van der Waals forces
• dipole forces

Examples:
Dichloromethane, CH_2Cl_2
Chloroform, $CHCl_3$
Acetone, C_3H_6O

Hydrogen-bonded liquids
• van der Waals forces
• hydrogen bonding

Examples:
Ammonia, NH_3
Water, H_2O
Ethanol, C_2H_5OH

Polarity increasing

Figure 8: The classification of liquids used to operate the principle of 'like-dissolves-like'. Liquids in the same category are miscible and will likely be miscible with liquids in a neighbouring category.

Exercise 1.5B

1. Ammonia has a pyramidal structure and can form hydrogen bonds. Explain why ammonia is extremely soluble in water. *(CCEA January 2011)*

2. Carbon dioxide does not have a dipole but is very soluble in water. Explain this extreme solubility in terms of intermolecular forces. *(CCEA June 2011)*

Before moving to the next section, check that you are able to:

• Use molecular features to identify the types of intermolecular forces operating between the molecules in a substance.

• Recall that liquids containing molecules that experience similar types of intermolecular force are more likely to mix.

• Recall that liquids containing molecules that are held together by different types of intermolecular forces are unlikely to mix.

1.6 Oxidation and Reduction

CONNECTIONS
- Batteries and fuel cells use a combination of reduction and oxidation to produce a voltage.
- Green plants use a combination of reduction and oxidation to produce sugars from carbon dioxide, water and sunlight by photosynthesis.
- Antioxidants such as Vitamin C prevent disease by acting as reducing agents.

Redox Reactions

In this section we are learning to:

- Recall that oxidation and reduction occur simultaneously in reactions known as redox reactions.
- Recognise oxidation and reduction in terms of elements gaining or losing electrons.
- Identify the oxidising agent and reducing agent in a redox reaction.
- Use the chemical equation for a redox reaction to write half-equations describing oxidation and reduction.

Oxidation and reduction are chemical processes that occur simultaneously in reactions known as **redox reactions**. Many of the chemical processes used in industry, and the chemical reactions that occur in living organisms, are redox reactions. They are a very important class of chemical reactions. The burning of natural gas (mostly methane, CH_4) is a redox reaction. When natural gas burns, the carbon and hydrogen in the gas combine with oxygen to form CO_2 and H_2O.

Combustion: $CH_4 + 2O_2 \rightarrow CO_2 + 2H_2O$

In humans, sugars such as glucose are converted into energy, CO_2 and H_2O by the process known as respiration.

Respiration: $C_6H_{12}O_6 + 6O_2 \rightarrow 6CO_2 + 6H_2O$

The burning (combustion) of natural gas and respiration are both examples of redox reactions in which one or more elements in the reactants combine with oxygen to form the products. When a substance gains oxygen it is said to have been oxidised. In the case of the thermite reaction between aluminium and iron(III) oxide, the aluminium is oxidised when it gains oxygen from iron(III) oxide and forms aluminium oxide. The substance that provides the oxygen needed for oxidation to occur, in this case iron(III) oxide, is known as the **oxidising agent**.

Thermite reaction: $Fe_2O_3 + 2Al \rightarrow Al_2O_3 + 2Fe$

Conversely, a substance is reduced when it loses oxygen. In the thermite reaction above, iron(III) oxide is reduced to iron when it reacts with aluminium. The substance doing the reducing, in this case aluminium, is referred to as the **reducing agent**.

$$Fe_2O_3 \quad + \quad 2Al \quad \rightarrow \quad 2Fe \quad + \quad Al_2O_3$$

oxidising agent   reducing agent
(loses oxygen)   (gains oxygen)

The reaction between nitrogen and hydrogen to produce ammonia, NH_3 is another example of a redox reaction. The reaction does not involve oxygen and must instead be described in terms of the reactants gaining or losing hydrogen. In this reaction nitrogen is reduced when it gains hydrogen to form ammonia, NH_3. The substance that supplies the hydrogen, in this case hydrogen gas itself, is referred to as the reducing agent. Conversely, a substance is oxidised when it loses hydrogen. In this reaction the atoms of hydrogen in hydrogen gas (H_2) are oxidised when they combine with nitrogen to form ammonia and nitrogen is described as the oxidising agent.

$$N_2 \quad + \quad 3H_2 \quad \rightarrow \quad 2NH_3$$

oxidising agent   reducing agent
(gains hydrogen)   (loses hydrogen)

Together these examples demonstrate that *a redox reaction can always be described as a reaction between an oxidising agent and a reducing agent in which the oxidising agent is reduced and the reducing agent is oxidised.* This general feature of all redox reactions can prove very helpful when attempting to understand the nature of the reduction and oxidation processes occurring in more complex reaction mixtures.

Worked Example 1.6i

Identify the reducing agent in the following reactions.

(a) $2Cu + O_2 \rightarrow 2CuO$

(b) $CuO + H_2 \rightarrow Cu + H_2O$

(c) $2H_2 + O_2 \rightarrow 2H_2O$

Strategy

- Identify which reactant is oxidised and which is reduced.
- The reducing agent is oxidised in the reaction.

Solution

(a) Copper is oxidised (to CuO) and oxygen is reduced. The reducing agent is copper.

(b) Copper oxide is reduced (to Cu) and hydrogen is oxidised. The reducing agent is hydrogen.

(c) Hydrogen is oxidised (to H_2O) and oxygen is reduced. The reducing agent is hydrogen.

Defining oxidation and reduction in terms of the loss and gain of oxygen or hydrogen is limited to redox reactions involving these elements. A more general definition is needed to understand oxidation and reduction in reactions such as the metal displacement that occurs when an iron nail is placed in a solution of copper(II) sulfate.

$$Fe_{(s)} + CuSO_{4\ (aq)} \rightarrow FeSO_{4\ (aq)} + Cu_{(s)}$$

The atoms on the surface of the nail (Fe) lose electrons to form iron(II) ions (Fe^{2+}) in solution. The electrons from the iron atoms are gained by copper(II) ions (Cu^{2+}) in the solution which then form a layer of copper metal (Cu) on the surface of the nail. The sulfate ions (SO_4^{2-}) do not get involved in the reaction. The role of individual atoms and ions becomes clear on writing the ionic equation for the reaction.

Ionic equation: $Fe_{(s)} + Cu^{2+}_{(aq)} \rightarrow Fe^{2+}_{(aq)} + Cu_{(s)}$

If we now define **oxidation** to be a process in which electrons are lost and **reduction** to be a process in which electrons are gained, the displacement of copper from solution can be identified as a redox reaction in which iron is oxidised and copper(II) ions are reduced. The oxidation of iron and the reduction of copper(II) ions are the half-reactions that, together, make up the

redox reaction. Each half-reaction is described by a **half-equation**.

Half-equations: $Fe_{(s)} \rightarrow Fe^{2+}_{(aq)} + 2e^-$ (oxidation)

$Cu^{2+}_{(aq)} + 2e^- \rightarrow Cu_{(s)}$ (reduction)

If we recall that the reducing agent is oxidised and the oxidising agent is reduced, the half-equations can be used to clearly show that iron is acting as the reducing agent, and copper(II) ions are acting as the oxidising agent.

Worked Example 1.6ii

The equation for the redox reaction that occurs when a piece of copper wire is dipped in aqueous silver nitrate is given below. Write half-equations for the reaction.

$$Cu_{(s)} + 2AgNO_{3\ (aq)} \rightarrow 2Ag_{(s)} + Cu(NO_3)_{2\ (aq)}$$

Strategy

- Identify spectator ions and write the ionic equation for the reaction.
- Use the ionic equation to identify what is oxidised and what is reduced.

Solution

The ionic equation is:

$$Cu_{(s)} + 2Ag^+_{(aq)} \rightarrow 2Ag_{(s)} + Cu^{2+}_{(aq)}$$

Copper atoms lose electrons to form copper(II) ions (Cu^{2+}). The half-equation for oxidation is:

$$Cu_{(s)} \rightarrow Cu^{2+}_{(aq)} + 2e^-$$

Silver ions (Ag^+) gain electrons to form silver metal. The half-equation for reduction is:

$$Ag^+_{(aq)} + e^- \rightarrow Ag_{(s)}$$

> **Before moving to the next section, check that you are able to:**
>
> - Recall that oxidation and reduction occur simultaneously in a redox reaction.
> - Identify oxidation and reduction in terms of the gain or loss of electrons.
> - Identify the oxidising agent and reducing agent in a redox reaction on the basis of what is being oxidised and what is reduced in the reaction.
> - Use the chemical equation for a redox reaction to write half-equations describing oxidation and reduction.

Oxidation States

In this section we are learning to:

- Use the term oxidation state to describe the extent to which an element is oxidised when it combines with other elements to form compounds and ions.
- Associate oxidation and reduction with changes in the oxidation state of individual elements during a redox reaction.
- Use oxidation numbers to keep track of the oxidation state of elements during chemical reactions.

The oxidation and reduction processes occurring within a redox reaction can also be identified by considering the extent to which individual elements are oxidised by the reaction. For example, in the thermite reaction between aluminium and iron(III) oxide, Fe_2O_3, iron is produced by the reduction of the iron(III) ions (Fe^{3+}) in iron(III) oxide. The electrons needed for the reduction are produced when aluminium is oxidised to form the aluminium(III) ions (Al^{3+}) in aluminium(III) oxide, Al_2O_3.

$$Fe_2O_3 + 2Al \rightarrow Al_2O_3 + 2Fe$$

If we use the term **oxidation state** to describe the extent to which an element has been oxidised: *oxidation refers to a process in which the oxidation state of an element increases* and *reduction refers to a process in which the oxidation state of an element decreases*. In the case of the thermite reaction, the oxidation of aluminium to aluminium oxide, Al_2O_3 can be interpreted as an increase in the oxidation state of aluminium. Conversely, the reduction of iron(III) oxide, Fe_2O_3, to iron corresponds to a decrease in the oxidation state of iron.

The number of electrons involved in oxidation and reduction can be determined by assigning the elements in each reactant and product an **oxidation number**. A positive oxidation number is used to indicate the number of electrons lost by an element when forming a compound. For example, the iron(III) ions (Fe^{3+}) ions in iron(III) oxide are assigned an oxidation number of +3 to indicate that an iron(III) ion is formed when an iron atom loses three electrons. Conversely, a negative oxidation number is used to indicate the number of electrons gained by an element when forming a compound. For example, the chloride (Cl^-) ions in sodium chloride, NaCl are assigned an oxidation number of –1 to indicate that chloride is

formed when a chlorine atom gains one electron. Having defined oxidation number in this way, *an increase in the oxidation number of an element can be used to indicate that the element has lost electrons and been oxidised.* Conversely, *a decrease in the oxidation number of an element indicates that the element has gained electrons and been reduced.*

Clearly this method for assigning oxidation numbers is only possible when working with ionic compounds and we must devise an alternative method to assign oxidation numbers in covalently bonded compounds. Consider for example the production of ammonia by the reaction between hydrogen and nitrogen.

$$N_2 + 3H_2 \rightarrow 2NH_3$$

In the process of forming ammonia (NH_3) the nitrogen atom acquires a small negative charge ($\delta-$) by using a total of three electrons from the hydrogen atoms to form covalent bonds. This is indicated by assigning the nitrogen atom in ammonia an oxidation number of –3. Similarly each hydrogen atom in ammonia is assigned an oxidation number of +1 to remind us that it has acquired a small positive charge ($\delta+$) by sharing one electron with nitrogen to form a covalent bond.

The atoms in a molecule of nitrogen (N_2) or hydrogen (H_2) do not gain or lose electrons as a result of forming the molecule. This is recognised by assigning the atoms in each molecule an oxidation number of zero. The changes in oxidation number that accompany the oxidation of hydrogen and the reduction of nitrogen are summarised in Figure 1.

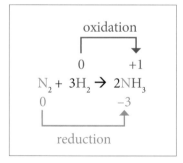

Figure 1: The changes in oxidation number that accompany the formation of ammonia from nitrogen and hydrogen.

Worked Example 1.6iii

Use oxidation numbers to explain the redox change taking place when sodium reacts with chlorine to form sodium chloride.

$$2Na_{(s)} + Cl_{2(g)} \rightarrow 2NaCl_{(s)}$$

Strategy

- Assign oxidation numbers to the elements in each reactant and product.
- Identify which element is oxidised and which is reduced.

Solution

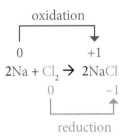

Sodium is oxidised (0 to +1) and chlorine is reduced (0 to –1).

....

Exercise 1.6A

1. Define (a) *oxidation* in terms of electron transfer and (b) *reduction* in terms of changes in oxidation state. *(CCEA June 2010)*

2. Use oxidation numbers to explain the redox change taking place in the following reaction.

$$H_{2\ (g)} + Cl_{2\ (g)} \rightarrow 2HCl_{(g)}$$

3. Determine the oxidation number of each underlined element and use the oxidation numbers to explain the redox change taking place.

$$\underline{Cu}O_{(s)} + \underline{H}_{2\ (g)} \rightarrow \underline{Cu}_{(s)} + \underline{H}_2O_{(l)}$$

> Before moving to the next section, check that you are able to:
>
> - Associate oxidation with an increase in the oxidation state of an element and reduction with a decrease in the oxidation state of an element.
> - Use oxidation numbers to identify changes in the oxidation states of elements during chemical a reaction.
> - Associate oxidation with an increase in the oxidation number of an element resulting from the loss of electrons by the element.
> - Associate reduction with a decrease in the oxidation number of an element resulting from the gain of electrons by the element.

Assigning Oxidation Numbers

> **In this section we are learning to:**
>
> - Assign oxidation numbers to individual elements in compounds and ions.

Elements

The outermost electrons in a metal are free to move and are shared equally by the atoms in the metal. As a result the individual atoms in the metal do not lose or gain electrons by forming bonds between the metal atoms. This is recognised by assigning the atoms in a metal an oxidation number of zero.

The atoms in elements with a molecular covalent structure such as chlorine (Cl_2) and sulfur (S_8), or a giant covalent structure such as diamond, are held together by nonpolar covalent bonds. The atoms do not gain or lose electrons as a result of forming nonpolar covalent bonds and are assigned an oxidation number of zero.

Ionic Compounds

The oxidation number of an element in an ionic compound is equal to the charge on the ion formed by the element. For example, a sodium ion (Na^+) in an ionic compound such as sodium oxide (Na_2O) is assigned an oxidation number of +1 to indicate that it is formed when an atom of sodium (metal) loses one electron. Similarly, an oxide ion (O^{2-}) in Na_2O can be assigned an oxidation number of –2 to indicate that it was formed by adding two electrons to an oxygen atom.

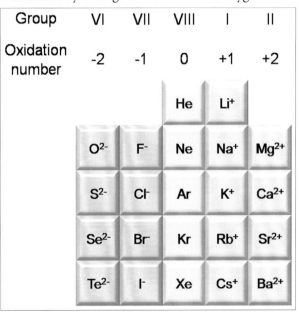

Figure 2: Oxidation numbers for the ions formed by the elements towards the left and right sides of the Periodic Table.

When the elements in Groups I, II and III combine to form ionic compounds, they lose electrons to form positive ions with a full outer shell. In contrast, when the elements in Groups VI and VII combine with metals to form ionic compounds they gain electrons to form negative ions with a full outer shell. The number of electrons lost or gained by an element is the same for each element in the Group, allowing the oxidation number for the element to be determined by its location in the Periodic Table. The relationship between the oxidation number of an element and its location in the Periodic Table is summarised in Figure 2.

Worked Example 1.6iv

Determine the oxidation number of each element in (a) MgO, (b) Na_2O and (c) $AlBr_3$.

Strategy

- The oxidation number of Mg, Na, Al, O and Br can be determined from the location of the element in the Periodic Table.

Solution

(a) Magnesium (Group II) has an oxidation number of +2. Oxygen (Group VI) has an oxidation number of −2.

(b) Sodium (Group I) has an oxidation number of +1. Oxygen (Group VI) has an oxidation number of −2.

(c) Aluminium (Group III) has an oxidation number of +3. Bromine (Group VII) has an oxidation number of −1.

Elements towards the middle of the Periodic Table are less likely to achieve a full outer shell of electrons when they form ionic compounds. For example, iron routinely forms compounds containing iron(II) ions, Fe^{2+} or iron(III) ions, Fe^{3+}. Neither ion has a full outer shell. The iron(II) ion is assigned an oxidation number of +2 and the iron(III) ion is assigned an oxidation number of +3 to indicate the number of electrons lost when forming the ion from an atom of iron.

When determining the oxidation number of an element with more than one stable oxidation state it is helpful to remember that *the oxidation numbers of the ions in one formula of the compound add to zero*. This

is always true because the electrons lost by elements trying to achieve full outer shell are gained by other elements as they attempt to achieve a full outer shell.

> **Rules** for assigning oxidation numbers in ionic compounds:
> - Use the Periodic Table to assign oxidation numbers to monatomic ions such as K^+, Ba^{2+}, Al^{3+}, O^{2-} and Cl^-.
> - Determine any remaining oxidation numbers by requiring the oxidation numbers of the atoms in the formula to add to zero.

Worked Example 1.6v

Determine the oxidation number of each element in the following compounds.

(a) FeO (b) Ag_2O (c) $FeBr_3$ (d) $CuCl_2$ (e) Cu_2O

Solution

(a) Oxygen (Group VI) has an oxidation number of −2. The oxidation number of iron must be +2 if the oxidation numbers add to zero.

(b) Oxygen (Group VI) has an oxidation number of −2. Combining the oxidation numbers of the silver atoms (2Ag) gives +2. The oxidation number for each silver atom (Ag) is +1.

(c) Bromine (Group VII) has an oxidation number of −1. The oxidation number of iron must be +3 if the oxidation numbers add to zero.

(d) Chlorine (Group VII) has an oxidation number of −1. The oxidation number of copper must be +2 if the oxidation numbers add to zero.

(e) Oxygen (Group VI) has an oxidation number of −2. Combining the oxidation numbers of the copper atoms (2Cu) gives +2. The oxidation number of each copper atom (Cu) is +1.

Exercise 1.6B

Nuclear power plants use chlorine(III) fluoride, ClF_3 to produce uranium hexafluoride, UF_6 from uranium tetrafluoride, UF_4. Deduce the oxidation number of uranium in UF_4 and UF_6 and determine the role of ClF_3 in the reaction. *(CCEA June 2003)*

Covalently Bonded Compounds

A number of rules can be applied to determine the oxidation numbers of the elements in covalently bonded compounds and ions. There are, however, a small number of exceptions that can only be understood by considering the nature of the bonding between atoms.

Figure 3: Assigned oxidation numbers for the atoms in (a) water, H_2O and (b) hydrogen peroxide, H_2O_2.

The oxidation numbers assigned to each atom in water, H_2O and hydrogen peroxide, H_2O_2 are shown in Figure 3. In water, each hydrogen atom is assigned an oxidation number of +1 to remind us that it has acquired a small positive charge by sharing one electron with oxygen. Similarly, the oxygen atom in water is assigned an oxidation number of –2 to remind us that it has acquired a small negative charge by using two electrons from the hydrogen atoms to form a polar covalent bond with each hydrogen atom.

The bonding in hydrogen peroxide, H_2O_2 is similar to the bonding in water. Each hydrogen atom is assigned an oxidation number of +1 to reflect the small positive charge acquired by sharing one electron with an oxygen atom. In return, the oxygen atoms are each assigned an oxidation number of –1 to reflect the small negative charge acquired by sharing one electron with a hydrogen atom to form a polar covalent bond. The electrons in the O-O bond are shared equally between the oxygen atoms and do not affect the oxidation state of the oxygen atoms. In this way the oxygen atoms in hydrogen peroxide are each assigned an oxidation number of –1 to indicate that they have not been reduced to the same extent as the oxygen atom in water (oxidation number –2).

In this way we see that the oxidation state of an atom in a covalently bonded compound depends on the ability of the atom to attract electrons when forming covalent bonds, and the way in which the atoms are connected in the molecule. In general, atoms with a high electronegativity will be more able to attract electrons and will achieve more negative oxidation states when forming compounds. This principle allows us to construct a number of rules that can be used to assign oxidation states in nonmetal compounds on the basis of electronegativity. As in the case of hydrogen peroxide, exceptions to these rules will result from a specific bonding arrangement within the molecule or ion and must be considered separately.

Rules for assigning oxidation numbers in nonmetal compounds:

- Hydrogen always has an oxidation number of +1.
- Fluorine always has an oxidation number of –1.
- With the exception of peroxides oxygen has an oxidation number of –2.
- In peroxides oxygen has an oxidation number of –1.
- Chlorine, bromine and iodine have an oxidation number of –1 except when bonding with more electronegative elements such as oxygen and fluorine.

The rules for assigning oxidation numbers are particularly helpful when attempting to assign oxidation numbers in compounds containing elements that have the ability to exist in different oxidation states. It is also helpful to recall that, as in ionic compounds, *the oxidation numbers of the atoms in one formula of a nonmetal compound add to zero.* For example, in dinitrogen tetroxide, N_2O_4 each oxygen atom is first assigned an oxidation number of –2. It then follows that the nitrogen atoms must each have an oxidation number of +4 if their combined oxidation number (+8) is to balance the combined oxidation number for the four oxygen atoms (–8).

$$N_2O_4$$

Oxidation numbers: $2\times(+4) + 4\times(-2) = 0$

The same rules can also be used to assign oxidation numbers in materials with a giant covalent structure. For example in quartz, SiO_2 each oxygen atom in the giant structure is first assigned an oxidation number of –2. The oxidation number of each silicon atom in the giant structure must then be +4 if the oxidation numbers of the atoms in the formula are to add to zero.

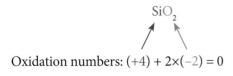

Oxidation numbers: $(+4) + 2\times(-2) = 0$

Exercise 1.6C

Ammonia can act as a reducing agent. When passed over heated copper(II) oxide the following reaction occurs:

$$2NH_3 + 3CuO \rightarrow 3Cu + N_2 + 3H_2O$$

Deduce the oxidation numbers for nitrogen and copper in the reactants and products and use them to explain the redox change. *(CCEA June 2006)*

Polyatomic Ions

The atoms in polyatomic ions such as sulfate (SO_4^{2-}), nitrate (NO_3^-) and bromate (BrO_3^-) are held together by covalent bonds. This allows us to apply the rules for assigning oxidation numbers in nonmetal compounds when assigning oxidation numbers to the atoms in a polyatomic ion. If we consider the charge on a polyatomic ion to be the net number of electrons lost or gained when the ion was formed from its elements, *the oxidation numbers of the atoms in a polyatomic ion must add to the charge on the ion*. This principle becomes very helpful when assigning oxidation numbers in ions containing atoms such as sulfur and nitrogen that have the ability to exist in different oxidation states.

For example, in sulfate ion (SO_4^{2-}) we can begin by assigning each oxygen atom an oxidation number of –2. If the oxidation numbers of all five atoms in the ion combine to give a charge of –2, sulfur must be assigned an oxidation number of +6 to counter a combined oxidation number of –8 for the four oxygen atoms.

SO_4^{2-}

$(+6) + 4\times(-2) =$ charge on ion

Similarly in bromate ion (BrO_3^-) we can begin by assigning each oxygen atom an oxidation number of –2. If the oxidation numbers of all four atoms in the ion combine to give a charge of –1, bromine must be

assigned an oxidation number of +5 to counter a combined oxidation number of –6 for the three oxygen atoms.

BrO_3^-

$(+5) + 3\times(-2) =$ charge on ion

> **Rules** for assigning oxidation numbers in polyatomic ions:
> * Use the rules for nonmetal compounds to assign oxidation numbers to individual atoms in the polyatomic ion.
> * Determine any remaining oxidation numbers by requiring the oxidation numbers of the atoms in the ion to add to the charge on the ion.

Worked Example 1.6vi

Determine the oxidation number of chlorine in the following compounds.

(a) NaCl (b) Cl_2O_7 (c) NaOCl (d) $NaClO_3$

(CCEA January 2003)

Strategy

* If the compound is ionic use the Periodic Table to identify the oxidation number of monatomic ions and then apply the rules for polyatomic ions if needed.
* If the compound is a nonmetal compound apply the rules to determine oxidation numbers in nonmetal compounds.

Solution

(a) NaCl is an ionic compound. Na (Group I) has an oxidation number of +1. Cl (Group VII) has an oxidation number of –1.

(b) Cl_2O_7 is a nonmetal compound. Oxygen has an oxidation number of –2. The combined oxidation number for the two chlorine atoms must balance the combined oxidation number of $7 \times (-2) = -14$ for the seven oxygen atoms. Each chlorine atom has an oxidation number of +7.

(c) NaOCl is an ionic compound. The oxidation number of oxygen in OCl^- is –2. The oxidation number for chlorine must offset the oxidation number of oxygen to produce a charge of –1. Chlorine has an oxidation number of +1.

(d) $NaClO_3$ is an ionic compound. The oxidation number of oxygen in ClO_3^- is –2. The oxidation number of chlorine must offset a combined oxidation number of $3 \times (-2) = -6$ for the oxygen atoms to produce a charge of –1. Chlorine has an oxidation number of +5.

Exercise 1.6D

1. Deduce the oxidation number of nitrogen in (a) HNO_3 and (b) NO. *(CCEA June 2010)*

2. The equation for the reaction of silver with nitric acid is given below. Determine the oxidation numbers of the underlined elements and use them to explain the redox reaction taking place.

$$3\,\underline{Ag} + 4H\underline{NO}_3 \rightarrow 3\,\underline{Ag}NO_3 + 2H_2O + \underline{N}O$$

(CCEA January 2007)

3. Determine the oxidation numbers of potassium and manganese in potassium permanganate, $KMnO_4$. *(CCEA June 2002)*

4. Which one of the following reactions shows hydrogen peroxide, H_2O_2 behaving as a reducing agent?
   (a) $H_2O_2 + Ag_2O \rightarrow 2Ag + O_2 + H_2O$
   (b) $H_2O_2 + 2FeSO_4 + H_2SO_4 \rightarrow Fe_2(SO_4)_3 + 2H_2O$
   (c) $H_2O_2 + Na_2SO_3 \rightarrow Na_2SO_4 + H_2O$
   (d) $H_2O_2 + 2KI + 2HCl \rightarrow I_2 + 2KCl + 2H_2O$

(CCEA June 2003)

5. Chlorine reacts with cold dilute sodium hydroxide according to the following equation. Determine the oxidation number of chlorine in each species and explain, using the oxidation numbers of chlorine, why this is a redox reaction.

$$Cl_2 + 2NaOH \rightarrow NaCl + NaOCl + H_2O$$

(CCEA January 2008)

6. Which one of the following reactions is a redox reaction?
   (a) $2NH_3 \rightarrow N_2 + 3H_2$
   (b) $CuO + H_2SO_4 \rightarrow CuSO_4 + H_2O$
   (c) $H_2O + H^+ \rightarrow H_3O^+$
   (d) $AgNO_3 + KI \rightarrow KNO_3 + AgI$

(CCEA June 2008)

7. Which one of the following reactions is a redox reaction?
   (a) $2HBr + H_2SO_4 \rightarrow Br_2 + SO_2 + 2H_2O$
   (b) $NaOH + HCl \rightarrow NaCl + H_2O$
   (c) $NH_3 + HCl \rightarrow NH_4Cl$
   (d) $Ag^+ + Cl^- \rightarrow AgCl$

(CCEA June 2004)

> Before moving to the next section, check that you are able to:
>
> - Assign oxidation numbers to individual elements in compounds and ions.
> - Use changes in oxidation number to identify oxidation and reduction.

Balancing Redox Reactions

In this section we are learning to:

- Use half-equations to write chemical equations for redox reactions.
- Write balanced half-equations for oxidation and reduction.

The chemical equation for a redox reaction is obtained by adding the half-equations describing oxidation and reduction in a way that makes the number of electrons generated by oxidation equal to the number of electrons used for reduction. For example, sodium bromide is formed when sodium metal reacts with bromine vapour.

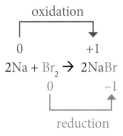

The oxidation number of sodium increases from zero to +1 as sodium is oxidised to form sodium (Na^+) ions in NaBr. Conversely, the oxidation number of bromine decreases from zero to –1 as bromine is reduced to form bromide (Br^-) ions in NaBr. The numbers of electrons involved in oxidation and reduction are given in the half-equations describing oxidation and reduction.

Half-equations: $Na \rightarrow Na^+ + e^-$ (oxidation)
$Br_2 + 2e^- \rightarrow 2Br^-$ (reduction)

If the number of electrons produced by oxidation is to equal the number required for reduction, two sodium atoms (2Na) must be oxidised for every molecule of bromine (Br_2) reduced. As a result, the next step towards writing a chemical equation for the reaction is to write balanced half-equations in which the number of electrons produced by oxidation equals the number of electrons required for reduction.

Balanced half-equations:
$2Na \rightarrow 2Na^+ + 2e^-$ (oxidation)
$Br_2 + 2e^- \rightarrow 2Br^-$ (reduction)

The balanced equation for the reaction can then be obtained by adding the balanced half-equations for oxidation and reduction.

Chemical equation:
$2Na_{(s)} + Br_{2\,(l)} \rightarrow 2NaBr_{(s)}$

When combining half-equations care must be taken to ensure that ions formed by the redox process are used to form the products of the reaction. In this instance the sodium (Na^+) ions and bromide (Br^-) ions formed by the redox process must be combined to form solid sodium bromide; the actual product obtained from the reaction.

If a redox reaction occurs in solution, adding the balanced half-equations produces the ionic equation for the reaction. For example, placing a copper wire in a solution of silver nitrate displaces silver from the solution.

$Cu_{(s)} + 2AgNO_{3\,(aq)} \rightarrow Cu(NO_3)_{2\,(aq)} + 2Ag_{(s)}$

Half-equations: $Cu_{(s)} \rightarrow Cu^{2+}_{(aq)} + 2e^-$ (oxidation)
$Ag^+_{(aq)} + e^- \rightarrow Ag_{(s)}$ (reduction)

The half-equations are balanced when the electrons produced by the oxidation of one copper atom are used to reduce two silver ions. Adding the balanced half-equations gives the ionic equation for the reaction.

Balanced half-equations:
$Cu_{(s)} \rightarrow Cu^{2+}_{(aq)} + 2e^-$ (oxidation)
$2Ag^+_{(aq)} + 2e^- \rightarrow 2Ag_{(s)}$ (reduction)

Ionic equation:
$Cu_{(s)} + 2Ag^+_{(aq)} \rightarrow Cu^{2+}_{(aq)} + 2Ag_{(s)}$

In this reaction the nitrate ions (NO_3^-) are spectator ions. The chemical equation for the reaction is obtained by adding the spectator ions to the ionic equation.

Worked Example 1.6vii

(a) Use the following half-equations to write the ionic equation for the reaction of chlorine with a solution of potassium iodide. (b) Explain the role of iodide ions in this reaction.

$I_{2\,(aq)} + 2e^- \rightarrow 2I^-_{(aq)}$

$Cl_{2\,(aq)} + 2e^- \rightarrow 2Cl^-_{(aq)}$

(Adapted from CCEA June 2004)

Solution

(a) The half-equations for the reaction of chlorine (Cl_2) with iodide (I^-) are:

$$Cl_{2\,(aq)} + 2e^- \rightarrow 2Cl^-_{(aq)}$$

and $2I^-_{(aq)} \rightarrow I_{2\,(aq)} + 2e^-$

The half-equations are balanced. Adding the half-equations gives the ionic equation for the reaction.

$$Cl_{2\,(aq)} + 2I^-_{(aq)} \rightarrow I_{2\,(aq)} + 2Cl^-_{(aq)}$$

(b) Iodide (I^-) reduces chlorine (Cl_2) to chloride (Cl^-) ion. Iodide is acting as a reducing agent.

Exercise 1.6E

1. The half-equation for the reduction of concentrated nitric acid is shown below. Write a half-equation for the oxidation of iodide ions to form an iodine molecule then combine the half-equations to give the ionic equation for the reaction.

$HNO_3 + 3H^+ + 3e^- \rightarrow NO + 2H_2O$

(CCEA June 2010)

2. Acidified chloric (I) acid reacts with aqueous iron(II) to form iron(III) ions. Use the following half-equations to write the equation for the reaction.

$2HOCl_{(aq)} + 2H^+_{(aq)} + 2e^- \rightarrow Cl_{2\,(aq)} + 2H_2O_{(l)}$
$Fe^{2+}_{(aq)} \rightarrow Fe^{3+}_{(aq)} + e^-$

(CCEA January 2003)

3. Use the following half-equations to write an ionic equation for the reaction between acidified manganate(VII) ions and ethanedioate ions.

$$MnO_4^- + 8H^+ + 5e^- \rightarrow Mn^{2+} + 4H_2O$$
$$C_2O_4^{2-} \rightarrow 2CO_2 + 2e^-$$

(CCEA June 2009)

4. (a) Use the following half-equations to write the equation for the reaction between hydrogen peroxide and hydrazine. (b) Use oxidation numbers to explain why this is a redox reaction.

$$N_2H_4 \rightarrow N_2 + 4H^+ + 4 e^-$$
$$H_2O_2 + 2H^+ + 2e^- \rightarrow 2H_2O$$

(CCEA January 2005)

If an ionic equation has been constructed correctly the total charge on the products should be the same as the total charge on the reactants. This is also true for any half-equation and can be used to help construct half-equations.

Worked Example 1.6viii

When concentrated sulfuric acid reacts with solid sodium bromide the acid reacts with bromide ion to form sulfur dioxide and bromine.

(a) State how the oxidation number for sulfur changes during the reaction.

(b) Write the half-equation for the formation of bromine from bromide ion.

(c) Complete the following half-equation for the formation of sulfur dioxide.

$$H_2SO_4 + H^+ \rightarrow SO_2 + H_2O$$

(d) Write the ionic equation for the reaction of bromide ions with sulfuric acid.

(e) Describe the role of bromide ions in the reaction.

$\left(\text{CCEA January 2010}\right)$

Solution

(a) The oxidation number of sulfur decreases from +6 in sulfuric acid (H_2SO_4) to +4 in sulfur dioxide (SO_2).

(b) The half-equation for the formation of bromine (Br_2) is: $2Br^- \rightarrow Br_2 + 2e^-$

(c) Balance the number of hydrogen atoms before adding the 2 electrons needed to reduce the oxidation number of sulfur from +6 to +4.

$$H_2SO_4 + 2H^+ + 2e^- \rightarrow SO_2 + 2H_2O$$

(d) The half-equations in (b) and (c) are balanced. Adding gives the ionic equation for the reaction.

$$2Br^- + H_2SO_4 + 2H^+ \rightarrow Br_2 + SO_2 + 2H_2O$$

(e) Bromide ion acts as a reducing agent by reducing the sulfur in the sulfuric acid.

Exercise 1.6F

Bromate(V) ion, BrO_3^- can be reduced to bromine. Determine the values of x, y and z if the half-equation for the reduction has the form:

$$2BrO_3^-{}_{(aq)} + x\,H^+{}_{(aq)} + y\,e^- \rightarrow Br_2{}_{(aq)} + z\,H_2O_{(l)}$$

(CCEA January 2006)

Before moving to the next section, check that you are able to:

- Use half-equations to write the equation for a redox reaction.
- Write half-equations for oxidation and reduction.

Disproportionation Reactions

In this section we are learning to:

- Refer to the simultaneous oxidation and reduction of an element as disproportionation.
- Identify and explain examples of disproportionation by assigning oxidation numbers.

The term **disproportionation** refers to a redox reaction in which an element is simultaneously oxidised and reduced. The reaction that occurs when chlorine gas dissolves in water is an example of a disproportionation reaction. Chlorine dissolves in water to give a mixture of hydrochloric acid, HCl $_{(aq)}$ and hypochlorous or chloric (I) acid, HOCl $_{(aq)}$.

$$Cl_2{}_{(g)} + H_2O_{(l)} \rightarrow HCl_{(aq)} + HOCl_{(aq)}$$

The resulting solution contains chloride ions, Cl^- and chlorate (I) ions, OCl^-. Chlorine has an oxidation number of –1 in chloride and +1 in chlorate (I). As a result, when chlorine dissolves in water, the oxidation number of the chlorine atoms involved in forming chlorate (I) increases from zero to +1, and the oxidation number of the chlorine atoms involved in forming chloride ions decreases from zero to –1. In this way chlorine disproportionates by being simultaneously oxidised to form chlorate(I) ions and reduced to form chloride ions.

Basic oxides such as copper(II) oxide react with acids to produce a salt and water. The copper(II) ion,

Cu^{2+} is stable in aqueous solution and gives the resulting solution its characteristic blue colour.

$$CuO_{(s)} + H_2SO_{4\,(aq)} \rightarrow CuSO_{4\,(aq)} + H_2O_{(l)}$$

In contrast, the copper(I) ion, Cu^+ is not stable in aqueous solution. When copper(I) oxide reacts with acid the copper(I) ions disproportionate to form copper metal and copper(II) ions in solution.

$$Cu_2O_{(s)} + H_2SO_{4\,(aq)} \rightarrow Cu_{(s)} + CuSO_{4\,(aq)} + H_2O_{(l)}$$

Half-equations:

$$Cu_2O + 2H^+ \rightarrow 2Cu^{2+} + H_2O + 2e^- \text{ (oxidation)}$$

$$Cu_2O + 2H^+ + 2e^- \rightarrow 2Cu + H_2O \quad \text{(reduction)}$$

Worked Example 1.6ix

Which one of the following equations involves disproportionation?

(a) $Cl_2 + 2Br^- \rightarrow 2Cl^- + Br_2$

(b) $Cl_2 + 2OH^- \rightarrow OCl^- + Cl^- + H_2O$

(c) $Cl_2 + 2Fe^{2+} \rightarrow 2Cl^- + 2Fe^{3+}$

(d) $Cl_2 + H_2 \rightarrow 2HCl$

(CCEA June 2002)

Solution

Reactions (a), (b) and (d) are simple redox reactions.

Reaction (b) is an example of disproportionation in which chlorine disproportionates to form chlorate(I), ClO^- and chloride, Cl^-.

Exercise 1.6G

1. The reaction between hydrogenxenate ions and hydroxide ions is given below. (a) Deduce the oxidation number of xenon in each species and (b) explain why this is considered an example of disproportionation.

    $$2OH^- + 2HXeO_4^- \rightarrow Xe + 2H_2O + XeO_6^{4-} + O_2$$

    (CCEA January 2009)

2. The equation for the reaction of chlorine with hot concentrated sodium hydroxide is given here. (a) Deduce the oxidation number of chlorine in $NaClO_3$ and $NaCl$ and (b) explain

why this is a disproportionation reaction.

$$6\,NaOH_{(aq)} + 3Cl_{2\,(g)} \rightarrow$$
$$NaClO_{3\,(aq)} + 5NaCl_{(aq)} + 3H_2O_{(l)}$$

(CCEA June 2004)

3. Aqueous iodine reacts readily with sodium hydroxide solution to form sodium iodate, $NaIO_3$. The reaction occurs via the following 2-step process. (a) Write the overall equation for the reaction of iodine with sodium hydroxide to form sodium iodate. (b) Deduce the oxidation number of iodine in NaIO, NaI and $NaIO_3$ and use these oxidation numbers to explain why this process is an example of disproportionation.

    $$I_{2\,(aq)} + 2NaOH_{(aq)} \rightarrow NaI_{(aq)} + NaIO_{(aq)} + H_2O_{(l)}$$

    $$3NaIO_{(aq)} \rightarrow 2NaI_{(aq)} + NaIO_{3\,(aq)}$$

    (CCEA January 2006)

Before moving to the next section, check that you are able to:

- Identify examples of disproportionation by assigning oxidation numbers.
- Use oxidation numbers to explain disproportionation.

1.7 The Periodic Table

In this section we are learning to:

- Recall the organisation of elements within the Periodic Table in terms of atomic number, groups, periods and blocks.
- Determine the electron configuration of an element from its location in the Periodic Table.
- Explain trends in the melting point, first ionisation energy and atomic radius of the elements in the third period.

Organisation and Structure

In the modern Periodic Table the elements are arranged in order of increasing atomic number. Elements with similar chemical properties are arranged in columns known as **groups**, a number of which have common names and are referred to using roman numerals as shown in Figure 1. The rows of elements formed by arranging the elements in this way are known as **periods**. Many properties of the elements vary in a predictable way across periods, and within groups. Trends in the properties of the elements within a period or group are referred to as **periodic trends**. Arranging the elements in this way reveals properties that are shared by the elements in an entire 'block' of the Periodic Table. The classification of the elements into s, p and d blocks is shown in Figure 1.

The form of the modern Periodic Table also allows for the elements to be classified as metals and nonmetals based on their location in the Periodic Table. The distribution of metals and nonmetals within the Periodic Table is shown in Figure 2. A number of elements have been identified as **semimetals** on account of their having properties in common with both metals and nonmetals. The location of the semimetals reminds us that the transition from metallic behaviour to nonmetallic behaviour is gradual and is an example of a periodic trend. The trends in **metallic character** shown in Figure 2 remind us that the metals in the s-block have more metallic character, and are 'better' metals, than those in the d-block. The trend in metallic character within a group also reveals that the metals towards the bottom of the s-block have the most metallic character of all metals.

The transition from metallic behaviour to

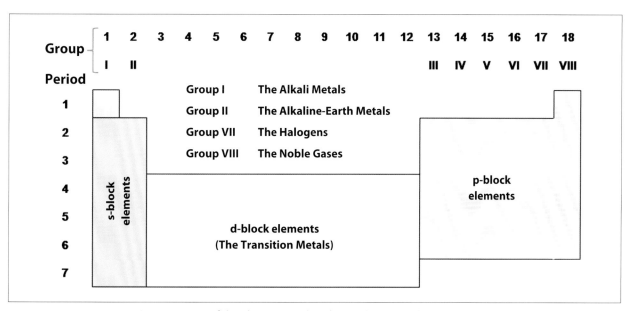

Figure 1: Organisation of the elements within the modern Periodic Table into periods, groups and blocks.

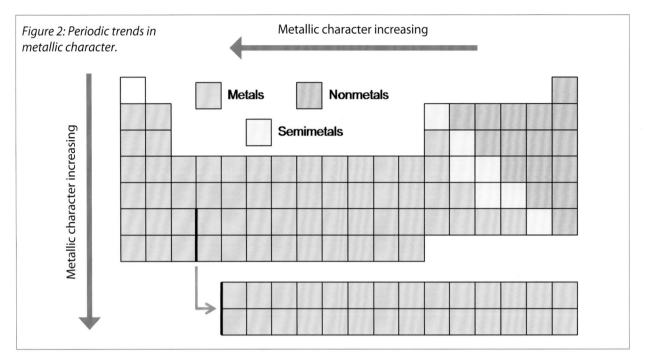

Figure 2: Periodic trends in metallic character.

nonmetallic behaviour can also be experienced within several groups of elements located in the p-block. For example, the elements at the bottom of Group IV, lead (Pb) and tin (Sn), are metals. The metallic character of the elements decreases towards the top of the group with the result that germanium (Ge) and silicon (Si) are semimetals, and carbon (C) is a nonmetal.

Many properties of the elements are determined by their electron configuration. The electron configuration of an element can be determined from the Periodic Table by superimposing the subshell filling order on the Periodic Table as shown in Figure 3. The electron configuration for an element is obtained by filling the subshells in order until the atomic number of the

element is reached. For example, the electron configuration for an oxygen atom (atomic number = 8) is determined by first adding two electrons to the 1s subshell (H to He), followed by two electrons to the 2s subshell (Li to Be), and a further four electrons to the 2p subshell (Be to O).

The electron configurations for the elements in the second period reveal that the 2s and 2p subshells belonging to the second shell (n=2) fill from left to right across the second period.

filling the 2s subshell		filling the 2p subshell					→
Li $(2s)^1$	Be $(2s)^2$	B $(2s)^2(2p)^1$	C $(2s)^2(2p)^2$	N $(2s)^2(2p)^3$	O $(2s)^2(2p)^4$	F $(2s)^2(2p)^5$	Ne $(2s)^2(2p)^6$

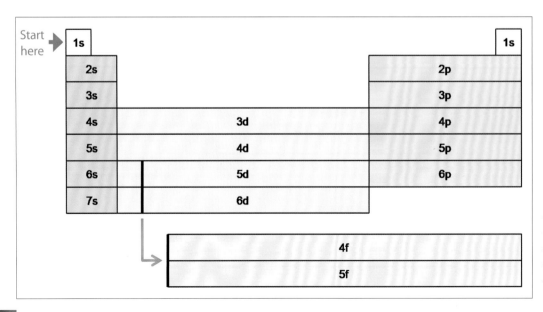

Figure 3: Subshell filling order for a multielectron atom superimposed on the Periodic Table.

Similarly, the 3s and 3p subshells belonging to the third shell (n=3) fill from left to right across the third period and the 4s, 3d and 4p subshells fill in order from left to right across the fourth period. The grouping of the 4s, 3d and 4p subshells in this way reminds us that, in effect, the outer shell of an element in the fourth period consists of the 4s, 3d and 4p subshells that together hold a total of 18 electrons.

By using the subshell filling order in this way Figure 3 reveals that the outermost electrons in an s-block element are located in an s-subshell, the outermost electrons in a p-block element are located in a p-subshell, and the outermost electrons in a d-block element are located in a d-subshell. Further, the arrangement of the outer shell electrons amongst the subshells is the same for each element in a group. The relationship between the arrangement of the outer shell electrons in s- and p-block elements and their location in the Periodic Table is shown in Figure 4.

Worked Example 1.7i

Which one of the following represents the first five ionisation energies in kJ mol^{-1} of an s-block element?

	First	Second	Third	Fourth	Fifth
A	580	1800	2700	11600	14800
B	740	1500	7700	10500	13600
C	1000	2300	3400	4600	7000
D	14800	11600	2700	1800	580

(CCEA June 2009)

Strategy

- The electron configuration for an s-block element is s^1 or s^2.
- If the configuration is s^1 the second IE will be much larger than the first and the ionisation energies will then increase steadily as electrons are removed from a full p-subshell.
- If the configuration is s^2 the third IE will be much larger than the second and the ionisation energies will then increase steadily as electrons are removed from a full p-subshell.

Solution

Answer B is consistent with an s^2 configuration.

....

Exercise 1.7A

1. Elements Q and R have ground state electron structures $1s^2 2s^2 2p^6 3s^2$ and $1s^2 2s^2 2p^5$ respectively. Write the formula of the compound formed when Q and R combine.

   (Adapted from CCEA January 2010)

2. (a) What property is used to order the elements in the Periodic Table? (b) Explain why transition metals are classified as d-block elements.

   (CCEA June 2009)

3. (a) Explain why all of the Group I elements are described as being s-block elements. (b) Explain why the ions of the Group I elements get bigger down the group. *(Adapted from CCEA June 2011)*

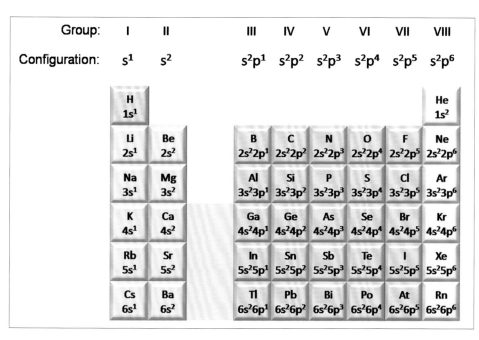

Figure 4: The relationship between the arrangement of the outer shell electrons in s- and p-block elements and their location in the Periodic Table. Filled d-subshells have been omitted for clarity.

4. Use the following electron configurations to identify which block of the Periodic Table contains the elements X, Y and Z.

X $1s^2 2s^2 2p^6 3s^2 3p^6 3d^3 4s^2$

Y^{2-} $1s^2 2s^2 2p^6 3s^2 3p^6$

Z^+ $1s^2 2s^2 2p^6 3s^2 3p^6$

(CCEA June 2008)

5. The first six ionisation energies in kJ mol^{-1} of an element M are 578, 1817, 2745, 11578, 14831 and 18378. What is the formula of the oxide of M? *(CCEA January 2006)*

6. (a) Using outer electrons only draw diagrams to explain the formation of caesium chloride from caesium atoms and chlorine atoms. *(CCEA June 2011)* (b) Use spd-notation to write the electron configuration for the caesium and chloride ions in caesium chloride.

7. An element X has 3 electrons in its outermost shell. Element Y has 6 electrons in its outermost shell. What is the empirical formula of the compound formed by X and Y? *(CCEA June 2008)*

8. The element europium reacts with hydrogen to form europium hydride. Atoms of europium have their outer electrons in levels 5 and 6, i.e. $5s^2 5p^6 6s^2$. What is the formula of europium hydride? *(Adapted from CCEA June 2011)*

Before moving to the next section, check that you are able to:

- Recall that the elements are organised in order of increasing atomic number within the Periodic Table.
- Describe the organisation of elements within the Periodic Table in terms of groups, periods and blocks.
- Determine the electron configuration of an atom from its location in the Periodic Table.
- Determine the location of an element in the Periodic Table from the arrangement of the electrons in its outer shell.

Trends Across a Period

The elements in the third period (Na to Ar) can be used to illustrate a number of important Periodic Trends. The first three elements in the period: sodium (Na), magnesium (Mg), and aluminium (Al) are metals. All three are good conductors of heat and electricity on account of the formation of metallic bonds involving delocalised outer shell electrons that can move freely through the metal. Metallic bonding in sodium results from the sharing of one outer shell electron per metal atom. It is considerably weaker than the bonding in magnesium and aluminium that results from the sharing of more than one outer shell electron from each metal atom. As a result, the atoms in magnesium and aluminium are more tightly packed and harder to separate than the atoms in sodium. This explains why magnesium and aluminium are relatively dense, and have considerably higher melting points than sodium. The relatively weak bonding in sodium also explains why sodium is much softer than either magnesium or aluminium.

The fourth element in the period, silicon (Si) is a semimetal. The atoms in silicon are bonded together to form a giant covalent structure identical to that formed by the carbon atoms in diamond. The formation of strong covalent bonds between neighbouring silicon atoms can be used to explain why silicon has a high melting point. As in diamond, the outer shell electrons from each silicon atom are involved in forming covalent bonds and are not free to move within the solid. The absence of delocalised electrons that are able to move through the solid can be used to explain why silicon is unable to conduct electricity.

The remaining elements in the period are nonmetals. Phosphorus (P_4), sulfur (S_8) and chlorine (Cl_2) have molecular covalent structures while argon (Ar) is a monatomic gas. Their properties are typical of molecular and atomic materials; all have low melting and boiling points and do not conduct electricity. The van der Waals attractions between the atoms and molecules in these elements are much weaker than the covalent bonds in silicon and the metallic bonding in the metals earlier in the period. As a result, the melting points of phosphorus, sulfur, chlorine and argon are all very much lower than the melting points of the elements earlier in the period. The melting points of the elements in the third period are compared in Figure 5.

The trend in the melting points for P, S, Cl and Ar can be understood by considering the effect of molecular size on the magnitude of the van der Waals attraction between the atoms and molecules in the

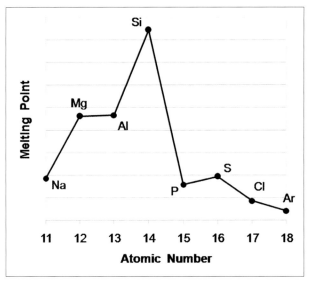

Figure 5: Melting points of the Period 3 elements.

van der Waals attraction.

The relationship between van der Waals attraction and melting point in Figure 6 demonstrates that, in the absence of other intermolecular forces, *the melting point of a molecular material increases as the molecular mass of the substance increases.*

Exercise 1.7B

Only one of the lettered responses (A–D) is correct. Select the correct response.

The melting point of the elements on going across the Periodic Table from sodium to argon

    A   increases steadily.

    B   decreases steadily.

    C   increases to silicon and then decreases.

    D   decreases to silicon and then increases.

(CCEA January 2009)

elements. The relationship between molecular size and melting point that results from van der Waals attraction between the atoms and molecules in the elements is illustrated in Figure 6.

The S_8 molecules in sulfur have more electrons than the smaller P_4 molecules in phosphorus. As a result the molecules in sulfur experience greater van der Waals attraction and sulfur has a higher melting point than phosphorus. Similarly, phosphorus has a higher melting point than chlorine as the P_4 molecules in phosphorus have more electrons than the Cl_2 molecules in chlorine and therefore experience greater van der Waals attraction. The melting point of chlorine is, in turn, greater than the melting point of argon (Ar) as the atoms in argon have fewer electrons than the Cl_2 molecules in chlorine and therefore experience less

The elements in the third period can also be used to exemplify trends in the properties of atoms across a period. For example, as the charge on the nucleus increases from left to right across the period, the outer shell electrons experience greater attraction to the nucleus while the amount of shielding remains approximately constant. As a result, the outer shell electrons are pulled closer to the nucleus and become harder to remove. This explains why the atoms become smaller and the first ionisation energy of the elements generally increases from left to right across the period.

The distance between the electrons in the outermost subshell and the nucleus of an atom is known as the

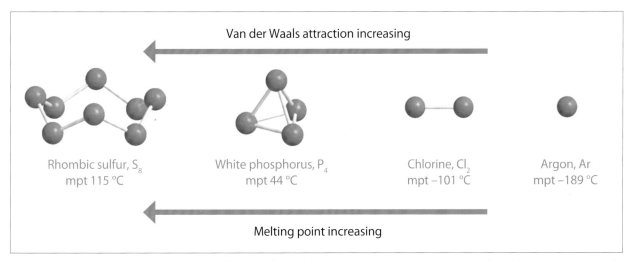

Figure 6: The relationship between molecular size and melting point that results from van der Waals attraction between molecules.

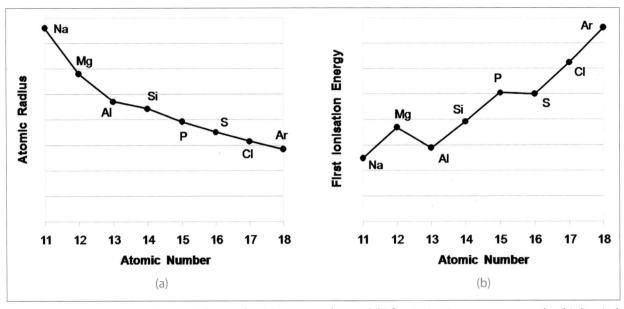

Figure 7: The trend in (a) atomic radius and (b) first ionisation energy across the third period.

atomic radius and represents the size of the atom. The opposing trends in atomic radius and first ionisation energy for the elements in the third period are shown in Figure 7.

Exercise 1.7C

A number of distinct trends can be seen in the third period from sodium to argon. (a) Describe the change in melting point across this period. (b) Describe and explain the change in atomic radius across this period. (c) On the axis below sketch the change in the first ionisation energy across the third period.

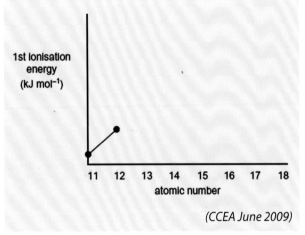

(CCEA June 2009)

Before moving to the next section, check that you are able to:

- Explain the trend in melting point across the third period in terms of the nature and strength of the bonding within each element.

- Explain why the first ionisation energy generally increases across the third period in terms of nuclear charge and shielding of the outermost electrons.

- Explain why the atomic radius decreases across the third period in terms of nuclear charge and shielding of the outermost electrons.

1.8 Group VII: The Halogens

Properties

In this section we are learning to:

- Recall the colour and physical state of the halogens under normal conditions.
- Explain trends in melting and boiling point within the group in terms of intermolecular forces.
- Account for the solubility of the halogens in water and nonpolar solvents such as hexane in terms of intermolecular forces.
- Account for trends in atomic size and first ionisation energy within the group.

Physical Properties

The halogens (Group VII) are a group of reactive nonmetals. Under normal laboratory conditions fluorine (formula: F_2) and chlorine (formula: Cl_2) are diatomic gases, bromine is a diatomic liquid (formula: Br_2), and iodine is a diatomic solid (formula: I_2). The colours and physical states of the halogens under normal laboratory conditions are summarised in Figure 1. The element astatine, At, is also a halogen. It is a solid under normal laboratory conditions and has properties characteristic of a semimetal. Astatine is radioactive and has only ever been made in very small quantities. As a result, very little is known about the chemistry of astatine.

The relationship between the atomic number of the halogen and its physical state in Figure 1 demonstrates that the van der Waals attraction between halogen molecules (X_2) increases as the number of electrons in the molecule increases. The increase in van der Waals attraction as atomic number (number of electrons) increases down the group is also evidenced by the relative ease with which bromine and iodine can be vaporised. Liquid bromine vaporises readily at room temperature as shown in Figure 2a. In contrast, solid iodine will only vaporise when heated as shown in Figure 2b.

The halogens dissolve readily in nonpolar solvents such as hexane (C_6H_{14}). They are much less soluble in polar solvents such as water. The solubility of the halogens can be explained by using the principle that like-dissolves-like. Halogen molecules are held together by van der Waals attractions. The molecules in nonpolar solvents such as hexane are also held together by van der Waals attractions. In contrast, the molecules in more polar solvents such as water are held together by a combination of van der Waals attraction and dipole forces or hydrogen bonds. When halogen molecules mix with the molecules in a nonpolar solvent such as hexane, much less energy is needed to disrupt the weaker van der Waals forces in the solvent and form a solution. As a result it becomes easier for the halogens to dissolve in nonpolar solvents such as hexane and form a solution.

Chlorine dissolves in water to form a colourless

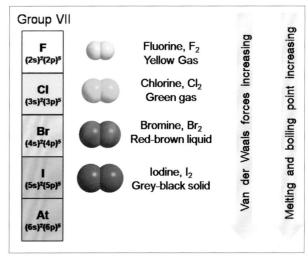

Figure 1: The effect of atomic number (number of electrons) on the melting and boiling points of the halogens.

Figure 2: (a) Bromine vapour, $Br_{2(g)}$ from the vaporisation of liquid bromine. (b) Iodine vapour, $I_{2(g)}$ formed by heating solid iodine.

solution known as 'chlorine water', Cl_2 (aq). In contrast, when chlorine dissolves in nonpolar solvents such as hexane, the solution has a pale-green colour. The colour of chlorine in hexane can be seen by shaking a small sample of chlorine water with an equal volume of hexane as shown in Figure 3. The results of shaking samples of bromine water, $Br_{2\ (aq)}$ and aqueous iodine, $I_{2\ (aq)}$ with hexane are also shown in Figure 3 and reveal that while the characteristic yellow/orange colour of aqueous bromine persists in hexane, the purple colour of iodine in hexane contrasts the brown colour of aqueous iodine.

Exercise 1.8A

1. Which one of the following statements is **not** correct?
   A   Iodine has a molecular covalent structure.
   B   Iodine contains nonpolar molecules.
   C   Iodine exists as a grey-black shiny solid.
   D   Iodine is more soluble in water than in hexane. *(CCEA January 2010)*

2. Iodine is a grey-black shiny solid. Describe the bonding in solid iodine and explain the structure of iodine crystals. Also explain the relative solubility of iodine in water and hexane.

   (CCEA June 2010)

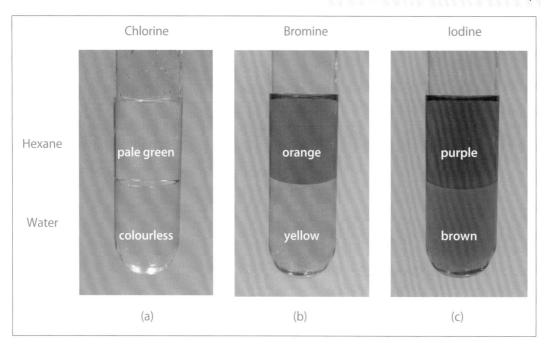

Figure 3: The colour of (a) chlorine, (b) bromine and (c) iodine in hexane (top layer) and water.

3. The boiling points of the halogens are: fluorine (–188 °C), chlorine (–35 °C), bromine (59 °C) and iodine (183 °C). Explain the trend in boiling point.

(CCEA January 2009)

4. Astatine was predicted to exist by Mendeleev in his original Periodic Table and was given the name eka-iodine. Complete the following table by predicting some of the properties of astatine.

Property	Result for Astatine
molecular formula	
physical state at room temperature	
colour at room temperature	
colour of vapour	
solubility in water (answer yes or no)	
solubility in hexane (answer yes or no)	

(CCEA June 2011)

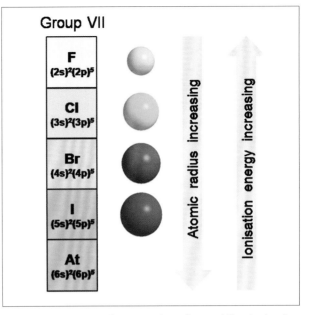

Figure 4: Trends in atomic radius and first ionisation energy for the halogens.

Atomic Properties

The halogens each have seven electrons in their outer shell arranged in an s^2p^5 configuration. As the atomic number increases down the group, the electrons in the outermost shell are further from the nucleus and better shielded. As a result, the electrons in the outermost shell are easier to remove and the first ionisation energy of the halogens decreases as the halogens get bigger down the group. The opposing trends in atomic size and ionisation energy are illustrated in Figure 4.

The electronegativity of an element refers to its ability to attract bonding electrons to itself when forming covalent bonds. The electrons involved in forming covalent bonds are located in the outermost shell of an atom. As a result, elements in which the outer shell electrons are strongly attracted to the nucleus have a higher electronegativity than those in which the outer shell electrons are less strongly attracted to the nucleus. In the case of the halogens, the electrons in the outermost shell are less shielded and more strongly attracted to the nucleus as the halogen atoms become smaller towards the top of the group. This explains why the electronegativity of the halogens increases as the halogen atoms become smaller towards the top of the group.

Exercise 1.8B

1. (a) Explain why the halogens are referred to as p-block elements. (b) State and explain the trend in atomic radius as Group VII is descended.

(CCEA January 2003)

2. (a) Define the term electronegativity. (b) State and explain the trend in the electronegativity of the elements down Group VII from fluorine to iodine. *(CCEA January 2010)*

Before moving to the next section, check that you are able to:

- Recall the colour and physical state of the halogens under normal laboratory conditions.

- Recall and explain the trend in the melting point, boiling point, atomic size, first ionisation energy and electronegativity of the halogens within the group.

- Explain the solubility of the halogens in aqueous solution and nonpolar solvents such as hexane in terms of intermolecular forces.

- Recall the colour of the halogens in aqueous solution and nonpolar solvents such as hexane.

Reactions

In this section we are learning to:

- Recall that the halogens become less reactive as their oxidising ability decreases down the group.
- Describe the reactions of the halogens with hydrogen, phosphorus and metals in terms of the oxidising ability of the halogens.
- Account for the colour changes that occur when a halogen displaces a halide from aqueous solution.

Reactivity

Fluorine is very reactive and often reacts violently with other substances. Chlorine and bromine are much less reactive than fluorine. For example, fluorine gas reacts violently with water to produce hydrofluoric acid (HF) and oxygen gas as per Equation 1. In contrast, chlorine dissolves in water to form a mixture of hydrochloric acid, $HCl_{(aq)}$ and hypochlorous acid, $HOCl_{(aq)}$ as per Equation 2. Bromine reacts in a similar way to form a mixture of hydrobromic acid, $HBr_{(aq)}$ and hypobromous acid, $HOBr_{(aq)}$. Iodine is, by far, the least reactive halogen. Iodine does not react with water and is only sparingly soluble in cold water.

$$2F_{2\,(g)} + 2H_2O_{(l)} \rightarrow 4HF_{(aq)} + O_{2\,(g)} \qquad \text{Equation 1}$$

$$Cl_{2\,(g)} + H_2O_{(l)} \rightarrow HCl_{(aq)} + HOCl_{(aq)} \quad \text{Equation 2}$$

The halogens react readily with metals in Groups I, II and III to form metal halides. For example, chlorine gas reacts vigorously with sodium metal to form solid sodium chloride (equation 3). Similarly, aluminium turnings react vigorously with liquid bromine to produce white fumes of solid aluminium bromide, $AlBr_3$ (equation 4). The reaction between aluminium and iodine is less vigorous, again demonstrating that iodine is lower in the group and is therefore less reactive than bromine.

$$2Na_{(s)} + Cl_{2\,(g)} \rightarrow 2NaCl_{(s)} \qquad \text{Equation 3}$$

$$2Al_{(s)} + 3Br_{2\,(l)} \rightarrow 2AlBr_{3\,(s)} \qquad \text{Equation 4}$$

Oxidising Ability

The halogens react with hydrogen gas to form hydrogen halides, HX where X = F, Cl, Br, I (equation 5). Fluorine gas reacts explosively when it comes into contact with hydrogen. The reaction between chlorine and hydrogen is also explosive when a mixture of hydrogen gas and chlorine gas is exposed to a spark or sunlight. Bromine and iodine react more slowly. If we consider the reactivity of the mixture to be a measure of how able the oxidising and reducing agents are, the observations demonstrate that the ability of the halogens to oxidise hydrogen decreases towards the bottom of the group.

$$H_2 + X_2 \rightarrow 2HX \quad \text{where } X = F, Cl, Br, I \quad \text{Equation 5}$$

The relative **oxidising ability** of the halogens can again be seen by comparing the reaction of the halogens with elements such as iron and phosphorus. When iron wool is heated in an atmosphere of chlorine, the iron in the wool reacts to form iron(III) chloride, $FeCl_3$ (Equation 6). Similarly, heating iron wool in an atmosphere of bromine vapour produces iron(III) bromide, $FeBr_{3\,(s)}$. The reaction between iron wool and iodine vapour is less vigorous and produces iron(II) iodide, $FeI_{2\,(s)}$.

$$2Fe_{(s)} + 3Cl_{2\,(g)} \rightarrow 2FeCl_{3\,(s)} \qquad \text{Equation 6}$$

In each reaction iron is oxidised and the halogen is reduced. The relative reactivity of chlorine and bromine, and the inability of iodine to oxidise iron to the +3 oxidation state and form iron(III) iodide, is further evidence that the oxidising ability of the halogens decreases going down the group.

Similarly, chlorine reacts with phosphorus (P_4) to form phosphorus(V) chloride, PCl_5 in which phosphorus has an oxidation state of +5 (Equation 7). In contrast, the reaction between phosphorus and bromine produces a mixture of phosphorus(III) bromide, PBr_3 and phosphorus(V) bromide, PBr_5 an unstable solid that decomposes above 100 °C. The reaction between phosphorus and iodine produces only phosphorus(III) iodide, PI_3 which is unstable (Equation 8).

$$P_{4\,(s)} + 10Cl_{2\,(g)} \rightarrow 4PCl_{5\,(s)} \qquad \text{Equation 7}$$

$$P_{4\,(s)} + 6I_{2\,(s)} \rightarrow 4PI_{3\,(s)} \qquad \text{Equation 8}$$

The formation of phosphorus(III) bromide, and the instability of phosphorus(V) bromide, indicates that bromine is not as capable of oxidising phosphorus to the +5 oxidation state as chlorine. Further, the inability of iodine to form phosphorus(V) iodide and the instability of phosphorus(III) iodide demonstrates that iodine is less able to oxidise phosphorus than bromine. In this way we again see that the oxidising ability of the halogens decreases down the group.

Halogen Displacement

A more reactive halogen (better oxidising agent) will oxidise a less reactive halogen (lower in the group). If the less reactive halogen is in the form of halide ions in solution, the halide ions will be oxidised to form the corresponding halogen. In this way a more reactive halogen will be seen to displace a less reactive halogen from the solution. For example, bromine will displace iodine from solution (Equation 9) but will not displace chlorine (Equation 10) as chlorine is more reactive than bromine.

$$Br_2 \text{ (aq)} + 2I^- \text{ (aq)} \rightarrow 2Br^- \text{ (aq)} + I_2 \text{ (aq)} \qquad \text{Equation 9}$$
$$Br_2 \text{ (aq)} + 2Cl^- \text{ (aq)} \rightarrow \text{no reaction} \qquad \text{Equation 10}$$

Worked Example 1.8i

A compound produces a lilac colour in a flame test. When chlorine is bubbled into an aqueous solution of the compound the solution turns from colourless to yellow/orange. Identify the compound.

(CCEA January 2010)

Strategy

- The flame colour can be used to identify the metal in the compound.
- The halogen displacement reaction indicates that the compound contains halide ions and is a metal halide.

Solution

The flame colour indicates that the compound contains potassium.

The yellow/orange colour indicates that bromine is produced when chlorine reacts with bromide ions in the solution.

The compound is potassium bromide.

Exercise 1.8C

1. (a) Write the ionic equation for the reaction between bromine solution and aqueous sodium iodide. (b) Describe the observations that would indicate a reaction has taken place when aqueous sodium iodide is added to a solution of bromine.

(CCEA January 2011)

2. (a) Write the equation for the reaction between chlorine solution and aqueous sodium bromide. (b) Describe what is observed when chlorine solution is added to aqueous sodium bromide.

(CCEA January 2011)

3. Astatine, the last element in the halogen group, was synthesised in 1940. Write the equation for the reaction of iodine with sodium astatide.

(CCEA June 2011)

Reactivity of Fluorine

Reacting the halogens with hydrogen, metals and phosphorus clearly demonstrates that the halogens become less reactive as their oxidising ability decreases down the group. The reactions also reveal that fluorine is significantly more reactive than might be expected. The very high reactivity of fluorine results from its oxidising ability and the weak bond between fluorine atoms in a fluorine (F_2) molecule. The relationship between the reactivity of the halogens, their oxidising ability, and the strength of the halogen bond is shown in Figure 5.

Weak bonds are easily broken and substances such as fluorine (F_2) that contain weak bonds tend to be more reactive than those containing stronger bonds. Having said this, the decrease in halogen bond strength from chlorine to iodine does not produce an increase in reactivity down the group and instead reminds us that the reactivity of the halogens is principally determined by their oxidising ability.

Figure 5: The relationship between the reactivity of the halogens, their oxidising ability, and the strength of the halogen bond.

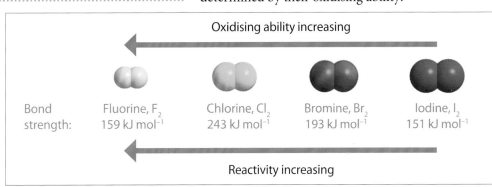

Before moving to the next section, check that you are able to:

- Recall that the halogens become less reactive as their oxidising ability decreases down the group.
- Explain trends in the reactivity of the halogens with hydrogen, phosphorus, and metals in terms of their oxidising ability.
- Account for the colour changes that occur when a halogen displaces a halide from aqueous solution.

Halide Ions in Solution

In this section we are learning to:

- Detect and verify the presence of chloride, bromide and iodide ion in aqueous solution.
- Recall the principal arguments for and against the fluoridation of public water supplies.

Salts such as sodium chloride and magnesium bromide contain **halide ions**. The halide ions: fluoride (F^-), chloride (Cl^-), bromide (Br^-) and iodide (I^-) are stable in aqueous solution. Chloride, bromide and iodide can be detected by adding acidified silver nitrate solution to form a precipitate of the corresponding silver halide (Equation 11). Silver fluoride is soluble and does not form a precipitate on adding acidified silver nitrate solution to a solution containing fluoride ion.

$$Ag^+_{(aq)} + X^-_{(aq)} \rightarrow AgX_{(s)} \quad \text{where} \quad X = Cl, Br, I$$

Equation 11

The colour of the silver halide precipitate can be used to identify the halide ion. The identity of the halide ion can then be confirmed by determining the solubility of the silver halide in aqueous ammonia. The appearance of the silver halide precipitates, and the solubility of each in ammonia solution, is summarised in Figure 6.

Talking Point

In many parts of the world fluoride (F^-) is added to toothpaste and public water supplies in an attempt to prevent tooth decay; a process known as **fluoridation**. The fluoridation of public water supplies is often opposed on the grounds that it represents an attempt to mass medicate whole populations and does give individuals the freedom to choose non-fluoridated water.

Worked Example 1.8ii

The presence of chloride ions in water can be established by adding aqueous silver nitrate. (a) What would be observed in this reaction? (b) Write an ionic equation, including state symbols, for the reaction. (c) State what is observed when an excess of dilute aqueous ammonia is then added.

(CCEA June 2010)

Solution

(a) A white precipitate of silver chloride forms.

(b) $Cl^-_{(aq)} + Ag^+_{(aq)} \rightarrow AgCl_{(s)}$

(c) The precipitate of silver chloride dissolves.

(a)

	Soluble in dilute ammonia	Soluble in conc. ammonia
Silver chloride	✓	✓
Silver bromide	✗	✓
Silver iodide	✗	✗

(b)

Figure 6: (a) Precipitates of silver chloride, silver bromide and silver iodide formed by the addition of acidified silver nitrate solution to a solution containing halide ion. (b) The solubility of silver halides in dilute and concentrated ammonia solution.

Exercise 1.8D

1. When sodium bromide is dissolved in water the presence of bromide ions can be established by using aqueous silver nitrate followed by concentrated ammonia solution. (a) What is observed when aqueous silver nitrate is added to sodium bromide solution? (b) Write the ionic equation, including state symbols, for the reaction. (c) What is observed when an excess of concentrated ammonia solution is added? *(CCEA January 2010)*

2. If you had poured solutions of sodium iodide, bromide and chloride into beakers A, B and C and forgotten to label them, describe how, using aqueous silver nitrate and both dilute and concentrated ammonia solutions, you would determine which sodium salt was in which beaker. Each beaker must be tested. *(CCEA January 2011)*

3. A solution of a metal salt gave a red colour when sprayed into a Bunsen flame. The same solution gave a yellow precipitate with acidified silver nitrate solution. Identify the metal salt.

   A calcium bromide   B lithium bromide

   C sodium iodide   D strontium iodide

   (CCEA June 2007)

4. Explain why the public water supply may be fluoridated and why some people are opposed to this. *(CCEA January 2009)*

Before moving to the next section, check that you are able to:

- Explain how to detect and verify the presence of chloride, bromide and iodide ions in aqueous solution using a combination of silver nitrate solution and aqueous ammonia.
- Recall the principal arguments for and against the fluoridation of public water supplies.

Redox Chemistry

In this section we are learning to:

- Recall the reaction of chlorine with water and the reactions of the halogens with cold, dilute and hot concentrated sodium hydroxide solution.
- Explain the redox changes that occur when the halogens react with water and sodium hydroxide solution in terms of disproportionation.

The oxidation state of the halogen in a halide ion is -1. Nonmetal compounds such as hydrogen bromide (HBr), phosphorus pentachloride (PCl_5) and thionyl chloride ($SOCl_2$) also contain halogens with an oxidation state of -1.

As the oxidising ability of the halogens decreases down the group the halogens become better reducing agents and increasingly form compounds in which the halogen has an oxidation state of $+1$, $+5$ or even $+7$. This trend can be demonstrated by reacting the halogens with water and aqueous solutions such as sodium hydroxide solution. For example, chlorine gas reacts with water to form a mixture of hydrochloric acid, HCl and hypochlorous acid, HClO (Equation 12).

$$Cl_{2\,(g)} + H_2O_{\,(l)} \rightarrow HCl_{\,(aq)} + HClO_{\,(aq)} \quad \text{Equation 12}$$

A solution of hypochlorous acid turns universal indicator red then colourless as the hypochlorite (ClO^-) ions in the solution 'bleach' the indicator. Hypochlorite ion is the active ingredient in bleach. Hydrochloric acid, HCl is an aqueous solution of hydrogen ions (H^+) and chloride ions (Cl^-). The chloride ions contain chlorine in the -1 oxidation state and are formed by the reduction of chlorine (Cl_2). In contrast, hypochlorous acid, HClO is a weak acid that partially dissociates to give hydrogen ions and hypochlorite (ClO^-) ions. The systematic name for hypochlorite ion is chlorate(I) ion. A chlorate(I) ion, ClO^- contains chlorine in the $+1$ oxidation state and is formed by the oxidation of chlorine (Cl_2). In this way we can see that chlorine atoms are simultaneously oxidised to chlorate(I) ions and reduced to chloride ions in the reaction.

Previously the term disproportionation has been used to describe a redox reaction in which the same element is oxidised and reduced. The simultaneous oxidation and reduction of chlorine that occurs when chlorine reacts with water reveals that the reaction between chlorine and water is an example of disproportionation.

Chlorine also disproportionates when dissolved in sodium hydroxide solution. In cold dilute sodium hydroxide chlorine disproportionates to form a solution containing sodium chloride, NaCl and sodium chlorate(I), NaClO. The ionic equation for the reaction is given in Equation 13.

$$Cl_{2\ (g)} + 2OH^-_{\ (aq)} \rightarrow Cl^-_{\ (aq)} + ClO^-_{\ (aq)} + H_2O_{\ (l)}$$

Equation 13

In cold sodium hydroxide solution chlorine is simultaneously reduced to chloride ion (Cl^-) and oxidised to form chlorate(I) ions (ClO^-). If the solution is heated to 70 °C the chlorate(I) ions disproportionate to give a mixture of chloride, Cl^- and chlorate(V), ClO_3^- ions (equation 14). The chlorate(V) ion contains chlorine in the +5 oxidation state. Chlorate(V) salts such as sodium chlorate(V), $NaClO_3$ are powerful oxidising agents.

$$3ClO^-_{\ (aq)} \rightarrow 2Cl^-_{\ (aq)} + ClO_3^-_{\ (aq)}$$ Equation 14

The disproportionation of chlorate(I) ion involves the reduction of chlorate(I) ion to chloride ion (Cl^-). The electrons needed to reduce chlorine from the +1 oxidation state in chlorate(I) ion to the –1 oxidation state in chloride ion are provided by the simultaneous oxidation of chlorine from the +1 oxidation state in chlorate(I) ion to the +5 oxidation state in chlorate(V) ion.

When chlorine gas dissolves in hot concentrated sodium hydroxide, chlorate(I) ions from the disproportionation of chlorine (Equation 13) disproportionate to form a mixture of chloride ions and chlorate(V) ions (Equation 14). The overall reaction that occurs when chlorine dissolves in hot concentrated sodium hydroxide is summarised by Equation 15.

$$3Cl_{2\ (g)} + 6OH^-_{\ (aq)} \rightarrow 5Cl^-_{\ (aq)} + ClO_3^-_{\ (aq)} + 3H_2O_{\ (l)}$$

Equation 15

Bromine and iodine react in a similar way to chlorine. The corresponding bromate(I), BrO^- and iodate(I), IO^- ions are less stable than chlorate(I) with the result that bromate(I) disproportionates to bromide and bromate(V) at 15 °C, and iodate (I), IO^- rapidly disproportionates to iodide and iodate(V) at 0 °C. The relative ease with which the halate(I) ions ClO^-, BrO^- and IO^- disproportionate to give the corresponding halate(V) ions: ClO_3^-, BrO_3^- and IO_3^-

reflects the greater stability of the +5 oxidation state as the oxidising ability of the halogens decreases down the group.

Exercise 1.8E

1. The reaction between chlorine and cold dilute sodium hydroxide is used in the manufacture of bleach. (a) Write the equation for this reaction. (b) This reaction is described as disproportionation. Explain the meaning of this term. (CCEA June 2010)

2. Acidified iodate(V) ions react with iodide ions according to the following equation. Which description (A-D) best describes the redox reaction and colour change that occurs?

$$IO_3^-_{\ (aq)} + 5I^-_{\ (aq)} + 6H^+_{\ (aq)} \rightarrow 3I_{2\ (aq)} + 3H_2O_{\ (l)}$$

	Redox	Colour Change
A	iodide ions are oxidised	brown to colourless
B	iodide ions are reduced	colourless to brown
C	iodate(V) ions are oxidised	brown to colourless
D	iodate(V) ions are reduced	colourless to brown

(CCEA June 2004)

Before moving to the next section, check that you are able to:

- Write chemical equations for the reaction of chlorine with water, cold dilute sodium hydroxide and hot concentrated sodium hydroxide.
- Explain the redox changes that occur when chlorine reacts with water and sodium hydroxide solution in terms of disproportionation.

The Hydrogen Halides

In this section we are learning to:

- Account for trends in the boiling points of the hydrogen halides.
- Explain trends in the thermal stability and acid strength of the hydrogen halides in terms of the hydrogen-halogen bond strength.
- Account for the products formed when preparing a hydrogen halide by the reaction of concentrated sulfuric acid with the corresponding halide salt.

Figure 7: The effect of van der Waals attraction and hydrogen bonding on the boiling points of the hydrogen halides.

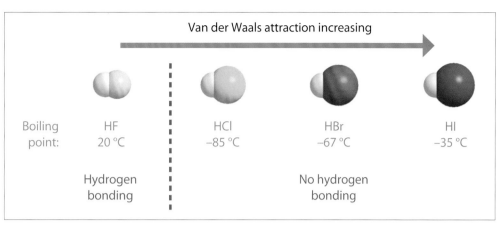

Van der Waals attraction increasing

Boiling point:	HF	HCl	HBr	HI
	20 °C	−85 °C	−67 °C	−35 °C

Hydrogen bonding | No hydrogen bonding

Physical Properties

The hydrogen halides, HX (X = F, Cl, Br, I) are gases under normal laboratory conditions. The more electronegative halogen atom acquires a small negative charge (δ−) as a result of forming a polar covalent bond with hydrogen. The resulting permanent dipole $H^{\delta+}X^{\delta-}$ gives rise to dipole forces between neighbouring molecules. Neighbouring HX molecules also experience van der Waals attraction that becomes stronger as the number of electrons in the halogen atom increases. The relationship between the boiling point of the hydrogen halides and the strength of the van der Waals attraction between HX molecules is shown in Figure 7. As expected, the boiling points of the hydrogen halides increase from HCl to HI as the van der Waals attraction between molecules increases. The boiling point of hydrogen fluoride (HF) is, however, unexpectedly high due to the presence of hydrogen bonds between hydrogen fluoride molecules.

The hydrogen halides HCl, HBr and HI dissociate in water to form hydrochloric acid, HCl $_{(aq)}$ hydrobromic acid, HBr $_{(aq)}$ and hydroiodic acid, HI $_{(aq)}$ as per Equation 16. All three solutions behave as **strong acids**. In this context the term 'strong' refers to an acid in which most of the molecules dissociate to form hydrogen ions.

$$HX_{(aq)} \rightarrow H^+_{(aq)} + X^-_{(aq)} \quad \text{where } X = Cl, Br, I$$

Equation 16

In contrast hydrofluoric acid, HF$_{(aq)}$ – a solution of hydrogen fluoride (HF) in water – is a **weak acid**. In this context the term 'weak' is used to describe an acid in which only a small fraction of the molecules dissociate to form hydrogen ions. This 'partial dissociation' of HF in aqueous solution is described by using a double arrow (⇌) as in Equation 17.

$$HF_{(aq)} \rightleftharpoons H^+_{(aq)} + F^-_{(aq)}$$

Equation 17

The relative strengths of the acids HX (X = F, Cl, Br, I) can be explained by considering the strength of the H-X bond. As the halogen gets bigger the H-X bond becomes longer and weaker. This makes it easier to break the H-X bond and form ions as the halogen gets bigger down the group. The trends in H-X bond strength and acid strength in Figure 8 demonstrate that, as expected, the hydrogen halides (HX) become stronger acids as the H-X bond becomes weaker down the group.

The strength of the H-X bond also influences the **thermal stability** of the hydrogen halides where the term *thermal stability* refers to the ability of a substance

Figure 8: Trends in the acid strength and thermal stability of the hydrogen halides that result from a decrease in the H-X bond strength from fluorine to iodine.

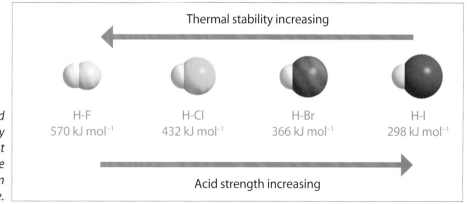

Thermal stability increasing

	H-F	H-Cl	H-Br	H-I
	570 kJ mol⁻¹	432 kJ mol⁻¹	366 kJ mol⁻¹	298 kJ mol⁻¹

Acid strength increasing

to resist the effects of heating. The trends in H-X bond strength and thermal stability in Figure 8 indicate that the hydrogen halides are more likely to decompose when heated as the H-X bond becomes weaker. This relationship can be used to explain why HI decomposes on a hot wire (Equation 18) while HF and HCl do not decompose when heated.

$$2HI_{(g)} \rightarrow H_{2\,(g)} + I_{2\,(g)} \qquad \text{Equation 18}$$

Exercise 1.8F

1. (a) Place the hydrides HF, HCl, HBr and HI in order of increasing hydrogen-halogen bond strength (weakest first). (b) Which one of the acids HF, HCl, HBr and HI has the highest pH when in the form of a 1 M solution?

    (CCEA June 2008)

2. (a) Place hydrobromic, hydrochloric and hydrofluoric acids in order of increasing acid strength (weakest first). (b) Explain what is meant by the term strong acid. (c) Write the formula for each ion present in hydrobromic acid. *(CCEA June 2002)*

3. Which one of the following gaseous hydrides most readily decomposes into its elements when in contact with a hot glass rod?

    A ammonia   B hydrogen fluoride
    C hydrogen iodide D steam

    (CCEA January 2011)

4. Explain why hydrogen chloride is more thermally stable than hydrogen iodide.

    (CCEA June 2010)

Preparation

The hydrogen halides, HX can be prepared by reacting the corresponding sodium halide, NaX with concentrated sulfuric acid, H_2SO_4 (Equation 19).

$$NaX + H_2SO_4 \rightarrow NaHSO_4 + HX$$
where X = F, Cl, Br, I   Equation 19

The hydrogen fluoride and hydrogen chloride prepared by this method are pure. However, as the oxidising ability of the halogens decreases down the group, the corresponding halide (X^-) becomes a better reducing agent to the extent that it reduces the concentrated sulfuric acid and forms the corresponding halogen. For example, bromide ions from the dissociation of HBr are able to reduce sulfuric acid. As a result the reaction between sodium bromide and sulfuric acid (Equation 19) produces a mixture of HBr, bromine and pungent fumes of sulfur dioxide (Equation 20). The bromine formed is observed as a red-brown vapour. Similarly, iodide ions from the dissociation of HI reduce sulfuric acid to produce a mixture of iodine and sulfur dioxide (Equation 21). The iodine formed in the reaction is observed as a purple vapour and may also accumulate in the form of a grey-black solid.

$$2HBr_{(g)} + H_2SO_{4\,(aq)} \rightarrow Br_{2\,(g)} + SO_{2\,(g)} + 2H_2O_{(l)}$$

Equation 20

$$2HI_{(g)} + H_2SO_{4\,(aq)} \rightarrow I_{2\,(g)} + SO_{2\,(g)} + 2H_2O_{(l)}$$

Equation 21

In the presence of iodide ions from the dissociation of HI sulfur dioxide is further reduced to form a mixture of hydrogen sulfide (H_2S) and sulfur (S). The production of hydrogen sulfide results in the smell of rotten-eggs and the production of sulfur results in the

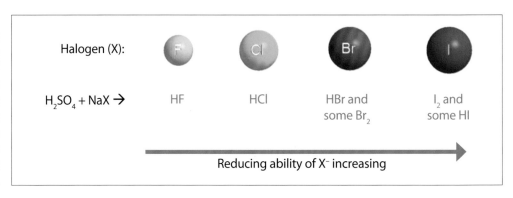

Figure 9: The relationship between the products formed when concentrated sulfuric acid reacts with a sodium halide salt and the reducing ability of the halide ion formed in the reaction.

formation of a yellow solid. The relationship between the products of the reaction and the reducing ability of the halide formed in the reaction is summarised in Figure 9.

. . . .

Worked Example 1.8iii

The diagram below shows a common method of preparing hydrogen chloride gas in the laboratory.

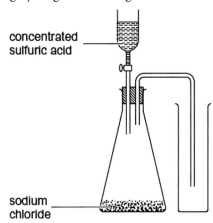

concentrated sulfuric acid

sodium chloride

(a) Write the equation for the reaction of sodium chloride with concentrated sulfuric acid.

(b) Explain why sodium hydroxide pellets would not be suitable to dry the gas produced in the reaction.

(c) Explain whether this method could be used to prepare hydrogen bromide by reacting concentrated sulfuric acid with sodium bromide.

(Adapted from CCEA June 2011)

Solution

(a) $NaCl + H_2SO_4 \rightarrow NaHSO_4 + HCl$

(b) Sodium hydroxide is not a suitable drying agent as it would react with the hydrogen chloride gas produced in the reaction.

(c) The method is not suitable as hydrogen bromide would be oxidised to bromine by the sulfuric acid.

. . . .

Exercise 1.8G

1. Which one of the following is **not** produced when concentrated sulfuric acid reacts with sodium bromide?

   A bromine   B hydrogen sulfide

   C hydrogen bromide   D sulfur dioxide

   (CCEA January 2005)

2. Which one of the following is **not** produced in the reaction between concentrated sulfuric acid and sodium iodide at room temperature?

   A I_2 B HI

   C $NaHSO_4$ D SO_3

   (CCEA June 2008)

3. Give two observations when concentrated sulfuric acid is added to sodium iodide.

   (CCEA June 2009)

Before moving to the next section, check that you are able to:

- Explain why the boiling point of the hydrogen halides increases down the group and why the boiling point of HF is unusually high.

- Explain trends in the thermal stability and acid strength of the hydrogen halides in terms of the hydrogen-halogen bond strength.

- Write chemical equations for the preparation of a hydrogen halide by the reaction of concentrated sulfuric acid with the corresponding halide salt.

- Account for the products formed in the preparation of the hydrogen halides in terms of the reducing ability of the corresponding halide.

1.9 Volumetric Analysis

Working with Solutions

In this section we are learning to:

- Determine the level of accuracy that can be achieved when using a scale to estimate the volume of a solution.
- Recall how to use volumetric glassware to measure, prepare and transfer volumes of solution accurately.
- Identify procedures to maximise the accuracy and reliability of volumes measured, prepared and transferred.

Volumetric analysis refers to the procedures and techniques used to analyse the composition of solutions. If a solution is to be analysed accurately it is necessary to develop special techniques for handling solutions. This section of the course introduces the techniques used to handle solutions in the laboratory and accurately analyse their composition.

Volumetric Glassware

The items of glassware shown in Figure 1 are used to measure and transfer volumes of solution in the laboratory. A **volumetric pipette** (A) is used when it is necessary to accurately measure out and transfer a volume of solution. Measuring cylinders (B) are less accurate and should only be used when the volume to be measured does not affect the outcome of the analysis.

A **burette** (C) is used in experiments where it is necessary to keep an accurate record of the volume of solution used. Beakers (D) and conical flasks (E) are used to hold volumes of solution. They are not used to measure volumes of solution or prepare solutions. In contrast, a **volumetric flask** (F) can be used to accurately prepare solutions of a specified concentration by dissolving a solid or diluting a concentrated solution.

Measuring cylinders and burettes come in different

Figure 1: Common items of volumetric glassware include a volumetric pipette (A), measuring cylinders (B), a burette (C), beakers (D), conical flasks (E) and volumetric flasks (F).

sizes and have a scale. The accuracy of the volumes measured using the scale depends on the size of the interval between divisions on the scale. The scales on a 50 cm³ measuring cylinder, a 10 cm³ measuring cylinder and a 50 cm³ burette are shown in Figure 2. The scale on a burette (Figure 2c) is distinct from the scales on other pieces of glassware as it increases downwards, allowing the amount of liquid dispensed from the burette to be measured.

At this level of introduction, volumes read from a scale should be considered accurate to one-half the size of the smallest division on the scale. For instance, the scale on the 50 cm³ measuring cylinder in Figure 2a is marked at 1 cm³ intervals and is therefore accurate to 0.5 cm³. Volumes measured using this scale should therefore be recorded to the nearest 0.5 cm³. For example, the volume of solution shown in Figure 2a is closer to 32.5 than 32.0 and is recorded as 32.5 cm³.

The scale on the 10 cm³ measuring cylinder in Figure 2b is marked at intervals of 0.2 cm³ and is accurate to $0.2 \div 2 = 0.1$ cm³. As a result, the volume of solution

Figure 2: Scales on a (a) 50 cm³ measuring cylinder, (b) 10 cm³ measuring cylinder and (c) 50 cm³ burette.

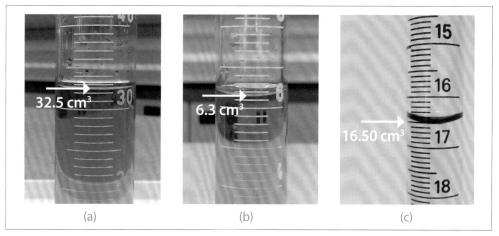

(a)   (b)   (c)

shown in Figure 2b is judged to be closer to 6.3 cm³ than 6.2 cm³ and is recorded as 6.3 cm³.

The scale on the 50 cm³ burette in Figure 2c is even more accurate than the scale on the small measuring cylinder. The scale on the burette is marked at intervals of 0.1 cm³ and is accurate to 0.05 cm³. As a result, the volume of solution shown in Figure 2c is judged to be nearer to 16.50 cm³ than 16.55 cm³ and is recorded as 16.50 cm³.

In contrast, volumetric flasks and many types of volumetric pipette do not have a scale. The volume of liquid held by the flask or pipette is instead measured by requiring the lowest point on the **meniscus** – the surface of the liquid – to reach the calibration line or 'fill line' on the glassware as shown in Figure 3.

Making Solutions

A fixed volume of solution with a specified concentration is made by transferring a known amount of substance to a volumetric flask that holds the required volume of solution and adding deionised water to make-up the required volume of solution.

Method

1. Dissolve a known (weighed) amount of solid in a minimum of deionised water and transfer the solution to a volumetric flask.
2. Use a wash bottle filled with deionised water to wash any drops of solution remaining on the glassware into the volumetric flask.
3. Add deionised water to the contents of the volumetric flask until the bottom of the meniscus lies on the fill line.
4. Stopper the flask and invert several times to mix.

The procedure used to transfer the sample to a volumetric flask is illustrated in Figure 4. A similar procedure is used when making solutions from liquids. The following steps can be taken to ensure that the concentration of the resulting solution is accurate.

Ensuring Accuracy

1. Ensure that the solid has completely dissolved.
2. Ensure that every drop of solution has been

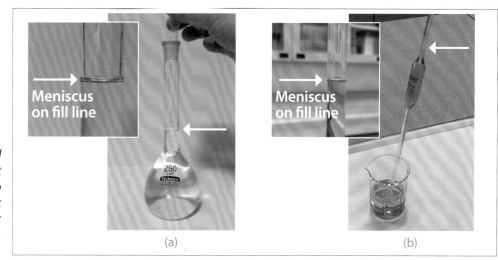

Figure 3: Use of the fill line to add the correct amount of solution to (a) a volumetric flask and (b) a volumetric pipette.

Meniscus on fill line

Meniscus on fill line

(a)   (b)

washed into the volumetric flask.

3. Wash the inside surface of the volumetric flask with deionised water when making-up the solution to the fill line.

4. Ensure that the bottom of the meniscus lies on the fill line.

Diluting Solutions

A volumetric flask can also be used to make a solution with a specified concentration by diluting a more concentrated solution whose concentration is known.

Method

1. Wash the inside surfaces of a volumetric pipette with 2–3 cm³ of the concentrated solution.

2. Use the volumetric pipette to transfer a fixed volume of the concentrated solution to the volumetric flask.

3. Dilute the solution by adding deionised water until the bottom of the meniscus lies on the fill line.

4. Stopper the flask and invert several times to mix.

The procedure used to dilute a solution is illustrated in Figure 5. The following steps can be taken to ensure that the concentration of the resulting solution is accurate.

Ensuring Accuracy

1. Wash the entire inside surface of the pipette when rinsing.

2. Use a wash bottle to wash the inside surface of the volumetric flask with deionised water when making-up the solution to the fill line.

3. Ensure that the bottom of the meniscus lies on the fill line.

Exercise 1.9A

Some liquid oven cleaners contain sodium hydroxide. You have been provided with a solution containing 25.0 cm³ of oven cleaner diluted to 500 cm³ with distilled water. Give an account of how you would prepare the diluted solution of oven cleaner and then how you would safely transfer 25.0 cm³ of the diluted solution to a conical flask.

(CCEA June 2010)

Using a Volumetric Pipette

A volumetric pipette is used to accurately measure out a fixed volume of solution. The only markings on a volumetric pipette are the volume held by the pipette and the fill line.

Method

1. Use a pipette filler to draw 2–3 cm³ of solution into the pipette.

2. Wash the entire inner surface of the pipette with the solution.

3. Allow the wash to drain from the pipette.

4. Use a pipette filler to draw solution into the pipette until the bottom of the meniscus lies on the fill line.

(a)   (b)

Figure 4: Making a solution using a volumetric flask.
(a) The solid is dissolved in a minimum of deionised water.
(b) Deionised water is used to wash the solution into the volumetric flask.

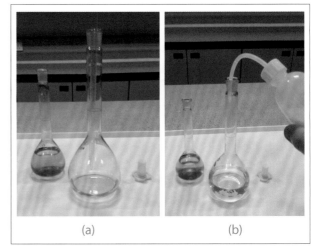

(a)   (b)

Figure 5: Diluting a solution using a volumetric flask.
(a) A volumetric pipette is used to transfer a fixed volume of concentrated solution into the volumetric flask. (b) Deionised water is used to make-up the solution to the fill line.

The solution can then be transferred to a new container by allowing it to flow freely from the pipette as illustrated in Figure 6. The following steps can be taken to ensure that the volume of solution measured and transferred using the pipette is accurate.

Ensuring Accuracy

1. Be sure to wash the entire inside surface of the pipette when rinsing.
2. Remove any air bubbles that remain in the pipette after filling.
3. Ensure that the bottom of the meniscus lies on the fill line.
4. Do not force the final drop from the pipette when transferring the solution.

Using a Burette

A burette is used to dispense measured amounts of solution accurately. A burette is often used when the amount of reactant added to a reaction mixture must be carefully controlled during an experiment.

Method

1. Use a funnel to add 2–3 cm³ of solution to the burette.
2. Wash the entire inner surface of the burette with the solution.
3. Open the tap and allow the solution to drain.
4. Use a funnel to overfill the burette by 2–3 cm³ then remove the funnel.
5. Use the tap to fill the volume below the tap with solution.
6. Use the tap to further reduce the volume until the bottom of the meniscus is on the scale and close to the zero mark.

The procedure for filling a burette is illustrated in Figure 7. The following steps can be taken to ensure

Figure 6: Using a volumetric pipette to transfer a fixed volume of solution. A drop of solution remains in the pipette when the solution flows freely from the pipette.

that the burette is capable of dispensing measured amounts of solution accurately.

Ensuring Accuracy

1. Be sure to wash the entire inside surface of the burette when rinsing.
2. Remove any air bubbles that have formed above and below the tap after filling.
3. Ensure that the bottom of the meniscus is on the scale after filling.

Before moving to the next section, check that you are able to:

- Use a volumetric pipette to measure and transfer a fixed volume of solution.
- Use a volumetric flask to prepare a fixed volume of solution by dissolving a solid.
- Use a volumetric flask and pipette to prepare a solution by diluting a more concentrated solution.
- Identify procedures to ensure that the volumes of solution measured, prepared and transferred using volumetric glassware are accurate and reliable.

Figure 7: The procedure for filling a burette. (a) Solution is added using a funnel. (b) The volume below the tap is filled with solution. (c) The bottom of the meniscus is on the scale and close to the zero mark.

No air bubbles below the tap

Meniscus on the scale

(a)　　　　　　　　(b)　　　　　　　　(c)

Calculations with Solutions

In this section we are learning to:

- Calculate the concentration of a solution in mol dm^{-3}, g dm^{-3} and related units as required given appropriate conversion factors.
- Use the term molarity (M) when referring to the concentration of a solution in units of mol dm^{-3}.
- Calculate amounts of solution involved in chemical reactions.
- Calculate the volume of solution required to make a specified volume of a more dilute solution.

Concentration

The **concentration** or 'strength' of a solution refers to the amount of solute dissolved in the solution. Solutions containing a lot of solute in a small amount of solvent are very concentrated. Solutions containing less solute or the same amount of solute in a greater amount of solvent are less concentrated. In chemistry the concentration of a solution is typically reported in units of moles per cubic decimetre (mol dm^{-3}) or grams per cubic decimetre (g dm^{-3}) where 1 cubic-decimetre (1 dm^3) is equivalent to 1 litre (1 l = 1000 cm^3) of solution. The concentration of a solution in units of moles per cubic decimetre (mol dm^{-3}) is also known as the **molarity** of the solution and is calculated using the equation:

$$\text{Molarity (M)} = \frac{\text{Moles of solute (mol)}}{\text{Volume of solvent (dm}^3)}$$

Worked Example 1.9i

A solution of magnesium sulfate is made by dissolving 0.2 mol of magnesium sulfate in 500 cm^3 of water. Calculate the concentration of the solution in units of (a) mol dm^{-3} and (b) g dm^{-3}.

Solution

(a) $\text{Molarity} = \dfrac{\text{Moles}}{\text{Volume}} = \dfrac{0.2 \text{ mol}}{0.500 \text{ dm}^3} = 0.4 \text{ mol dm}^{-3}$

(b) Use the equation:

$$\text{Mass in 1 dm}^3 = \text{Molarity} \times \text{Molar Mass}$$

Molar mass of MgSO$_4$ = 120 g mol^{-1}

Mass of MgSO$_4$ in 1 dm^3
$$= 0.4 \text{ mol dm}^{-3} \times 120 \text{ g mol}^{-1} = 48 \text{ g dm}^{-3}$$

Exercise 1.9B

1. 2.65 g of anhydrous sodium carbonate, Na$_2$CO$_3$ was dissolved in water and the solution made up to 250 cm^3 in a volumetric flask. Calculate the molarity of the resulting solution.

   (CCEA January 2010)

2. 8.70 g of potassium sulfate, K$_2$SO$_4$ is dissolved in water and made up to 250 cm^3. What is the concentration of sulfate ion in mol dm^{-3}?

   (CCEA January 2003)

Reacting Volumes

The relationship between molarity and moles (of solute) can be used to calculate the amounts of substance involved in chemical reactions that involve solutions.

Worked Example 1.9ii

Calculate the mass of calcium carbonate needed to neutralise 500 cm^3 of 0.1 M hydrochloric acid.

(CCEA June 2011)

Strategy

Write the chemical equation for the reaction then:
1. Calculate the moles of acid used.
2. Calculate the moles of CaCO$_3$ needed.
3. Calculate the mass of CaCO$_3$ needed.

Solution

$$CaCO_{3\,(s)} + 2HCl_{(aq)} \rightarrow CaCl_{2\,(aq)} + CO_{2\,(g)} + H_2O_{(l)}$$

1. Moles of HCl = Molarity × Volume
   $$= 0.1 \text{ mol dm}^{-3} \times 0.500 \text{ dm}^3 = 0.05 \text{ mol}$$

2. Moles of CaCO$_3$ = $\dfrac{\text{Moles of HCl}}{2}$
   $$= \frac{0.05 \text{ mol}}{2} = 0.025 \text{ mol}$$

3. Mass of CaCO$_3$ = Moles × Molar Mass
   $$= 0.025 \text{ mol} \times 100 \text{ g mol}^{-1} = 2.5 \text{ g}$$

Exercise 1.9C

1. Calculate the volume of 0.20 mol dm^{-3} potassium hydroxide solution needed to neutralise 50 cm^3 of 0.20 mol dm^{-3} sulfuric acid.

   (CCEA January 2011)

2. 0.84 g of a Group II carbonate, MCO$_3$ reacts with 20.0 cm^3 of a 1.0 mol dm^{-3} solution of hydrochloric acid. Identify the metal, M.

   (CCEA June 2007)

The scales on many pieces of laboratory glassware measure volume in units of millilitres (Unit: ml) where 1 ml = 1 cm^3. Therefore, if we recall that 1 l contains 1000 cm^3 we can use the following conversion factors to convert volumes in units of cm^3, l and ml to dm^3.

Conversion factors for volumes:

$$1 \text{ dm}^3 = 1000 \text{ cm}^3 = 1 \text{ l} = 1000 \text{ ml}$$

Worked Example 1.9iii

A solution of sodium chloride has a concentration of 0.10 M. Calculate the concentration of the solution in units of (a) g dm^{-3} and (b) mg cm^{-3} given that there are 1000 milligrams in 1 gram (1 g = 1000 mg).

Solution

(a) Molar mass of NaCl = 58.5 g mol^{-1}

Mass of NaCl in 1 dm^3 =
0.10 mol dm^{-3} × 58.5 g mol^{-1} = 5.85 g dm^{-3}

(b) 1 dm^3 = 1000 cm^3 therefore:

Mass of NaCl in 1 cm^3 = 5.85 g dm^{-3} × $\dfrac{1 \text{ dm}^3}{1000 \text{ cm}^3}$

= 5.85 × 10^{-3} g cm^{-3}

1 g = 1000 mg therefore:

Mass of NaCl in 1 cm^3 = 5.85 × 10^{-3} g cm^{-3}

$\times \dfrac{1000 \text{ mg}}{1\text{g}}$ = 5.85 mg cm^{-3}

Diluting Solutions

A solution is diluted by adding solvent. The particle picture in Figure 8 shows how the solute particles become more spread out and the solution becomes less concentrated as solvent is added. The amount of solute in the solution does not change as a result of adding solvent. As a result we are able to relate the concentration and volume of the solution before dilution (M_C and V_C) to the concentration and volume after dilution (M_D and V_D) as follows.

Before dilution (concentrated solution):

Moles of solute = Molarity (M_C) × Volume (V_C)

After dilution (diluted solution):

Moles of solute = Molarity (M_D) × Volume (V_D)

Therefore it follows that:

Molarity (M_C) × Volume (V_C) = Molarity (M_D)
× Volume (V_D)

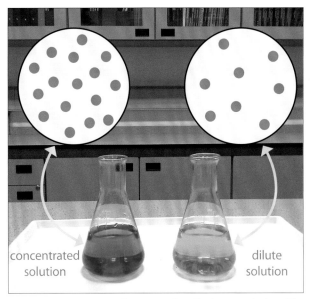

Figure 8: Particle picture for diluting a solution. The concentrated solution contains more solute particles per unit of volume.

Worked Example 1.9iv

Calculate the concentration of a copper(II) sulfate solution prepared by diluting 10 cm^3 of 1.0 M copper(II) sulfate in a 100 cm^3 volumetric flask.

Solution

Molarity of diluted solution, $M_D = \dfrac{M_C \times V_C}{V_D}$

$= \dfrac{(1.0)(10)}{(100)} = 0.1$ M $= 0.1$ mol dm^{-3}

Exercise 1.9D

50 cm^3 of 3.0 M hydrochloric acid was diluted with 150 cm^3 of water. What is the concentration of hydrogen ions in the resultant solution?

(CCEA January 2006)

Before moving to the next section, check that you are able to:

- Use volumes and amounts of substance to calculate the concentration of a solution in mol dm^{-3}, g dm^{-3} and related units.
- Use the term molarity (M) when referring to the concentration of a solution in units of mol dm^{-3}.
- Use chemical equations to calculate the volumes of solutions involved in chemical reactions such as neutralisation.
- Calculate the volume of solution required to make a specified volume of a more dilute solution.

Titration Experiments

In this section we are learning to:

- Recall the procedures used to accurately and reliably determine the concentration of a solution by titration.

- Explain how the method of back titration can be used to determine the composition of insoluble substances such as limestone.

- Record and analyse the results of titration experiments using procedures designed to produce accurate and reliable outcomes.

Before the end point (colourless when mixed)

At the end point (pink after mixing)

Figure 9: Using phenolphthalein to detect the end point when an acid (in the conical flask) is titrated against an alkali (in the burette).

A **titration** is an experiment to accurately determine the concentration of a solution. For example, the concentration of an acid could be determined by accurately measuring the volume of a **standard** alkali needed to neutralise a sample of the acid and using the result to calculate the moles of acid in the sample. In this context we are using the term standard to refer to a stable solution whose concentration has been accurately determined. Similarly, the concentration of an alkali could be determined by measuring the volume of a standard acid needed to neutralise a sample of the alkali. Titration experiments that make use of neutralisation reactions are referred to as **acid-base titrations**.

Acid-Base Titrations

The concentration of an acid can be determined by titrating a sample of the acid against a standard solution of a strong alkali such as sodium hydroxide. A sample of the acid is placed in a conical flask and the alkali added in measured amounts using a burette. The assembled apparatus used to conduct a titration experiment is shown in Figure 9. The amount of acid in the sample decreases after each addition as the alkali reacts with the acid to form a salt and water: acid + alkali → salt + water. The point at which the acid in the sample has been completely neutralised is known as the **equivalence point** of the titration. The volume of solution needed to reach the equivalence point is referred to as the **titre**. Adding a drop of alkali at the equivalence point is sufficient to produce an alkaline solution. The associated rise in pH is significant and can be detected by adding a few drops of an **indicator** to the acid in the conical flask at the beginning of the experiment.

An indicator is a substance, or combination of substances, that changes colour over a range of pH values. For instance, the indicator methyl orange changes from red to yellow when the pH of a solution containing methyl orange increases from 3 to 5. The pH change at the equivalence point when a strong acid is titrated against a strong alkali is sufficiently large to cause most indicators to change colour.

The point in the titration at which the indicator changes colour is known as the **end point** of the titration. An indicator can only be used to identify the equivalence point in an acid-base titration if the end point occurs at the equivalence point. The colour change that occurs at the end point when the indicator phenolphthalein is used to titrate an acid against an alkali is shown in Figure 9.

When titrating a weakly acidic solution such as vinegar against a standard solution of a strong alkali (in the burette) the pH of the solution rises steadily as the acid reacts. As a result, the change in pH at the end point begins at a high pH, and it becomes necessary to use an indicator that changes colour at even higher pH values. The indicator phenolphthalein changes colour between pH 8 and 10, and is suitable for the titration of a weak acid such as vinegar. Vinegar is the common name for an aqueous solution of ethanoic acid, CH_3COOH. The chemical equation for the neutralisation of ethanoic acid by sodium hydroxide is:

$$CH_3COOH_{(aq)} + NaOH_{(aq)}$$

ethanoic acid → $CH_3COONa_{(aq)} + H_2O_{(l)}$

sodium ethanoate

Similarly the concentration of an alkali can be determined by titrating a sample of the alkali against a standard solution of a strong acid such as hydrochloric acid or sulfuric acid. If the alkali is a strong alkali the pH of the solution remains high as the acid is added from the burette and the colour of the solution reflects the colour of the indicator at high pH values. Adding a drop of acid at the equivalence point produces a large drop in pH that is sufficient to cause most indicators to change colour. Phenolphthalein (changes colour between pH 8 and 10) and methyl orange (changes colour between pH 3 and 5) would both be suitable indicators for the titration of a strong alkali against a strong acid.

When a weak base such as sodium carbonate solution is titrated against a strong acid the pH decreases steadily as the acid is added. As a result, the decrease in pH at the equivalence point begins at a moderate pH, and it becomes necessary to use an indicator that changes colour at even lower pH values. The indicator methyl orange changes colour between pH 3 and 5, and is suitable for the titration of a weak base such as sodium carbonate. Phenolphthalein would be unsuitable for the titration of a weak base as it changes colour before the equivalence point is reached. The suitability of phenolphthalein and methyl orange for use in acid-base titrations is summarised in Table 1.

Worked Example 1.9v

Which one of the following would not be a suitable combination? *(CCEA June 2007)*

Titration	Acid	Alkali	Indicator
A	sulfuric acid	sodium carbonate	phenolphthalein
B	hydrochloric acid	sodium carbonate	methyl orange
C	hydrochloric acid	sodium hydroxide	methyl orange
D	ethanoic acid	sodium hydroxide	phenolphthalein

Strategy

- Classify the acids and alkalis as strong or weak.
- Recall that any indicator can be used to detect the end point of a titration that involves a strong acid and a strong alkali.
- Recall that methyl orange cannot be used in titrations involving a weak acid and that phenolphthalein cannot be used in titrations involving a weak alkali.

Solution

Titration A involves a strong acid and a weak alkali. Phenolphthalein indicator is not suitable for this titration.

Table 1: The suitability of phenolphthalein and methyl orange indicators for use in acid-base titrations.

Titration of a ... (in conical flask)	Against a ... (in burette)	Colour change
strong acid eg: $HCl_{(aq)}$	strong base eg: $NaOH_{(aq)}$	Methyl orange: *red → yellow* Phenolphthalein: *colourless → pink*
weak acid eg: $CH_3COOH_{(aq)}$	strong base eg: $NaOH_{(aq)}$	Methyl orange: *NOT suitable* Phenolphthalein: *colourless → pink*
strong base eg: $KOH_{(aq)}$	strong acid eg: $H_2SO_{4\,(aq)}$	Methyl orange: *yellow → red* Phenolphthalein: *pink → colourless*
weak base eg: $Na_2CO_{3\,(aq)}$	strong acid eg: $HCl_{(aq)}$	Methyl orange: *yellow → red* Phenolphthalein: *NOT suitable*

Exercise 1.9E

1. (a) Explain what is meant by a standard solution. (b) Name a suitable indicator for the titration of hydrochloric acid with standard sodium hydroxide solution. (c) Describe the colour change observed at the end point.

   (CCEA June 2009)

2. (a) Write the chemical equation for the titration of sodium carbonate solution with a standard solution of hydrochloric acid. (b) Name a suitable indicator for the titration and describe the colour change observed at the end point.

   ((Adapted from CCEA June 2010)

Practical Details

The basic procedure for conducting an acid-base titration and the steps that can be taken to improve the accuracy and reliability of the results are as follows.

Method

1. Rinse the volumetric pipette using 2–3 cm^3 of solution before filling the pipette and transferring the solution to the conical flask.
2. Add several drops of indicator to the solution in the conical flask.
3. Rinse the burette with 2–3 cm^3 of solution before filling the burette and recording the initial reading on the burette scale.
4. Perform a rough titration by adding solution from the burette in 1 cm^3 amounts and swirling the solution several times after each addition until the end point is reached.
5. Record the final reading on the burette and calculate the total volume of solution added (the titre).
6. Perform an accurate titration by adding solution dropwise near the end point.
7. Repeat to obtain accurate titres that differ by less than 0.1 cm^3.
8. Use the accurate titres to calculate an average titre.

Ensuring Accuracy

1. Ensure that the entire inside surface of the pipette and burette are washed.
2. Ensure that there are no bubbles in the pipette and burette after filling.
3. Add solution dropwise from the burette when approaching the end point.

4. Repeat the titration to obtain more accurate titres.
5. Average the accurate titres to improve the reliability of the results.

Exercise 1.9F

(a) Describe how you would use a 0.10 mol dm^{-3} solution of sodium hydroxide and phenolphthalein indicator to determine the concentration of ethanoic acid in a sample of vinegar. (b) State the colour change at the end point and write the chemical equation for the reaction of sodium hydroxide with the ethanoic acid in vinegar. Include state symbols. *(CCEA June 2009)*

Analysis of Results

The results of a titration experiment are recorded in a standard format. The following examples illustrate how to record and analyse the results of a titration experiment to the required level of accuracy.

Worked Example 1.9vi

The following results were obtained by titrating 25 cm^3 of sulfuric acid, H_2SO_4 against a 0.100 mol dm^{-3} solution of sodium hydroxide. Calculate the concentration of the sulfuric acid in units of g dm^{-3}.

	Initial Burette Reading (cm^3)	Final Burette Reading (cm^3)	Titre (cm^3)
Rough	0.00	26.00	26.00
First Accurate	0.10	25.70	25.60
Second Accurate	0.05	25.70	25.65

Strategy

1. Use the accurate titres to calculate the average titre.
2. Calculate the moles of sodium hydroxide used in the titration.
3. Calculate the moles of acid neutralised.
4. Calculate the concentration of the acid in units of mol dm^{-3}.
5. Calculate the concentration of the acid in units of g dm^{-3}.

Solution

STEP 1 Use the accurate titres to calculate the average titre.

$$\text{Average titre} = \frac{25.60 + 25.65}{2} = 25.63 \text{ cm}^3$$

STEP 2 Calculate the moles of sodium hydroxide used in the titration.

$$\text{Moles} = \text{Volume (in dm}^3) \times \text{Molarity (in mol dm}^{-3})$$

$$\text{Moles} = \frac{\text{Average Titre}}{1000} \times 0.100$$

$$= 2.563 \times 10^{-2} \times 0.100 = 2.56 \times 10^{-3} \text{ mol}$$

STEP 3 Calculate the moles of acid neutralised.

Neutralisation reaction:

$$H_2SO_4 + 2NaOH \rightarrow Na_2SO_4 + 2H_2O$$

$$\text{Moles of acid} = \frac{\text{Moles of hydroxide}}{2} = \frac{2.56 \times 10^{-3}}{2}$$

$$= 1.28 \times 10^{-3} \text{ mol}$$

STEP 4 Calculate the concentration of the acid in units of mol dm^{-3}.

$$25 \text{ cm}^3 \text{ of acid} = 25 \text{ cm}^3 \times \frac{1 \text{ dm}^3}{1000 \text{ cm}^3} = 0.025 \text{ dm}^3$$

$$\text{Molarity of acid} = \frac{\text{Moles of acid}}{\text{Volume of acid}} = \frac{1.28 \times 10^{-3}}{0.025}$$

$$= 0.0512 \text{ mol dm}^{-3}$$

STEP 5 Calculate the concentration of the acid in units of g dm^{-3}.

Molar mass of $H_2SO_4 = 98$ g dm^{-3}

Concentration in g dm^{-3} = Molarity × Molar Mass

$$= 0.0512 \times 98 = 5.02 \text{ g dm}^{-3}$$

Exercise 1.9G

The following results were obtained by diluting 25.0 cm^3 of a vinegar solution using a 250 cm^3 volumetric flask and titrating 25.0 cm^3 portions of the diluted vinegar using 0.1 mol dm^{-3} sodium hydroxide solution. (a) Name a suitable indicator for the titration and state the colour change at the end point. (b) Use the results in the table to calculate the concentration of ethanoic acid in the undiluted vinegar.

	Initial Burette Reading (cm³)	Final Burette Reading (cm³)	Titre (cm³)
Rough	0.0	21.7	21.7
First Accurate	21.7	43.1	
Second Accurate	0.0	21.3	

Use the following headings to structure your work.

1. Calculate the average titre.
2. Moles of sodium hydroxide used.
3. Concentration of ethanoic acid in diluted vinegar in mol dm^{-3}.
4. Concentration of ethanoic acid in undiluted vinegar in mol dm^{-3}.

(Adapted from CCEA January 2010)

Worked Example 1.9vii

The following results were obtained by titrating 25 cm^3 of a solution containing 1.20 g of hydrated sodium carbonate, $Na_2CO_3.xH_2O$ in 100 cm^3 of water against 0.100 M hydrochloric acid. Calculate the amount of water of crystallisation (x) in the hydrate.

	Initial Burette Reading (cm³)	Final Burette Reading (cm³)	Titre (cm³)
Rough	0.00	22.00	22.00
First Accurate	0.10	21.40	21.30
Second Accurate	0.20	21.60	21.40

Strategy

1. Use the accurate titres to calculate the average titre.
2. Calculate the moles of acid used in the titration.
3. Calculate the moles of carbonate neutralised.
4. Calculate the mass of water in the hydrate.
5. Calculate the moles of water in the hydrate.

Solution

STEP 1 Use the accurate titres to calculate the average titre.

$$\text{Average titre} = \frac{21.30 + 21.40}{2} = 21.35 \text{ cm}^3$$

STEP 2 Calculate the moles of acid used in the titration.

Moles = Volume (in dm³) × Molarity (in mol dm⁻³)

$$\text{Moles} = \frac{\text{Average Titre}}{1000} \times 0.100$$

$$= 2.135 \times 10^{-2} \times 0.100 = 2.14 \times 10^{-3} \text{ mol}$$

STEP 3 Calculate the moles of carbonate neutralised.

Neutralisation reaction:

$$Na_2CO_3 + 2HCl \rightarrow 2NaCl + H_2O + CO_2$$

$$\text{Moles of carbonate} = \frac{\text{Moles of acid}}{2} = \frac{2.14 \times 10^{-3}}{2}$$

$$= 1.07 \times 10^{-3} \text{ mol}$$

STEP 4 Calculate the mass of water in the hydrate.

Molar mass of $Na_2CO_3 = 106 \text{ g mol}^{-1}$

Mass of Na_2CO_3 = Moles × Molar Mass

$$= 1.07 \times 10^{-3} \times 106 = 0.113 \text{ g}$$

Mass of hydrate in 25 cm³ of solution

$$= \frac{1.20 \text{ g}}{4} = 0.300 \text{ g}$$

Mass of water in 0.300 g of hydrate

$$= 0.300 - 0.113 = 0.187 \text{ g}$$

STEP 5 Calculate the moles of water in the hydrate.

Molar mass of $H_2O = 18 \text{ g mol}^{-1}$

Moles of water in 0.3 g of hydrate

$$= \frac{\text{Mass}}{\text{Molar mass}} = \frac{0.187}{18} = 0.0104 \text{ mol}$$

$$x = \frac{\text{Moles of water}}{\text{Moles of carbonate}} = \frac{0.0104}{1.07 \times 10^{-3}} = 10.2$$

Rounding to the nearest whole number gives
x = 10

The formula of the hydrate is $Na_2CO_3.10H_2O$

Exercise 1.9H

1. 25.0 cm³ of a solution made by dissolving 4.64 g of hydrated sodium carbonate, $Na_2CO_3.xH_2O$ in 1.00 dm³ of water was neutralised by 20.0 cm³ of 0.05 mol dm⁻³ hydrochloric acid. Calculate x. *(CCEA June 2009)*

2. (a) 20.0 cm³ of a solution made by dissolving 3.05 g of hydrated barium chloride, $BaCl_2.xH_2O$ in 250 cm³ of water was titrated with 0.100 M silver nitrate solution. The equivalence point was reached when 20.0 cm³ of silver nitrate had been added. Write (a) the chemical equation and (b) the ionic equation for the titration reaction. (c) Calculate x. *(Adapted from CCEA June 2011)*

> Before moving to the next section, check that you are able to:
>
> • Recall procedures to determine the concentration of a solution by titration and ensure that the results are accurate and reliable.
>
> • Record and analyse the results of titration experiments in a way that ensures accurate and reliable outcomes.
>
> • Determine the suitability of methyl orange and phenolphthalein indicators for use in specified acid·base titrations.

Back-Titration Methods

We have seen that titrations can be used to determine the concentration of an acid or alkali by using an indicator to signal that the equivalence point has been reached. We can also use titration methods to determine the purity of insoluble bases such as metal carbonates and oxides by employing a technique known as **back-titration**. In a back-titration experiment a sample of the base is first allowed to react with an excess of acid. The amount of base in the sample can then be determined by titrating the remaining acid in the reaction mixture against a standard solution of a strong alkali such as sodium hydroxide. Back-titration procedures are used widely in industry to determine the purity of products such as the limestone produced by quarries.

....

Worked Example 1.9vii

0.80 g of limestone (mostly $CaCO_3$) was allowed to completely react with 40.0 cm³ of 1.00 M hydrochloric acid. The following results were then obtained by titrating the resulting mixture against 1.00 M NaOH. Calculate the % purity of the limestone.

	Initial Burette Reading (cm³)	Final Burette Reading (cm³)	Titre (cm³)
Rough	0.00	29.00	29.00
First Accurate	0.10	28.80	28.70
Second Accurate	0.00	28.80	28.80

Strategy

The % purity refers to the % by mass of calcium carbonate in the sample. The steps needed to calculate the % purity of the limestone are:

1. Use the accurate titres to calculate the average titre.
2. Calculate the moles of sodium hydroxide used in the titration.
3. Calculate the moles of acid titrated.
4. Calculate the moles of acid that reacted with the carbonate.
5. Calculate the moles of carbonate in the sample
6. Calculate the % purity of the sample.

Solution

STEP 1 Use the accurate titres to calculate the average titre.

$$\text{Average titre} = \frac{28.70 + 28.80}{2} = 28.75 \text{ cm}^3$$

STEP 2 Calculate the moles of sodium hydroxide used in the titration.

$$\text{Moles} = \text{Volume (in dm}^3) \times \text{Molarity (in mol dm}^{-3})$$

$$\text{Moles} = \frac{\text{Average Titre}}{1000} \times 1.00$$

$$= 2.875 \times 10^{-2} \times 1.00 = 2.88 \times 10^{-2} \text{ mol}$$

STEP 3 Calculate the moles of acid titrated.

Titration reaction: $HCl + NaOH \rightarrow NaCl + H_2O$

Moles of acid = Moles of hydroxide
$$= 2.88 \times 10^{-2} \text{ mol}$$

STEP 4 Calculate the moles of acid that reacted with the carbonate.

Moles of acid in 40.0 cm³ of 1.00 M HCl:

$$\text{Moles} = \text{Volume (in dm}^3) \times \text{Molarity}$$

$$= \frac{40.0}{1000} \times 1.00 = 0.0400 \text{ mol}$$

Moles of acid reacted = $0.0400 - 2.88 \times 10^{-2}$
$$= 0.0112 \text{ mol}$$

STEP 5 Calculate the moles of carbonate in the sample.

$$CaCO_3 + 2HCl \rightarrow CaCl_2 + H_2O + CO_2$$

$$\text{Moles of carbonate} = \frac{\text{Moles of acid reacted}}{2}$$

$$= 5.60 \times 10^{-3} \text{ mol}$$

STEP 6 Calculate the % purity of the sample.

Molar mass of $CaCO_3 = 100 \text{ g mol}^{-1}$

Mass of carbonate = Moles × Molar Mass

$$= 5.60 \times 10^{-3} \times 100 = 0.560 \text{ g}$$

$$\text{\% Purity} = \frac{\text{Mass of carbonate}}{\text{Mass of sample}} \times 100$$

$$= \frac{0.560}{0.80} \times 100 = 70\%$$

Exercise 1.9I

The percentage of calcium carbonate present in egg shells can be found by back titration. 1.12 g of egg shell was allowed to react with 20.0 cm³ of 2.00 M hydrochloric acid and the solution formed made up to 250 cm³ in a volumetric flask. 25.0 cm³ of this solution completely reacted with 18.6 cm³ of 0.100 M sodium hydroxide. Calculate the percentage of calcium carbonate in the egg shell using the following headings to structure the calculation.

1. Moles of hydrochloric acid added to the egg shell.
2. Moles of sodium hydroxide used.
3. Moles of hydrochloric acid in 250 cm³.
4. Moles of hydrochloric acid needed to react with the egg shell.
5. Mass of calcium carbonate in the egg shell.
6. Percentage of calcium carbonate in the egg shell.

(CCEA June 2009)

Before moving to the next section, check that you are able to:

- Explain the method of back-titration and use the results of a back-titration experiment to determine the percent purity of an insoluble base.

Unit AS 2:

Further Physical and Inorganic Chemistry and Introduction to Organic Chemistry

2.1 Further Calculations

Percentage Yield

In this section we are learning to:

- Calculate the percentage yield of a reaction.
- Use the percentage yield for a reaction to relate the amounts of reactants and products in a chemical reaction.

The amount of product formed in a chemical reaction may be less than expected if the reactants do not completely react, or if some of the product is lost when attempting to recover it from the reaction mixture. The amount of product lost as a result of incomplete reaction and loss during transfer can be determined by calculating the **percentage yield** for the reaction.

$$\text{Percentage yield} = \frac{\text{Actual yield}}{\text{Expected yield}} \times 100\ \%$$

The **expected yield** refers to the amount of product that would be formed if the reactants completely reacted, and the product was completely recovered from the reaction mixture after reaction.

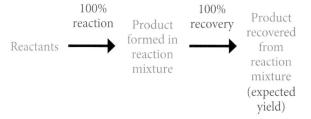

In contrast, the **actual yield** refers to the actual amount of product recovered from the reaction mixture. The actual yield is lower than the expected yield as a result of incomplete reaction and loss of product during its recovery from the reaction mixture.

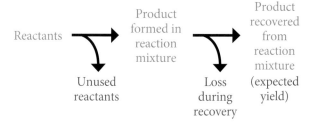

Worked Example 2.1i

In industry ethanol, C_2H_6O is made by reacting ethene, C_2H_4 with steam. Calculate the percentage yield of the reaction if 4.6 tonnes of ethene are needed to produce 4.7 tonnes of ethanol (1 tonne = 1000 kg).

$$C_2H_4 + H_2O \rightarrow C_2H_6O$$

Strategy

- Use the mass of ethene reacted to calculate the expected yield.
- Use the moles of ethanol formed to calculate the actual yield.

Solution

Mass of ethene = 4.6 tonnes = 4.6×10^6 g

$$\text{Moles of ethene reacted} = \frac{4.6 \times 10^6\ \text{g}}{26\ \text{g mol}^{-1}} = 1.77 \times 10^5\ \text{mol}$$

Expected yield of ethanol = 1.77×10^5 mol

$$\text{Actual yield of ethanol} = \frac{4.7 \times 10^6\ \text{g}}{46\ \text{g mol}^{-1}} = 1.02 \times 10^5\ \text{mol}$$

$$\text{\% yield} = \frac{1.02 \times 10^5\ \text{mol}}{1.77 \times 10^5\ \text{mol}} \times 100 = 58\%$$

Exercise 2.1A

1. 12.3 g of 1-bromobutane, C_4H_9Br was obtained from 11.1 g of butan-1-ol, C_4H_9OH. Calculate the percentage yield for the reaction.

   $$C_4H_9OH + HBr \rightarrow C_4H_9Br + H_2O$$

   (CCEA June 2010)

2. Calculate the percentage yield of t-butyl chloride, $(CH_3)_3CCl$ if 28 g of t-butyl chloride are obtained by reacting 25 g of t-butyl alcohol, $(CH_3)_3COH$ with hydrochloric acid.

   $$(CH_3)_3COH + HCl \rightarrow (CH_3)_3CCl + H_2O$$

   (CCEA June 2011)

3. The compound cisplatin, $Pt(NH_3)_2Cl_2$ is used to treat several different forms of cancer. It is prepared by reacting the salt K_2PtCl_4 with ammonia. Calculate the percentage yield for the reaction if 2.08 g of cisplatin is formed when 3.42 g of K_2PtCl_4 react with 1.61 g of ammonia.

The percentage yield can also be used to calculate the amount of product formed in a reaction, or the amount of reactants needed to form a given amount of product.

....

Worked Example 2.1ii

The solvent dichloromethane, CH_2Cl_2 is used to make decaffeinated coffee by extracting the compound caffeine from coffee beans. Dichloromethane is formed by reacting methane, CH_4 with chlorine.

$$CH_4 + 2Cl_2 \rightarrow CH_2Cl_2 + 2HCl$$

Calculate the mass of dichloromethane formed when 1.00 tonne of methane reacts with an excess of chlorine. The yield for the reaction is 43.1%.

Strategy

- Use the moles of methane to calculate the expected yield of dichloromethane.
- Use the percent yield to calculate the actual yield of dichloromethane.

Solution

Moles of CH_4 reacted $= \dfrac{1.00 \times 10^6 \text{ g}}{16 \text{ g mol}^{-1}} = 6.25 \times 10^4$ mol

Expected yield of $CH_2Cl_2 = 6.25 \times 10^4$ mol

Actual Yield $=$ Expected yield $\times \dfrac{\% \text{ yield}}{100} = 2.69 \times 10^4$ mol

Mass of $CH_2Cl_2 = (2.69 \times 10^4 \text{ mol})(85 \text{ g mol}^{-1})$
$= 2.29 \times 10^6 \text{ g} = 2.29$ tonnes

....

Exercise 2.1B

1. Decane, $C_{10}H_{22}$ can be converted to octane, C_8H_{18} by heating at 500 °C in the presence of a catalyst. Ethene, C_2H_4 is a useful by-product of the reaction. Calculate the mass of decane needed to produce 1.00 tonne of ethene by this method if the percentage yield for the reaction is 94.0%.

$$C_{10}H_{22} \rightarrow C_8H_{18} + C_2H_4$$

2. Ethanoic acid, $C_2H_4O_2$ reacts with isopentyl alcohol, $C_5H_{12}O$ to form isopentyl acetate, $C_7H_{14}O_2$ an artificial flavour that smells and tastes like bananas. The percentage yield for the reaction is 45%. Calculate the mass of isopentyl acetate formed when 3.58 g of ethanoic acid reacts with 4.75 g of isopentyl alcohol.

$$C_2H_4O_2 + C_5H_{12}O \rightarrow C_7H_{14}O_2 + H_2O$$

Before moving to the next section, check that you are able to:

- Calculate the percentage yield for a reaction given the amounts of reactants used and the amounts of products formed.
- Use the percentage yield for a reaction to relate the amounts of reactants used and the amounts of products formed in the reaction.

Atom Economy

In this section we are learning to:

- Use atom economy as a measure of the amount of reactants converted into useful products in a reaction.
- Recall that reactions with a high atom economy generate little waste and have a more positive impact on the economy and the environment than reactions with a low atom economy.
- Describe the ways in which a reaction with a low atom economy negatively impacts the economy and the environment.

Percentage yield measures the amount of product produced by a chemical reaction and does not take into account the amount of waste generated by the reaction. For example calcium oxide, CaO or 'lime' is used by the farming industry to reduce the acidity of soil and is produced by heating limestone (mostly $CaCO_3$).

$$CaCO_{3 \text{ (s)}} \rightarrow CaO_{\text{ (s)}} + CO_{2 \text{ (g)}}$$

The reaction is expected to yield 560 g of CaO for every 1 kg of $CaCO_3$ that reacts. If the percentage yield for the process is 75%, the actual yield is only 420 g of CaO and the reaction generates 330 g of carbon dioxide for every 1 kg of $CaCO_3$ reacted. If the carbon dioxide produced in the reaction is not used it is considered waste. The amount of waste generated by the process is measured by calculating the **atom economy** for the reaction.

$$\text{Atom economy} = \frac{\text{mass of useful products}}{\text{Mass of all products}} \times 100\%$$

The decomposition of limestone produces 420 g of useful product (CaO) and 330 g of waste (carbon dioxide) for every 1 kg of limestone that reacts. The atom economy for this process is:

$$\frac{420 \text{ g}}{420 \text{ g} + 330 \text{ g}} \times 100\% = 56\%$$

An atom economy of 56% indicates that $(100 - 56) = 44\%$ of the products are waste. In this way we can see that reactions with a low atom economy generate a lot of waste and that reactions with a fairly high percentage yield (75%) can still generate a lot of waste.

The waste generated by chemical processes must be disposed of safely if damage to the environment is to be avoided. The allocation of money and resources to dispose of waste has a negative effect on the economy by making the process more expensive to operate and reducing the amount of profit that can be made from the process. As a result, atom economy can be used to help develop **green chemistry** where we are using the term 'green' to describe chemical processes that generate less waste and have a less negative impact on our economy and the environment. In addition to designing processes that produce less waste, the negative impact of a chemical process on the economy and the environment can be reduced through the use of renewable resources, the recycling of unused reactants, and the use of sustainable energy such as wind and solar power as illustrated in Figure 1.

Worked Example 2.1iii

In industry, iron is extracted from iron(III) oxide by reducing the oxide with carbon monoxide. Calculate the atom economy for the reaction if the carbon dioxide formed in the reaction is (a) released into the atmosphere and (b) used to produce more carbon monoxide.

$$Fe_2O_3 + 3CO \rightarrow 2Fe + 3CO_2$$

Solution

(a) The carbon dioxide is a waste product of the reaction.

Each mole of Fe_2O_3 that reacts produces 2 mol of Fe and 3 mol of CO_2.

Mass of 2 mol of Fe = 2 mol × 56 g mol^{-1} = 112 g

Mass of 3 mol of CO_2 = 3 mol × 44 g mol^{-1} = 132 g

Atom economy =

$$\frac{\text{Mass of iron}}{\text{Total mass of products}} = \frac{112 \text{ g}}{112 \text{ g} + 132 \text{ g}} \times 100\%$$

$$= 45.9\%$$

(b) Both products are useful. The reaction produces no waste.

Atom economy = 100%

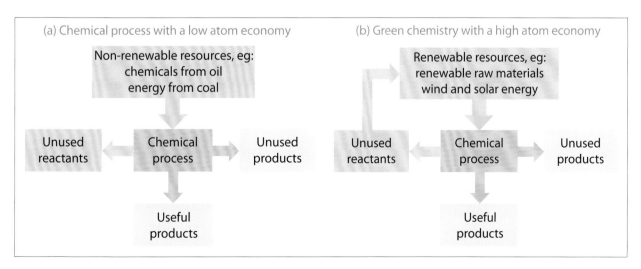

Figure 1: (a) A chemical process with a low atom economy. (b) The same process with a higher atom economy achieved by reducing the amount of waste and recycling unused reactants. The process has also been made 'greener' by the use of renewable resources.

Exercise 2.1C

1. Barium carbonate is roasted with carbon to produce barium oxide. Calculate the atom economy of the reaction.

$$BaCO_3 \rightarrow BaO + CO_2$$

(CCEA June 2011)

2. In industry decane, $C_{10}H_{22}$ is 'cracked' to produce octane, C_8H_{18} and ethene, C_2H_4. The octane produced by the process is used to produce gasoline (petrol). Calculate the atom economy of the reaction if ethene is discarded.

$$C_{10}H_{22} \rightarrow C_8H_{18} + C_2H_4$$

3. Titanium can be extracted from its ore (mostly TiO_2) by reacting the ore with a more reactive metal such as magnesium. Titanium can also be extracted from its ore by electrolysis. Calculate the atom economy when titanium is produced from its ore by (a) reaction with magnesium and (b) electrolysis.

Reaction with magnesium:

$$TiO_2 + 2Mg \rightarrow Ti + 2MgO$$

Electrolysis: $TiO_2 \rightarrow Ti + O_2$

Before moving to the next section, check that you are able to:

- Use atom economy to describe the amount of reactants converted into useful products in a chemical reaction.
- Recall that reactions with a high atom economy generate little waste and have a more positive impact on the economy and the environment than reactions with a low atom economy.
- Explain how the negative impact of a reaction with a low atom economy on the economy and the environment can be reduced.

Calculating Gas Volumes

In this section we are learning to:

- Recall Avogadro's law and use it to relate the amount of a gas to its volume.
- Use Avogadro's law to calculate the volumes of gases involved in chemical reactions.

The volume of gas produced or used by a chemical reaction can be calculated using **Avogadro's law** which states that *the volume of one mole of any gas is exactly 24 dm³ if measured at 20 °C and 1 atmosphere pressure.* This relationship between the amount of gas and its volume is summarised by the equation:

$$\text{Moles of gas} = \frac{\text{Volume of gas (in dm}^3\text{)}}{24 \text{ dm}^3}$$

Worked Example 2.1iv

Mercury(II) oxide decomposes on heating. Calculate the mass of mercury(II) oxide needed to produce 10.0 dm³ of oxygen at 20 °C and 1 atmosphere pressure.

$$2HgO_{(s)} \rightarrow 2Hg_{(l)} + O_{2\,(g)}$$

Strategy

- Calculate the moles of oxygen in 10.0 dm³.
- Calculate the mass of mercury(II) oxide needed to form 10.0 dm³ of oxygen.

Solution

Moles of oxygen in 10.0 dm³ =

$$\frac{10.0 \text{ dm}^3}{24 \text{ dm}^3 \text{ mol}^{-1}} = 0.417 \text{ mol}$$

Moles of mercury(II) oxide needed

$$= 0.417 \text{ mol} \times 2 = 0.834 \text{ mol}$$

Mass of mercury(II) oxide needed

$$= (0.834 \text{ mol})(217 \text{ g mol}^{-1}) = 181 \text{ g}$$

Exercise 2.1D

1. Ammonium chloride, NH_4Cl is quite soluble in water. 37.2 g dissolve in 100 cm³ of water at 20 °C. Calculate the maximum volume of ammonia gas that could be obtained from this solution at 20 °C and 1 atmosphere pressure.

(CCEA June 2011)

2. Calculate the volume of hydrogen produced at 20 °C and 1 atmosphere pressure when 8 g of magnesium reacts with an excess of steam.

$$Mg_{(s)} + H_2O_{(g)} \rightarrow MgO_{(s)} + H_{2\,(g)}$$

(CCEA January 2006)

3. Airbags in cars contain sodium azide, NaN_3. The airbag inflates when sodium azide decomposes to produce nitrogen gas. When inflated, an airbag

holds 50 dm^3 of nitrogen at 20 °C and 1 atmosphere pressure. What mass of sodium azide is needed to inflate the airbag?

$$2NaN_{3\ (s)} \rightarrow 2Na_{(s)} + 3N_{2\ (g)}$$

(CCEA January 2011)

4. Calculate the volume of hydrogen produced at 20 °C and 1 atmosphere pressure when an excess of magnesium is added to 50.0 cm^3 of 2 M hydrochloric acid.

$$Mg_{(s)} + 2HCl_{(aq)} \rightarrow MgCl_{2\ (aq)} + H_{2\ (g)}$$

(CCEA January 2008)

5. Manganese(IV) oxide catalyses the decomposition of hydrogen peroxide. Calculate the volume of oxygen produced at 20 °C and 1 atmosphere pressure when 50.0 cm^3 of 2 mol dm^{-3} hydrogen peroxide solution decomposes.

$$2H_2O_2 \rightarrow 2H_2O + O_2$$

(CCEA June 2010)

6. Nitrogen dioxide reacts with sodium hydroxide to form a mixture of sodium nitrate and sodium nitrite in solution. Calculate the volume of 2 M NaOH needed to react with 720 dm^3 of nitrogen dioxide at 20°C and 1 atmosphere pressure.

$$2NO_2 + 2NaOH \rightarrow NaNO_3 + NaNO_2 + H_2O$$

(CCEA January 2007)

Avogadro's law can also be used to calculate the **density** of a gas. By using Avogadro's law to first calculate the number of moles of gas in 1 cm^3 of the gas, the number of moles in 1 cm^3 of gas can then be converted into grams to give the density of the gas in units of g cm^{-3}. The density of nitrogen gas (N$_2$) is calculated as follows.

Moles in 1 cm^3 of any gas =

$$\frac{\text{Volume of gas (in dm}^3)}{24\,\text{dm}^3} = \frac{0.001\,\text{dm}^3}{24\,\text{dm}^3} = 4 \times 10^{-5}\,\text{mol}$$

Mass of N$_2$ in 1 cm^3 = Moles × Molar Mass =

$$(4 \times 10^{-5})(28) = 1.12 \times 10^{-3}\,\text{g}$$

Density of nitrogen gas (N$_2$) = 1.12×10^{-3} g cm^{-3}

1. Calculate the density of (a) hydrogen, (b) oxygen and (c) carbon dioxide.

2. You have two identical flasks: one contains nitrogen and the other contains hydrogen. How could you tell which is nitrogen without opening the flasks? Explain your answer.

Before moving to the next section, check that you are able to:

- Recall Avogadro's law and use it to relate the amount of a gas to its volume.
- Use Avogadro's law to calculate the volumes of gases involved in chemical reactions.

Percent Composition Calculations

In this section we are learning to:

- Calculate the mass percent of an element in a compound.
- Describe the amount of each element in a compound by writing the percent composition for the compound.

Mass Percent and Percent Composition

The amount of each element in a compound is often expressed as the **mass percent** of the element in the compound. The mass percent of an element is the mass of the element in 100 g of the compound expressed as a percentage. For example, 100 g of the compound aspirin, C$_9$H$_8$O$_4$ contains 4.4 g of hydrogen, 60.0 g of carbon and 35.6 g of oxygen. In terms of mass percent, this is equivalent to stating that aspirin is 4.4% hydrogen, 60.0% carbon and 35.6% oxygen by mass.

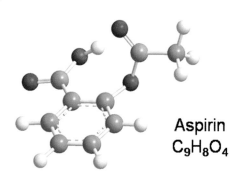

Aspirin
C₉H₈O₄

The mass percent of an element in a compound is calculated using the formula:

Mass % of an element =

$$\frac{\text{Mass of element in 1 mole}}{\text{Molar mass of compound}} \times 100\%$$

Worked Example 2.1v

Calculate the mass percent carbon in aspirin, $C_9H_8O_4$.

Solution

One mole of aspirin contains 9 moles of carbon atoms.

Mass of carbon in 1 mol of aspirin =

$$9 \text{ mol} \times 12 \text{ g mol}^{-1} = 108 \text{ g of C}$$

Molar mass of aspirin = $108 + 8 + 64 = 180$ g mol^{-1}

Mass percent carbon = $\dfrac{108}{180} \times 100\% = 60\%$

When combined, the mass percents for the element in a compound describe the composition of the substance. A list detailing the mass percent of each element in a substance is known as the **percent composition** of the substance. The percent composition of aspirin is: 60.0% C, 4.4% H, 35.6% O.

Exercise 2.1F

1. Calculate the percent composition of (a) propane, C_3H_8 and (b) hexane, C_6H_{14}.

2. Calculate the percent composition of glucose, $C_6H_{12}O_6$.

> Before moving to the next section, check that you are able to:
>
> • Use the formula of a compound to calculate the mass percent of an element in the compound.
>
> • Describe the amount of each element in a compound by writing the percent composition for the compound.

Empirical Formula

The chemical formula of a newly discovered substance is often determined with the help of percent composition data. The formula obtained from percent composition data is known as the empirical formula for the compound. The **empirical formula** describes the simplest ratio of the elements in the compound. By defining empirical formula in this way, the chemical formula of an ionic compound also becomes the empirical formula of the compound. For example, the ionic lattice in magnesium chloride, $MgCl_2$ contains two chloride ions for every magnesium ion. The ratio of magnesium to chlorine in the lattice is described by the chemical formula $MgCl_2$ and, as a result, the chemical formula also serves as the empirical formula for the compound.

In contrast, the molar mass corresponding to the empirical formula of a molecular compound is often less than the actual molar mass of the compound. To understand why it is helpful to examine how percent composition is used to calculate the empirical formula for a molecular compound.

Worked Example 2.1vi

The percent composition of ascorbic acid is: 40.9% C, 4.6% H, 54.5% O. Calculate the empirical formula for ascorbic acid.

Strategy

• Calculate the moles of each element in 100 g of the compound.

• Use the mole ratio for the elements to write a formula for the compound.

• Convert the mole ratio to the simplest whole number ratio.

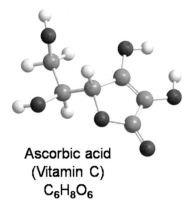

Ascorbic acid
(Vitamin C)
$C_6H_8O_6$

Solution

100 g of ascorbic acid contains:

$$100 \text{ g} \times \frac{40.9\%}{100\%} = 40.9 \text{ g of C} = \frac{40.9 \text{ g}}{12 \text{ g mol}^{-1}} = 3.4 \text{ mol of C}$$

$$100 \text{ g} \times \frac{4.6\%}{100\%} = 4.6 \text{ g of H} = \frac{4.6 \text{ g}}{1 \text{ g mol}^{-1}} = 4.6 \text{ mol of H}$$

$$100 \text{ g} \times \frac{54.5\%}{100\%} = 54.5 \text{ g of O} = \frac{54.5 \text{ g}}{16 \text{ g mol}^{-1}} = 3.4 \text{ mol of O}$$

The mole ratio of the elements corresponds to the formula $C_{3.4}H_{4.6}O_{3.4}$

Converting to whole numbers:

$$C_{\frac{3.4}{3.4}}H_{\frac{4.6}{3.4}}O_{\frac{3.4}{3.4}} = C_1H_{\frac{4}{3}}O_1 = C_3H_4O_3$$

The empirical formula for ascorbic acid is $C_3H_4O_3$

．．

The empirical formula for ascorbic acid corresponds to a RMM of 88. In contrast, the molecular ion peak (M^+) in the mass spectrum for ascorbic acid corresponds to a RMM of 176. A RMM of 176 is exactly twice the RMM for the empirical formula, $C_3H_4O_3$ and indicates that the formula for a molecule of ascorbic acid is $C_6H_8O_6$ (= $2 \times C_3H_4O_3$'s). In this way the molecular mass of a new compound can be combined with percent composition data to determine the formula of a new molecule. The molecular and empirical formulas for several common molecular compounds are compared in Table 1.

Exercise 2.1G

1. Disilane, Si_2H_x is 90.3% silicon by mass. Find x.

2. The metal sulfide, MS_2 is 40.1% sulfur by mass. Identify M.

3. The refrigerant CFC-114 is 14.0% carbon and 44.4% fluorine by mass. The remainder is chlorine. Calculate the empirical formula of CFC-114. *(CCEA January 2011)*

4. Analysis of a compound containing carbon, hydrogen and bromine showed that the compound is 22.2% carbon and 3.7% hydrogen by mass. The relative molecular mass of the compound is 216. Calculate the molecular formula of the compound. *(CCEA June 2010)*

5. The compound tetraethyllead (TEL) contains carbon, hydrogen and lead and is the chemical form of lead in petrol. TEL is 29.7% carbon and 6.23% hydrogen by mass. Calculate the empirical formula of tetraethyl lead.

6. 0.8 moles of a liquid X was found to contain 19.2 g of carbon, 3.2 g of hydrogen and 56.8 g of chlorine. Calculate the empirical formula of X.
   (Adapted from CCEA June 2007)

Before moving to the next section, check that you are able to:

- Use the percent composition for a compound to determine the empirical formula of the compound.
- Recall that the formula of an ionic compound is an empirical formula.
- Recall that the molecular formula of a molecular material may be a multiple of the empirical formula.

Table 1: Molecular and empirical formulas for several common molecular substances.

Substance	Molecular Formula	Empirical Formula
Methane (natural gas)	CH_4	CH_4
Octane (petrol)	C_8H_{18}	C_4H_9
Ethylene glycol (anti-freeze)	$C_2H_6O_2$	CH_3O
Glucose (sugar)	$C_6H_{12}O_6$	CH_2O
Ascorbic acid (Vitamin C)	$C_6H_8O_6$	$C_3H_4O_3$

2.2 Organic Chemistry

CONNECTIONS
- Organic chemistry is the branch of chemistry concerned with the synthesis and study of organic compounds.
- Many plastics and fibres such as polythene and Nylon are made from the organic compounds found in crude oil.
- Many medicines contain organic compounds that are based on Natural Products obtained directly from plants.

In this section we are learning to:

- Identify organic compounds and recall how they can exist in different structural forms known as isomers.
- Recall that organic compounds have systematic names and common 'everyday' names.
- Explain how organic compounds can be grouped together to form a homologous series of compounds.
- Recall the use of molecular models to describe the size and shape of molecules, and the use of structural and condensed formulas to describe the bonding within an organic compound.
- Recall that the properties and reactions of an organic compound are determined by the functional groups present in the compound.

Organic Compounds

An **organic compound** is a substance whose structure is based on the element carbon. Many of the compounds found in nature are organic compounds. The compounds carvone and eugenol give spearmint leaves and cloves their distinctive smells, and are examples of organic compounds. Much of the food and medicine we consume is also made-up of organic compounds. Common pain-killers such as aspirin, dietary supplements such as Vitamin C, and sugars such as glucose are all organic compounds. The structures and molecular formulas for carvone, Vitamin C and Aspirin are shown in Figure 1.

The mirror image of the spearmint form of carvone produces the odour of caraway seeds. The relationship between the spearmint and caraway forms of carvone is shown in Figure 2. Compounds with the same chemical formula but a different arrangement of atoms are known as **isomers**. The spearmint and caraway forms of carvone are isomers and are distinguished by including the prefix *D-* or *L-* when naming the isomers.

Talking Point

Every organic compound has a systematic name based on the rules developed and maintained by the International Union of Pure and Applied Chemistry (IUPAC). A large number of organic compounds such as lactic acid and glucose are still referred to by their common 'everyday' names.

Lactic acid, $C_3H_6O_3$
2-hydroxypropanoic acid

Glucose, $C_6H_{12}O_6$
2, 3, 4, 5, 6-pentahydroxyhexanal

Organic compounds can be very large. The carbohydrates and proteins in our food are constructed from much smaller organic molecules such as simple sugars and amino acids. Plastics such as polythene and fibres such as Nylon are also organic compounds constructed from many smaller organic molecules.

Many of the plastics and other materials we use in our everyday lives are made from the organic compounds in crude oil. Crude oil is a complex mixture of organic compounds known as hydrocarbons, where the term **hydrocarbon** refers to

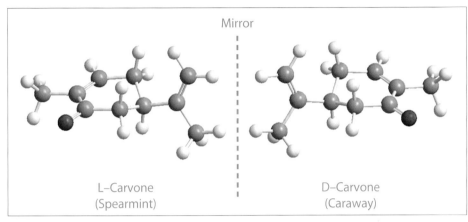

Carvone (Spearmint)
Formula: $C_{10}H_{14}O$

(a)

Ascorbic acid (Vitamin C)
Formula: $C_6H_8O_6$

(b)

Acetylsalicylic acid (Aspirin)
Formula: $C_9H_8O_4$

(c)

Mirror

L–Carvone
(Spearmint)

D–Carvone
(Caraway)

Figure 1: Structures and molecular formulas for (a) carvone (spearmint), $C_{10}H_{14}O$ (b) ascorbic acid (Vitamin C), $C_6H_8O_6$ and (c) acetylsalicylic acid (Aspirin), $C_9H_8O_4$.

Figure 2: Mirror image isomers of the compound carvone. The isomers have the same chemical formula ($C_{10}H_{14}O$) but have a different arrangement of atoms and cannot be superimposed.

a compound that contains only carbon and hydrogen. A large number of hydrocarbons belong to a family of compounds known as the alkanes. The molecular formulas for the alkanes can be obtained by setting n = 1, 2, 3 ... in the general formula C_nH_{2n+2}. The effect of increasing n on the size of the alkanes can be seen by constructing **space-filling models** in which each atom is represented by a sphere centred on the nucleus of the atom. The space-filling models in Figure 3 clearly show that the alkane molecules become longer as the number of carbon atoms (n) increases.

Worked Example 2.2i

Which one of the following is an alkane?

(a) $C_{10}H_{18}$ (b) $C_{10}H_{20}$ (c) $C_{10}H_{22}$ (d) $C_{10}H_{24}$

(CCEA January 2006)

Solution

The formula of an alkane with 10 carbon atoms is obtained by inserting n = 10 into the general formula, C_nH_{2n+2}.

$C_{10}H_{22}$ is an alkane (Answer c).

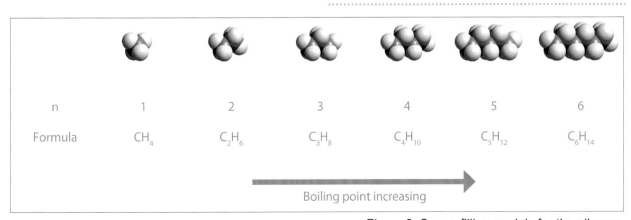

n	1	2	3	4	5	6
Formula	CH_4	C_2H_6	C_3H_8	C_4H_{10}	C_5H_{12}	C_6H_{14}

Boiling point increasing

Figure 3: Space-filling models for the alkanes.

121

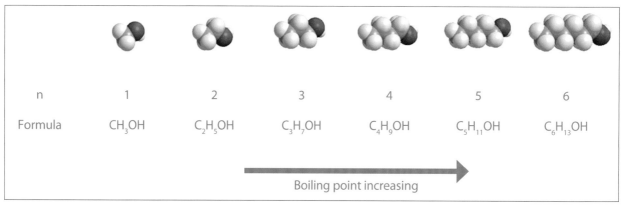

n	1	2	3	4	5	6
Formula	CH_3OH	C_2H_5OH	C_3H_7OH	C_4H_9OH	$C_5H_{11}OH$	$C_6H_{13}OH$

Boiling point increasing

Figure 4: Space-filling models for the alcohols.

The alkanes are an example of a **homologous series**. The term homologous series refers to a series of compounds with similar chemical properties whose formulas are related by a general formula and differ by CH_2. Ethanol, C_2H_5OH belongs to a different homologous series known as the alcohols. The molecular formulas for the alcohols are obtained by setting n = 1, 2 ... in the general formula $C_nH_{2n+1}OH$. The space-filling models in Figure 4 clearly show that, as with the alkanes, the alcohol molecules become longer as the number of carbon atoms (n) increases.

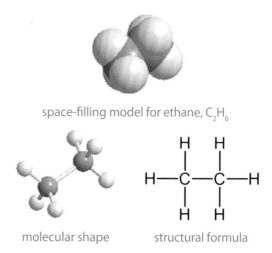

space-filling model for ethane, C_2H_6

molecular shape   structural formula

In practice, a structural formula is only used when it is necessary to detail the bonds formed between individual atoms in the structure. In many molecules the nature of the bonding between atoms can be inferred by writing the **condensed formula** for the compound in which formulas are used to represent different parts of the structure.

> Before moving to the next section, check that you are able to:
>
> • Recognise compounds whose structure is based on carbon as organic compounds and explain why a compound can exist as isomers.
>
> • Recall that hydrocarbons are a type of organic compound, and that most hydrocarbons are obtained from natural sources such as crude oil.
>
> • Explain how the members of a homologous series are related, and how a general formula can be used to generate a formula for each member of the series.

Structural Formulas

Space-filling models are useful when comparing the size of molecules but cannot be used to describe chemical bonding within molecules. The bonding within a compound must instead be described by drawing the structural formula for the compound. Comparing the space-filling model, the molecular shape, and the structural formula for ethane, C_2H_6 reminds us that the structural formula describes the bonding between atoms and may not reflect the shape of the molecule.

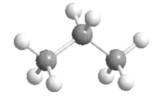

molecular shape for propane, C_3H_8

structural formula   condensed formula

$CH_3CH_2CH_3$

A condensed formula can be used to quickly convey the arrangement of the atoms in a molecule and the size of the molecule, making it a convenient tool to describe the structure and bonding in larger molecules such as hexane, C_6H_{14}.

space-filling model for hexane, C_6H_{14}

$$CH_3CH_2CH_2CH_2CH_2CH_3$$

condensed formula

> **Before moving to the next section, check that you are able to:**
>
> - Recall the use of space-filling models to describe the size of molecules.
> - Distinguish the use of molecular models to describe the shapes of molecules and the use of structural formulas to describe bonding in molecules.
> - Explain how a condensed formula can be used to describe the structure of an organic compound and the bonding within the compound.

Functional Groups

When an organic compound reacts with another substance the reaction will involve small groups of atoms at specific sites in the molecule known as **functional groups**.

For example, when wine 'goes bad' some of the alcohol in the wine (ethanol) is oxidised to form ethanoic acid.

ethanol, C_2H_6O ethanoic acid, $C_2H_4O_2$

$$CH_3CH_2OH \rightarrow CH_3COOH$$

The reaction transforms the $-CH_2-$ group adjacent to the hydroxyl (-OH) group into part of the larger carboxyl (-COOH) group in the acid. The hydroxyl (-OH) group is a functional group whose presence confers the properties of an alcohol. Similarly, the presence of a carboxyl (-COOH) group confers the properties of a carboxylic acid; a type of organic acid that reacts with metals and bases to form salts in the same way as non-organic acids such as sulfuric acid and nitric acid. The conversion of the hydroxyl (-OH) group to a carboxyl (-COOH) group demonstrates that the hydroxyl group must be present if the carboxyl group is to be formed. In this way we can see that the reactions of a compound are determined by the nature of the functional groups present in the molecule.

Worked Example 2.2ii

The compound cinnamyl alcohol contains several functional groups. Explain the meaning of the term *functional group*.

$$C_6H_5-C=C-C-OH$$

cinnamyl alcohol

(CCEA January 2003)

Solution

A functional group is a group of atoms within a compound that together determine the reactions of the compound.

> **Before moving to the next section, check that you are able to:**
>
> - Recall that the reactions of an organic compound are determined by the functional groups present in the compound.
> - Explain what is meant by the term functional group.

2.3 Hydrocarbons: Alkanes

Structure and Properties

In this section we are learning to:

- Recognise the alkanes as a homologous series of hydrocarbons.
- Explain the properties of the alkanes in terms of the nonpolar nature of the bonding within the alkane molecules.
- Use structural and condensed formulas to represent the structure of alkanes.
- Recognise and draw structural isomers of alkanes.
- Use systematic (IUPAC) rules to name alkanes.

The alkanes are a homologous series of hydrocarbons with the general formula C_nH_{2n+2}. The structural formulas in Figure 1 reveal that alkanes contain only C-C and C-H bonds. Both types of bond are strong and difficult to break. As a result, alkanes are unreactive and will only react when in contact with very reactive substances. The structures in Figure 1 also reveal that the alkanes are **saturated hydrocarbons** as they only contain single bonds between carbon atoms.

The bond dipoles associated with the C-H bonds in alkanes are very small. As a result, alkanes do not have a significant permanent dipole, and experience only van der Waals attraction between neighbouring molecules. The nonpolar nature of the alkanes makes liquids such as hexane, C_6H_{14} good solvents for other nonpolar molecules such as bromine, Br_2. The van der Waals attraction between alkane molecules increases as the number of electrons in the molecule increases. This explains why the lighter alkanes (small n) are gases while the heavier alkanes (large n) are solids. The effect of increasing van der Waals attraction on boiling point is illustrated in Figure 2.

The 'straight-chain' alkanes in Figures 1 and 2 are based on a simple chain of carbon atoms and are referred to as the **parent alkanes** on which more branched structures are based. The alkanes in Figure 3 are isomers; both have the formula C_5H_{12}. Pentane has a higher boiling point as the more branched structure of neopentane reduces the amount of contact between the electrons on neighbouring molecules. This reduces the van der Waals attraction between neopentane molecules and ensures that neopentane has a lower boiling point than pentane.

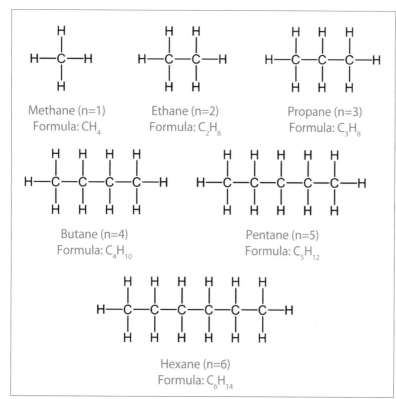

Methane (n=1)
Formula: CH_4

Ethane (n=2)
Formula: C_2H_6

Propane (n=3)
Formula: C_3H_8

Butane (n=4)
Formula: C_4H_{10}

Pentane (n=5)
Formula: C_5H_{12}

Hexane (n=6)
Formula: C_6H_{14}

Figure 1: Structural formulas for the first six alkanes (n=1–6).

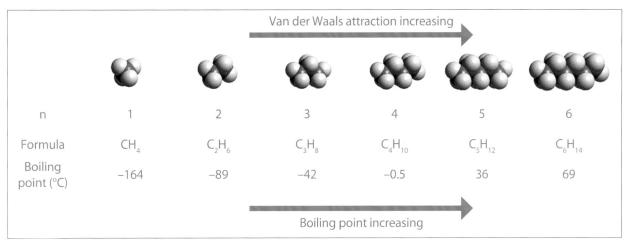

Figure 2: The effect of van der Waals attraction on boiling point for the first six alkanes (n=1–6).

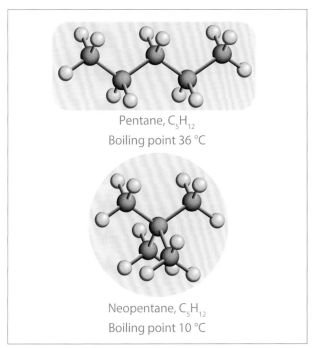

Pentane, C_5H_{12}
Boiling point 36 °C

Neopentane, C_5H_{12}
Boiling point 10 °C

Figure 3: The effect of molecular shape on the boiling point of pentane isomers.

Naming Alkanes

Alkanes are named according to the parent (straight-chain) alkane on which their structure is based. The names of the parent alkanes consist of a prefix to indicate the number of carbon atoms in the molecule, and the suffix *ane* to indicate that the compound is an alkane. For example pentane, C_5H_{12} is named using the prefix *pent* to indicate that the molecule contains a chain of five carbon atoms. The prefixes used to name alkanes based on a chain of up to six carbon atoms are summarised in Table 1.

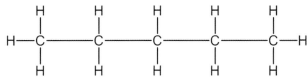

Structural formula for pentane, C_5H_{12}

$$CH_3CH_2CH_2CH_2CH_3$$

Condensed formula for pentane, C_5H_{12}

The compound 2-methylbutane is an isomer of pentane. It is based on a chain of four carbon atoms

Table 1: Naming prefixes for alkanes based on a chain of up to six carbon atoms.

Carbon atoms in longest chain	Naming prefix	Name of parent alkane	Condensed formula of parent alkane
1	meth-	meth**ane**	CH_4
2	eth-	eth**ane**	CH_3CH_3
3	prop-	prop**ane**	$CH_3CH_2CH_3$
4	but-	but**ane**	$CH_3CH_2CH_2CH_3$
5	pent-	pent**ane**	$CH_3CH_2CH_2CH_2CH_3$
6	hex-	hex**ane**	$CH_3CH_2CH_2CH_2CH_2CH_3$

with a fifth carbon atom, in the form of a methyl group (-CH$_3$), attached to the second carbon atom in the chain. The compound is considered a butane as the longest carbon chain in the molecule contains four carbon atoms.

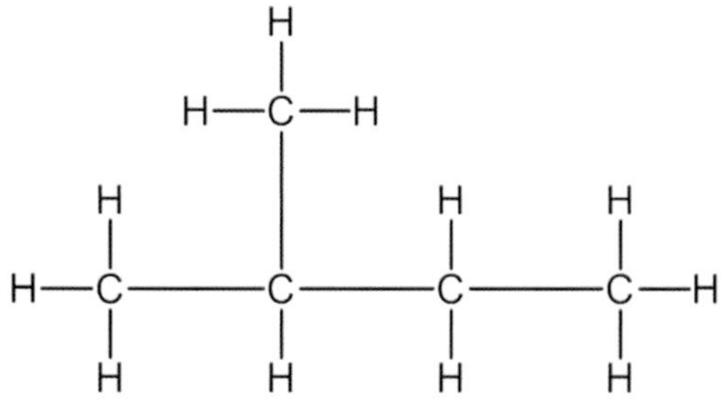

Structural formula for 2-methylbutane, C$_5$H$_{12}$

$$CH_3CH(CH_3)CH_2CH_3$$

Condensed formula for 2-methylbutane, C$_5$H$_{12}$

In 2-methylbutane, the presence of the methyl group is indicated by including the prefix *methyl* when naming the compound. An additional prefix *2-* is then added to indicate that the methyl group is attached to the second carbon in the chain.

The use of the prefix *2-methyl* is potentially confusing. The methyl group is only attached to the second carbon atom if we choose to number the carbon atoms from left to right. If we instead choose to number the carbon atoms from right to left, the location of the methyl group is described by the prefix *3-methyl*. To avoid confusion the carbon atoms are always numbered in a way that produces the lowest number prefixes.

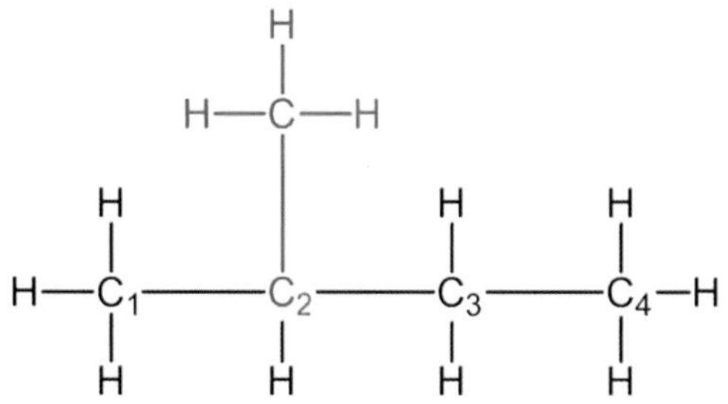

2-methylbutane ✓

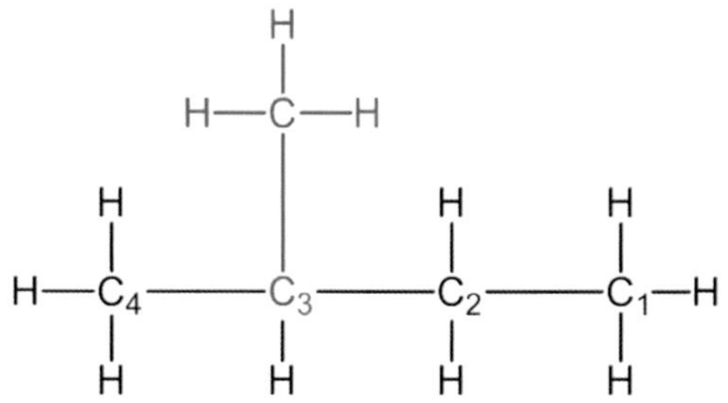

3-methylbutane ✗

The compound 2,2-dimethylpropane is also an isomer of pentane. It is based on a chain of three carbon atoms with the remaining two carbon atoms in the form of methyl groups (-CH$_3$) attached to the second carbon atom in the chain.

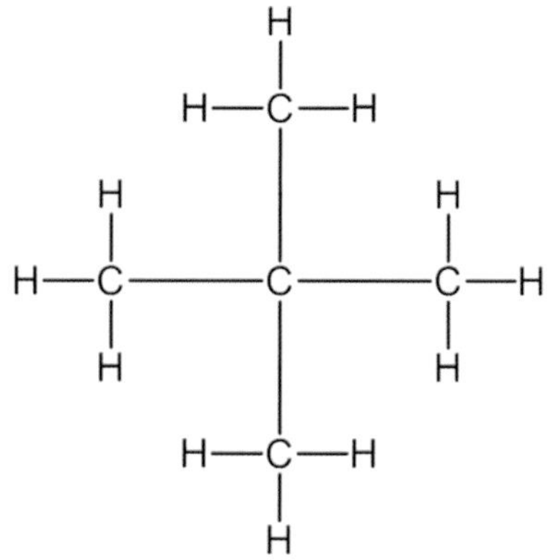

Structural formula for 2,2-dimethylpropane, C$_5$H$_{12}$

$$CH_3C(CH_3)_2CH_3$$

Condensed formula for 2,2-dimethylpropane, C$_5$H$_{12}$

The molecule is considered to be a propane as the longest carbon chain in the molecule contains three carbon atoms. The presence of two methyl groups on the chain is indicated by use of the prefix *dimethyl* and the additional prefix *2,2-* is added to indicate that both methyl groups are attached to the second carbon atom in the chain.

The presence of additional methyl groups in a molecule can be described by using the number prefixes *di*, *tri*, *tetra*, *penta*, *hexa*, ... to construct naming prefixes such as *trimethyl* and *tetramethyl*. An additional prefix such as *1,2,2-* or *2,2,3,3-* can then be added to describe the location of each methyl group as in 2,2,4-trimethylpentane.

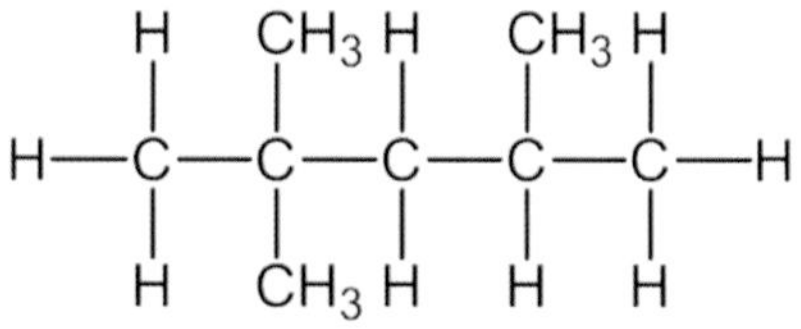

2,2,4-trimethylpentane

....

Worked Example 2.3i

What is the systematic name of:

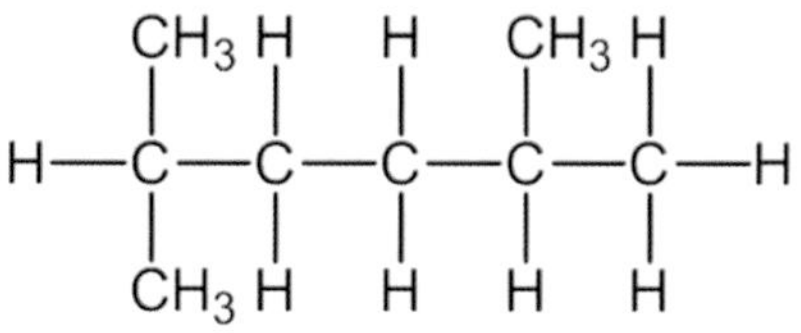

(a) 2,2-dimethylhexane

(b) 2,5-dimethylhexane

(c) 1,1,4-trimethylpentane

(d) 2,5,5-trimethylpentane

(CCEA June 2001)

Strategy

- The molecule is a hexane if the longest carbon chain contains 6 carbon atoms and a pentane if the longest carbon chain contains 5 carbon atoms.
- Locate the methyl groups by numbering the carbon atoms in the longest chain from the end that generates the lowest number prefixes.

Solution

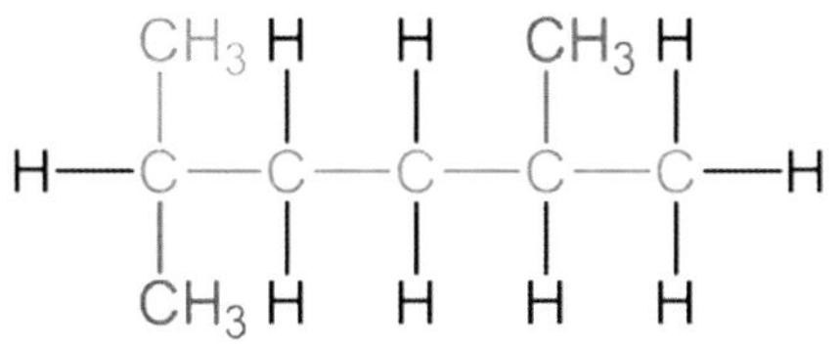

The molecule is a hexane with methyl groups attached to the second and fifth carbon atoms in the chain.

The compound is 2,5-dimethylhexane (Answer b).

Exercise 2.3A

1. What is the IUPAC name for the hydrocarbon shown below?

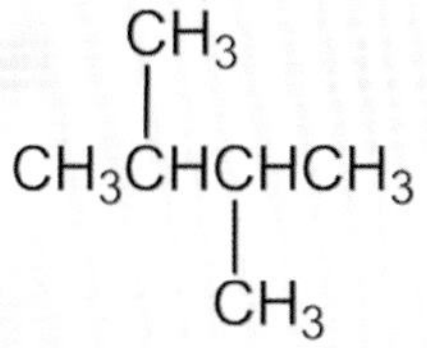

(a) 1,4-dimethylbutane

(b) 2,3-dimethylbutane

(c) 1,4-dimethylhexane

(d) 2,3-dimethylhexane   *(CCEA June 2011)*

2. The correct name for the following compound is

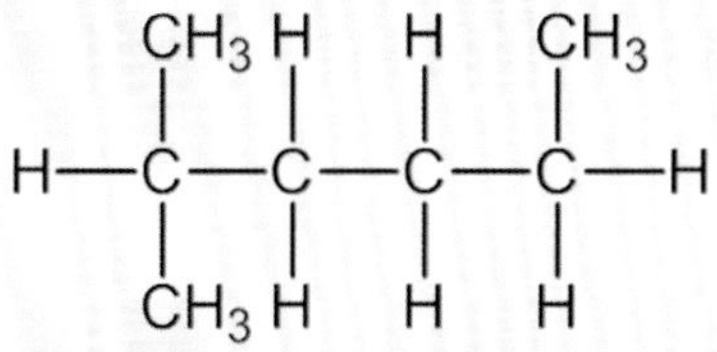

(a) 1,1,4-trimethylbutane.

(b) 1,4-dimethylpentane.

(c) 1,4,4-trimethylbutane.

(d) 2-methylhexane.   *(CCEA June 2010)*

Structural Isomers

Compounds with the same molecular formula but different structural formulas are known as **structural isomers**. The compounds pentane, 2-methylbutane and 2,2-dimethylpropane named in the previous section are structural isomers and can be distinguished by comparing their structural formulas or condensed formulas.

Worked Example 2.3ii

Draw the structural formula for all possible butane isomers with the formula C_6H_{14}. Write the condensed formula and systematic (IUPAC) name for each isomer.

Strategy

- Begin by drawing a chain of four carbon atoms (butane).
- Add the remaining atoms to generate a hydrocarbon containing only C-H and C-C bonds in which the longest carbon chain contains four carbon atoms.
- Repeat until all possible structures have been found.

Solution

There are two butanes with the formula C_6H_{14}

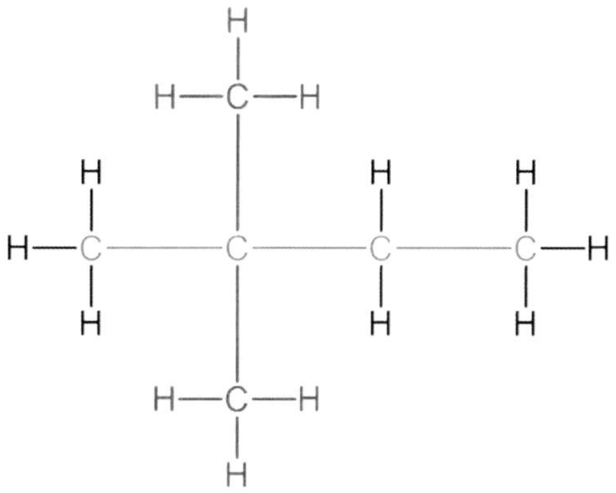

$CH_3C(CH_3)_2CH_2CH_3$ 2,2-dimethylbutane

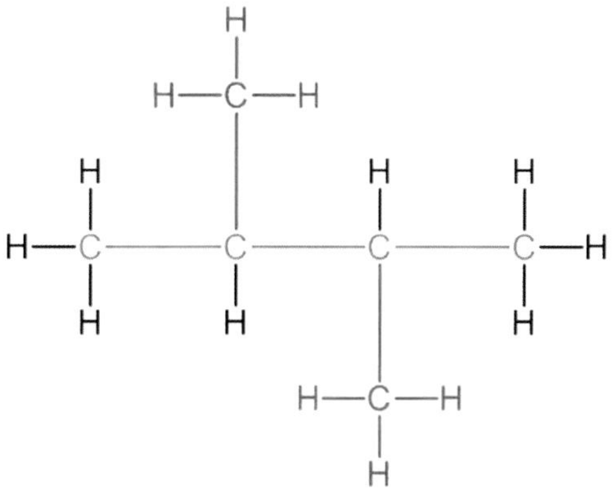

$CH_3CH(CH_3)CH(CH_3)CH_3$ 2,3-dimethylbutane

Exercise 2.3B

1. (a) Write the general formula for an alkane. (b) The pentanes in the table are structural isomers. Explain the term structural isomer. (c) Write IUPAC names for isopentane and neopentane. (d) Explain why the pentanes have different boiling points. *(CCEA January 2010)*

structure	name	boiling point
$CH_3CH_2CH_2CH_2CH_3$	normal pentane	36 °C
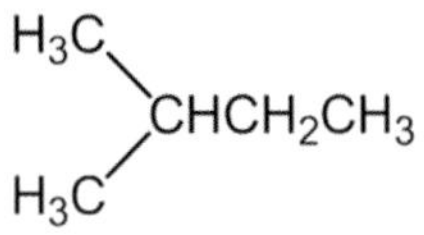 H_3C $CHCH_2CH_3$ H_3C	isopentane	28 °C
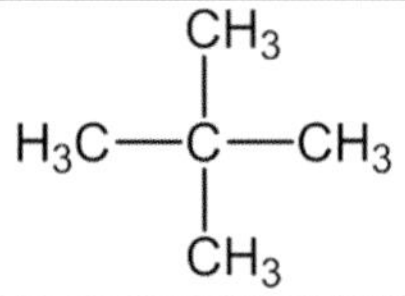 CH_3 $H_3C-C-CH_3$ CH_3	neopentane	9 °C

2. How many structural isomers have the formula C_4H_{10}?

(CCEA June 2009)

3. How many isomers have the formula C_5H_{12}?

(CCEA January 2002)

Alkyl Groups

An **alkyl group** is a functional group that consists of carbon and hydrogen atoms held together by single bonds. There are many different types of alkyl groups in organic compounds. Common alkyl groups include:

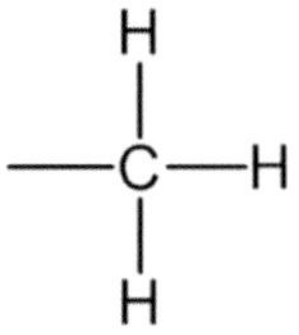

Methyl, -CH_3 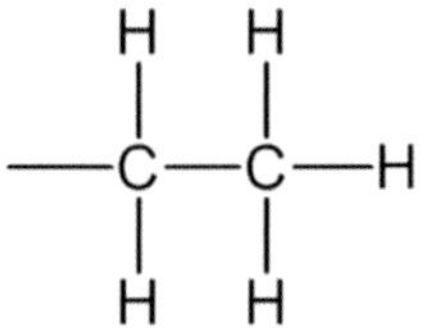   Ethyl, -C_2H_5

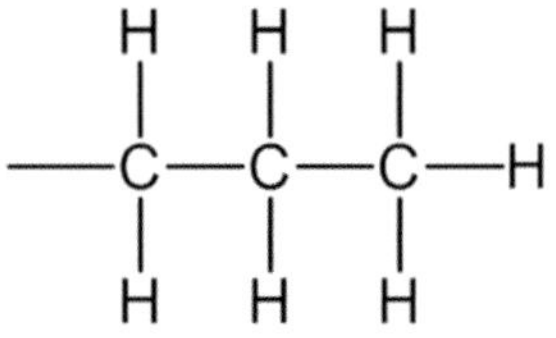

Propyl, -C_3H_7

The presence of an alkyl group in a molecule is indicated by a prefix that describes the type of alkyl group and its location in the molecule. For instance, the prefix *3-ethyl* is used to indicate that an ethyl group

(-C_2H_5 or -CH_2CH_3) is located on the third carbon atom within the longest carbon chain. Similarly the prefix *2,4-diethyl* indicates that there are ethyl groups attached to the second and fourth carbon atoms within the longest carbon chain.

When using prefixes to identify different types of alkyl group, the prefixes are written in alphabetical order. For example, the prefix *4-ethyl-2-methyl* is used to indicate that an ethyl group is attached to the fourth carbon atom and a methyl group is attached to the second carbon atom within the longest carbon chain.

Rules for naming alkanes:

- The name of an alkane consists of a prefix followed by the suffix *ane*. The prefix is determined by the number of carbon atoms in the longest carbon chain within the molecule.

- Additional prefixes are added to describe the type and location of each alkyl group. The prefixes are written in alphabetical order and are based on a numbering of the longest carbon chain that produces the lowest number prefixes.

Exercise 2.3C

What is the systematic name for the molecule shown below?

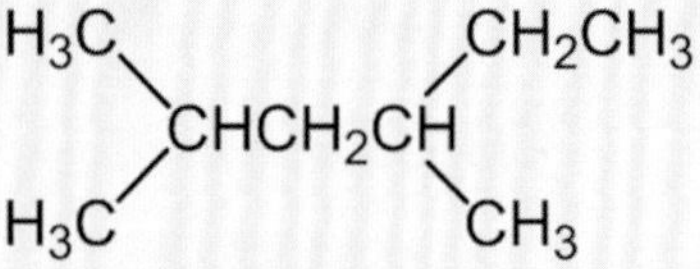

H_3C CH_2CH_3
    $CHCH_2CH$
H_3C CH_3

(a) 2,4-dimethylhexane
(b) 2-ethyl-4-methylpentane
(c) 2-methyl-4-ethylpentane
(d) 3,5-dimethylhexane   *(CCEA June 2008)*

Before moving to the next section, check that you are able to:

- Recall the general formula for an alkane and use the general formula to generate molecular formulas for alkanes.

- Explain how molecular size and shape affects the boiling point of alkanes.

- Draw structural formulas and write condensed formulas for alkanes.

- Recognise and draw structural isomers of alkanes.

- Deduce systematic names for alkanes.

Sources of Alkanes

- Recall that crude oil is a major source of hydrocarbons and explain how hydrocarbons are obtained by the refining of crude oil.
- Describe the environmental problems associated with the spillage of crude oil.
- Explain how smaller hydrocarbons are obtained from larger hydrocarbons by cracking and write equations for the cracking of alkanes.

Crude oil (petroleum) is a complex mixture of hydrocarbons and can be separated by fractional distillation to produce more useful mixtures of hydrocarbons such as gasoline (petrol) and kerosene (jet fuel). Many of the hydrocarbons in crude oil are alkanes. The 'refining' of crude oil by distillation is illustrated in Figure 4. The first step in the refining of crude oil is to heat the oil to around 350 °C. The more **volatile** (lighter) compounds in the oil vaporise and enter the distillation column where they cool as they rise towards the top of the column. Heavier nonvolatile compounds in the oil remain as liquids and fall to the bottom of the distillation column. The compounds in the vapour have different boiling points and condense at different heights within the distillation column. The condensed hydrocarbons are collected at various heights within the distillation column to form mixtures of hydrocarbons known as **fractions**. The composition and primary use of each fraction is detailed in Table 2.

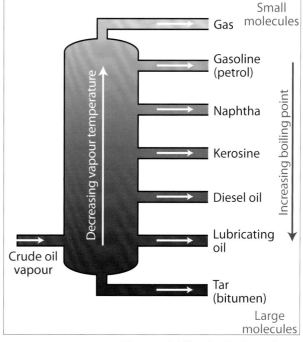

Figure 4: (a) The distillation column in an oil refinery. (b) The separation of crude oil into fractions within the distillation column.

Fraction (alternative name)	Primary Use	Carbon atoms
Refinery gas	Domestic heating	1–4
Gasoline (Petrol)	Fuel for motor vehicles	5–8
Naphtha	Chemicals for industry	9–10
Kerosene (Paraffin)	Fuel for jet aircraft	11–12
Diesel oil	Fuel for large engines	13–25
Lubricating oil	Lubrication	26–28
Tar (Bitumen)	Road surfacing	>28

Table 2: Fractions obtained from the fractional distillation of crude oil (petroleum).

Exercise 2.3D

Crude petroleum is the source of hydrocarbons such as alkanes. (a) How are alkanes obtained from crude petroleum? (b) Octane, C_8H_{18} is a saturated hydrocarbon. What is meant by the terms saturated and hydrocarbon? (c) Write the systematic name for the isomer of octane shown below. *(CCEA January 2011)*

$$H_3C - \overset{\overset{\displaystyle CH_3}{|}}{\underset{\underset{\displaystyle CH_3}{|}}{C}} - \overset{\overset{\displaystyle CH_3}{|}}{\underset{\underset{\displaystyle CH_3}{|}}{C}} - CH_3$$

The accidental spillage of crude oil has a very negative impact on wildlife and the landscape. When an oil spill occurs the oil must be quickly contained and sprayed with detergents to break the oil into small particles that can be digested by bacteria. The containment and dispersal of the oil following a spill at sea is shown in Figure 5. If the oil is not contained and dispersed, wildlife habitats directly affected by the spill will be seriously damaged, making it difficult for wildlife dependent on the habitats to survive. Animals that come into direct contact with the oil may also be seriously harmed by the spill. When sea-birds come into contact with crude oil, their feathers are no longer able to sustain flight, leaving the birds unable to feed themselves and vulnerable to predators. Sea-birds and

other animals can also suffer serious organ damage as a result of ingesting the oil. Oil spills at sea can also affect aquatic plant life by covering the surface of the water and reducing the amount of sunlight available for photosynthesis below the surface.

Exercise 2.3E

Crude petroleum is a major source of hydrocarbons. Discuss the environmental problems associated with the spillage of hydrocarbons. *(CCEA June 2011)*

Cracking of Alkanes

The amount of gasoline (petrol) produced by refining oil is not sufficient to meet demand and must be increased by breaking apart larger hydrocarbons from fractions with a higher boiling range; a process known as cracking. For example, the supply of octane, C_8H_{18} from crude oil can be increased by cracking decane, $C_{10}H_{22}$ to produce a mixture of octane, C_8H_{18} and ethene, C_2H_4.

$$C_{10}H_{22} \rightarrow C_8H_{18} + C_2H_4$$

Cracking hydrocarbons by heating to high temperatures is known as **thermal cracking**. If the hydrocarbon is heated in the presence of a catalyst the cracking process is referred to as **catalytic cracking**. Catalytic cracking occurs at much lower temperatures than thermal cracking and, as a result, is much less expensive to operate on an industrial scale.

*Figure 5: (a) The use of a floating barrier to contain an oil spill.
(b) Spraying affected areas with detergent to disperse the oil into tiny droplets.*

Exercise 2.3F

1. Long chain hydrocarbons may be converted into shorter more useful ones by catalytic cracking. Write an equation for the cracking of the hydrocarbon $C_{20}H_{42}$ in which pentane is one of the products.

   (CCEA June 2007)

2. Annual production of polythene in the UK is about half a million tonnes. The ethene needed for the process is obtained from the catalytic cracking of naphtha. Explain the term catalytic cracking.

   (CCEA January 2009)

Before moving to the next section, check that you are able to:

- Recall that crude oil (petroleum) is the major source of hydrocarbons and explain how gasoline, diesel and other fractions are obtained by the fractional distillation of crude oil.
- Describe the environmental problems associated with the spillage of crude oil.
- Recall the conditions for thermal and catalytic cracking and write equations to describe the cracking of alkanes.

Combustion of Alkanes

In this section we are learning to:

- Explain the difference between complete and incomplete combustion, and recall the products of the complete and incomplete combustion of hydrocarbons.
- Describe the environmental problems associated with the combustion of hydrocarbons and explain the use of a catalytic converter to reduce environmental pollution resulting from the burning of hydrocarbon-based fuels in motor vehicles.

Complete Combustion

The term combustion refers to the reaction between a compound and oxygen. If a compound is burnt in an excess of air (oxygen), the compound completely reacts with oxygen, and the reaction is referred to as **complete combustion**. The complete combustion of hydrocarbons produces carbon dioxide (CO_2), water (H_2O) and energy in the form of heat.

The **COMPLETE** combustion of butane, C_4H_{10}:

$$C_4H_{10 \, (g)} + \frac{13}{2}O_{2 \, (g)} \rightarrow 4CO_{2 \, (g)} + 5H_2O_{(l)}$$

Or

$$2C_4H_{10 \, (g)} + 13O_{2 \, (g)} \rightarrow 8CO_{2 \, (g)} + 10H_2O_{(l)}$$

Worked Example 2.3iii

10 cm³ of a hydrocarbon was reacted with 70 cm³ of oxygen. The mixture contained 30 cm³ of carbon dioxide and 20 cm³ of oxygen after reaction. Calculate the formula of the hydrocarbon.

(Adapted from CCEA January 2010)

Strategy

- Write a balanced equation for the combustion of a hydrocarbon C_xH_y.
- Use Avogadro's law to relate volumes of gas to moles of gas.
- Deduce x and y from the moles of gas reacted and the moles of gas formed.

Solution

$$C_xH_y + zO_2 \rightarrow xCO_2 + \frac{y}{2}H_2O$$

Moles of CO_2 in 30 cm³ = 3 × Moles of C_xH_y in 10 cm³. x=3 and the formula of the hydrocarbon is C_3H_y.

The hydrocarbon reacts with 50 cm³ of oxygen. Moles of O_2 in 50 cm³ = 5 × Moles of C_xH_y in 10 cm³. z=5 and the equation becomes:

$$C_3H_y + 5O_2 \rightarrow 3CO_2 + \frac{y}{2}H_2O$$

Balancing oxygen in the equation gives y=8. The formula of the hydrocarbon is C_3H_8.

Exercise 2.3G

1. 20 cm³ of a gaseous hydrocarbon reacts with exactly 90 cm³ of oxygen to produce 60 cm³ of carbon dioxide. Calculate the formula of the hydrocarbon. *(CCEA January 2008)*

2. Branched hydrocarbons such as 2,2,4-trimethylpentane, C_8H_{18} burn smoothly in car engines. (a) Draw the structural formula for 2,2,4-trimethylpentane. (b) Write an equation for the complete combustion of 2,2,4-trimethylpentane. *(CCEA January 2002)*

Incomplete Combustion

If a hydrocarbon burns in a limited supply of oxygen, the carbon within the hydrocarbon is instead converted to carbon monoxide (CO) and the process referred to as **incomplete combustion**. The incomplete combustion of alkanes and other hydrocarbons may also produce soot (carbon) as there is not enough oxygen available to react with all of the carbon in the compound.

The **INCOMPLETE** combustion of butane, C_4H_{10}:

$$C_4H_{10\,(g)} + \frac{9}{2}O_{2\,(g)} \rightarrow 4CO_{(g)} + 5H_2O_{(l)}$$

Or

$$2C_4H_{10\,(g)} + 9O_{2\,(g)} \rightarrow 8CO_{(g)} + 10H_2O_{(l)}$$

Exercise 2.3H

1. Write an equation for (a) the complete combustion of pentane and (b) the incomplete combustion of pentane to form carbon monoxide. *(CCEA January 2010)*

2. Write an equation for the incomplete combustion of heptadecane, $C_{17}H_{36}$ to form carbon monoxide. *(CCEA June 2010)*

3. Carbon (soot) can be formed by the incomplete combustion of hydrocarbons. (a) Name two other products formed by the incomplete combustion of hydrocarbons. (b) What causes incomplete combustion to occur?

(CCEA January 2009)

4. Branched-chain alkanes are less likely to cause 'knocking' when a mixture of the alkane and air is ignited in car engines. (a) Write the systematic name for the alkane shown below. (b) The branched-chain alkane is a structural isomer of a straight-chain alkane. Explain the term structural isomer. (c) Write the equation for the incomplete combustion of this alkane. (d) Explain why incomplete combustion produces smoke.

$$H_3C \qquad CH_3$$
$$| \qquad\qquad |$$
$$CH_3CHCH_2CH_2CHCH_3$$

(CCEA June 2005)

Before moving to the next section, check that you are able to:

- Explain the difference between complete and incomplete combustion.
- Recall the products of the complete and incomplete combustion of alkanes.
- Write equations for the complete and incomplete combustion of alkanes.

Air Pollution

The burning of hydrocarbon-based fuels such as gasoline (petrol), diesel and kerosene (jet fuel) releases large quantities of carbon dioxide into the atmosphere. Increasing amounts of carbon dioxide in the atmosphere have been linked to **global warming**; a warming of the earth's atmosphere that occurs as a result of natural processes and human activity. The exhaust fumes produced by motor vehicles also contain significant amounts of carbon monoxide (CO), nitrogen oxides (NO and NO_2), unburnt hydrocarbons and particulate matter that is mostly carbon in the form of soot. Carbon monoxide is very toxic; even brief exposure to elevated levels results in acute breathing difficulties. In the presence of sunlight the nitrogen oxides and hydrocarbons react to produce a hazardous mixture of volatile organic compounds that combine with the particulates to form a thick smoky fog known as **photochemical smog**. Photochemical smog causes short-term breathing difficulties and, with repeated exposure, longer term respiratory problems in humans.

Exercise 2.3I

1. Crude petroleum is a major source of hydrocarbons. Discuss the environmental problems associated with the combustion of hydrocarbons. *(CCEA June 2011)*

The amount of carbon monoxide, nitrogen oxides and hydrocarbons in exhaust emissions can be reduced by passing the exhaust gases through a **catalytic converter**. A catalytic converter contains a 'honeycomb' made of a ceramic material. The inside surfaces of the honeycomb are coated in small particles of metals such as palladium (Pd), rhodium (Rh) and platinum (Pt). When exhaust gases from the engine pass through the ceramic honeycomb they bond to the

Figure 6: (a) A catalytic converter which can be fitted to the exhaust system of a motor vehicle. (b) The honeycomb used to support the metal catalyst in the catalytic converter.

metal particles dispersed on the honeycomb and are transformed into less toxic products. The metal particles act as a **catalyst** by speeding up the reactions involving the exhaust gases without being consumed by the reactions. The honeycomb in a typical catalytic converter is shown in Figure 6.

The metal catalyst in a catalytic converter is known as a three-way catalyst as it catalyses three types of reactions: the oxidation of carbon monoxide, the reduction of nitrogen oxides and the combustion of unburnt hydrocarbons.

The reactions catalysed by a three-way catalyst:

1. The oxidation of carbon monoxide

   $2CO + O_2 \rightarrow 2CO_2$

2. The reduction of nitrogen oxides

   $2NO_x \rightarrow N_2 + xO_2$

3. The combustion of unburnt hydrocarbons

   hydrocarbon + oxygen $\rightarrow$ carbon dioxide + water

Worked Example 2.3iv

Write an equation to show how (a) unburnt heptane, C_7H_{16} is removed, and (b) carbon monoxide reacts with nitrogen(II) oxide to form nitrogen, when vehicle exhaust emissions are passed through a catalytic converter. *(Adapted from CCEA January 2011)*

Solution

(a) Hydrocarbons react to form carbon dioxide and water:

   $C_7H_{16} + 11O_2 \rightarrow 7CO_2 + 8H_2O$

(b) Combining the reactions $2CO + O_2 \rightarrow 2CO_2$ and $2NO \rightarrow N_2 + O_2$ gives:

   $2CO + 2NO \rightarrow 2CO_2 + N_2$

The bonding of the exhaust gases to the metal particles in a catalytic converter is an example of **chemisorption**. The chemisorption and subsequent oxidation of carbon monoxide on the surface of a metal particle is illustrated by the flow scheme in Figure 7. Oxygen atoms from the decomposition of nitrogen oxides are present on the metal surface and react with carbon monoxide. Chemisorption weakens the bonding within the reactants. It also brings the reactants closer together and arranges them in the correct orientation. In this way chemisorption makes it easier for the reaction to occur. Once formed, carbon dioxide desorbs from the surface leaving the metal catalyst unchanged by the reaction.

Worked Example 2.3v

The catalytic converter in a car exhaust system may contain metals such as platinum and palladium. The metals act as heterogeneous catalysts. Explain their catalytic behaviour in terms of chemisorption. *(Adapted from CCEA June 2008)*

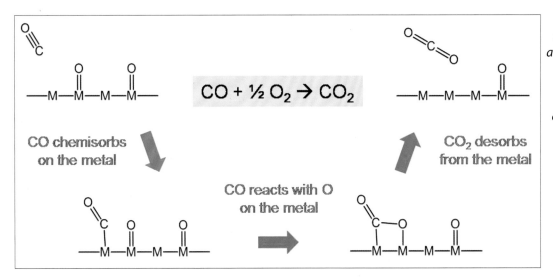

Figure 7: The chemisorption and subsequent oxidation of carbon monoxide to carbon dioxide on the surface of a metal catalyst.

Solution

The molecules in the exhaust gases chemisorb on the surface of the metal. Chemisorption brings the reactants closer together, aligns them in the correct orientation for a reaction to occur, and weakens the bonds within the gases. In this way chemisorption makes it easier for the reaction to occur. Once formed, the products desorb from the surface.

....

The chemisorption of exhaust gases in a catalytic converter is also an example of **heterogeneous catalysis**; a term that describes a reaction in which the catalyst is in a different physical state than the reactants. The ceramic honeycomb greatly increases the efficiency of the metal catalyst by creating a larger surface over which the exhaust gases can come into contact with the metal catalyst. The efficiency of the metal catalyst is further improved by using **finely divided metals** consisting of small particles with a large surface area on which the reacting gases can chemisorb and react.

The efficiency of the catalytic converter can be maintained if the catalytic converter is used in conjunction with unleaded fuels. A catalytic converter cannot be used with leaded fuels as the lead in additives such as tetraethyllead, $Pb(C_2H_5)_4$ bonds to the metal particles and 'poisons' the catalyst by preventing exhaust gases from bonding to the metal particles.

Exercise 2.3J

1. What is formed when (a) carbon monoxide (b) unburnt hydrocarbons and (c) nitrogen oxides are passed through a catalytic converter?

   (CCEA January 2010)

2. The reactions that occur in a catalytic converter are examples of heterogeneous catalysis involving chemisorption. (a) Explain the term chemisorption. (b) Explain why the ceramic support in a catalytic converter has a 'honeycomb' structure. *(CCEA June 2005)*

3. A catalytic converter contains a ceramic honeycomb structure coated in finely divided metals. (a) Suggest why the metals are finely divided. (b) Explain how chemisorption takes place on the surface of the metals and leads to a reaction. (c) Explain why lead-free petrol must be used with a catalytic converter.

   (CCEA January 2009)

4. (a) Write the equation for the reaction between CO and NO in a catalytic converter. (b) Name one metal used in catalytic converters. (c) Suggest why the metal particles in a catalytic converter are spread very thinly on a ceramic support. (d) Why are the reactions in a catalytic converter described as examples of heterogeneous catalysis?

   (CCEA January 2008)

Before moving to the next section, check that you are able to:

- Recall the environmental problems associated with the combustion of hydrocarbon-based fuels in motor vehicles.
- Explain how a catalytic converter can be used to reduce environmental pollution resulting from the burning of hydrocarbon-based fuels in motor vehicles.

- Describe the role of chemisorption in the reactions that occur in a catalytic converter and why the catalysis is an example of heterogeneous catalysis.
- Explain why the efficiency of a catalytic converter is increased by the use of a honeycomb coated in finely divided metals, and decreased by the use of leaded fuels.

Halogenation of Alkanes

In this section we are learning to:

- Describe the mechanism for the free radical substitution of methane and explain the role of ultraviolet light in the reaction.

Alkanes are generally unreactive and will only react when they come into contact with very reactive substances. A **free radical** is an atom, molecule or ion with one or more unpaired electrons. Free radicals are very reactive and will react with alkanes. When a halogen molecule absorbs ultraviolet (UV) light, the energy provided by the UV light breaks the covalent bond in the halogen molecule and produces two halogen atoms, each with one unpaired electron in its outer shell.

$$Cl_2 \text{ (g)} \rightarrow 2Cl\bullet \text{ (g)}$$

Homolytic fission of the Cl-Cl bond

$$Br_2 \text{ (g)} \rightarrow 2Br\bullet \text{ (g)}$$

Homolytic fission of the Br-Br bond

The formulas for the halogen atoms are written Cl• and Br• to indicate that they are free radicals with an unpaired electron (•) in their outer shell. This reaction is an example of **homolytic fission** in which the atoms forming the bond each receive one of the electrons shared in the bond when the bond breaks.

When a mixture of methane, CH_4 and chlorine, Cl_2 is exposed to UV light, chlorine radicals formed by the homolytic fission of the Cl-Cl bond in chlorine react with methane to form chlorinated hydrocarbons such as chloromethane, CH_3Cl.

$$CH_4 \text{ (g)} + Cl_2 \text{ (g)} \rightarrow CH_3Cl \text{ (g)} + HCl \text{ (g)}$$

Smaller amounts of more substituted hydrocarbons such as dichloromethane, CH_2Cl_2 and trichloromethane, $CHCl_3$ are also formed in the reaction.

$$CH_3Cl \text{ (g)} + Cl_2 \text{ (g)} \rightarrow CH_2Cl_2 \text{ (g)} + HCl \text{ (g)}$$

$$CH_2Cl_2 \text{ (g)} + Cl_2 \text{ (g)} \rightarrow CHCl_3 \text{ (g)} + HCl \text{ (g)}$$

The chlorination of methane is an example of a **photochemical reaction** as the reaction only occurs when light is absorbed by one or more of the reactants. The light provides the energy needed for the reaction to occur and is consumed by the reaction. As a result, light cannot be considered a catalyst for the reaction as a catalyst would speed up the reaction without being consumed by the reaction.

The photochemical chlorination of methane is also an example of a **chain reaction**. Chain reactions occur in three stages: initiation, propagation and termination. When the reactions occurring at each stage are combined the resulting scheme is known as the **reaction mechanism**.

Mechanism for the photochemical chlorination of methane:

INITIATION

$$Cl_2 \text{ (g)} \rightarrow 2Cl\bullet \text{ (g)}$$

Chlorine molecules absorb UV light and undergo homolytic fission to produce chlorine radicals.

PROPAGATION

$$CH_4 \text{ (g)} + Cl\bullet \text{ (g)} \rightarrow CH_3\bullet \text{ (g)} + HCl \text{ (g)}$$

Chlorine radicals abstract hydrogen from methane to form hydrogen chloride (HCl).

$$CH_3\bullet \text{ (g)} + Cl_2 \text{ (g)} \rightarrow CH_3Cl \text{ (g)} + Cl\bullet \text{ (g)}$$

A methyl radical ($CH_3\bullet$) then abstracts a chlorine atom from a chlorine molecule (Cl_2) to form chloromethane. The chlorine radical ($Cl\bullet$) produced in this step can then 'propagate' the reaction by reacting with another molecule of methane.

TERMINATION

$$2CH_3\bullet \text{ (g)} \rightarrow C_2H_6 \text{ (g)}$$

$$2Cl\bullet \text{ (g)} \rightarrow Cl_2 \text{ (g)}$$

$$CH_3\bullet \text{ (g)} + Cl\bullet \text{ (g)} \rightarrow CH_3Cl \text{ (g)}$$

The termination reactions slow the reaction by removing the methyl and chlorine radicals needed for propagation.

Bromine (Br_2) reacts with alkanes in the same way as chlorine to produce brominated alkanes such as bromomethane, CH_3Br and dibromomethane, CH_2Br_2. The photochemical halogenation of an alkane is an example of a **substitution reaction** as it involves the replacement or 'substitution' of atoms in the alkane by halogen atoms. It is also an example of free radical substitution as the reaction is propagated by free radicals.

Talking Point

Halogen radicals are produced when chlorofluorocarbons (CFCs) such as freon-11, CCl_3F and freon-12, CCl_2F_2 are exposed to UV radiation from the sun in the upper atmosphere. The halogen radicals react with ozone, O_3 reducing the levels of ozone in the upper atmosphere, and increasing levels of UV radiation at the earth's surface. The reaction is an example of a photochemical chain reaction with one halogen radical destroying thousands of ozone molecules.

$$Cl\bullet + O_3 \rightarrow ClO\bullet + O_2$$

$$ClO\bullet + O_3 \rightarrow Cl\bullet + 2O_2$$

Exercise 2.3K

1. The chlorination of methane in sunlight occurs by a free radical mechanism. (a) Explain what is meant by the term free radical. (b) Write the equation for the formation of chloromethane from chlorine and methane. (c) Write equations for (i) the initiation step, (ii) both propagation steps and (iii) one possible termination step.

   (CCEA June 2008)

2. (a) Explain how chlorine radicals, $Cl\bullet$ are formed in the free radical substitution reaction that occurs between methane and chlorine. (b) Methyl radicals, $\bullet CH_3$ are formed during the propagation step. Draw a dot-cross diagram for a methyl radical using only the outer electrons on each atom. *(Adapted from CCEA January 2002)*

3. Which one of the following substances is **not** formed when methane reacts with chlorine in the presence of ultraviolet light?

   (a) dichloromethane   (b) ethane

   (c) hydrogen   (d) hydrogen chloride

   (CCEA June 2010)

4. Light is sometimes wrongly regarded as a catalyst in the chlorination of methane. Using an appropriate definition of a catalyst, explain why light cannot be considered a catalyst for this reaction. *(Adapted from CCEA January 2007)*

Before moving to the next section, check that you are able to:

- Explain how homolytic fission results in the formation of free radicals.

- Recall the mechanism for the reaction between chlorine and methane, and explain the role of UV light in the reaction.

2.4 Hydrocarbons: Alkenes

CONNECTIONS

- Hydrocarbons containing one or more C=C bonds can combine to form the long chain molecules found in plastics such as polythene and polystyrene.
- Fats and oils containing two or more C=C bonds are known as polyunsaturates and are an essential part of our diet.

Structure and Properties

In this section we are learning to:

- Recognise the alkenes as a homologous series of hydrocarbons.
- Explain the properties of the alkenes in terms of the nonpolar nature of the bonding within alkene molecules.
- Recall that alkenes are obtained by cracking hydrocarbons and write equations for the cracking of hydrocarbons to form alkenes.
- Use structural and condensed formulas to represent the structure of alkenes.
- Recognise and draw structural isomers of alkenes.
- Use systematic (IUPAC) rules to name alkenes.

The alkenes are a homologous series of hydrocarbons with the general formula C_nH_{2n}. The molecular formulas for the members of the series are obtained by setting n = 2, 3, 4 ... in the general formula. The structural formulas in Figure 1 reveal that alkenes are **unsaturated hydrocarbons** as they contain one or more multiple bonds between carbon atoms (C=C or C≡C). The structures of the isomers but-1-ene and but-2-ene in Figure 1 also demonstrate how a C=C bond can give rise to structural isomers.

The bond dipoles associated with the C-H bonds in alkenes are very small. As a result, alkenes do not have a significant permanent dipole and experience only van der Waals attraction between molecules. The strength of the van der Waals attraction between molecules increases as the number of electrons in the molecule increases, and explains why the lighter alkenes (small n) are gases while the heavier alkanes (large n) are solids.

Exercise 2.4A

Which one of the following hydrocarbons contains a double bond?

(a) CH_4 (b) C_2H_2 (c) C_2H_4 (d) C_2H_6

(CCEA June 2009)

Sources of Alkenes

Alkenes are formed by the thermal cracking of larger hydrocarbons. When a hydrocarbon is heated it decomposes to form a mixture of products that may include smaller alkanes and one or more alkenes. If the hydrocarbon is heated in the presence of a catalyst the process is known as catalytic cracking and can be operated at a much lower temperature.

Worked Example 2.4i

Write an equation for the thermal cracking of heptadecane, $C_{17}H_{36}$ in which ethene and propene are produced in a 2:1 ratio and one other product is formed. *(CCEA June 2010)*

Solution

Both of the following equations have the required ratio of alkenes and one additional product. Either can

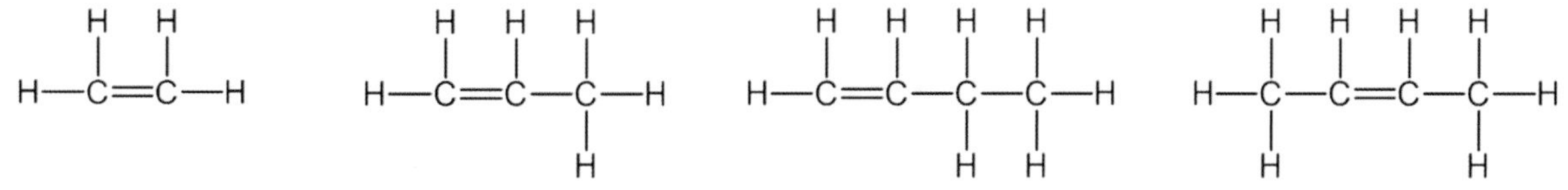

Ethene (n=2) Formula: C_2H_4 | Propene (n=3) Formula: C_3H_6 | But-1-ene (n=4) Formula: C_4H_8 | But-2-ene (n=4) Formula: C_4H_8

Figure 1: (a) Structural formulas for ethene, C_2H_4 (n = 2) and propene, C_3H_6 (n = 3). (b) The structural isomers of butene, C_4H_8 (n = 4).

be used as the correct answer to the question.

$$C_{17}H_{36} \rightarrow 2C_2H_4 + C_3H_6 + C_{10}H_{22}$$

or

$$C_{17}H_{36} \rightarrow 4C_2H_4 + 2C_3H_6 + C_3H_8$$

Exercise 2.4B

1. (a) What name is given to the process of forming alkenes from alkanes? (b) State one condition necessary for this process. (c) Write an equation for the formation of propene from octane, C_8H_{18}. *(CCEA January 2011)*

2. Alkenes can be made from alkanes with high relative molecular masses. Write an equation for the formation of ethene from dodecane, $C_{12}H_{26}$.

   (CCEA June 2008)

3. Hydrocarbons in the range C_{15}–C_{19} can be cracked by strong heating. Write an equation for the cracking of $C_{16}H_{34}$ to produce ethene and propene in the ratio 2:1 and only one other compound. *(CCEA January 2007)*

Naming Alkenes

Alkenes are named according to the parent (straight-chain) alkene on which their structure is based. The names of the parent alkenes consist of a prefix to indicate the number of carbon atoms in the molecule, and the suffix *ene* to indicate that the compound is an alkene. The prefixes used to name straight-chain (parent) alkenes with up to six carbons are given in Table 1.

According to the classification in Table 1, the structural isomers pent-1-ene and pent-2-ene (shown below) are both pentenes as they are based on a chain of five carbon atoms that also contains the C=C bond. In pent-1-ene the number prefix *1-* is used to indicate that the C=C bond is between the first pair of carbon atoms ($C_1=C_2$). Similarly, in pent-2-ene the number prefix *2-* is used to locate the C=C bond between the second pair of carbon atoms ($C_2=C_3$). In both cases the position of the C=C bond is described by numbering the carbon atoms in a way that produces the lowest number prefixes.

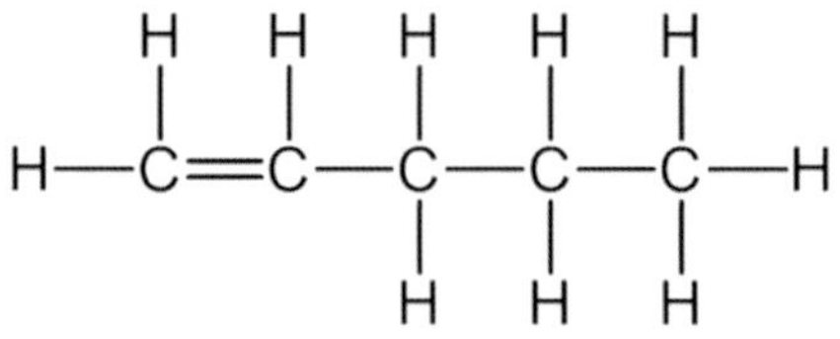

pent-1-ene   CH$_2$=CHCH$_2$CH$_2$CH$_3$

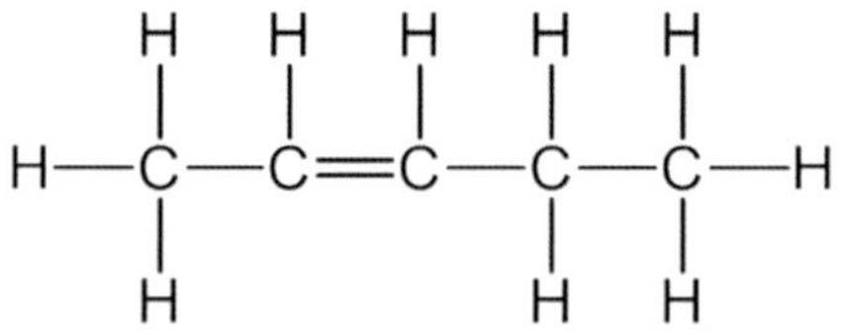

pent-2-ene   CH$_3$CH=CHCH$_2$CH$_3$

The alkenes 2-methylbut-1-ene and 2-methylbut-2-ene are structural isomers of pent-1-ene and pent-2-ene. Both are methylbutenes as they are based on a chain of four carbon atoms that

Table 1: Naming prefixes for alkenes based on a chain of up to six carbon atoms.

Carbon atoms in longest chain	Naming prefix	Parent alk**ene**	Structural isomers of parent alkene
2	eth-	eth**ene**	CH$_2$=CH$_2$
3	prop-	prop**ene**	CH$_2$=CHCH$_3$
4	but-	but**ene**	CH$_2$=CHCH$_2$CH$_3$ CH$_3$CH=CHCH$_3$
5	pent-	pent**ene**	CH$_2$=CHCH$_2$CH$_2$CH$_3$ CH$_3$CH=CHCH$_2$CH$_3$
6	hex-	hex**ene**	CH$_2$=CHCH$_2$CH$_2$CH$_2$CH$_3$ CH$_3$CH=CHCH$_2$CH$_2$CH$_3$ CH$_3$CH$_2$CH=CHCH$_2$CH$_3$

also contains the C=C bond. As in pent-1-ene and pent-2-ene, the suffix *1-ene* or *2-ene* is used to locate the C=C bond within the carbon chain. With the location of the C=C bond established, the same numbering of the carbon chain is used to locate the methyl group on the second carbon atom.

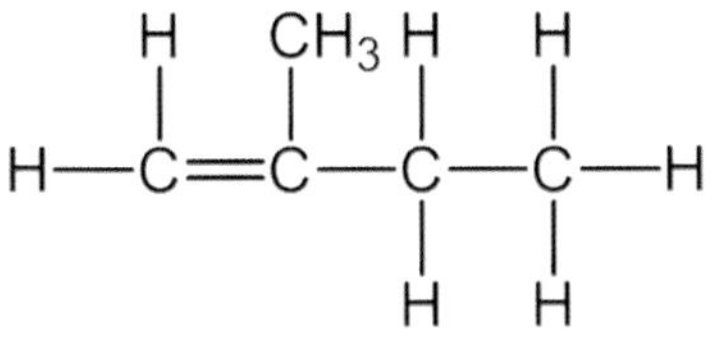

2-methylbut-1-ene $CH_2=C(CH_3)CH_2CH_3$

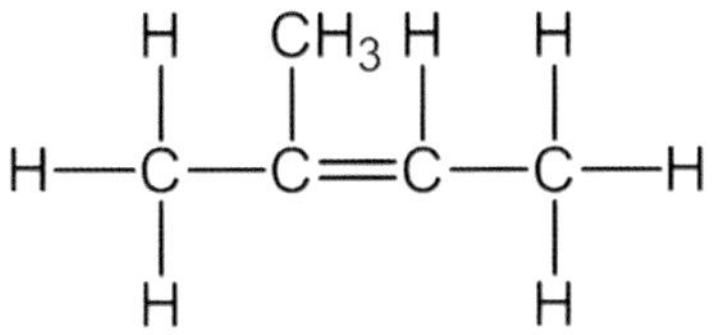

2-methylbut-2-ene $CH_3C(CH_3)=CHCH_3$

Dienes

Alkenes containing two C=C bonds are known as **dienes** and are named using the suffix *diene*. The compound penta-1,4-diene is an example of a diene. It is considered a pentadiene as it is based on a chain of five carbon atoms that contains two C=C bonds. The suffix *1,4-diene* is used to locate the C=C bonds between the first and fourth pairs of carbon atoms in the chain. Similarly, the compound 2-methylbuta-1,3-diene is considered a butadiene as it is based on a chain of four carbon atoms (*buta*) that also contains two C=C bonds (*diene*). The suffix *1,3-diene* is used to locate the C=C bonds between the first and third pairs of carbon atoms in the chain.

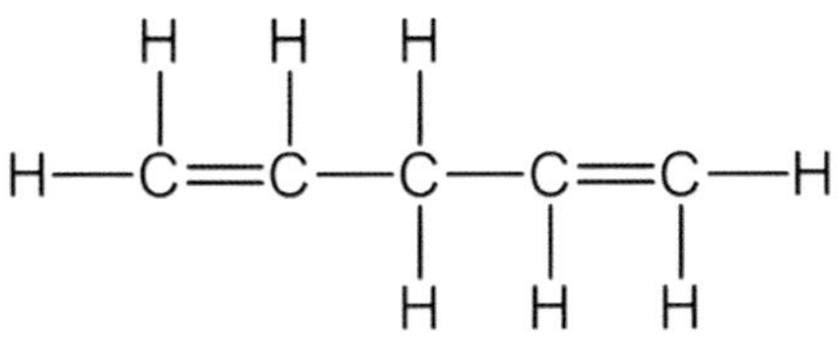

penta-1,4-diene $CH_2=CHCH_2CH=CH_2$

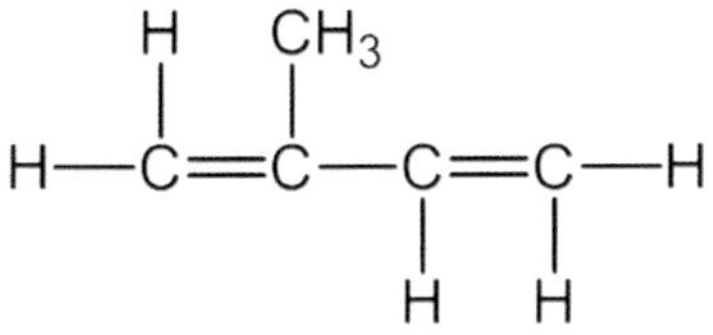

2-methylbuta-1,3-diene $CH_2=C(CH_3)CH=CH_2$

Rules for naming alkenes (including dienes):

- The name of an alkene consists of a prefix followed by the suffix *ene* or *diene*. The prefix is determined by the number of carbon atoms in the longest carbon chain that also contains the C=C bond(s).

- The location of each C=C bond is described by adding a number prefix before the suffix. The number prefix is based on a numbering of the carbon atoms that produces the smallest number prefixes.

- Additional prefixes are then added to describe the type and location of functional groups on the carbon chain. The prefixes are given in alphabetical order and are based on the numbering of carbons used to locate the C=C bond(s).

Exercise 2.4C

1. The systematic name for the alkene is

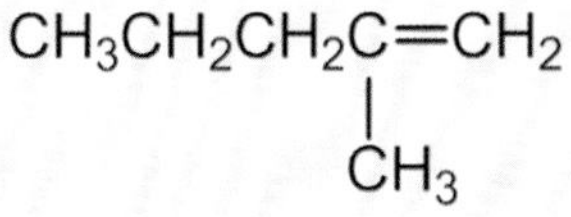

$$CH_3CH_2CH_2C=CH_2$$
$$|$$
$$CH_3$$

   (a) 2-propylprop-1-ene.
   (b) 2-methylpent-1-ene.
   (c) 2,4-dimethylbut-1-ene.
   (d) 2-methylhex-1-ene.

   (CCEA June 2003)

2. The IUPAC name for the alkene is

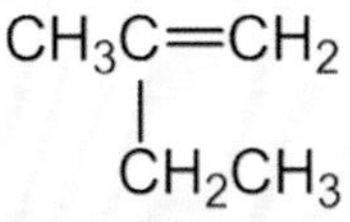

$$CH_3C=CH_2$$
$$|$$
$$CH_2CH_3$$

   (a) 1,2-dimethylpropene.
   (b) 2-ethylpropene.
   (c) 2-methylbut-1-ene.
   (d) 1-ethyl-1-methylethene.

   (CCEA January 2003)

Before moving to the next section, check that you are able to:

- Recall the general formula for an alkene and use the general formula to generate molecular formulas for alkenes.

- Explain how molecular size affects the boiling point of alkenes.
- Write equations for the cracking of hydrocarbons to form alkenes.
- Draw structural formulas and write condensed formulas for alkenes.
- Recognise and draw structural isomers of alkenes.
- Deduce systematic names for alkenes (including dienes).

The C=C Functional Group

In this section we are learning to:

- Describe the electronic structure of C-C and C=C bonds, and explain the properties of C-C and C=C bonds in terms of their electronic structure.
- Explain why a C=C bond gives rise to geometric isomers.
- Draw geometric isomers for alkenes and use both cis-trans and E-Z notation to distinguish between geometric isomers.

Properties of the C=C bond

In ethene, $CH_2=CH_2$, the repulsion between the electrons in the C-H and C=C bonds is minimised when the atoms around each carbon atom are directed towards the corners of a triangle in a trigonal planar arrangement. The structural formulas used to represent the trigonal planar arrangement of atoms about each carbon in ethene are shown in Figure 2.

A C=C bond is formed when a pair of carbon atoms share two pairs of electrons. One bonding pair results from the head-on overlap of p-orbitals to form a

sigma (σ) bond. When the p-orbitals overlap, the electron in each p-orbital combines to form a shared pair of electrons that occupies the region of space between the carbon atoms where the p-orbitals overlap.

head-on overlap of p-orbitals   C-C σ-bond

The second pair of electrons in the C=C bond results from the side-on overlap of p-orbitals on the carbon atoms to form a **pi (π) bond**. The electrons in the overlapping p-orbitals again pair-up to form a shared pair that occupies the space above and below the C-C σ-bond where the p-orbitals forming the π-bond overlap.

side-on overlap of p-orbitals   C-C π-bond

Worked Example 2.4ii

A C=C bond contains a σ (sigma) bond and a π (pi) bond. Draw a labelled diagram to show the formation of (a) a σ-bond and (b) a π-bond from p orbitals.

(Adapted from CCEA June 2003)

Solution

(a)

two p-orbitals   σ-bond

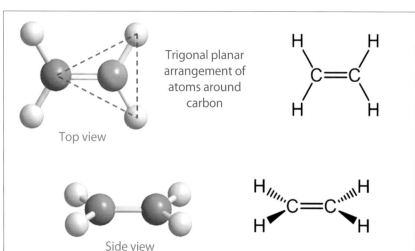

Trigonal planar arrangement of atoms around carbon

Top view

Side view

Figure 2: The structural formulas used to represent the arrangement of the atoms about each carbon in ethene, $CH_2=CH_2$. Solid and dashed wedges are used to indicate bonds coming out of the page (solid wedge) and going behind the page (dashed wedge).

(b)

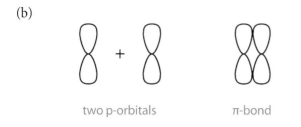

two p-orbitals   π-bond

Exercise 2.4D

Ethene, C_2H_4 contains

(a) 4 sigma (σ) and 2 pi (π) bonds.

(b) 5 sigma (σ) and 1 pi (π) bonds.

(c) 2 sigma (σ) and 4 pi (π) bonds.

(d) 1 sigma (σ) and 5 pi (π) bonds.

(CCEA January 2008)

A single bond between two carbon atoms (C-C) is a σ-bond. The additional bonds in a C=C bond or C≡C bond are π-bonds. The combination of σ and π-bonds in a C=C bond results in the carbon atoms being held more tightly in the bond than the carbon atoms in a C-C (σ) bond. As a result, a C=C bond has a shorter bond length than a C-C bond where the term **bond length** refers to the distance between the nuclei of the atoms forming the bond.

The electrons in a σ-bond behave differently than the electrons in a π-bond. The electrons in a σ-bond are closer to the nuclei of the atoms forming the bond. As a result they are held more tightly in the bond making a σ-bond more difficult to break than a π-bond. The strength of a C-C σ-bond or C-C π-bond can be estimated by considering the amount of energy needed to break the C-C and C=C bonds found in typical organic compounds. On average, C-C (σ) bonds have a bond energy of around 350 kJ mol⁻¹ where the term **bond energy** refers to the amount of energy needed to break one mole of bonds. The strength of a C-C π-bond can be estimated by subtracting the bond energy for a C-C (σ) bond (350 kJ mol⁻¹) from the bond energy for a C=C (σ+π) bond (590 kJ mol⁻¹). By this calculation the bond energy for a C-C π-bond is approximately 590 – 350 = 240 kJ mol⁻¹. In this way we see that while a C=C (σ+π) bond is significantly stronger than a C-C (σ) bond, the π-bond within the C=C bond (240 kJ mol⁻¹) is weaker than a C-C (σ) bond (350 kJ mol⁻¹). As a result, the π-bond within the C=C

bond will break under more moderate reaction conditions than a C-C (σ) bond, making alkenes considerably more reactive than alkanes. The exposed nature of the electrons in the C-C π-bond also makes the π-bond a region of high electron density that is vulnerable to attack by atoms, molecules or ions seeking electrons to bond with.

Exercise 2.4E

The bond length and bond energy for the carbon-carbon bonds in ethane and ethene are compared in the following table. (a) Explain the difference in bond length and bond energy in terms of sigma (σ) and pi (π) bonding. (b) Explain why ethene is more reactive despite its bond energy being greater.

	Ethane	Ethene
Bond length /nm	0.154	0.134
Bond energy /kJ mol⁻¹	346	598

(CCEA June 2008)

Before moving to the next section, check that you are able to:

- Describe with the aid of diagrams how the overlap of orbitals results in the formation of C-C σ-bonds and C-C π-bonds.

- Explain the relative strength and length of C-C and C=C bonds in terms of the formation of σ- and π-bonds.

Geometric Isomers

The electrons in a C-C (σ) bond are not disturbed when the molecule rotates about the bond. This makes it possible for molecules to rotate freely about each of the σ-bonds in the molecule. In contrast, rotating the molecule about a C=C bond involves breaking the π-bond and results in molecules being unable to rotate about a C=C bond unless the bond is being broken as part of a reaction. Molecules with the same structural formula, but different arrangements of atoms due to one or more C=C bonds, are referred to as **geometric isomers**. The compound but-2-ene has two geometric isomers: *cis*-but-2-ene and *trans*-but-2-ene. The prefix *cis*- or *trans*- is used to indicate that the methyl groups are on the same side (*cis*-) or opposite sides (*trans*-) of the C=C bond.

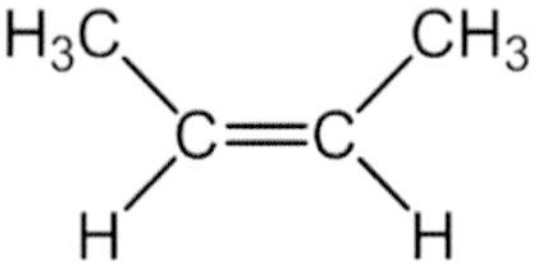

cis-but-2-ene 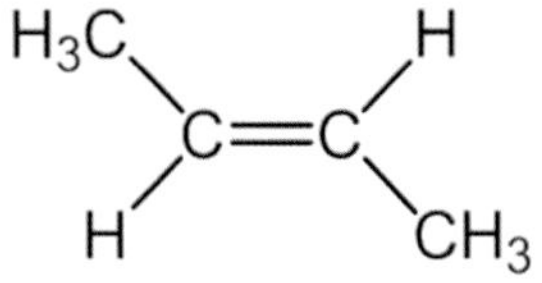   trans-but-2-ene

Worked Example 2.4iii

Cinnamyl alcohol exhibits *cis-trans* isomerism. (a) Draw the structure of each isomer. (b) Explain why cinnamyl alcohol exhibits *cis-trans* isomerism.

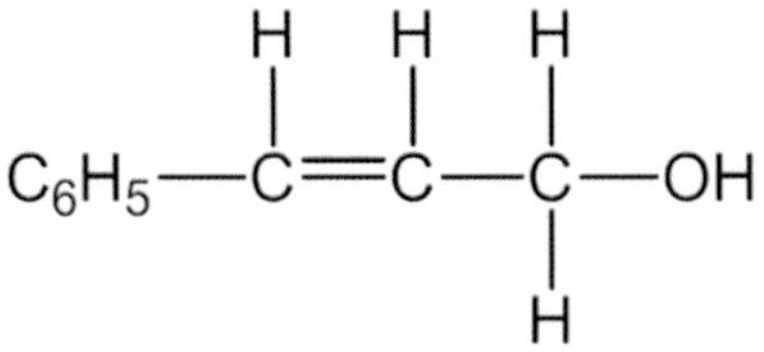

(CCEA January 2003)

Solution

(a)

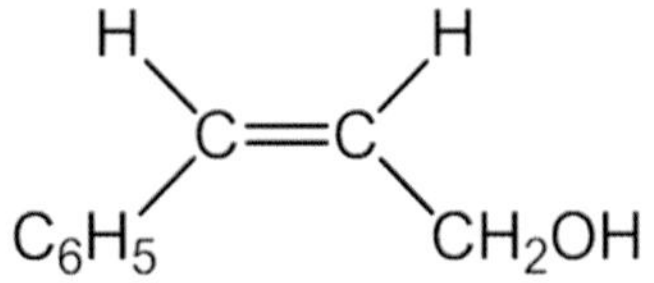

cis isomer

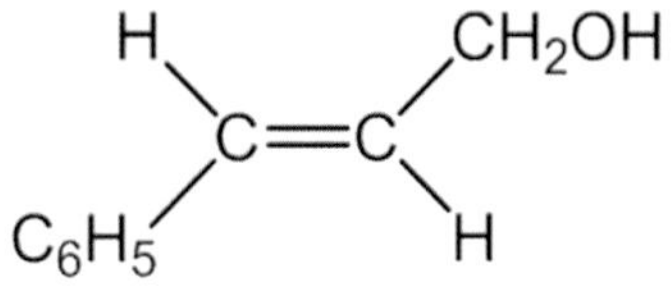

trans isomer

(b) The molecule cannot rotate about the C=C bond.

....

If the groups attached at one end of the C=C bond are the same the C=C bond will not be able to generate geometric (*cis-trans*) isomers. For example, the C=C bond in 2-methylbut-2-ene is unable to generate geometric isomers as two methyl groups are attached to the same end of the C=C bond.

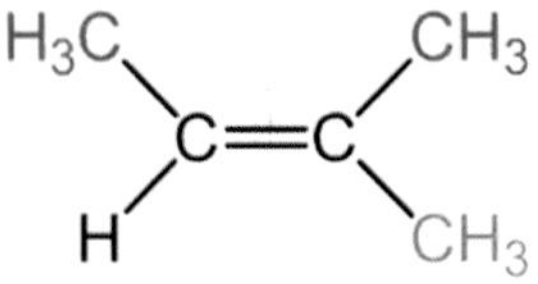

2-methylbut-2-ene 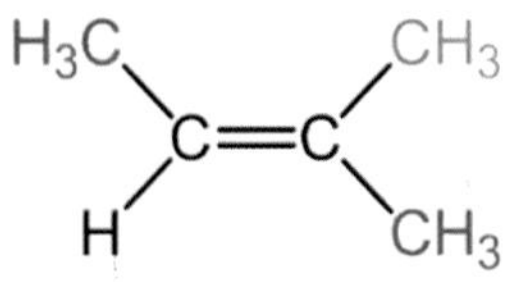   switching the groups produces the same structural isomer

Exercise 2.4F

1. Which one of the following exists as *cis-trans* isomers?

    (a) $CH_2=CHCH(CH_3)CH_3$

    (b) $CH_2=CHCH_2CH_2CH_3$

    (c) $CH_3CH=CHCH_2CH_3$

    (d) $CH_3C(CH_3)=CHCH_3$

    (CCEA January 2011)

2. Which one of the following molecules exists as *cis-trans* isomers?

    (a) $(CH_3)_2C=C(CH_3)_2$

    (b) $CH_3CH_2CH=CHCH_2CH_3$

    (c) $CH_3CH_2CH=C(CH_3)_2$

    (d) $(CH_3)_2CHCH_2CH=CH_2$

    (CCEA June 2008)

3. (a) Draw the structure of a branched alkene C_6H_{12} which exhibits geometric isomerism. (b) Name the alkene. (c) Draw the geometric isomers of the alkene.

    (CCEA June 2010)

E-Z Notation

The prefixes *cis-* and *trans-* can be used to distinguish geometric isomers when the same type of group is attached at both ends of a C=C bond. In the case of 3-methylpent-2-ene the prefixes *cis-* and *trans-* describe the relative positioning of the methyl groups about the C=C bond.

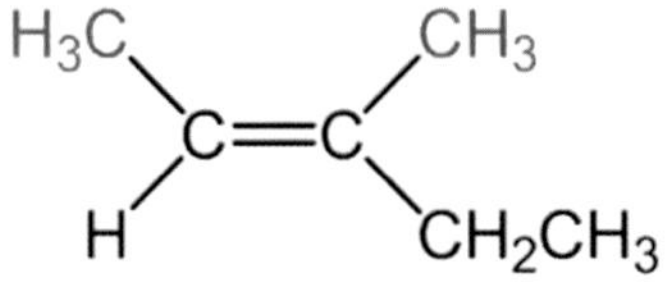

cis-3-methylpent-2-ene

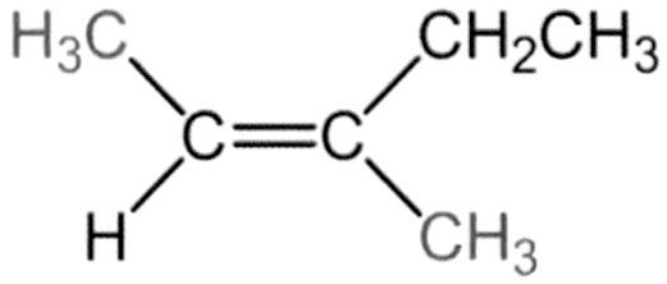

trans-3-methylpent-2-ene

In cases where the same type of group is not attached at either end of the C=C bond, the prefixes *cis-* and *trans-* can no longer be used, and we must use the Cahn-Ingold-Prelog rules to distinguish between the geometric isomers by assigning the prefixes *E-* and *Z-*

to the isomers. The first step in assigning the prefix *E*- or *Z*- is to identify which of the two groups attached at either end of the C=C bond will be used to describe the positioning of the groups about the C=C bond in the isomer. This is accomplished by assigning one of the groups attached to each end of the C=C bond a high priority and the other group a low priority. If the high priority groups are located on the same side of the C=C bond the isomer is assigned the prefix *Z*- and if the high priority groups are on opposite sides of the C=C bond the isomer is assigned the prefix *E*-. The relationship between high priority groups in *E-Z* isomers is effectively illustrated by the case of 3-methylpent-2-ene.

H3C⟍   ⟋CH3
    C=C
H⟋   ⟍CH2CH3

E-3-methylpent-2-ene

H3C⟍   ⟋CH2CH3
    C=C
H⟋   ⟍CH3

Z-3-methylpent-2-ene

In order to assign high and low priority to the groups attached at either end of the C=C bond it is necessary to determine that methyl (-CH$_3$) has a higher priority than hydrogen (-H) and that ethyl (-CH$_2$CH$_3$) has a higher priority than methyl.

The relative priority of the methyl and hydrogen groups can be determined by considering the atomic number of the atoms attached to the C=C bond. The methyl group is attached to the C=C bond via a carbon atom (C) and the hydrogen group is attached to the C=C bond via a hydrogen atom (H). The atomic number of carbon is greater than the atomic number of hydrogen and, as a result, the methyl group is assigned a higher priority than the hydrogen group.

H
|
H—C—C═   H—C═
|
H

methyl, -CH$_3$ hydrogen, -H

The ethyl and methyl groups attached at the other end of the C=C bond are both connected to the C=C

bond via a carbon atom and, as a result, cannot be distinguished by the type of atom connected to the C=C bond. In cases such as this it becomes necessary to compare the types of atoms further from the C=C bond. In an ethyl group (-CH$_2$CH$_3$) the carbon attached to the C=C bond is bonded to two hydrogen atoms and one carbon atom. In contrast, the carbon atom in a methyl group (-CH$_3$) is bonded to three hydrogen atoms. The combination of two hydrogen atoms and a carbon atom is used to assign a higher priority to the ethyl group as the carbon atom (C) has a greater atomic number than the hydrogen atom in the corresponding position within the methyl group (H).

H H   H
| | |
═C—C—C—H   ═C—C—H
| | |
H H   H

ethyl, -CH$_2$CH$_3$ methyl, -CH$_3$

Worked Example 2.4iv

Draw and label the structural (E-Z) isomers for the compound CH$_3$CH=C(OH)CH$_3$.

Solution

On the left end of the C=C bond -CH$_3$ has a higher priority than -H as carbon (C) has a higher atomic number than hydrogen (H).

On the right end of the C=C bond -CH$_3$ has a lower priority than -OH as oxygen (O) has a higher atomic number than carbon (C).

H3C⟍   ⟋CH3   H3C⟍   ⟋OH
    C=C   C=C
H⟋   ⟍OH   H⟋   ⟍CH3

E isomer   Z isomer
(high priority on opposite sides)

Exercise 2.4G

1. Draw and label the structural (E-Z) isomers for the compound CH$_3$CCl=CHCH$_3$.

2. Draw and label the structural (E-Z) isomers for the compound CH$_3$CH=CHCH$_2$OH.

3. Draw and label the structural (E-Z) isomers for the compound CHCl=C(CH$_3$)CH$_2$OH.

Before moving to the next section, check that you are able to:

- Recall how the presence of one or more C=C bonds in a molecule can result in geometric isomers.
- Draw structural formulas to represent geometric isomers and use *cis-trans* and *E-Z* notation to identify geometric isomers.

Reactions of Alkenes

In this section we are learning to:

- Use structural formulas to describe the addition of hydrogen, halogens and hydrogen halides across a C=C bond.
- Recall the conditions used to hydrogenate alkenes and the use of hydrogenation to harden polyunsaturated oils.
- Describe the use of bromine water to test for the presence of C=C bonds in a molecule.

Hydrogenation

When a mixture of an alkene and hydrogen gas is heated in the presence of a catalyst hydrogen molecules 'add across' the C=C bonds in the alkene to form the corresponding alkane. For example, when a mixture of propene, $CH_3CH=CH_2$ and hydrogen is heated, a molecule of hydrogen gas (H_2) adds across the C=C bond to form propane, $CH_3CH_2CH_3$. In the process the pair of electrons in the H-H bond and the pair of electrons in the C-C π-bond are used to form two new C-H bonds. The C-C σ-bond within the C=C bond is not involved in the reaction.

propene $CH_3CH=CH_2$

propane $CH_3CH_2CH_3$

The addition of a hydrogen molecule (H_2) across a C=C bond is referred to as **hydrogenation** and is an example of an **addition reaction** as the product results from the addition of a molecule across a C=C bond. In the food industry hydrogenation is used to convert polyunsaturated vegetable oils containing several C=C bonds into the harder saturated fats and oils used in margarine. The hydrogenation of unsaturated oils and other alkenes is catalysed by finely divided nickel and is an example of heterogeneous catalysis as the catalyst (solid) is in a different physical phase than the reactants (liquid or gas).

Worked Example 2.4v

The Smoky Mountains in the United States are enveloped by a blue haze which contains simple gaseous hydrocarbons emitted by trees and plants. One such hydrocarbon is isoprene.

(a) Write an equation for the hydrogenation of isoprene and name the product.

(b) Name the catalyst used.

isoprene

(CCEA June 2007)

Solution

(a) $C_5H_8 + 2H_2 \rightarrow C_5H_{12}$

The product is methylbutane:
$CH_3CH(CH_3)CH_2CH_3$.

(b) Finely divided nickel.

Exercise 2.4H

1. (a) Draw the structure for penta-1,4-diene.
   (b) Write an equation for the conversion of penta-1,4-diene to pentane. (c) State the catalyst used. *(CCEA June 2006)*

2. (a) Write an equation for the hydrogenation of cinnamyl alcohol. (b) Suggest a suitable catalyst for the reaction.

   $C_6H_5CH=CHCH_2OH + H_2 \rightarrow$

   (Adapted from CCEA January 2003)

Before moving to the next section, check that you are able to:

* Use structural formulas and equations to describe the addition of hydrogen across a C=C bond.
* Recall the conditions used for the hydrogenation of alkenes and the use of hydrogenation to harden polyunsaturated oils.

Addition of Halogens

Halogens such as chlorine (Cl_2) and bromine (Br_2) will add across a C=C bond to form a halogenated alkane. When bromine adds to propene, $CH_3CH=CH_2$ the pair of electrons in the Br-Br bond and the pair of electrons in the C-C π-bond are used to form two new C-Br bonds in the product.

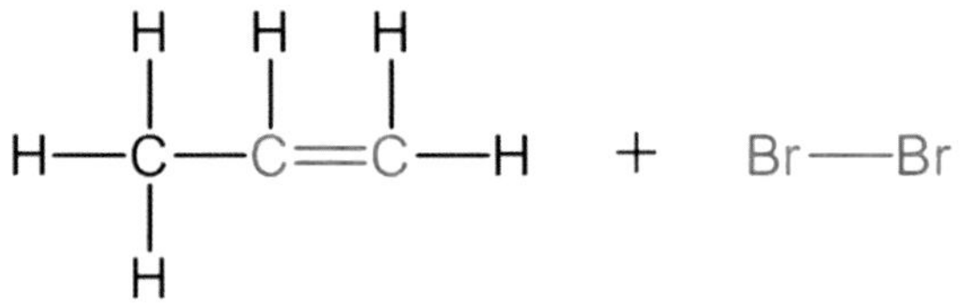

propene $CH_3CH=CH_2$

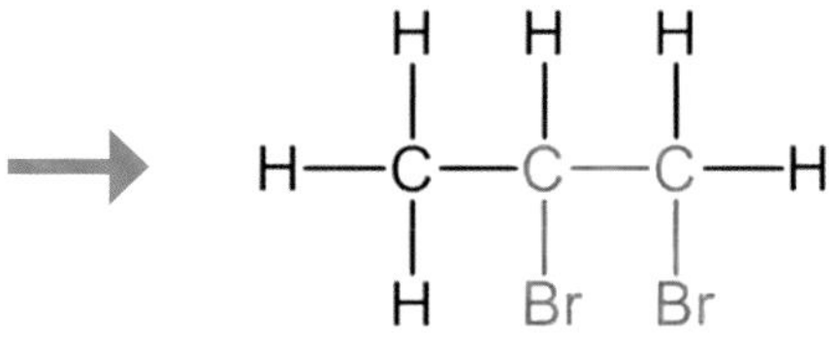

1,2-dibromopropane $CH_3CHBrCH_2Br$

The addition of bromine to a C=C bond can be used to test for the presence of one or more C=C bonds in a molecule. When a molecule containing one or more C=C bonds is reacted with bromine water, $Br_{2\ (aq)}$ the orange colour of the bromine water is replaced by a colourless solution containing the product of the addition reaction.

Worked Example 2.4vi

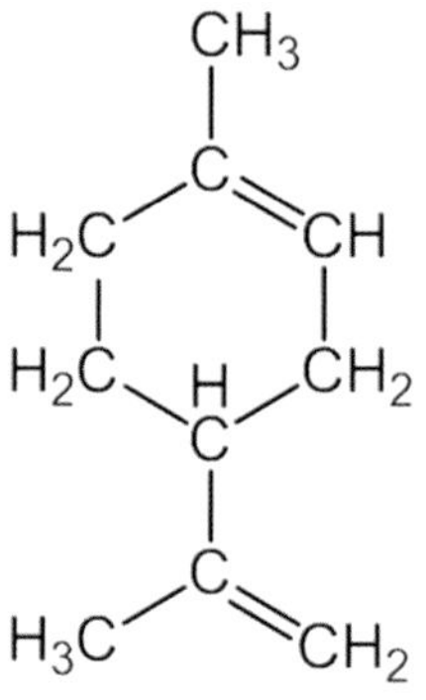

limonene

Limonene belongs to a family of compounds known as terpenes. It is a colourless liquid found in significant quantities in the rind of citrus fruits.

(a) State what would be observed when a sample of limonene was shaken with an excess of bromine water.

(b) Write an equation for the reaction that occurs when limonene is shaken with an excess of bromine water.

Solution

(a) The bromine water would be decolourised to form a colourless solution.

(b) $C_{10}H_{16} + 2Br_2 \rightarrow C_{10}H_{16}Br_4$

Exercise 2.4I

1. (a) Write a chemical equation for the reaction that occurs when but-1-ene is shaken with chlorine water, $Cl_{2\ (aq)}$. (b) Draw the structure of the product showing all bonds present.

2. (a) Write an equation for the reaction that occurs when penta-1,4-diene is shaken with an excess of bromine water. (b) Draw the structure of the product showing all bonds present.

3. Myrcene is found in many natural oils including lemon oil.

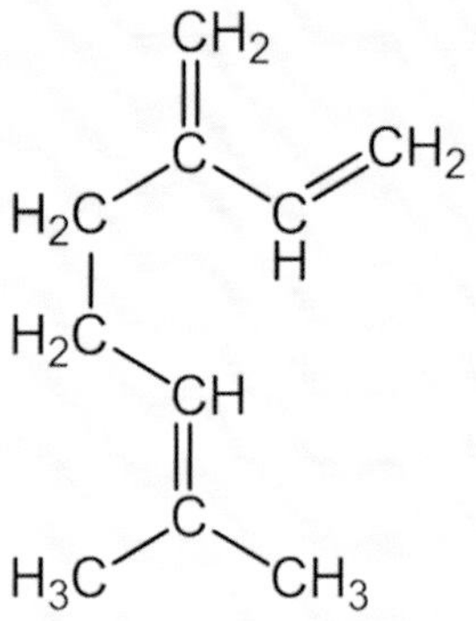

myrcene

(a) Write the molecular formula and empirical formula for myrcene.

(b) State what would be observed when a small amount of myrcene was shaken with an excess of bromine water.

(c) Draw the structure of the product when myrcene is reacted with an excess of chlorine in the absence of light.

(CCEA January 2006)

4. 2.1 g of an alkene reacts with 8.0 g of bromine to produce a dibromoalkane. Write the formula for the alkene. *(CCEA January 2007)*

5. 1.4 g of an alkene reacts with chlorine to produce 3.8 g of a dichloroalkane. Write the formula for the alkene. *(CCEA June 2011)*

6. Calculate the volume of liquid bromine (density = 3.2 g cm^{-3}) required to react with 120 cm^3 of ethene at 20 °C and 1 atmosphere pressure.

$$C_2H_4 + Br_2 \rightarrow C_2H_4Br_2$$

(CCEA January 2008)

Before moving to the next section, check that you are able to:

- Use structural formulas and equations to describe the addition of halogens (Cl_2, Br_2 ...) across a C=C bond.

- Describe the use of bromine water to test for the presence of one or more C=C bonds in a molecule.

Addition of Hydrogen Halides

Hydrogen halides (HCl, HBr ...) will also add across a C=C bond to produce a halogenated alkane. The flow scheme in Figure 3 reveals that the reaction occurs in two steps. In the first step, the pair of electrons in the C-C π-bond is used to bond the hydrogen in HBr to one of the carbon atoms. The C-H bond results from the attraction between the positive end of the H-Br dipole ($H^{\delta+}$) and the electrons in the C-C π-bond. In this way HBr acts as

an **electrophile** by 'attacking' the region of high electron density produced by the C-C π-bond. Formation of the C-H bond results in **heterolytic fission** of the H-Br bond to form bromide ion.

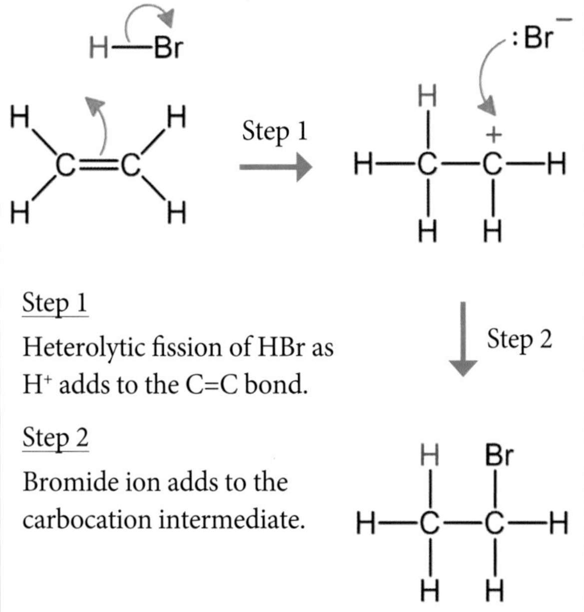

$$H\text{-}Br \rightarrow H^+ + Br^-$$

Heterolytic fission of the H-Br bond

$$H\text{-}Br \rightarrow H\bullet + Br\bullet$$

Homolytic fission of the H-Br bond

When drawing the mechanism for a reaction, the movement of a pair of electrons is described using a 'curly arrow', ↺. In the reaction between HBr and ethene, curly arrows are used to describe the electron pair in the C-C π-bond moving to form a bond between carbon and hydrogen, and the electron pair in the H-Br bond moving onto bromine during heterolytic fission of the H-Br bond.

The cation formed by the addition of H^+ to the C=C bond contains an electron deficient carbon atom with only six electrons in its outer shell (C^+). A cation containing an electron deficient carbon (C^+) is known as a **carbocation**. Carbocations are unstable and will react quickly. In the second step of the reaction, bromide (Br^-) donates a pair of electrons to the electron deficient carbon (C^+) to form a coordinate bond. The second step is much faster than the first due to the attraction between the positive and negative ions.

The addition of a hydrogen halide across a C=C bond is an example of an **electrophilic addition** reaction. The term electrophilic addition is used to describe a reaction in which an electrophile; in this case a hydrogen halide (HCl, HBr ...), adds across a C=C bond.

Step 1

Heterolytic fission of HBr as H^+ adds to the C=C bond.

Step 2

Bromide ion adds to the carbocation intermediate.

Figure 3: Flow scheme detailing the mechanism for the addition of hydrogen bromide to ethene:
$C_2H_4 + HBr \rightarrow C_2H_5Br.$

Exercise 2.4J

1. The double bond in ethene allows the molecule to undergo an electrophilic addition reaction with hydrogen bromide. Explain the term electrophilic addition.

$$C_2H_4 + HBr \rightarrow C_2H_5Br$$

(CCEA June 2003)

2. Which one of the following equations represents a step in the mechanism for the reaction between hydrogen bromide and ethene?

(a) $C_2H_4 + Br^+ \rightarrow C_2H_4Br^+$

(b) $C_2H_4 + HBr \rightarrow C_2H_5^+ + Br^-$

(c) $C_2H_4 + HBr \rightarrow C_2H_5\bullet + Br\bullet$

(d) $C_2H_4 + HBr \rightarrow C_2H_4Br^- + H^+$

(CCEA January 2009)

3. (a) Explain why alkenes are more reactive than alkanes. (b) What name is given to the reaction between propene and hydrogen bromide? (c) Use a flow diagram to suggest the mechanism for the reaction between an alkene and hydrogen bromide. Represent the alkene as:

$$\begin{array}{c}\diagdown \\ \diagup \end{array} C = C \begin{array}{c}\diagdown \\ \diagup \end{array}$$

(CCEA January 2011)

4. The Smoky Mountains in the United States are enveloped by a blue haze which contains simple gaseous hydrocarbons emitted by trees and plants. One such hydrocarbon is isoprene:

Isoprene reacts as a typical unsaturated hydrocarbon. Draw a flow scheme to show the mechanism for the reaction between one molecule of hydrogen bromide and isoprene to form 3-bromo-3-methylbut-1-ene,

$CH_3CBr(CH_3)CH=CH_2$.

(Adapted from CCEA June 2007)

Before moving to the next section, check that you are able to:

- Use structural formulas and equations to describe the addition of hydrogen halides (HCl, HBr ...) across a C=C bond.
- Draw the mechanism for the addition of HBr to a C=C bond.
- Recall the role of heterolytic fission in the addition of HBr to a C=C bond and explain why the reaction is described as electrophilic addition.

Polymerisation

The presence of one or more C=C bonds in an alkene makes it possible for many alkene molecules to combine and form much larger molecules known as polymers. For example, when ethene is heated in the presence of a catalyst, many ethene molecules combine to form a polymer known as 'polythene'.

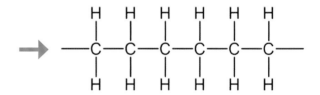

three ethene monomers

a section of a polythene molecule containing three identical subunits

The term **polymer** is used to describe a large molecule formed from many smaller molecules that are referred to as **monomers**. The process of forming a polymer from its monomers is referred to as a **polymerisation reaction**. The reaction between ethene monomers to form a molecule of polythene is an example of a polymerisation reaction. The formation of polythene from ethene is also an example of **addition polymerisation** in which the polymer is formed as a result of addition reactions between ethene monomers. The polymerisation of ethene to form polythene can be summarised in the form of an equation.

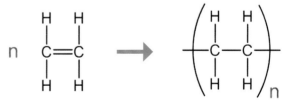

one subunit in a polythene molecule formed from n monomers

The addition polymerisation of substituted ethenes, $CHR=CH_2$ is used to form polymers such as polypropylene (R = CH_3), polyvinylchloride (R = Cl) and polystyrene (R = phenyl, C_6H_5).

147

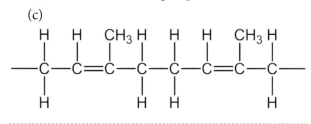

Worked Example 2.4vii

Natural rubber is a polymer of isoprene (2-methylbuta-1,3-diene). (a) Explain the meaning of the term polymer. (b) State the functional group which enables isoprene to polymerise. (c) Draw a section of natural rubber showing how isoprene units combine to form the polymer.

(Adapted from CCEA January 2005)

Strategy

The electrons from one of the two C-C π-bonds in isoprene are needed to add isoprene to the polymer. The electrons in the second C-C π-bond are used to complete the octet around each carbon when isoprene adds to the polymer.

Solution

(a) A polymer is a large molecule that is formed when many identical molecules known as monomers combine.

(b) The C=C functional group.

(c)

Exercise 2.4K

1. Propenonitrile, CH_2=CHCN can be polymerised to form a fibre known as Orlon that is used for making clothes. (a) Draw the structure of propenonitrile, showing all of the bonds present. (b) Explain if propenonitrile can exist as *cis* and *trans* (E-Z) forms. (c) Draw the structure of two repeating units in Orlon. (d) State the type of polymerisation taking place. *(CCEA June 2009)*

2. Polytetrafluoroethene is made by the polymerisation of tetrafluoroethene, CF_2=CF_2. (a) Write the equation for the polymerisation reaction. (b) Why is tetrafluoroethene able to polymerise? (c) State the type of reaction that occurs when tetrafluoroethene polymerises.

   (Adapted from CCEA January 2010)

3. Ethene and propene can be converted into polythene and polypropene respectively. (a) Name the type of reaction involved in the conversion of propene to polypropene. (b) Suggest the equation for the conversion of styrene to polystyrene.

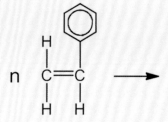

(CCEA June 2010)

Before moving to the next section, check that you are able to:

- Write equations to describe the formation of polymers containing a large number (n) of monomers.

- Recall that polymers based on ethene monomers are formed by addition polymerisation and that addition polymerisation can only occur when the monomer contains one or more C=C bonds.

2.5 Halogenoalkanes

CONNECTIONS

• Very few compounds in nature contain halogens. Most are toxic and are used by living organisms to fight disease or defend against predators.

• Halogenated alkanes such as halothane, $CF_3CHClBr$ and chloroform, $CHCl_3$ have been widely used as anaesthetics.

• Halogenated alkanes are also used in fire suppression systems as they terminate the free radical reactions that sustain flames.

Structure and Properties

In this section we are learning to:

• Account for the properties of halogenoalkanes in terms of the bonding within halogenoalkane molecules.

• Classify the structures of halogenoalkanes as primary, secondary or tertiary.

• Use systematic (IUPAC) rules to name halogenoalkanes.

Factors Affecting Solubility

A **halogenoalkane** is a saturated hydrocarbon containing one or more halogen atoms. Small halogenoalkanes such as chloromethane, CH_3Cl and bromomethane, CH_3Br are gases, while larger halogenoalkanes such as bromobutane, C_4H_9Br are oily liquids with a sweet smell. The carbon-halogen bonds within a halogenoalkane are the functional groups that determine the reactions of the halogenoalkane. The remainder of the molecule is constructed from alkyl groups and is essentially nonpolar. The remainder of the molecule consists of alkyl groups and is nonpolar as illustrated by the halogenoalkanes in Figure 1.

Smaller halogenoalkanes such as chloromethane, CH_3Cl and bromoethane, C_2H_5Br experience a combination of attractive dipole forces and van der Waals attraction between molecules. As a result they are soluble in nonpolar solvents such as hexane, and are only sparingly soluble in water. As the halogenoalkanes become larger the van der Waals attraction dominates and molecules as small as bromobutane, C_4H_9Br become **immiscible** with water. The solubility of halogenoalkanes in polar and nonpolar solvents can be demonstrated by shaking a mixture of bromobutane and copper sulfate solution with hexane as shown in Figure 2. When the mixture is shaken the bromobutane (bottom layer) dissolves in the hexane to form a single nonpolar layer that is immiscible with the copper sulfate solution.

Chlorine, bromine and iodine are considerably heavier than the atoms in most liquids. As a result, halogenoalkanes containing these elements have a greater density than water and liquids made from lighter elements such as C, H, N and O. When a halogenoalkane containing chlorine, bromine or iodine is mixed with an aqueous solution it forms a separate non-aqueous layer below the aqueous solution as shown in Figure 2.

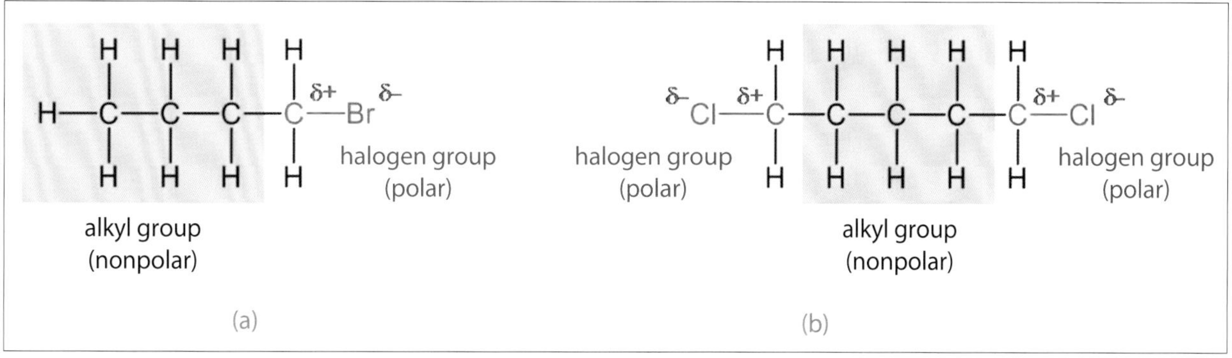

Figure 1: Polar and nonpolar regions within (a) 1-bromobutane, C_4H_9Br and (b) 1,5-dichloropentane, $C_5H_{10}Cl_2$.

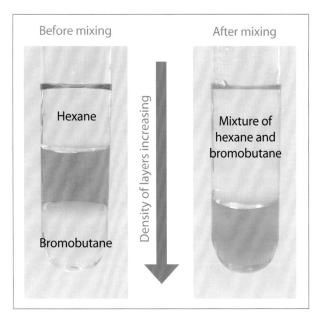

Figure 2: The effect of mixing hexane and bromobutane with aqueous copper sulfate. Bromobutane mixes with hexane to form a single nonpolar layer.

Factors Affecting Boiling Point

The chloroalkanes are a homologous series of halogenoalkanes. The formula for each member of the series is obtained by inserting n = 1, 2, 3 ... in the general formula $C_nH_{2n+1}Cl$. The boiling points for the straight-chain chloroalkanes in Figure 3 demonstrate that the boiling points of the chloroalkanes increase as the molar mass of the compound increases. As in alkanes, the increase in boiling point is due to an increase in the van der Waals attraction between neighbouring molecules as the number of electrons in the molecule increases. Other homologous series such as the fluoroalkanes ($C_nH_{2n+1}F$), bromoalkanes ($C_nH_{2n+1}Br$) and iodoalkanes ($C_nH_{2n+1}I$) behave in a

similar way.

As with alkanes, a straight-chain halogenoalkane will have a higher boiling point than a more branched isomer. For instance, the compound 2-bromo-2-methylpropane is a structural isomer of bromobutane. The molecular shapes in Figure 4 reveal it has a branched structure that reduces the amount of contact between the electrons in neighbouring molecules. This, in turn, decreases the strength of the van der Waals attraction between molecules and lowers the boiling point.

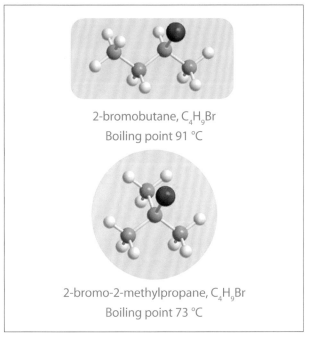

2-bromobutane, C_4H_9Br
Boiling point 91 °C

2-bromo-2-methylpropane, C_4H_9Br
Boiling point 73 °C

Figure 4: The effect of van der Waals attraction on the boiling points of bromobutane isomers.

The magnitude of the van der Waals attraction

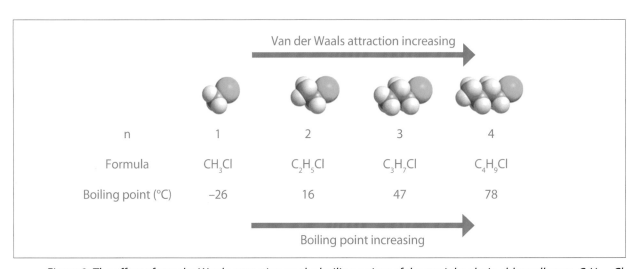

Van der Waals attraction increasing

n	1	2	3	4
Formula	CH_3Cl	C_2H_5Cl	C_3H_7Cl	C_4H_9Cl
Boiling point (°C)	−26	16	47	78

Boiling point increasing

Figure 3: The effect of van der Waals attraction on the boiling points of the straight-chain chloroalkanes, $C_nH_{2n+1}Cl$.

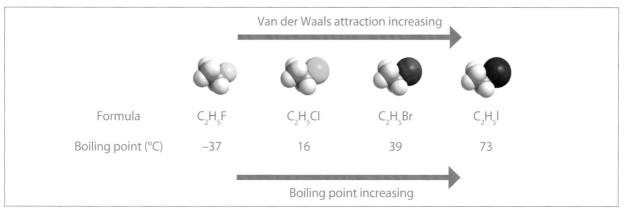

Figure 5: The effect of van der Waals attraction on the boiling points of the ethyl halides, C_2H_5X (X = F, Cl, Br, I)

between molecules is also determined by the nature of the halogen atoms in the molecule. The boiling points for the ethyl halides, C_2H_5X (X = F, Cl, Br, I) in Figure 5 demonstrate that the van der Waals attraction between molecules increases as the number of electrons in the molecule increases.

Adding halogens to a molecule further increases the van der Waals attraction between neighbouring molecules. The increase in boiling point that results from adding chlorine atoms is illustrated by the sequence of chloropropanes in Figure 6a. The even more substantial increases in boiling point that result from adding larger halogens are illustrated by the corresponding bromopropanes in Figure 6b.

Exercise 2.5A

1. (a) Use δ+ and δ– to indicate the polarity of the carbon-bromine bond in 2-bromobutane. (b) Explain why the carbon-bromine bond is polar.

```
     H   H   H   H
     |   |   |   |
H —  C — C — C — C — H    2-bromobutane
     |   |   |   |
     H   H   Br  H
```

(CCEA June 2005)

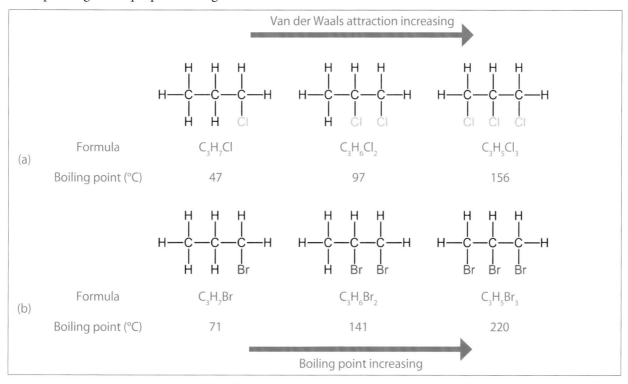

Figure 6: The effect of additional halogen atoms on the boiling point of (a) chloropropane, C_3H_7Cl and (b) bromopropane, C_3H_7Br.

2. Account for the boiling points of the following halogenoalkanes in terms of the intermolecular forces operating between the molecules.

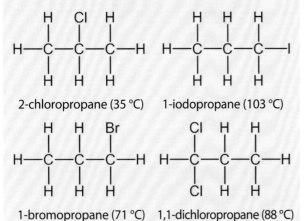

2-chloropropane (35 °C)   1-iodopropane (103 °C)

1-bromopropane (71 °C)   1,1-dichloropropane (88 °C)

3. Account for the boiling points of the following halogenoalkanes in terms of the intermolecular forces operating between the molecules.

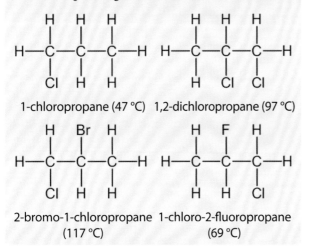

1-chloropropane (47 °C)   1,2-dichloropropane (97 °C)

2-bromo-1-chloropropane   1-chloro-2-fluoropropane
(117 °C)   (69 °C)

Factors Affecting Reactivity

The reactivity of a halogenoalkane is determined by the extent to which the individual carbon-halogen bonds in the molecule participate in a reaction. The extent to which a particular carbon-halogen bond will react is determined by the strength of the bond, the polarity of the bond, and the number of carbon atoms attached to the bond.

The relationship between the structure of a halogenoalkane and the reactivity of the carbon-halogen bond can be understood if we classify halogenoalkanes as primary, secondary or tertiary according to the number of carbon atoms attached to the carbon-halogen bond. The compound 1-bromobutane is an example of a **primary**

halogenoalkane as the halogen atom is bonded to a carbon (C) with one carbon atom (C) attached. The isomer 1-bromo-2-methylpropane is also a primary halogenoalkane.

1-bromobutane (*primary*)
$CH_3CH_2CH_2CH_2Br$

1-bromo-2-methylpropane (*primary*)
$CH_3CH(CH_3)CH_2Br$

The isomer 2-bromobutane is an example of a **secondary halogenoalkane** as the halogen atom is bonded to a carbon (C) with two carbon atoms (C) attached. In contrast, the isomer 2-bromo-2-methylpropane is an example of a **tertiary halogenoalkane** as the halogen atom is bonded to a carbon (C) with three carbon atoms (C) attached.

2-bromobutane (secondary)
$CH_3CH_2CHBrCH_3$

2-bromo-2-methylpropane (*tertiary*)
$CH_3C(CH_3)BrCH_3$

The conditions under which primary, secondary and tertiary halogenoalkanes react are often quite different. As a result, the primary, secondary, or tertiary nature of the carbon-halogen bonds in a molecule is one of several factors that must be taken into account when describing the reactions of the compound.

Worked Example 2.5i

Draw the structure of 2-chloro-2-methylpropane, C_4H_9Cl and explain why the compound is described as a *tertiary* halogenoalkane.

(Adapted from CCEA January 2003)

Solution

The compound is described as a tertiary halogenoalkane as the carbon atom in the carbon-halogen bond is bonded to three other carbon atoms.

Exercise 2.5B

1. (a) Draw the structural formula for a secondary chloroalkane with a molecular formula C_3H_7Cl.
   (b) Explain what is meant by the term *secondary*.

2. (a) Draw the structure of each iodoalkane with a molecular formula C_3H_7I. Classify each isomer as a primary, secondary or tertiary iodoalkane.
   (b) Explain what is meant by the term *isomer*.

3. (a) Draw the structure of each primary fluoroalkane with a molecular formula C_4H_9F.
   (b) Explain what is meant by the term *primary*.

Naming Halogenoalkanes

The systematic (IUPAC) name for a halogenoalkane is based on the systematic name for the parent (straight-chain) alkane on which its structure is based. For example, 1-bromobutane and 2-bromobutane are considered bromobutanes as their structure is based on the straight-chain isomer of butane, $CH_3CH_2CH_2CH_3$.

1-bromobutane $CH_3CH_2CH_2CH_2Br$

2-bromobutane $CH_3CH_2CHBrCH_3$

The prefix *bromo* indicates that the molecule contains a bromine atom. The additional prefix *1-* or *2-* is then added to locate bromine on the carbon chain. As in alkanes, the prefix used to locate the bromine atom is based on a numbering of the carbon atoms that generates the lowest number prefix.

The compounds 1-bromo-2-methylpropane and 2-bromo-2-methylpropane are structural isomers of the bromobutanes. Both are considered propanes as their structure is based on the three carbon chain in propane, $CH_3CH_2CH_3$. As in alkanes, the prefixes describing the location of bromine and the methyl group are listed in alphabetical order, and are based on a numbering of the carbon atoms that produces the lowest number prefixes.

1-bromo-2-methylpropane $CH_3CH(CH_3)CH_2Br$

2-bromo-2-methylpropane $CH_3C(CH_3)BrCH_3$

The prefixes *fluoro*, *chloro*, *bromo* and *iodo* are used to locate halogen atoms and can be combined to locate several halogens within a molecule. For example, the prefix *2-bromo-1-chloro* could be used to locate bromine on the second carbon and chlorine on the first carbon in the molecule. Similarly, the prefix *1-chloro-1-fluoro* could be used to locate chlorine and fluorine on the first carbon in the molecule. Once again the prefixes are listed in alphabetical order and are based on a numbering of the carbons that produces the lowest number prefixes. The correct use of multiple prefixes is further illustrated by the following examples.

1-chloro-3-iodopropane
$CH_2ClCH_2CH_2I$

2-bromo-1-chloro-2-methylpropane

$CH_3C(CH_3)BrCH_2Cl$

The location of two or more halogen atoms of the same type can be described by using the number prefixes *di, tri, tetra* ... to construct naming prefixes such as *dibromo* and *trichloro*. An additional prefix such as *1,2-* or *1,1,2-* can then be added to describe the location of each halogen atom as in 1,1,1-trichloroethane, CCl_3CH_3. The correct use of number prefixes is further illustrated by the following examples.

1,3-dibromopropane

$CH_2BrCH_2CH_2Br$

1-chloro-1,1-difluoroethane

$CClF_2CH_3$

Rules for naming halogenoalkanes:

• The name of a halogenoalkane is based on the name of the parent (straight-chain) alkane on which its structure is based.

• The prefixes *fluoro, chloro, bromo* and *iodo* are combined with the prefixes *di, tri, tetra* ... to describe the type and location of each halogen atom.

• Prefixes such as *methyl* and *ethyl* are combined with the prefixes *di, tri, tetra* ... to describe and locate other functional groups.

• The prefixes are listed in alphabetical order and the carbon atoms numbered in a way that produces the lowest number prefixes.

Exercise 2.5 C

1. The compound trichlorofluoromethane, CCl_3F is known as CFC-11. Write systematic names for CFC-12, CCl_2F_2 and CFC-13, $CClF_3$.

2. The halogenoalkane CCl_3CH_3 is used as a solvent in correction fluid. (a) Draw the structure of the molecule and write the IUPAC name for the compound. (b) Draw remaining structural isomers of the compound and write the systematic name for each isomer.

3. (a) Draw the structure of the halogenoalkane CCl_2BrCH_3 and write the systematic name for the compound. (b) Draw the remaining structural isomers of the compound and write the systematic name for each isomer.

4. There are four bromoalkanes with the formula, C_4H_9Br. Complete the following table by drawing the missing structures, writing the name for each structure, and classifying each structure as primary, secondary or tertiary.

Structure	Name	Classification
	1-bromobutane	primary
	2-bromo-2-methylpropane	
	1-bromo-2-methylpropane	

(CCEA June 2010)

5. The chlorobutanes in the table are isomers. (a) Write the molecular formula for a chlorobutane. (b) Write the general formula for a chloroalkane. (c) Deduce the systematic name for t-butyl chloride. (d) Suggest what is meant by the term sec. (e) Suggest why the boiling point of t-butyl chloride is so different from the other chlorobutanes.

butyl chloride	structure	boiling point /°C
t-butyl chloride	$(CH_3)_3CCl$	51–52
n-butyl chloride	$CH_3CH_2CH_2CH_2Cl$	78–79
sec-butyl chloride	$CH_3CH_2CHClCH_3$	68–70
iso-butyl chloride	$(CH_3)_2CHCH_2Cl$	68–69

(Adapted from CCEA June 2011)

Before moving to the next section, check that you are able to:

- Explain why halogenoalkanes are denser than water and become less soluble in water as the molecules get bigger.
- Explain how the boiling point of a halogenoalkane is affected by the size and shape of the molecule, the type of halogen atoms in the molecule, and the number of halogen atoms in the molecule.
- Write structural and condensed formulas for halogenoalkanes.
- Classify the structures of halogenoalkanes as primary, secondary, or tertiary.
- Use IUPAC rules to write systematic names for halogenoalkanes.

Preparation

In this section we are learning to:

- Describe how to prepare a pure, dry sample of a halogenoalkane.
- Explain the role of reflux and distillation in the preparation of a halogenoalkane and the use of a separating funnel, drying agents and distillation in the purification of a halogenoalkane.

The process of making a pure organic compound from the starting materials is known as **organic synthesis**. In the first stage of a synthesis one or more chemical reactions are used to prepare a crude (impure) sample of the compound. The crude product is then extracted from the reaction mixture and purified. The synthesis of 1-bromobutane, C_4H_9Br illustrates the process and techniques used to prepare a pure, dry sample of a halogenoalkane in the laboratory.

Stage 1: Forming the product

Crude 1-bromobutane, C_4H_9Br is synthesised by reacting the alcohol butan-1-ol, C_4H_9OH with hydrogen bromide.

$$CH_3CH_2CH_2CH_2OH + HBr \rightarrow CH_3CH_2CH_2CH_2Br + H_2O$$
$$\text{butan-1-ol} \qquad\qquad \text{1-bromobutane}$$

The hydrogen bromide is produced within the reaction mixture – a technique referred to as *in situ* – by adding concentrated sulfuric acid to a mixture of solid sodium bromide and butan-1-ol as the reaction mixture is stirred.

$$NaBr + H_2SO_4 \rightarrow NaHSO_4 + HBr$$

The concentrated sulfuric acid is added one drop at a time using a dropping funnel as shown in Figure 7a. The concentrated sulfuric acid oxidises a portion of the hydrogen bromide to bromine, giving the reaction mixture a characteristic orange colour. The dropping funnel is then removed and several small pieces of ground glass or porcelain added to the reaction mixture. The reaction mixture is then refluxed for an extended period as shown in Figure 7b. In this context the term **reflux** describes the continuous boiling and condensing of a reaction mixture in a round-bottom flask fitted with a Liebig condenser in the vertical position. Refluxing increases the amount of product formed during the reaction by making it possible for the reactants to react at an elevated temperature over an extended period of time. The pieces of ground glass or porcelain added to the reaction mixture are referred to as **boiling chips** or **anti-bumping granules** as they ensure smooth boiling when the reaction mixture is refluxed.

....

Organic Synthesis

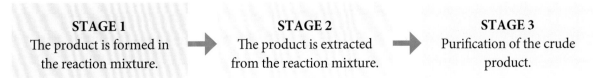

STAGE 1
The product is formed in the reaction mixture.

STAGE 2
The product is extracted from the reaction mixture.

STAGE 3
Purification of the crude product.

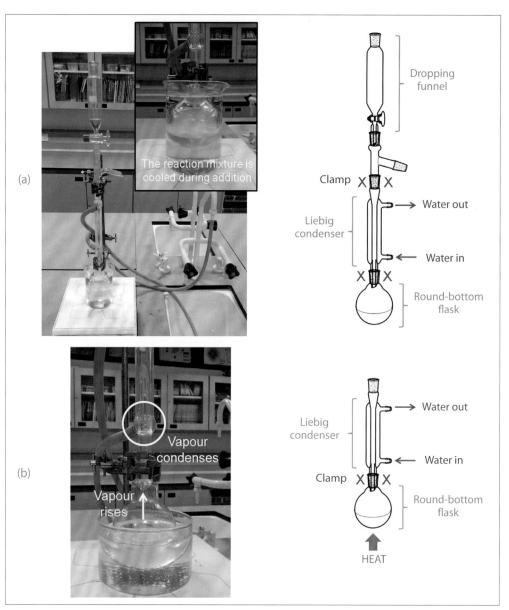

(a)

The reaction mixture is cooled during addition

(b)

Vapour condenses

Vapour rises

Dropping funnel

Clamp X X

Liebig condenser

Water out

Water in

Round-bottom flask

Liebig condenser

Water out

Water in

Clamp X X

Round-bottom flask

HEAT

Figure 7: (a) Using a dropping funnel to control the addition of concentrated sulfuric acid to the reaction mixture. (b) Refluxing the reaction mixture.

Worked Example 2.5ii

When bromobutane is prepared by the reaction of butanol with concentrated hydrobromic acid in the presence of concentrated sulfuric acid, which one of the following is not found in the reaction flask?

(a) bromine   (b) butanol

(c) butane   (d) hydrogen bromide

(CCEA June 2011)

Solution

The hydrobromic acid (HBr) is formed in situ and traces of the reactants (butanol and hydrobromic acid, HBr) may remain after reaction. Concentrated sulfuric acid will also oxidise some of the hydrobromic acid to bromine.

Answer (c).

Stage 2: Extracting the product

With the reflux complete the reaction mixture is left to cool. The apparatus is then reorganised with the condenser in the horizontal position and 1-bromobutane extracted from the reaction mixture by **distillation** as shown in Figure 8. Distillation involves slowly heating the reaction mixture until the 1-bromobutane in the mixture boils (boiling point 101 °C). The vapour produced by the boiling rises, enters the condenser, and condenses to form a liquid **distillate**. The distillate is referred to as crude 1-bromobutane as it contains 1-bromobutane and small amounts of impurities from the reaction mixture. A pure sample of 1-bromobutane would be collected over a range of 1-2 °C. The impurities in the

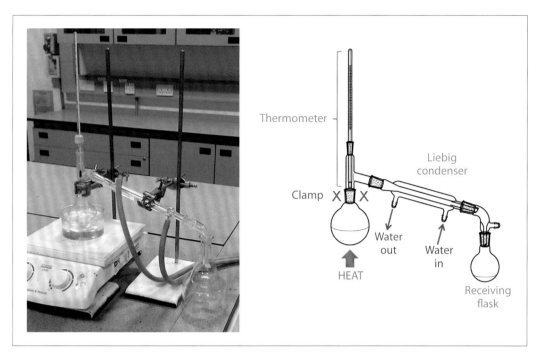

Figure 8: Separating crude 1-bromobutane from the reaction mixture by distillation.

crude distillate increase the temperature range over which the distillate is collected.

Worked Example 2.5iii

Separating a product from a mixture by distillation is an important practical technique in organic chemistry.

(a) Draw a labelled diagram of the apparatus used to carry out a distillation.

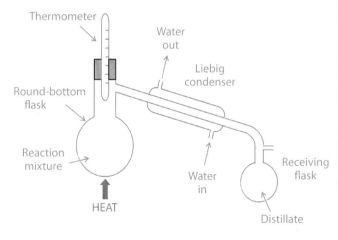

(b) Why are anti-bumping granules added to a mixture being distilled?

To ensure that the reaction mixture boils smoothly.

(CCEA June 2009)

Stage 3: Purifying the product

The first step in the purification process involves shaking the crude 1-bromobutane with dilute sodium hydrogencarbonate solution in a **separating funnel**. Acidic impurities in the crude 1-bromobutane react with the dilute alkali to form a salt and carbon dioxide gas which must be released to avoid the buildup of pressure in the separating funnel. This is achieved by inverting the separating funnel and using the tap to release the pressure inside the funnel at intervals as the mixture is being shaken. The technique of inverting and shaking to mix the contents of the separating funnel is illustrated in Figure 9a. The stopper is then removed and the mixture left to settle. The 1-bromobutane is immiscible in water and forms a separate (organic) layer as shown in Figure 9b. The lower (organic) layer containing the product can then be collected from the funnel and the upper (aqueous) layer discarded.

The lower (organic) layer containing the 1-bromobutane is then shaken with distilled water in a separating funnel to remove salts and other water soluble impurities before being collected in a small dry conical flask. A solid **drying agent** such as anhydrous calcium chloride or anhydrous sodium sulfate is then added to remove traces of water in the product. If the product contains small amounts of water it will appear cloudy and will become increasingly clear as the water is absorbed by the drying agent. The drying agent is then removed by filtering the mixture into a clean

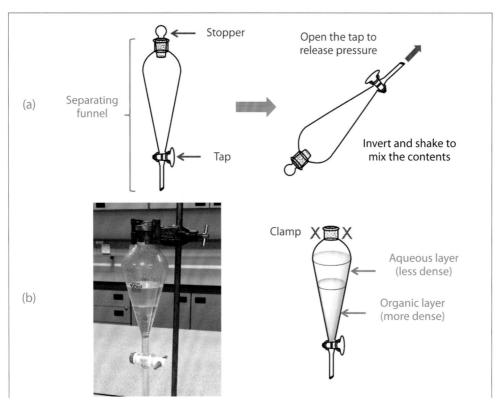

Figure 9: The use of a separating funnel to (a) mix and (b) separate the layers formed during the purification process.

round-bottom flask and the product distilled to obtain a pure, dry sample of bromobutane at its boiling point.

· ·

Worked Example 2.5iv

The compound 1-bromobutane is prepared by refluxing a mixture containing butan-1-ol, water, sodium bromide and concentrated sulfuric acid for 45 minutes. Describe the remaining steps required to produce a pure, dry sample of this haloalkane.

(CCEA June 2010)

Solution

- Distil the reaction mixture and collect crude 1-bromobutane at its boiling point.

- Add dilute sodium hydrogencarbonate solution to the crude product in a separating funnel. Stopper, invert and shake the separating funnel. Open the tap every few seconds to release any carbon dioxide formed as the mixture is shaken.

- Clamp the separating funnel, remove the stopper, and allow the layers to separate. Collect the lower (organic) layer containing the product.

- Wash the product with distilled water using a separating funnel and collect the lower (organic) layer. Add anhydrous sodium sulfate to the product in a small conical flask and swirl the

mixture until the product becomes clear.

- Filter the mixture into a clean, dry round-bottom flask and distil the product to obtain a pure, dry sample of 1-bromobutane at its boiling point.

· ·

Exercise 2.5D

1. Amphetamines can be synthesised by the following sequence. The liquid product obtained in Step 1 is impure. Explain, giving experimental details, how the product can be separated, dried and purified.

$$R-\underset{\underset{H}{|}}{\overset{\overset{CH_3}{|}}{C}}-OH \xrightarrow{\text{Step 1}} R-\underset{\underset{H}{|}}{\overset{\overset{CH_3}{|}}{C}}-Br$$

$$\xrightarrow{\text{Step 2}} R-\underset{\underset{H}{|}}{\overset{\overset{CH_3}{|}}{C}}-NH_2$$

(CCEA January 2011)

2. The following procedure is used to make t-butyl chloride from the corresponding alcohol.

$$(CH_3)_3COH + HCl \rightarrow (CH_3)_3CCl + H_2O$$

25 g of t-butyl alcohol and 85 cm³ of concentrated hydrochloric acid (an excess) are mixed in a separating funnel. The mixture is shaken from time to time over 20 minutes. The mixture is then allowed to stand for a few minutes and the acid layer removed. The crude t-butyl chloride is washed with sodium hydrogencarbonate solution and then with water. Anhydrous calcium chloride is swirled with the t-butyl chloride in a conical flask. The liquid is decanted, 2–3 chips of porous porcelain added and distilled to collect 28 g of t-butyl chloride at 51–52 °C.

Explain why the t-butyl chloride is (a) shaken with sodium hydrogencarbonate solution, (b) shaken with water and (c) swirled with anhydrous calcium chloride. Also explain why (d) porous porcelain is added before distillation and (e) the separating funnel is inverted and the tap opened after each shaking. (f) Calculate the percentage yield of t-butyl chloride.

(Adapted from CCEA June 2011)

3. 17.8 g of 1-bromobutane (RMM 137) was formed when 14.8 g of butan-1-ol (RMM 74) was refluxed with sodium bromide and sulfuric acid. Calculate the percentage yield for the reaction.

(CCEA June 2007)

Before moving to the next section, check that you are able to:

- Describe the use of reflux and distillation to prepare a crude sample of a halogenoalkane.
- Draw labelled diagrams of the apparatus used to reflux and distil a reaction mixture and explain the role of reflux and distillation in the preparation of a halogenoalkane.
- Describe the use of a separating funnel, drying agents and distillation in the purification of a halogenoalkane.
- Recall examples of drying agents and explain the role of a drying agent in the purification of a halogenoalkane.

Reactions

In this section we are learning to:

- Recognise the reactions of halogenoalkanes with dilute alkali, ammonia and cyanide ions as nucleophilic substitution and deduce the structure of the products formed.
- Explain the mechanism for the reaction that occurs when primary and tertiary halogenoalkanes react with dilute alkali.
- Recognise the hydrolysis of halogenoalkanes as nucleophilic substitution and explain how the nature of the carbon-halogen bond affects the rate of hydrolysis.
- Recognise the reaction of a halogenoalkane with an alcoholic solution of an alkali as elimination and deduce the structure of the products formed.

Substitution Reactions

When a halogenoalkane is refluxed with dilute alkali, the halogen atom is replaced by a hydroxyl (-OH) group to form the corresponding alcohol. For example, refluxing a mixture of 1-bromobutane and dilute sodium hydroxide produces the corresponding alcohol, butan-1-ol.

1-bromobutane
$CH_3CH_2CH_2CH_2Br$

butan-1-ol
$CH_3CH_2CH_2CH_2OH$

The reaction is an example of a substitution reaction as it involves replacement of the halogen by another group. It is also an example of **nucleophilic substitution** as it involves substitution of the halogen by a nucleophile.

The hydroxide ions in the alkali are nucleophiles. The term **nucleophile** is used to describe a molecule or ion that attacks regions of low electron density, and

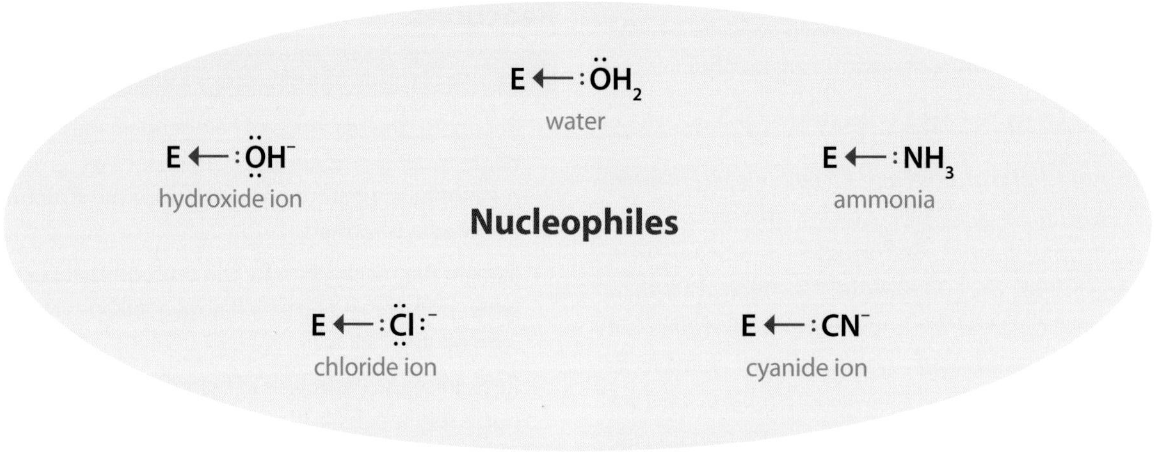

$$E \longleftarrow :\ddot{O}H_2$$
water

$$E \longleftarrow :\ddot{O}H^-$$
hydroxide ion

$$E \longleftarrow :NH_3$$
ammonia

Nucleophiles

$$E \longleftarrow :\ddot{\underset{..}{C}}l:^-$$
chloride ion

$$E \longleftarrow :CN^-$$
cyanide ion

has a lone pair that can form a coordinate bond with an electron-deficient atom.

Water (H_2O), ammonia (NH_3), halide ions (F^-, Cl^-, Br^-, I^-), and cyanide ion, CN^- are nucleophiles. Each is capable of using a lone pair of electrons to form a coordinate bond with another atom that is seeking electrons (E).

Exercise 2.5E

Explain why an ammonia molecule can act as a nucleophile but an ammonium ion cannot act as a nucleophile.

(CCEA June 2003)

If nucleophilic substitution occurs at a primary carbon, as in 1-bromobutane, $CH_3CH_2CH_2CH_2Br$ the reaction occurs in a single step. The mechanism for the reaction is described by the flow scheme in Figure 10. As hydroxide ion approaches the halogenoalkane it uses a lone pair to begin forming a coordinate bond with the electron-deficient carbon in the carbon-halogen bond ($C^{\delta+}$-$Br^{\delta-}$). In this instance the carbon is considered electron-deficient as the electrons in the carbon-halogen bond are not shared equally, leaving

carbon with fewer than eight electrons in its outer shell.

As the coordinate bond continues to form (C---OH) the carbon-halogen bond begins to break (C---Br). The process continues until the coordinate bond is fully formed (C-OH) and the carbon-halogen bond has undergone heterolytic fission to produce bromide ion. The intermediate structure (HO---C---Br) is referred to as a **transition state**, and illustrates how the bonds to the primary carbon change during the reaction. The transition state is not a stable substance and cannot be isolated as a compound.

In contrast, if nucleophilic substitution occurs at a tertiary carbon, as in 2-bromo-2-methylpropane, $CH_3C(CH_3)BrCH_3$ the substitution reaction occurs in two steps. The mechanism for the reaction is described by the flow scheme in Figure 11. The first step in the mechanism involves heterolytic fission of the carbon-halogen bond to produce a tertiary carbocation. Hydroxide ion then acts as a nucleophile by forming a coordinate bond with the electron-deficient carbon in the carbocation (C^+).

The situation at a secondary carbon atom is frequently more complex with one or both of these mechanisms operating simultaneously.

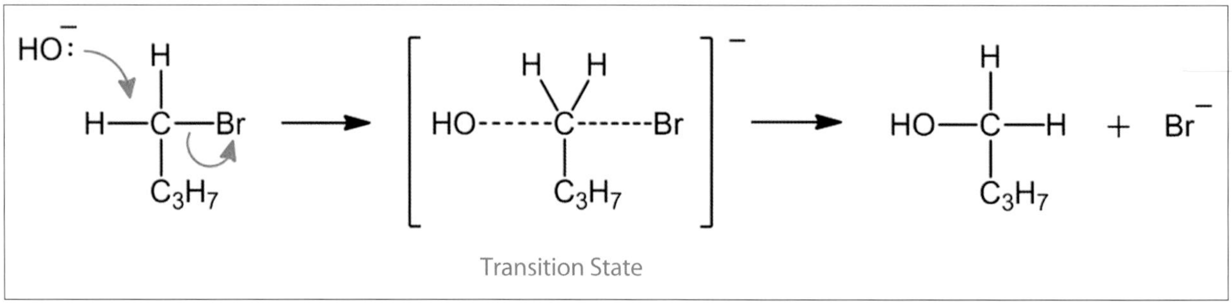

Transition State

Figure 10: The mechanism for the nucleophilic substitution reaction that occurs when 1-bromobutane (a primary halogenoalkane) reacts with dilute alkali. Dashed bonds (---) are used to indicate partially formed and partially broken bonds.

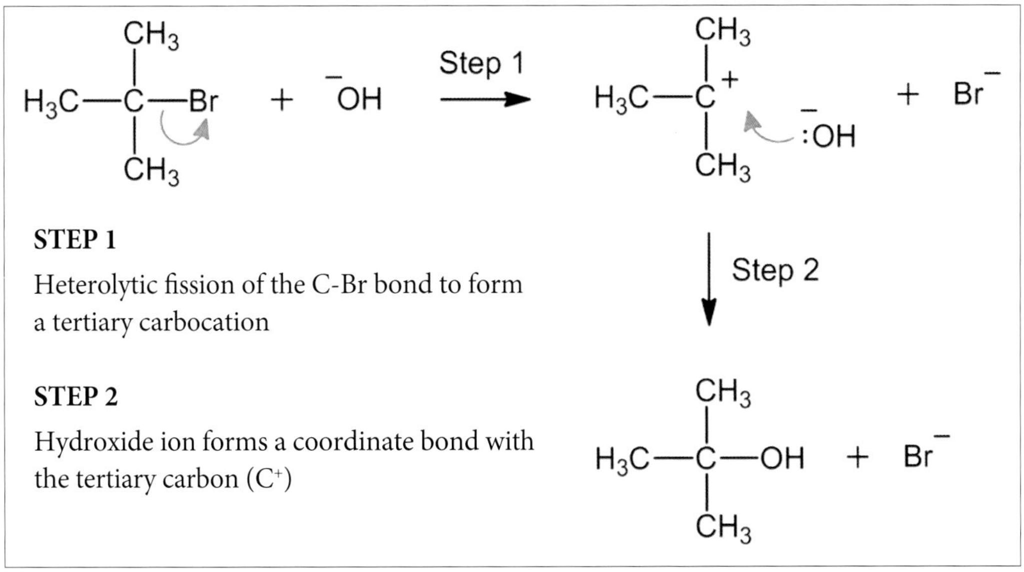

STEP 1

Heterolytic fission of the C-Br bond to form a tertiary carbocation

STEP 2

Hydroxide ion forms a coordinate bond with the tertiary carbon (C^+)

Figure 11: The mechanism for the nucleophilic substitution reaction that occurs when 2-bromo-2-methylpropane (a tertiary halogenoalkane) reacts with dilute alkali.

Exercise 2.5F

1. Draw a mechanism for the reaction between chloromethane and sodium hydroxide.

   (CCEA June 2004)

2. When 1-bromopropane reacts with aqueous potassium hydroxide the intermediate structure formed is:

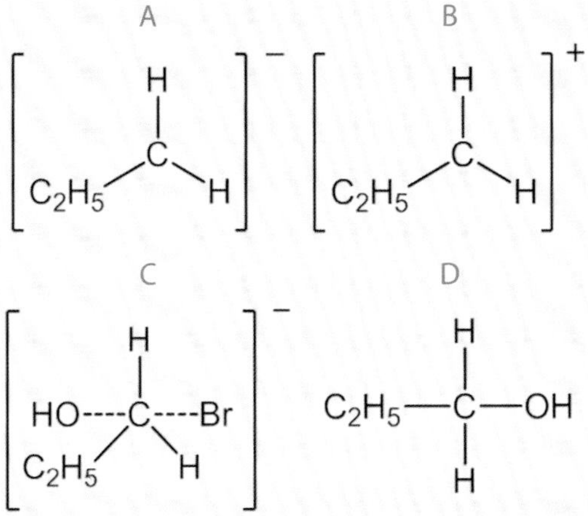

   (CCEA January 2003)

3. The compound 2-chloro-2-methylpropane is an isomer of 1-chlorobutane. (a) Explain why the compounds are isomers. (b) Write the mechanism for the reaction between 2-chloro-2-methylpropane and hydroxide ions.

   (Adapted from CCEA June 2006)

Before moving to the next section, check that you are able to:

- Recall the meaning of the terms nucleophile and nucleophilic substitution.

- Write and explain the mechanism for the nucleophilic substitution reaction that occurs when a primary halogenoalkane is refluxed with dilute alkali.

- Write and explain the mechanism for the nucleophilic substitution reaction that occurs when a tertiary halogenoalkane is refluxed with dilute alkali.

Amines and Nitriles

Refluxing a halogenoalkane with an excess of concentrated ammonia solution produces the corresponding **amine**. The reaction is an example of substitution as the halogen is replaced by an amino ($-NH_2$) group. The reaction is also an example of nucleophilic substitution as the ammonia molecule displaces the halogen by using its lone pair to form a coordinate bond with carbon. The substitution produces HBr which reacts with a second molecule of ammonia to form ammonium bromide, NH_4Br.

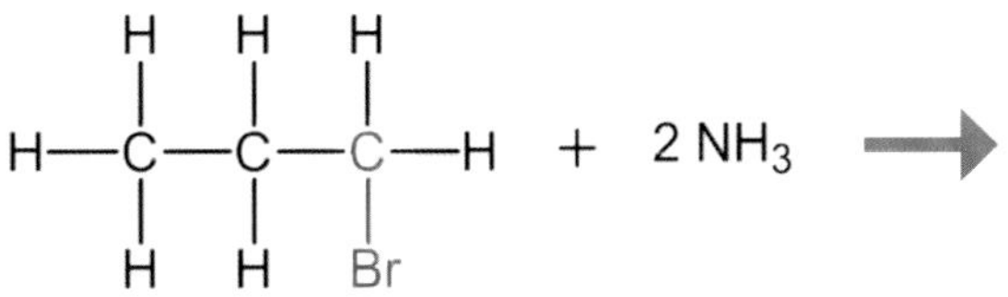

1-bromopropane
$CH_3CH_2CH_2Br$

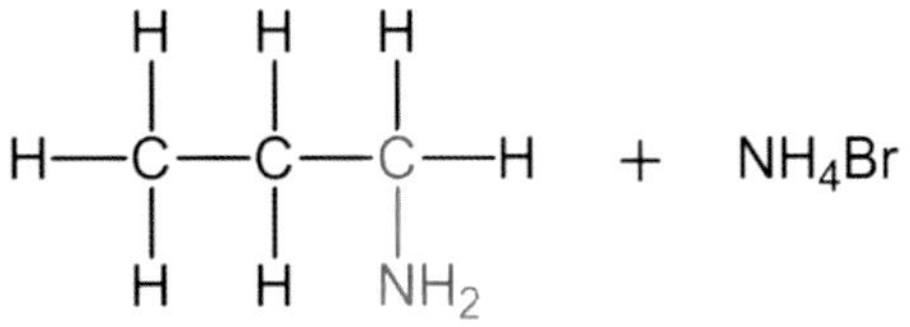

1-aminopropane
$CH_3CH_2CH_2NH_2$

Similarly, when a halogenoalkane is refluxed with an aqueous solution of sodium cyanide, the halogen is replaced by a cyano (-CN) group to form the corresponding **nitrile**. The reaction is considered nucleophilic substitution as cyanide ion (CN^-) displaces the halogen by using a lone pair to form a coordinate bond with carbon.

$$H-\overset{\overset{\displaystyle H}{|}}{\underset{\underset{\displaystyle H}{|}}{C}}-\overset{\overset{\displaystyle H}{|}}{\underset{\underset{\displaystyle H}{|}}{C}}-\overset{\overset{\displaystyle H}{|}}{\underset{\underset{\displaystyle Br}{|}}{C}}-H \quad + \quad NaCN \quad \longrightarrow$$

1-bromopropane
$CH_3CH_2CH_2Br$

$$H-\overset{\overset{\displaystyle H}{|}}{\underset{\underset{\displaystyle H}{|}}{C}}-\overset{\overset{\displaystyle H}{|}}{\underset{\underset{\displaystyle H}{|}}{C}}-\overset{\overset{\displaystyle H}{|}}{\underset{\underset{\displaystyle CN}{|}}{C}}-H \quad + \quad NaBr$$

butanenitrile
$CH_3CH_2CH_2CN$

Exercise 2.5G

1. Ammonia reacts with halogenoalkanes to form amines. Write an equation for the reaction of ammonia with chloroethane. *(CCEA June 2007)*

2. Write the structure for the product when 2-bromobutane reacts with (a) ammonia and (b) aqueous sodium cyanide.
   (Adapted from CCEA June 2005)

3. Excess ammonia reacts with 1,5-dichloropentane, $Cl(CH_2)_5Cl$ to produce cadaverine, $H_2N(CH_2)_5NH_2$ a putrid product formed from the decay of flesh. (a) Suggest an equation for this reaction. (b) The smell of cadaverine can be eliminated by adding hydrochloric acid. What does this suggest about the chemical nature of cadaverine?
   (CCEA June 2006)

Before moving to the next section, check that you are able to:

- Deduce the structure of the product when a halogenoalkane is refluxed with ammonia or cyanide ion and write an equation for the reaction.

- Explain why the displacement of a halogen to form the corresponding amine or nitrile is described as nucleophilic substitution.

Hydrolysis Reactions

The term **hydrolysis** describes a reaction in which bonds are broken as the result of a compound reacting with water. Forming an alcohol by refluxing a halogenoalkane with water is an example of hydrolysis.

$$CH_3CH_2CH_2CH_2Br + H_2O \rightarrow$$
$$CH_3CH_2CH_2CH_2OH + HBr$$

The reaction is also an example of nucleophilic substitution as it involves water forming a coordinate bond with the electron-deficient carbon in the carbon-halogen bond ($C^{\delta+}$-$Br^{\delta-}$). The same reaction occurs when a halogenoalkane is refluxed with dilute alkali, but is considerably faster as hydroxide ion is a better nucleophile than water. The reaction between a halogenoalkane and dilute alkali to produce the corresponding alcohol is known as **alkaline hydrolysis**.

$$CH_3CH_2CH_2CH_2Br + OH^- \rightarrow$$
$$CH_3CH_2CH_2CH_2OH + Br^-$$

Exercise 2.5H

Write the equation for the reaction that occurs when chloromethane is hydrolysed with 'heavy water', D_2O where deuterium, D is an isotope of hydrogen. *(Adapted from CCEA June 2011)*

Hydroxide ion is a better nucleophile than water as it is more strongly attracted to the electron-deficient carbon in the carbon-halogen bond ($C^{\delta+}$). As a result, increasing the attraction between the nucleophile and the electron-deficient carbon would be expected to increase the rate at which the carbon-halogen bond is hydrolysed. The expected increase in rate as the carbon-halogen bond becomes more polar is however reversed by a decrease in the carbon-halogen bond strength that makes it easier for the nucleophile to displace the halogen as the halogen gets bigger down the group.

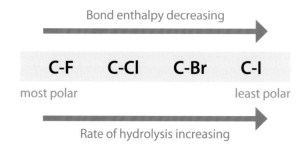

The hydrolysis of a halogenoalkane produces halide ions which can be detected by adding silver nitrate solution to the reaction mixture. As the reaction proceeds halide ions formed in the reaction combine with silver ions from the silver nitrate solution to form a precipitate of the corresponding silver halide.

Hydrolysis of the carbon-halogen bond:

$$R\text{-}X + H_2O \rightarrow R\text{-}OH + H^+ + X^-$$

where X = Cl, Br, I

Formation of a silver halide precipitate:

$$Ag^+ + X^- \rightarrow AgX$$

The rate at which a carbon-halogen bond undergoes hydrolysis can then be calculated by measuring the time it takes for the silver halide precipitate to form.

$$\text{Rate of hydrolysis} = \frac{1}{\text{Time for precipitate to form}}$$

The formation of silver halide precipitates during the hydrolysis of 1-chlorobutane, 1-bromobutane and 1-iodobutane is shown in Figure 12. The precipitates form in the order: AgI (yellow), AgBr (cream), AgCl (white) indicating that, as expected, the rate of hydrolysis increases as the carbon-halogen bond becomes weaker down the group.

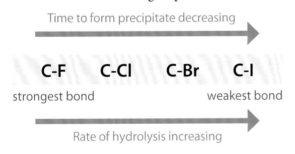

Time to form precipitate decreasing →

C-F   C-Cl   C-Br   C-I

strongest bond   weakest bond

Rate of hydrolysis increasing →

Worked Example 2.5v

Samples of 1-chloro, 1-bromo and 1-iodobutane were added to separate test tubes and heated gently. State what is be observed when silver nitrate solution is added to each test tube and explain the relative rates of reaction in terms of bond strength and bond polarity.

(Adapted from CCEA June 2003)

Solution

A yellow precipitate forms in the mixture containing 1-iodobutane. A cream precipitate then forms in the mixture containing 1-bromobutane and is followed by a white precipitate in the mixture containing 1-chlorobutane.

The rate of hydrolysis is expected to decrease as the carbon-halogen bond becomes less polar down the group. The rate is also expected to increase as the carbon-halogen bond becomes weaker down the group. The latter effect dominates as the rate is observed to increase as the carbon-halogen bond gets weaker down the group.

Exercise 2.5I

1. Samples of 1-iodobutane, 1-bromobutane and 1-chlorobutane are placed in separate test tubes labelled A, B and C respectively. Silver nitrate is added to each test tube and the mixtures warmed gently. (a) Describe the changes that occur in test tube A. (b) Explain the relative rates of hydrolysis in terms of the relative strength and polarity of the carbon-halogen bonds. (c) Write equations for the two reactions that occur in test tube B. *(Adapted from CCEA June 2006)*

Figure 12: The formation of silver halide precipitates during the hydrolysis of (from left to right): 1-chlorobutane, 1-bromobutane and 1-iodobutane. (a) Silver iodide forms first. (b) Silver bromide forms second.

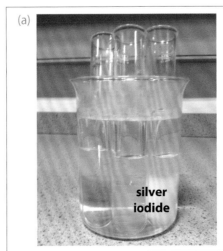

(a)

silver iodide

(b)

silver bromide

2. Bromochlorodifluoromethane, $BrClF_2C$ is used to extinguish fires. Suggest which carbon-halogen bond is most readily hydrolysed when $BrClF_2C$ is heated with aqueous sodium hydroxide. *(CCEA June 2007)*

3. When added to water t-butyl chloride, $(CH_3)_3CCl$ undergoes immediate hydrolysis to produce the corresponding alcohol. Suggest why the hydrolysis of n-butyl chloride, $CH_3CH_2CH_2CH_2Cl$ is significantly slower than the hydrolysis of t-butyl chloride.

(CCEA June 2011)

Before moving to the next section, check that you are able to:

- Describe how to measure the relative rates of hydrolysis for halogenoalkanes.
- Explain how the rate of hydrolysis for a halogenoalkane is affected by the polarity and strength of the carbon-halogen bonds in the molecule.

Elimination Reactions

Refluxing 2-bromopropane with a solution of potassium hydroxide dissolved in ethanol results in the elimination of hydrogen bromide (HBr) from the molecule.

2-bromopropane
$CH_3CHBrCH_3$

propene
$CH_3CH=CH_2$

The solution of potassium hydroxide in ethanol is referred to as ethanolic potassium hydroxide where the term **ethanolic** describes a solution in which ethanol is the solvent.

Reactions of this type are described as **elimination reactions** as they involve the loss of a small molecule

from a larger molecule or ion. Elimination occurs when a halogenoalkane is refluxed with an ethanolic solution of sodium or potassium hydroxide and results in the elimination of the corresponding hydrogen halide to form a C=C bond in the product.

halogenoalkane
(X = halogen)

alkene

Worked Example 2.5vi

Which one of the following is an elimination reaction?

A $CH_2=CH_2 + Br_2 \rightarrow CH_2BrCH_2Br$

B $CH_3Br + NaOH \rightarrow CH_3OH + NaBr$

C $CH_3CH_2Br + NaOH \rightarrow CH_2=CH_2 + NaBr + H_2O$

D $CH_3CH_2Br + NaCN \rightarrow CH_3CH_2CN + NaBr$

(CCEA June 2002)

Solution

Reaction A is an addition reaction.
Reactions B and D are substitution reactions.
Reaction C involves elimination of HBr to form a C=C bond.
Answer C.

Exercise 2.5J

1. (a) Write an equation for the reaction of 1-bromobutane with sodium hydroxide in alcohol. (b) Name the product of the reaction. (c) State the type of reaction that has occurred.

(Adapted from CCEA June 2007)

2. Ethene can be prepared from bromoethane. Write an equation for this reaction and state the reaction conditions. *(CCEA June 2008)*

An elimination reaction will often produce more than one product. For example, refluxing 2-bromobutane with ethanolic potassium hydroxide produces a mixture of but-1-ene and but-2-ene. Both isomers are produced by the elimination of hydrogen bromide.

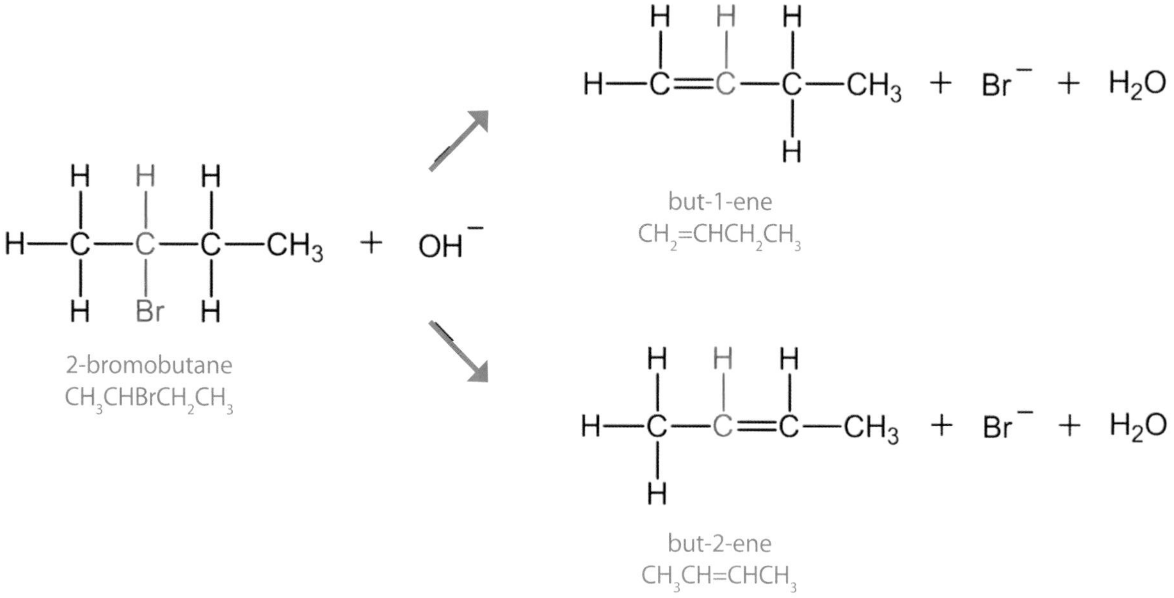

2-bromobutane
$CH_3CHBrCH_2CH_3$

but-1-ene
$CH_2=CHCH_2CH_3$

but-2-ene
$CH_3CH=CHCH_3$

Worked Example 2.5vii

(a) Write the equation for the reaction that occurs when 2-chlorobutane reacts with ethanolic potassium hydroxide. (b) Explain the term ethanolic. (c) Draw the structure of all possible products and write the systematic name for each product. *(Adapted from CCEA June 2005)*

Solution

(a) $C_4H_9Cl + KOH \rightarrow C_4H_8 + KCl + H_2O$

(b) The term ethanolic describes a solution in which the solvent is ethanol.

(c)

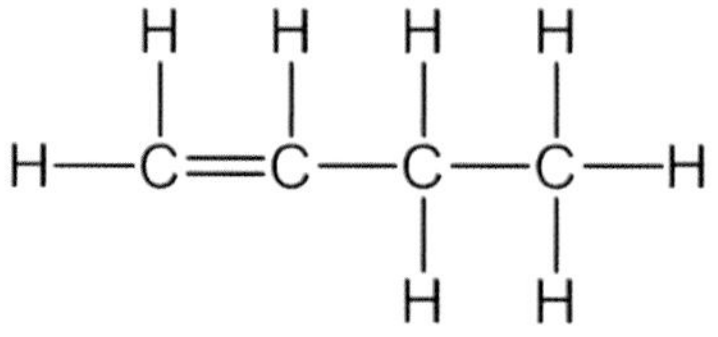

but-1-ene

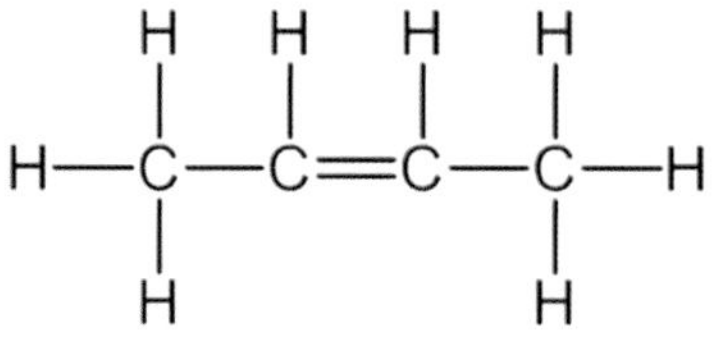

but-2-ene

Exercise 2.5K

1. Draw the structure of the product formed when 1-bromo-2-methylbutane is heated with (a) aqueous sodium hydroxide and (b) alcoholic sodium hydroxide. *(CCEA January 2008)*

2. State the type of reaction that occurs when 1,5-dichloropentane reacts with sodium hydroxide in ethanol to produce penta-1,4-diene.

$$2NaOH + Cl(CH_2)_5Cl \rightarrow$$
$$CH_2=CHCH_2CH=CH_2 + 2NaCl + 2H_2O$$

(CCEA June 2006)

Before moving to the next section, check that you are able to:

• Explain what is meant by an elimination reaction and recall the conditions for the elimination of a hydrogen halide from the corresponding halogenoalkane.

• Recognise that elimination may result in more than one product and deduce the structure of the products formed by an elimination reaction.

2.6 Alcohols

CONNECTIONS

- The 'sugar alcohols' sorbitol, xylitol and mannitol are found in many types of plants and are used as artificial sweeteners in many foods and drinks.
- In many countries a blend of gasoline and alcohol known as E10 or 'Gasohol' is used to fuel motor vehicles.

Structure and Properties

In this section we are learning to:

- Account for the properties of alcohols in terms of the bonding within alcohols.
- Classify the structures of alcohols as primary, secondary or tertiary.
- Use systematic (IUPAC) rules to name alcohols.

Factors Affecting Solubility

An **alcohol** is a saturated hydrocarbon that contains one or more hydroxyl (-OH) groups. The hydroxyl (-OH) group is the functional group that determines the reactions and properties of alcohols. The remainder of an alcohol molecule is composed of alkyl groups and is essentially nonpolar as illustrated in Figure 1.

Smaller alcohols such as methanol, CH_3OH and ethanol, C_2H_5OH experience a combination of van der Waals attraction and hydrogen bonding between molecules. The ability of alcohols to form hydrogen bonds results in smaller alcohols being **miscible** with water in all proportions. The formation of hydrogen bonds between molecules in methanol, CH_3OH and a mixture of methanol and water is illustrated in Figure 2. As the alcohols become larger the van der Waals attraction dominates to the extent that some isomers of hexanol, $C_6H_{13}OH$ are immiscible in water.

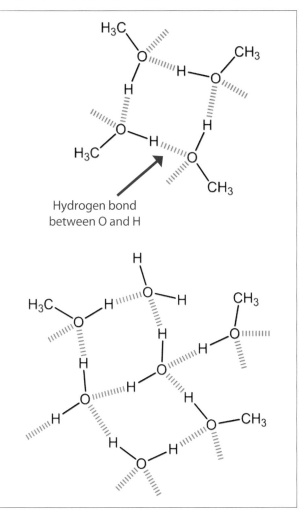

Figure 2: The formation of hydrogen bonds between neighbouring molecules in (a) methanol, CH_3OH and (b) a mixture of methanol and water.

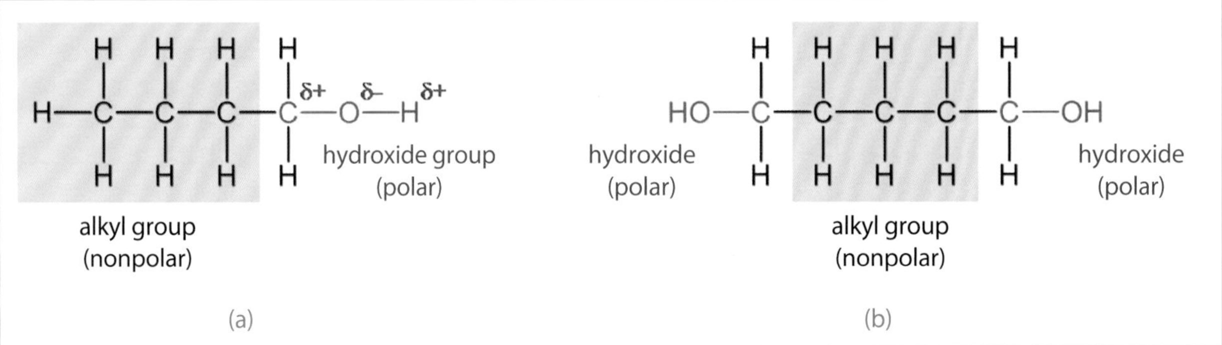

Figure 1: Polar and nonpolar regions within (a) butan-1-ol and (b) pentan-1,5-diol.

Exercise 2.6A

1. (a) Draw the structure of ethanol, C_2H_5OH showing all the bonds present. (b) Explain why ethanol is soluble in water. *(CCEA June 2004)*

2. The attraction between adjacent molecules in ethanol is due to

   A covalent bonds only.

   B hydrogen bonds only.

   C hydrogen bonds and van der Waals forces.

   D van der Waals forces only.

   (CCEA June 2011)

3. Explain why ethanol is soluble in water but ethene is immiscible with water.

   (CCEA June 2003)

4. Methylated spirits contains ethanol (b.p. 78 °C), methanol (b.p. 64 °C) and water. (a) Explain why ethanol, methanol and water are miscible. (b) Suggest how the components of methylated spirits could be separated. *(CCEA June 2007)*

Before moving to the next section, check that you are able to:

- Describe the nature of the attraction between molecules in smaller alcohols.

- Explain why alcohols become less soluble in polar solvents as they get larger.

Factors Affecting Boiling Point

Alcohols containing a single hydroxyl group form a homologous series with the general formula $C_nH_{2n+1}OH$. The formulas for the members of the series are obtained by inserting $n = 1, 2, ...$ in the general formula. The sequence of straight-chain alcohols in

Figure 3 demonstrates that the boiling points of the alcohols increase as the molar mass of the compound increases. As in alkanes, the increase in boiling point is due to an increase in the van der Waals attraction between neighbouring molecules as the number of electrons in the molecule increases.

As with alkanes, a straight-chain alcohol will have a higher boiling point than a more branched isomer. For instance, the compound 2-methylpropan-2-ol is a structural isomer of butan-2-ol. The molecular shapes in Figure 4 reveal that it has a branched structure that reduces the amount of contact between the electrons in neighbouring molecules. This, in turn, decreases the strength of the van der Waals attraction between molecules and lowers the boiling point.

The boiling point of an alcohol is also affected by the

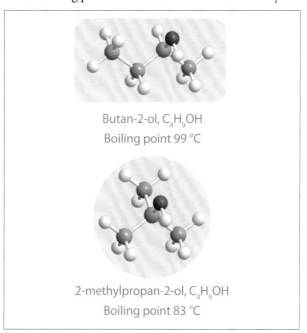

Butan-2-ol, C_4H_9OH
Boiling point 99 °C

2-methylpropan-2-ol, C_4H_9OH
Boiling point 83 °C

Figure 4: The effect of van der Waals attraction on the boiling points of the isomers butan-2-ol and 2-methylpropan-2-ol.

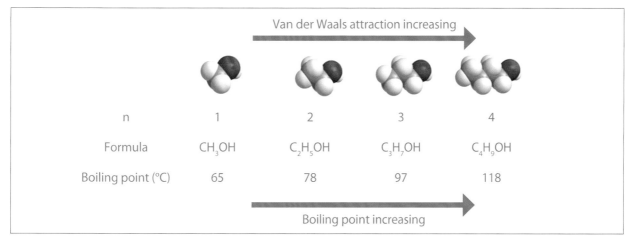

Van der Waals attraction increasing

n	1	2	3	4
Formula	CH_3OH	C_2H_5OH	C_3H_7OH	C_4H_9OH
Boiling point (°C)	65	78	97	118

Boiling point increasing

Figure 3: The effect of van der Waals attraction on the boiling points of the straight-chain alcohols, $C_nH_{2n+1}OH$.

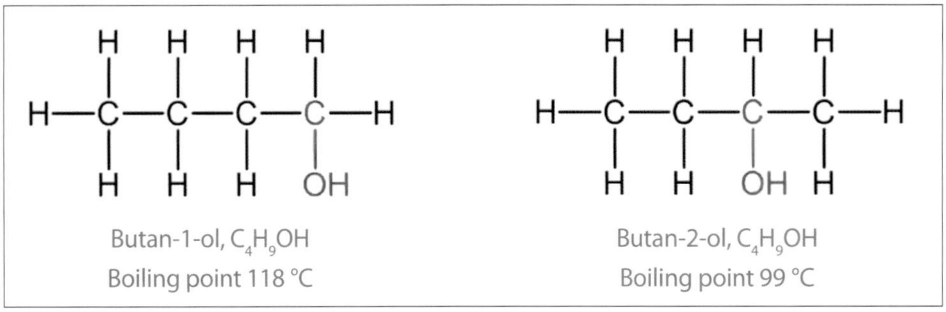

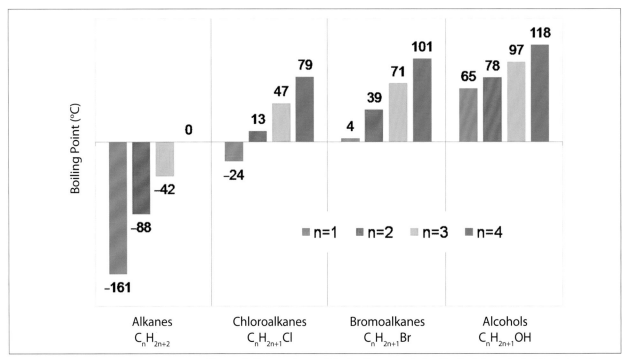

Butan-1-ol, C_4H_9OH
Boiling point 118 °C

Butan-2-ol, C_4H_9OH
Boiling point 99 °C

Figure 5: The effect of van der Waals attraction on the boiling points of the isomers butan-1-ol and butan-2-ol.

location of the hydroxyl group within the molecule. For example, the butanol isomers in Figure 5 have the same size and shape. The boiling point of butan-1-ol is however higher as the hydroxyl group is better able to hydrogen bond with neighbouring molecules.

The extent to which van der Waals attraction and hydrogen bonding influence boiling point can be assessed by the boiling point comparison in Figure 6. Comparing the boiling points for the alkanes (n=1–4) and chloroalkanes (n=1–4) reveals that adding chlorine increases the boiling point by an amount that is roughly equivalent to adding two carbon atoms to the alkane. For example, the boiling point of chloromethane, CH_3Cl (–24 °C) resembles the boiling point of propane, $CH_3CH_2CH_3$ (–42 °C) while the boiling point of chloroethane, CH_3CH_2Cl (13 °C) resembles the boiling point of butane, $CH_3CH_2CH_2CH_3$ (0 °C). The increase in boiling point on adding bromine is more substantial and is roughly equivalent to adding

three carbon atoms to the alkane. The increase in boiling point on adding a hydroxyl group to form the corresponding alcohol is even greater and is equivalent to adding four or more carbon atoms to the alkane.

Exercise 2.6B

1. The diagram shows the formation of a bond between molecule A and molecule B. (a) Name the molecules A and B. (b) State the type of bond formed between A and B. (c) State one physical property of substance A affected by this type of bond.

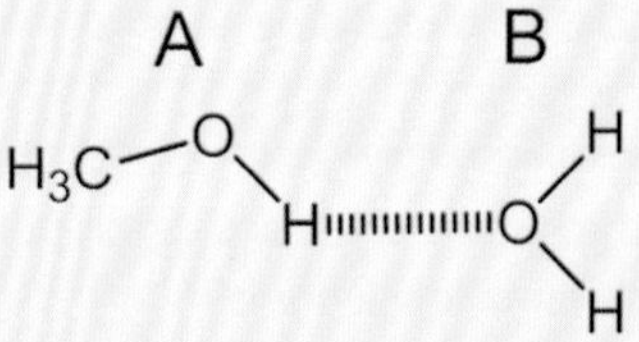

A   B

H_3C-O
      H⸺⸺⸺⸺O
                              H

(CCEA June 2002)

Figure 6: Comparison of the boiling points for the first four straight-chain alkanes, chloroalkanes, bromoalkanes and alcohols.

2. Which one of the following has the highest boiling point?

   A CH_3OH B CH_3CH_2OH

   C CH_3Cl D $CH_3CH_2CH_3$

   (CCEA January 2003)

3. Which one of the following has the highest boiling point?

   A CH_3CH_2Cl
   B $CH_3CH_2CH_2OH$
   C $CH_3CH_2CH_2CH_3$
   D $CH_3CH_2CH_2CH_2CH_3$

   (CCEA June 2009)

Before moving to the next section, check that you are able to:

- Recall that the alcohols are a homologous series and use the general formula $C_nH_{2n+1}OH$ to generate the formula for each member of the series.
- Explain how the boiling point of an alcohol is determined by the size and shape of the molecule.
- Recall that the boiling point of an alcohol is affected by the location of the hydroxyl group within the molecule.
- Rank the boiling points of alcohols, halogenoalkanes and alkanes.

Factors Affecting Reactivity

The reactivity of an alcohol is determined by the extent to which the individual hydroxyl groups in the molecule participate in a reaction. The extent to which a particular hydroxyl group will react is determined by the primary, secondary or tertiary nature of the carbon atom attached to the hydroxyl group.

The structures of primary, secondary and tertiary alcohols can be illustrated by considering the isomers of butanol. The compound butan-1-ol is an example of a **primary alcohol** as the hydroxyl (-OH) group is bonded to a carbon (C) with one carbon atom (C) attached. The isomer 2-methylpropan-1-ol is also a primary alcohol.

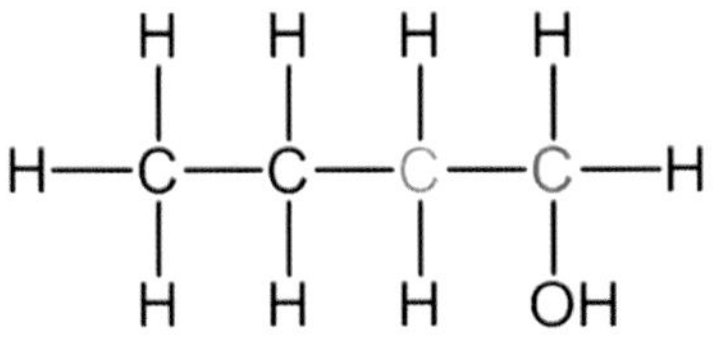

butan-1-ol (*primary*)
$CH_3CH_2CH_2CH_2OH$

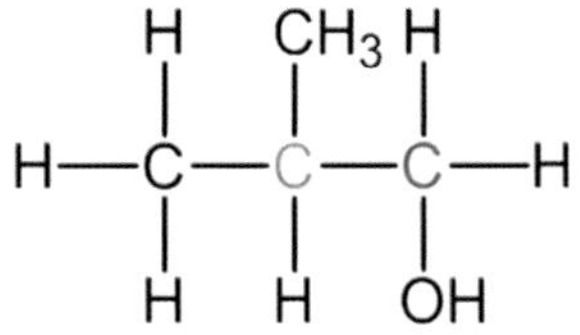

2-methylpropan-1-ol (*primary*)
$CH_3CH(CH_3)CH_2OH$

The isomer butan-2-ol is an example of a **secondary alcohol** as the hydroxyl group is bonded to a carbon (C) with two carbon atoms (C) attached. In contrast, the isomer 2-methylpropan-2-ol is an example of a **tertiary alcohol** as the hydroxyl group is bonded to a carbon (C) with three carbon atoms (C) attached.

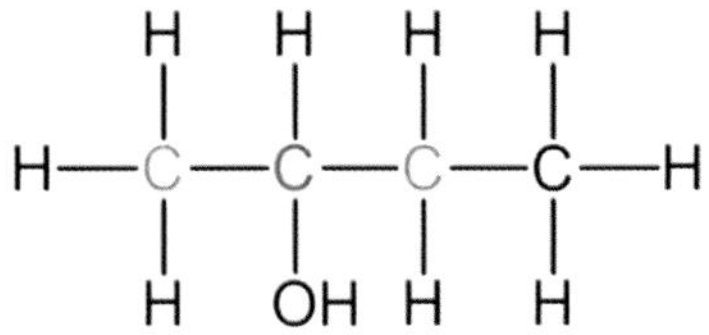

butan-2-ol (*secondary*)
$CH_3CH(OH)CH_2CH_3$

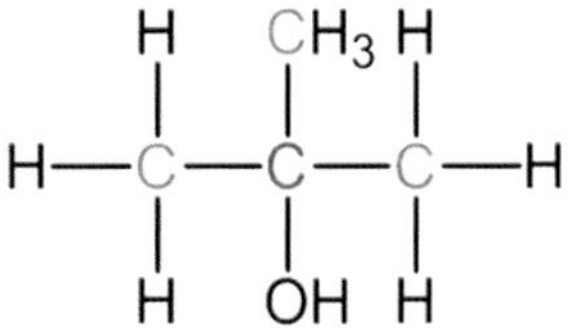

2-methylpropan-2-ol (*tertiary*)
$CH_3C(CH_3)(OH)CH_3$

Exercise 2.6C

1. (a) Ethylene glycol, $HOCH_2CH_2OH$ contains primary alcohol groups. Explain the term primary alcohol. (b) Explain why ethylene glycol is very soluble in water. *(CCEA January 2009)*

2. Which one of the following is a secondary alcohol?

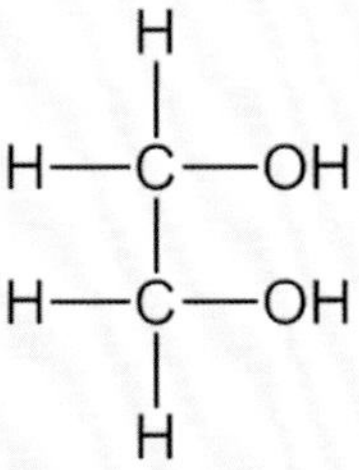

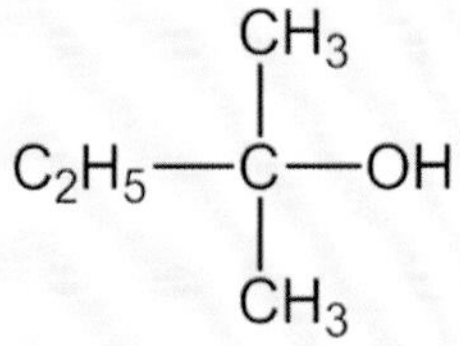

(Two more diagrams overleaf)

C

$H_3C-\overset{\displaystyle H}{\underset{\displaystyle H}{C}}-OH$

D

$H-\overset{\displaystyle CH_3}{\underset{\displaystyle C_2H_5}{C}}-OH$

(CCEA January 2007)

3. Classify the following alcohols as primary, secondary or tertiary.

A

H_3C-OH

B

$H_3C-\overset{\displaystyle OH}{\underset{\displaystyle H}{C}}-CH_3$

C

$H_3C-\overset{\displaystyle H}{\underset{\displaystyle CH_2OH}{C}}-CH_3$

D

$H_3C-\overset{\displaystyle CH_3}{\underset{\displaystyle CH_3}{C}}-\overset{\displaystyle OH}{\underset{\displaystyle CH_3}{C}}-CH_3$

(CCEA January 2006)

Naming Alcohols

The systematic (IUPAC) name for an alcohol consists of a prefix followed by the suffix *ol*. The prefix is derived from the name of the parent straight-chain alkane on which the structure of the alcohol is based. For example methanol, CH_3OH is named using the prefix *methan* as its structure is based on methane, CH_4. Similarly ethanol, CH_3CH_2OH is named using the prefix *ethan* as its structure is based on ethane, CH_3CH_3.

In larger alcohols such as butanol, C_4H_9OH the hydroxyl group generates structural isomers and it becomes necessary to describe the location of the hydroxyl group when naming the compound. In the case of butanol, the suffix *1-ol* or *2-ol* is used to locate the hydroxyl group when naming the isomers butan-1-ol and butan-2-ol. As in alkanes, the location of the hydroxyl group is described by numbering the carbon atoms in a way that generates the lowest number prefixes. The systematic names for structural isomers of straight-chain alcohols with up to six carbon atoms are summarised in Table 1.

butan-1-ol

$CH_3CH_2CH_2CH_2OH$

butan-2-ol

$CH_3CH(OH)CH_2CH_3$

The alcohols 2-methylpropan-1-ol and 2-methylpropan-2-ol are isomers of butan-1-ol. They are named using the prefix *propan* as their structure is based on the three carbon chain in propane, $CH_3CH_2CH_3$. The location of the hydroxyl group is described by the suffix *1-ol* or *2-ol* and is based on a numbering of the carbon atoms that produces the lowest number prefixes. Having established the hydroxyl group, the location of the methyl group is then described by adding the prefix *2-methyl*.

2-methylpropan-1-ol

$CH_3CH(CH_3)CH_2OH$

2-methylpropan-2-ol

$CH_3C(CH_3)(OH)CH_3$

The construction of prefixes to describe two or more functional groups is illustrated by the isomers 1-chloro-3-methyl-pentan-3-ol and 3-chloro-4-methylpentan-2-ol. Both isomers are named using the prefix *pentan* as their structure is based on the chain of five carbon atoms in pentane, $CH_3(CH_2)_3CH_3$. The prefixes used to describe the chlorine and methyl groups are listed in alphabetical

Table 1: Systematic names for the structural isomers of straight-chain alcohols (ROH) with up to six carbon atoms.

Parent alkane	Parent alcohol	Structural isomers
methane, CH_4 *(Naming prefix: methan)*	CH_3OH **methan**ol	CH_3OH methanol
ethane, CH_3CH_3 *(Naming prefix: ethan)*	C_2H_5OH **ethan**ol	CH_3CH_2OH ethanol
propane, $CH_3CH_2CH_3$ *(Naming prefix: propan)*	C_3H_7OH **propan**ol	$CH_3CH_2CH_2OH$ propan-1-ol $CH_3CH(OH)CH_3$ propan-2-ol
butane, $CH_3CH_2CH_2CH_3$ *(Naming prefix: butan)*	C_4H_9OH **butan**ol	$CH_3CH_2CH_2CH_2OH$ butan-1ol $CH_3CH_2CH(OH)CH_3$ butan-2-ol
pentane, $CH_3CH_2CH_2CH_2CH_3$ *(Naming prefix: pentan)*	$C_5H_{11}OH$ **pentan**ol	$CH_3CH_2CH_2CH_2CH_2OH$ pentan-1-ol $CH_3CH_2CH_2CH(OH)CH_3$ pentan-2-ol $CH_3CH_2CH(OH)CH_2CH_3$ pentan-3-ol
hexane, $CH_3CH_2CH_2CH_2CH_2CH_3$ *(Naming prefix: hexan)*	$C_6H_{13}OH$ **hexan**ol	$CH_3CH_2CH_2CH_2CH_2CH_2OH$ hexan-1-ol $CH_3CH_2CH_2CH_2CH(OH)CH_3$ hexan-2-ol $CH_3CH_2CH_2CH(OH)CH_2CH_3$ hexan-3-ol

order, and are based on the numbering of carbon atoms used to locate the hydroxyl group.

1-chloro-3-methylpentan-3-ol
$CH_2ClCH_2C(CH_3)(OH)CH_2CH_3$

3-chloro-4-methylpentan-2-ol
$CH_3CH(OH)CHClCH(CH_3)_2$

As in alkanes, the locations of two or more identical functional groups are described by using the number prefixes *di*, *tri*, *tetra* ... to construct prefixes such as *dimethyl* and *trichloro*. In contrast, the location of a second hydroxyl group is described by using the suffix *diol*. The following examples illustrate the appropriate numbering of the carbon atoms when using the suffix *diol* to name alcohols containing two hydroxyl groups.

2-methylpropan-1,2-diol
$CH_2(OH)C(OH)(CH_3)_2$

3-methylbutan-1,3-diol
$CH_2(OH)CH_2C(OH)(CH_3)_2$

Rules for naming alcohols (including diols):

- The name of an alcohol consists of a prefix followed by the suffix *ol* or *diol*. The prefix is based on the name of the parent (straight-chain) alkane on which the structure of the alcohol is based.

- The location of each hydroxyl group is described by adding a number prefix before the suffix. The number prefix is based on a numbering of the carbon atoms that produces the smallest number prefixes.

- Additional prefixes are then added to locate additional functional groups on the carbon chain. The prefixes are given in alphabetical order and are based on the numbering of the carbons used to locate the hydroxyl groups.

Exercise 2.6D

1. There are four alcohols with the formula, C_4H_9OH. Complete the following table by drawing the missing structures, writing the name for each structure, and classifying each structure as primary, secondary or tertiary.

Structure	Name	Classification
	butan-1-ol	primary
	2-methyl propan-2-ol	
	2-methyl propan-1-ol	

(CCEA January 2008)

2. Which one of the following is a tertiary alcohol?

    A   2-methylbutan-1-ol
    B   2-methylbutan-2-ol
    C   3-methylbutan-1-ol
    D   3-methylbutan-2-ol

(CCEA January 2009)

Before moving to the next section, check that you are able to:

- Write structural and condensed formulas for alcohols.
- Classify the structures of alcohols as primary, secondary or tertiary.
- Deduce systematic names for alcohols and diols.

Production and Uses of Ethanol

In this section we are learning to:

- Describe the manufacture of ethanol on an industrial scale by the hydration of ethene and the fermentation of sugars.
- Recall positive and negative effects of using alcohol as a recreational drug.
- Discuss how measuring alcohol in 'units' can be used to define safe limits for alcohol consumption.
- Describe the combustion of ethanol and its use as an alternative fuel.

Industrial Production of Ethanol

Ethanol, C_2H_5OH is produced on an industrial scale by reacting a mixture of ethene and steam at high temperature and high pressure in the presence of a phosphoric acid catalyst.

ethene
$CH_2{=}CH_2$

ethanol
CH_3CH_2OH

The reaction is an example of an addition reaction in which steam (H_2O) adds across the C=C bond in ethene to form ethanol. The reaction is also an example of a **hydration reaction** as it involves the addition of water to a compound to form a new substance.

Most of the ethanol used to make alcoholic drinks is instead manufactured by the **fermentation** of sugars obtained from fruit and grains such as grapes and barley. The sugars extracted from fruits and grains are fermented by adding yeast to a warm aqueous solution containing the sugars. In the absence of oxygen (anaerobic conditions) the yeast respires by converting the sugars in the solution to ethanol and carbon dioxide.

$$C_6H_{12}O_{6\,(aq)} \rightarrow 2C_2H_5OH_{\,(aq)} + 2CO_{2\,(g)}$$

In many countries sugar cane is grown specifically as a source of sugar for the production of ethanol by fermentation. Much of the ethanol manufactured in this way is intended for use as fuel in motor vehicles.

Exercise 2.6E

1. (a) Use an equation to help explain how ethanol is manufactured from ethene. (b) State another method of producing ethanol on an industrial scale. *(CCEA January 2010)*

2. Ethanol is produced commercially by the fermentation of sucrose which is initially converted to glucose, $C_6H_{12}O_6$. (a) Explain the term fermentation. (b) Write an equation for the production of ethanol from glucose.

    (CCEA June 2006)

3. Which one of the following is not a source of ethanol?
    A   Manufacture from sugar cane.
    B   Catalytic hydration of ethene.
    C   Hydrolysis of bromoethane with alkali.
    D   Reaction of bromoethane with ammonia.

    (CCEA June 2002)

Before moving to the next section, check that you are able to:

- Describe the large scale production of ethanol by the hydration of ethene.
- Explain what is meant by fermentation and describe the large scale production of ethanol by fermentation.

Recreational Use of Ethanol

Alcohol (ethanol) is widely used as a recreational drug and has both positive and negative effects. Consuming small amounts of alcohol can help people feel less inhibited and more relaxed in a social setting. Scientific studies also indicate that consuming small amounts of alcohol may help prevent heart disease. In contrast, consuming large quantities of alcohol impairs judgement, and may result in anti-social behaviour such as drink-driving. The excessive use of alcohol over long periods also results in permanent damage to organs such as the liver and brain, and has been linked to neurological disorders such as depression.

In the United Kingdom the alcohol content of drinks is measured in **units of alcohol** where a unit of alcohol contains 10 cm³ (8 g) of ethanol. On average, a unit of alcohol will increase the blood alcohol content (BAC) of a male by 15 mg per 100 cm³ of blood (0.015%) and a female by up to 30 mg per 100 cm³ of blood (0.03%). In the United Kingdom a BAC of 80 mg/100 cm³ (0.08%) is the legal limit for driving. A BAC above 0.08% is considered unsafe and anyone found driving with a BAC above 0.08% is considered legally unfit to drive.

Talking Point

A BAC of 80 mg/100 cm³ (0.08%) is the legal limit for driving in the United Kingdom. Drivers with a BAC below this limit are considered safe to drive. Countries such as Sweden and China have significantly lower BAC limits (0.02%) and countries such as Brazil and Pakistan have a zero tolerance policy (0.00%).

BAC (%)	Behaviour	Impairment
0.03–0.06	Relaxed, talkative	Concentration
0.06–0.09	Extraverted	Ability to reason Depth perception
0.09–0.20	Mood swings	Reflexes/ coordination Reaction time
> 0.20	Loss of sensation Loss of consciousness	Memory loss Low heart rate

Exercise 2.6F

1. Ethanol is considered a recreational drug. State one beneficial effect and one harmful effect of alcohol consumption. *(CCEA June 2008)*

2. In the UK it is illegal to drive with a blood alcohol level above 80 mg per 100 cm³. (a) Calculate the blood alcohol concentration in mol dm⁻³ for blood containing 90 mg of ethanol per 100 cm³. (b) Which organ of the body may be permanently affected by the consumption of alcohol? *(Adapted from CCEA June 2006)*

3. (a) A pint of beer contains two 'units' of alcohol and is 4% ethanol by mass. Calculate the moles of ethanol in one unit of alcohol if a pint of beer has a mass of 580 g. (b) State one harmful effect of alcohol on the body. *(CCEA June 2005)*

Before moving to the next section, check that you are able to:

- Discuss the positive and negative effects of alcohol consumption.
- Explain the concept of a unit of alcohol and how 'units' can be used to define safe limits for alcohol consumption

Ethanol as an Alternative Fuel

In many countries ethanol is manufactured on an industrial scale by the fermentation of sugars obtained from sugar cane or corn. Much of the ethanol produced by fermentation is then added to gasoline to produce blended fuels that can be burnt in motor vehicles. For example, a mixture of ethanol and gasoline that is 10% ethanol by volume is referred to as E10 and is commonly known as 'Gasohol'. The engines in modern cars can burn Gasohol without modification.

Ethanol contains less carbon per gram than the hydrocarbons in gasoline. As a result, burning ethanol produces less carbon dioxide for every mole of water formed. As a result, burning ethanol produces less carbon dioxide for every mole of water formed.

Complete combustion of octane (gasoline):

$$2C_8H_{18\,(l)} + 25O_{2\,(g)} \rightarrow 16CO_{2\,(g)} + 18H_2O_{\,(l)}$$

Complete combustion of ethanol:

$$2C_2H_5OH_{\,(l)} + 6O_{2\,(g)} \rightarrow 4CO_{2\,(g)} + 6H_2O_{\,(l)}$$

The amount of carbon in a fuel is reflected in the colour of the flame when the fuel burns. Fuels with a relatively high carbon content such as the hydrocarbons in gasoline burn with a 'smoky' yellow flame. A 'smoky' flame contains a considerable amount of soot (carbon) from the incomplete combustion of the fuel. In contrast, fuels with a relatively low carbon content such as ethanol burn with a cleaner 'blue flame'. The flames produced by the combustion of hexane, C_6H_{14} and ethanol, C_2H_5OH are compared in Figure 7.

Incomplete combustion of octane (gasoline):

$$2C_8H_{18\,(l)} + 17\,O_{2\,(g)} \rightarrow 16CO_{\,(g)} + 18H_2O_{\,(l)}$$

Incomplete combustion of ethanol:

$$2C_2H_5OH_{\,(l)} + 4\,O_{2\,(g)} \rightarrow 4CO_{\,(g)} + 6H_2O_{\,(l)}$$

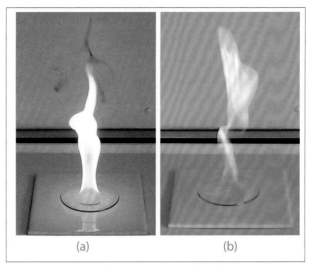

(a)   (b)

Figure 7: Flames produced by the combustion of (a) hexane, C_6H_{14} and (b) ethanol, C_2H_5OH.

The combustion of gasoline releases large quantities of carbon dioxide into the atmosphere that contribute to global warming. Gasoline also contains a significant amount of sulfur that is converted to sulfur dioxide when the gasoline is burnt. The sulfur dioxide then dissolves in rain droplets to form acid rain that damages the environment. In contrast, the ethanol used in blended fuels has a lower carbon content than gasoline and does not contain sulfur. As a result, blended fuels release less carbon dioxide and less sulfur dioxide into the atmosphere when they burn. Blended fuels are also better for the environment as the supply of ethanol can be sustained by growing more crops such as sugar cane and corn.

Worked Example 2.6i

(a) Write an equation for the complete combustion of ethanol. (b) Write an equation for the incomplete combustion of ethanol. (c) Explain the environmental advantage of using ethanol instead of petrol in cars.

(CCEA June 2006)

Solution

(a) Complete combustion:

$$C_2H_5OH + 3O_2 \rightarrow 2CO_2 + 3H_2O$$

(b) Incomplete combustion:

$$C_2H_5OH + 2O_2 \rightarrow 2CO + 3H_2O$$

(c) Ethanol has a lower carbon content than the hydrocarbons in petrol and does not contain sulfur. As a result, ethanol produces less carbon dioxide and less sulfur dioxide when it burns.

Reducing carbon dioxide emissions reduces damage to the environment from global warming and a reduction in sulfur dioxide emissions reduces damage to the environment caused by acid rain. Ethanol is also better for the environment as its use can be sustained by growing more crops such as sugar cane and corn.

Exercise 2.6G

(a) Write an equation for the complete combustion of methanol. (b) Write an equation for the incomplete combustion of methanol. (c) Explain the environmental advantage of using methanol instead of petrol in cars. *(CCEA January 2006)*

> **Before moving to the next section, check that you are able to:**
>
> - Write equations for the complete and incomplete combustion of alcohols.
> - Explain the advantages of using alcohols in fuels.

Laboratory Preparation of Alcohols

In this section we are learning to:

- Recall that alcohols can be prepared in the laboratory by the alkaline hydrolysis of a halogenoalkane.
- Deduce the structure of the alcohol formed by the alkaline hydrolysis of a halogenoalkane and write an equation for the reaction.

Alcohols are prepared in the laboratory by the alkaline hydrolysis of halogenoalkanes. For example, butan-1-ol can be prepared by refluxing 1-bromobutane with aqueous sodium hydroxide.

$$CH_3CH_2CH_2CH_2Br + OH^- \rightarrow$$
$$CH_3CH_2CH_2CH_2OH + Br^-$$

1-bromobutane   butan-1-ol

The reaction involves the substitution of bromine by hydroxide ion. If the structure of the bromoalkane is represented by the condensed formula RBr the equation can be written in a more general form that describes the hydrolysis of any bromoalkane.

> *Alkaline hydrolysis of a bromoalkane:*
> $$RBr + OH^- \rightarrow ROH + Br^-$$

Alcohols can also be prepared from the corresponding fluoroalkanes (RF), chloroalkanes (RCl) and iodoalkanes (RI). For example, butan-2-ol can be prepared by refluxing 2-chlorobutane with aqueous sodium hydroxide.

$$CH_3CHClCH_2CH_3 + OH^- \rightarrow$$
$$CH_3CH(OH)CH_2CH_3 + Cl^-$$

2-chlorobutane   butan-2-ol

> *Alkaline hydrolysis of a chloroalkane:*
> $$RCl + OH^- \rightarrow ROH + Cl^-$$

Exercise 2.6H

1. (a) Write the equation for the reaction that occurs when 2-chloropropane is refluxed with dilute potassium hydroxide. (b) Draw and name the product.

2. (a) State the type of reaction that occurs when an alcohol is formed by refluxing a halogenoalkane with aqueous alkali. (b) Explain why the mixture is refluxed.

3. (a) Write the equation for the reaction that occurs when 1,2-dichloroethane is refluxed with dilute sodium hydroxide. (b) Draw and name the product.

> **Before moving to the next section, check that you are able to:**
>
> - Recall that alcohols can be prepared in the laboratory by the alkaline hydrolysis of a halogenoalkane.
> - Deduce the structure of the alcohol formed by the alkaline hydrolysis of a halogenoalkane and write an equation for the reaction.

Reactions of Primary Alcohols

In this section we are learning to:

- Describe the reactions of primary alcohols with sodium, hydrogen halides, phosphorus(V) chloride and thionyl chloride.
- Deduce the structure of the product when a primary alcohol reacts with sodium, a hydrogen halide, phosphorus(V) chloride or thionyl chloride.
- Write equations for the reactions of primary alcohols.

Reaction with Sodium

The O-H bond in a hydroxyl (-OH) group behaves in the same way as the O-H bonds in water. As a result, reactive metals such as sodium will react with alcohols in the same way that they react with water. The state symbol (alc) is used to indicate a solution in alcohol.

Reaction of sodium with water:

$$2H_2O_{(l)} + 2Na_{(s)} \rightarrow 2NaOH_{(aq)} + H_{2(g)}$$

Reaction of sodium with ethanol:

$$2CH_3CH_2OH_{(l)} + 2Na_{(s)} \rightarrow$$
$$2CH_3CH_2ONa_{(alc)} + H_{2(g)}$$
sodium ethoxide

The reaction between sodium and ethanol is exothermic. The sodium ethoxide formed in the reaction is a strong base and reacts with water to form a colourless solution that is strongly alkaline.

$$CH_3CH_2ONa_{(alc)} + H_2O_{(l)} \rightarrow$$
$$CH_3CH_2OH_{(aq)} + NaOH_{(aq)}$$

Exercise 2.6I

1. Ethanol is a neutral liquid. When sodium is added to ethanol it sinks and reacts to form a strong base. Describe what is observed during this reaction. *(CCEA June 2005)*

2. (a) Write an equation for the reaction between propan-1-ol and sodium. (b) Name the salt formed in the reaction.

3. Sodium *tert*-butoxide is formed when sodium reacts with the alcohol shown below. (a) Write an equation for the reaction. (b) Name the alcohol. (c) Suggest the meaning of the prefix *tert*-.

$$H_3C-\underset{\underset{OH}{|}}{\overset{\overset{CH_3}{|}}{C}}-CH_3$$

Halogenation of Alcohols

The term **halogenation** refers to a reaction in which one or more halogen atoms add to a compound or replace atoms in the compound. A number of different reagents can be used to halogenate alcohols.

I. Reaction with Hydrogen Halides

Refluxing an alcohol, ROH with a hydrogen halide, HX where X = Cl, Br, ... produces the corresponding halogenoalkane, RX. The reaction is an example of halogenation as the hydroxyl (OH) group in the alcohol is replaced by a halogen (X).

Halogenation of an alcohol by HX:

$$ROH + HX \rightarrow RX + H_2O$$

The hydrogen halide (HX) is prepared *in situ* by reacting the corresponding sodium salt with concentrated sulfuric acid.

$$NaX + H_2SO_4 \rightarrow NaHSO_4 + HX$$

For example, refluxing a mixture of butan-2-ol, sodium bromide and concentrated sulfuric acid for an extended period produces the corresponding bromoalkane.

$$NaBr + H_2SO_4 \rightarrow NaHSO_4 + HBr$$
$$CH_3CH_2CH(OH)CH_3 + HBr \rightarrow$$
$$CH_3CH_2CHBrCH_3 + H_2O$$

butan-2-ol   2-bromobutane

II. Reaction with Phosphorus(V) Chloride

Phosphorus(V) chloride, PCl_5 is a white solid that reacts vigorously with alcohols (ROH) to produce the corresponding chloroalkane (RCl).

Chlorination by PCl_5:

$$ROH_{(l)} + PCl_{5(s)} \rightarrow RCl_{(l)} + HCl_{(g)} + POCl_{3(l)}$$

For example, when phosphorus(V) chloride is added to propan-1-ol it reacts to form 1-chloropropane.

$$CH_3CH_2CH_2OH_{(l)} + PCl_{5(s)} \rightarrow$$
$$CH_3CH_2CH_2Cl_{(l)} + HCl_{(g)} + POCl_{3(l)}$$

propan-1-ol   1-chloropropane

The reaction is exothermic and produces a colourless pungent smelling gas (HCl). As a result, the reaction between phosphorus(V) chloride and an alcohol must be carried out in a fume cupboard.

The addition of phosphorus(V) chloride can be used to test for the presence of an alcohol as the HCl gas turns damp blue litmus paper red and produces white fumes when it contacts the vapour produced by concentrated ammonia solution.

III. Reaction with Thionyl Chloride

Thionyl chloride, $SOCl_2$ is a colourless liquid that reacts with water vapour in the air to produce a mixture of sulfur dioxide and hydrogen chloride. Both are harmful gases with a pungent odour. As a result, reactions involving thionyl chloride must be carried out in a fume cupboard.

$$SOCl_{2\,(l)} + H_2O_{\,(g)} \rightarrow SO_{2\,(g)} + 2HCl_{\,(g)}$$

When thionyl chloride reacts with an alcohol, ROH the hydroxyl (OH) group in the alcohol is replaced by chlorine to form the corresponding chloroalkane, RCl. The reaction is generally preferred over other methods of making chloroalkanes as the by-products are gases and do not contaminate the chloroalkane formed in the reaction.

Chlorination by $SOCl_2$:

$$ROH_{\,(l)} + SOCl_{2\,(l)} \rightarrow RCl_{\,(l)} + HCl_{\,(g)} + SO_{2\,(g)}$$

Exercise 2.6J

1. Complete the flow scheme by writing the formula for each product.

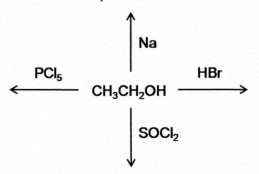

(CCEA January 2010)

2. (a) Write the equation for the reaction of butan-2-ol with hydrogen bromide. (b) Calculate the theoretical yield of 2-bromobutane if 11.1 g of butan-2-ol is used. (c) Calculate the mass of 2-bromobutane obtained if the percentage yield for the reaction is 85 %. *(CCEA June 2005)*

3. (a) Name the alcohol used to make 1-chlorobutane by reacting an alcohol with phosphorus pentachloride. (b) Write the equation for the reaction. (c) State two observations when phosphorus pentachloride is added to the alcohol.

(CCEA June 2001)

4. Thionyl chloride reacts with primary alcohols to form chloroalkanes. Write an equation for the reaction of ethanol with thionyl chloride.

(CCEA June 2004)

5. Which one of the following does not produce a gas when reacted with butanol?

   A   phosphorus pentachloride
   B   thionyl chloride
   C   hydrogen bromide
   D   sodium

(CCEA January 2007)

6. Which one of the following reagents could be used to detect the presence of ethanol in Gasohol – a mixture of alkanes, alkenes and ethanol.

   A   bromine   B   hydrogen chloride
   C   sodium   D   universal indicator

(CCEA June 2009)

> **Before moving to the next section, check that you are able to:**
>
> - Describe the reactions of primary alcohols with sodium, hydrogen halides, phosphorus(V) chloride and thionyl chloride.
> - Deduce the structure of the product when a primary alcohol reacts with sodium, a hydrogen halide, phosphorus(V) chloride or thionyl chloride.
> - Write equations for the reactions of a primary alcohol.

Oxidation of Alcohols

In this section we are learning to:

- Deduce the structure of the product when an alcohol is oxidised.
- Write balanced equations for the oxidation of alcohols.
- Describe the use of oxidising agents to distinguish between primary, secondary and tertiary alcohols.

Oxidation of Primary Alcohols

A solution of potassium dichromate $(K_2Cr_2O_7)$ in dilute sulfuric acid is referred to as acidified potassium dichromate and is a strong oxidising agent. When a primary alcohol is refluxed with acidified potassium dichromate the alcohol (RCH_2OH) is oxidised to the corresponding **carboxylic acid** (RCOOH).

$$R-\overset{\overset{\displaystyle H}{|}}{\underset{\underset{\displaystyle H}{|}}{C}}-OH + 2[O] \longrightarrow R-\overset{\overset{\displaystyle O}{\|}}{C}-OH + H_2O$$

primary alcohol
RCH_2OH

carboxylic acid
$RCOOH$

The oxidising agent is a source of oxygen and is represented by the symbol [O] when writing the equation for the reaction. When propan-1-ol is refluxed with acidified potassium dichromate the alcohol is oxidised to propanoic acid, CH_3CH_2COOH. The equation for the oxidation reveals that the dichromate provides two moles of oxygen atoms (2 [O]) for every mole of alcohol oxidised.

$$CH_3CH_2CH_2OH + 2[O] \rightarrow$$
$$CH_3CH_2COOH + H_2O$$

propan-1-ol   propanoic acid

The reactions of a carboxylic acid are determined by the carboxyl (-COOH) group. The systematic names for carboxylic acids with up to six carbon atoms are summarised in Table 2.

Acidified dichromate solution contains the dichromate ion, $Cr_2O_7^{2-}$. The dichromate ion contains chromium in an oxidation state of +6 and is responsible for the bright orange colour of the acidified dichromate solution. When dichromate oxidises an alcohol the orange colour of the dichromate ions is replaced by the green colour of the chromium III ions, Cr^{3+} that are formed as dichromate is reduced.

Parent alkane	Carboxylic acid (Suffix: -oic acid)
methane, CH_4 (Naming prefix: methan)	HCOOH **methan**oic acid
ethane, CH_3CH_3 (Naming prefix: ethan)	CH_3COOH **ethan**oic acid
propane, $CH_3CH_2CH_3$ (Naming prefix: propan)	CH_3CH_2COOH **propan**oic acid
butane, $CH_3CH_2CH_2CH_3$ (Naming prefix: butan)	$CH_3CH_2CH_2COOH$ **butan**oic acid
pentane, $CH_3CH_2CH_2CH_2CH_3$ (Naming prefix: pentan)	$CH_3CH_2CH_2CH_2COOH$ **pentan**oic acid
hexane, $CH_3CH_2CH_2CH_2CH_2CH_3$ (Naming prefix: hexan)	$CH_3CH_2CH_2CH_2CH_2COOH$ **hexan**oic acid

Table 2: Systematic names for carboxylic acids (RCOOH) with up to six carbon atoms.

Exercise 2.6K

1. Ethanol is oxidised when heated with acidified potassium dichromate. Write the equation for the oxidation of ethanol to ethanoic acid using [O] to represent acidified potassium dichromate.

   (CCEA June 2005)

2. The oxidation of ethanol to ethanoic acid is carried out using the following apparatus.

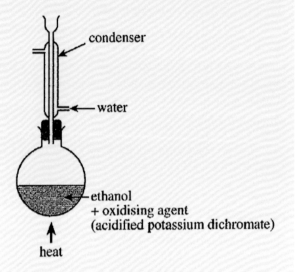

   The purpose of the condenser is to prevent

   A   air reacting with the ethanoic acid.
   B   air reacting with the ethanol.
   C   the oxidising agent from escaping.
   D   unreacted ethanol from escaping.

   (Adapted from CCEA January 2004)

The oxidation of a primary alcohol to the corresponding carboxylic acid occurs when the alcohol is refluxed with the oxidising agent for an extended period. If the mixture is instead distilled the alcohol is only partially oxidised to the corresponding **aldehyde** (RCHO) before being distilled from the reaction mixture.

$$R-\overset{\overset{\displaystyle H}{|}}{\underset{\underset{\displaystyle H}{|}}{C}}-OH + [O] \longrightarrow R-\overset{\overset{\displaystyle O}{\|}}{C}-H + H_2O$$

primary alcohol
RCH_2OH

aldehyde
RCHO

When a mixture of propan-1-ol, $CH_3CH_2CH_2OH$ and acidified potassium dichromate is distilled, the propan-1-ol is oxidised to propanal, CH_3CH_2CHO

Parent alkane	Aldehyde (Suffix: -al)
methane, CH_4 *(Naming prefix: methan)*	HCHO **methan**al
ethane, CH_3CH_3 *(Naming prefix: ethan)*	CH_3CHO **ethan**al
propane, $CH_3CH_2CH_3$ *(Naming prefix: propan)*	CH_3CH_2CHO **propan**al
butane, $CH_3CH_2CH_2CH_3$ *(Naming prefix: butan)*	$CH_3CH_2CH_2CHO$ **butan**al
pentane, $CH_3CH_2CH_2CH_2CH_3$ *(Naming prefix: pentan)*	$CH_3CH_2CH_2CH_2CHO$ **pentan**al
hexane, $CH_3CH_2CH_2CH_2CH_2CH_3$ *(Naming prefix: hexan)*	$CH_3CH_2CH_2CH_2CH_2CHO$ **hexan**al

Table 3: Systematic names for aldehydes (RCHO) with up to six carbon atoms.

which distils from the reaction mixture and is collected at its boiling point. The equation for the oxidation reveals that partial oxidation of the alcohol occurs as a result of dichromate providing one mole of oxygen atoms ([O]) for every mole of alcohol oxidised.

$$CH_3CH_2CH_2OH + [O] \rightarrow$$
$$CH_3CH_2CHO + H_2O$$

propan-1-ol   propanal

The properties and reactions of an aldehyde are determined by the aldehyde (-CHO) functional group. The systematic names for aldehydes with up to six carbon atoms are summarised in Table 3.

Exercise 2.6L

1. Methanol may be oxidised to methanal, HCHO and then to methanoic acid, HCOOH by acidified potassium dichromate. Draw the structures of (a) the aldehyde and (b) the acid showing all bonds present.

   (CCEA January 2006)

2. Ethanol can be oxidised to ethanal or ethanoic acid depending on the experimental technique used. (a) Name a suitable oxidising agent. (b) Give the formula of the ion formed by reduction of this oxidising agent. State the experimental techniques required to form (c) ethanal and (d) ethanoic acid.

   (CCEA January 2011)

Oxidation of Secondary Alcohols

When a secondary alcohol is refluxed with acidified dichromate solution, the alcohol is instead oxidised to the corresponding **ketone** (RCOR').

secondary alcohol   ketone
RCH(OH)R'   RCOR'

For example, when a mixture of propan-2-ol and acidified potassium dichromate is refluxed, the propan-2-ol is oxidised to propanone, CH_3COCH_3.

$$CH_3CH(OH)CH_3 + [O] \rightarrow CH_3COCH_3 + H_2O$$
propan-2-ol   propanone

The properties and reactions of a ketone are determined by the carbonyl (C=O) functional group. The systematic names for ketones with up to six carbon atoms are summarised in Table 4.

Parent alkane	Ketones (Suffix: -one)
propane, $CH_3CH_2CH_3$ *(Naming prefix: propan)*	CH_3COCH_3 **propan**one
butane, $CH_3CH_2CH_2CH_3$ *(Naming prefix: butan)*	$CH_3CH_2COCH_3$ **butan**one
pentane, $CH_3CH_2CH_2CH_2CH_3$ *(Naming prefix: pentan)*	$CH_3CH_2CH_2COCH_3$ **pentan**-2-one $CH_3CH_2COCH_2CH_3$ **pentan**-3-one
hexane, $CH_3CH_2CH_2CH_2CH_2CH_3$ *(Naming prefix: hexan)*	$CH_3CH_2CH_2CH_2COCH_3$ **hexan**-2-one $CH_3CH_2CH_2COCH_2CH_3$ **hexan**-3-one

Table 4: Systematic names for ketones (RCOR') with up to six carbon atoms.

Oxidation of Tertiary Alcohols

The oxidation of an alcohol to the corresponding aldehyde or ketone occurs when the oxidising agent provides one mole of oxygen atoms ([O]) for every mole of alcohol oxidised. Once a ketone is formed it cannot be oxidised further. In contrast, when a primary alcohol is oxidised to an aldehyde, the aldehyde can be further oxidised to form the corresponding carboxylic acid. In this way we see that secondary alcohols are more resistant to oxidation than primary alcohols. Tertiary alcohols are even more resistant to oxidation and will not react when refluxed with strong oxidising agents such as acidified dichromate.

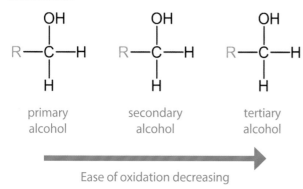

primary alcohol   secondary alcohol   tertiary alcohol

Ease of oxidation decreasing

Exercise 2.6M

1. Which one of the following molecules would not be oxidised by acidified dichromate?

   A
   $CH_3CH_2CH_2OH$

   B
   CH_3CHCH_3
   |
   OH

   C
   CH_3
   |
   CH_3CCH_3
   |
   OH

   D
   $CH_3CH_2CHCH_3$
   |
   OH

   (CCEA June 2003)

2. Which one of the following alcohols is not oxidised by acidified potassium dichromate solution?

   A   propan-1-ol
   B   propan-2-ol
   C   2-methylpropan-1-ol
   D   2-methylpropan-2-ol

   (CCEA June 2007)

Before moving to the next section, check that you are able to:

- Deduce the structure of the product formed when primary and secondary alcohols are refluxed with acidified dichromate.
- Deduce the structure of the aldehyde formed when a mixture of a primary alcohol and acidified dichromate is distilled.

- Recall that tertiary alcohols are not oxidised by strong oxidising agents such as acidified dichromate.
- Write balanced equations for the oxidation of alcohols using the symbol [O] to represent the oxidising agent.

Distinguishing Between Alcohols

The colour change that accompanies the oxidation of a primary or secondary alcohol can be used to distinguish primary and secondary alcohols from tertiary alcohols. If an alcohol is oxidised by acidified dichromate, the mixture changes colour from orange to green as dichromate ion ($Cr_2O_7^{2-}$) is reduced to form chromium III ions (Cr^{3+}). Alternatively, if an alcohol is oxidised by acidified potassium permanganate, $KMnO_4$ (aq) the mixture changes from purple to colourless as permanganate ion (MnO_4^-) is reduced to form manganese II ions (Mn^{2+}). The colour changes that accompany the oxidation of an alcohol by acidified dichromate and acidified permanganate are shown in Figure 8.

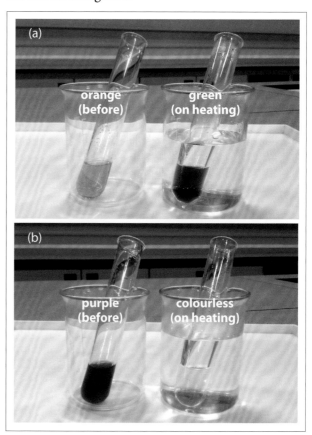

Figure 8: The colour change that occurs when an alcohol is oxidised by heating the alcohol with (a) acidified potassium dichromate and (b) acidified potassium permanganate.

Worked Example 2.6ii

Describe a chemical test which could be used to distinguish between the alcohols butan-1-ol and 2-methylpropan-2-ol. *(CCEA January 2008)*

Strategy

Describe the procedure and what would be observed when each alcohol is reacted with a strong oxidising agent.

Solution

Place samples of the alcohols in separate test tubes. Add an equal volume of acidified potassium dichromate solution to each alcohol and gently heat the mixtures. The mixture containing butan-1-ol will turn from orange to green. The mixture containing 2-methylpropan-2-ol will remain orange.

Alternative answer:

Place samples of the alcohols in separate test tubes. Add an equal volume of acidified potassium permanganate solution to each alcohol and gently heat the mixtures. The mixture containing butan-1-ol will turn from purple to colourless. The mixture containing 2-methylpropan-2-ol will remain purple.

Exercise 2.6N

1. Which one of the following alcohols will **not** cause the solution to turn from orange to green when heated with acidified potassium dichromate solution?

   A butan-1-ol
   B butan-2-ol
   C 2-methylpropan-1-ol
   D 2-methylpropan-2-ol

   (CCEA June 2010)

2. Explain why the structural isomers of propanol cannot be distinguished using acidified sodium dichromate solution.

3. Explain how acidified potassium permanganate solution can be used to distinguish between the isomers pentan-3-ol and 2-methylbutan-2-ol.

   (Adapted from CCEA June 2005)

4. A mixture of ethanol and gasoline (petrol) is known as Gasohol. Explain how you would carry out a chemical test to show that ethanol was present in a sample of Gasohol.

   (CCEA January 2010)

> **Before moving to the next section, check that you are able to:**
>
> - Describe the use of acidified dichromate and acidified permanganate to distinguish tertiary alcohols from primary and secondary alcohols.
> - Explain the colour change that occurs when an alcohol is oxidised by acidified dichromate or acidified permanganate in terms of the ions involved.

Esterification of Alcohols

In this section we are learning to:

- Deduce the structure of the ester formed when an alcohol reacts with a carboxylic acid or acyl chloride and write an equation for the reaction.
- Explain the role of concentrated sulfuric acid in the reaction between an alcohol and a carboxylic acid to form an ester.
- Write systematic names for esters.

Esters from Carboxylic Acids

When a mixture of an alcohol and a carboxylic acid is refluxed, the alcohol (R'OH) and the acid (RCOOH) combine to form an **ester** (RCOOR').

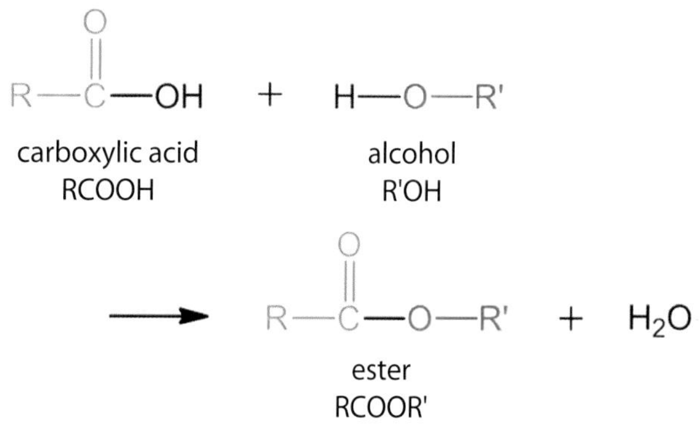

The reaction is an example of an **esterification reaction** as it produces an ester. The esterification of an alcohol is also an example of a **condensation reaction** as a small molecule is formed when the reactants combine to form the product.

The formation of the ester methyl ethanoate by

refluxing a mixture of methanol and ethanoic acid is an example of an esterification reaction.

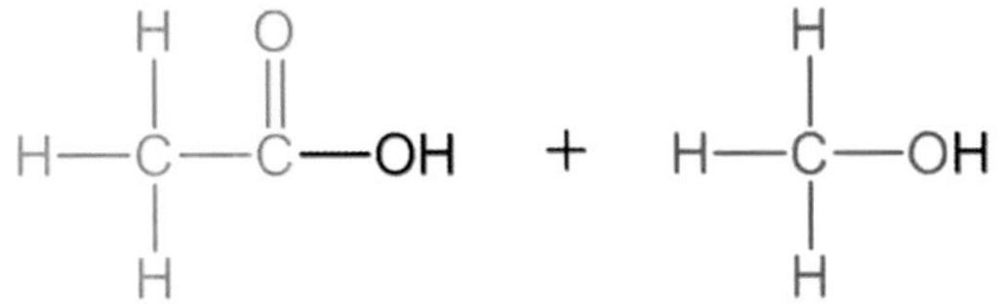

ethanoic acid
CH₃COOH

methanol
CH₃OH

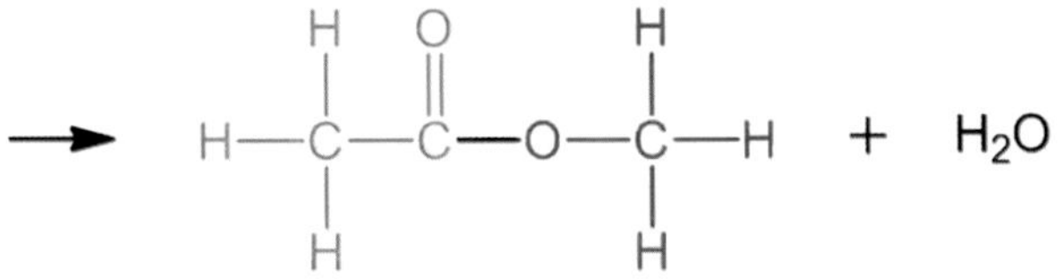

methyl ethanoate
CH₃COOCH₃

The formation of the ester ethyl propanoate by refluxing a mixture of ethanol and propanoic acid is also an example of esterification.

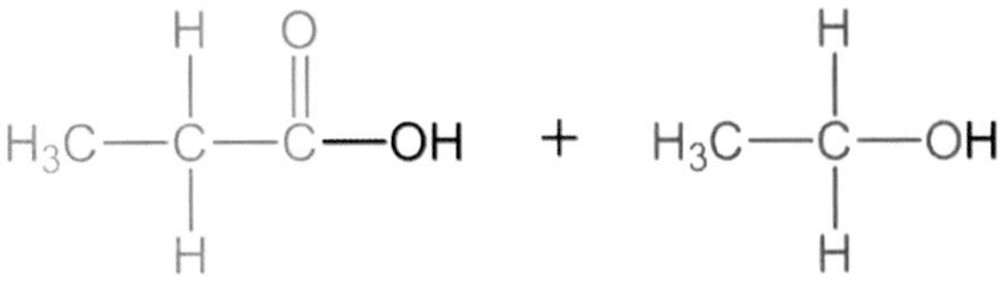

propanoic acid
CH₃CH₂COOH

ethanol
CH₃CH₂OH

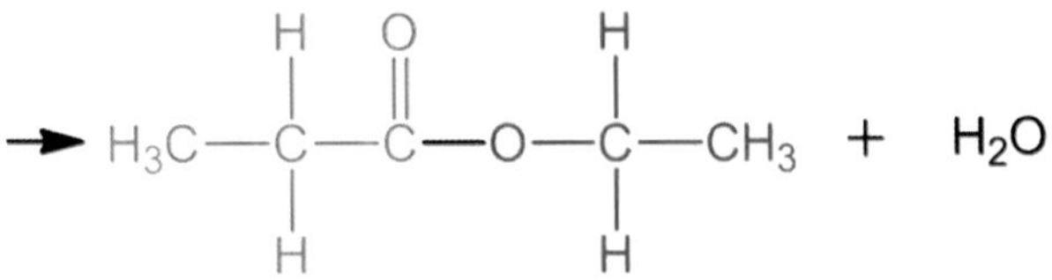

ethyl propanoate
CH₃CH₂COOCH₂CH₃

The systematic name for the ester is constructed from the name of the carboxylic acid by replacing the suffix *oic acid* with the suffix *oate*. A prefix such as *methyl* or *ethyl* is then added to describe the nature of the alkyl group (R') attached to the ester linkage (-COOR'). The structure of the alkyl group (R') is determined by the structure of the alcohol. For example, methyl esters (R' = CH_3) are formed from methanol, ethyl esters (R' = CH_2CH_3) are formed from ethanol, and so on.

....

Worked Example 2.6iii

Draw the structure of the esters formed by reacting ethanoic acid, CH_3COOH with each of the following alcohols.

A   B

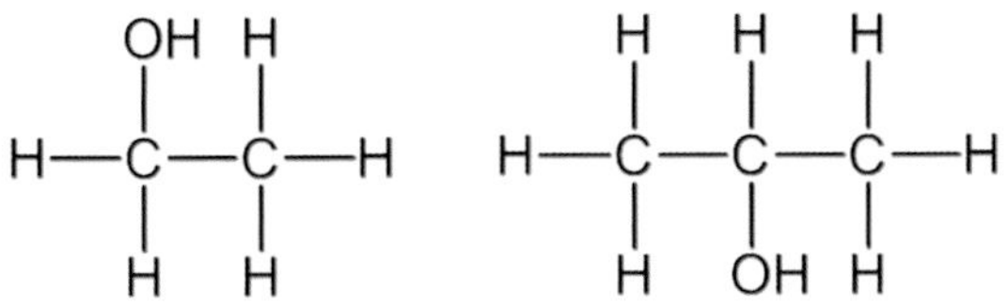

C

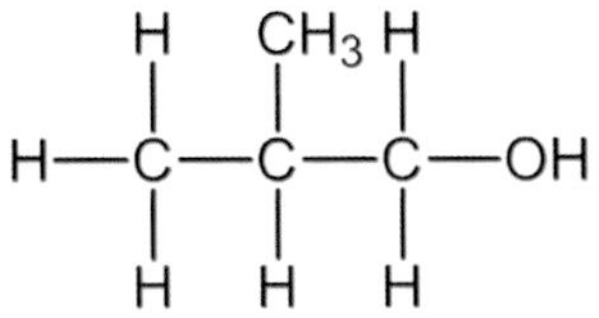

Strategy

• Ethanoic acid forms ethanoate esters (CH_3COOR')
• The alcohols contain the following alkyl groups (R').

A   B

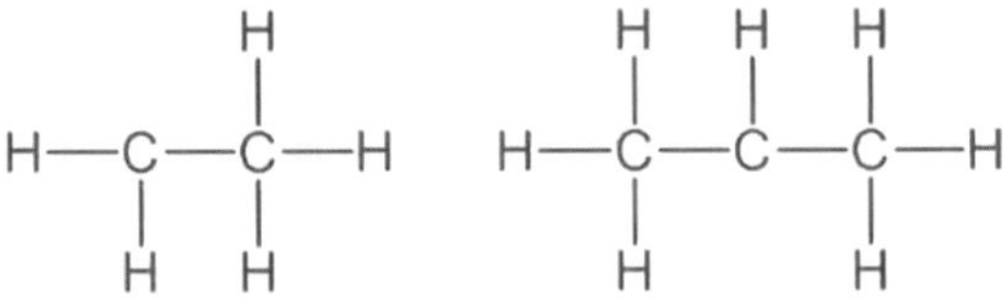

C

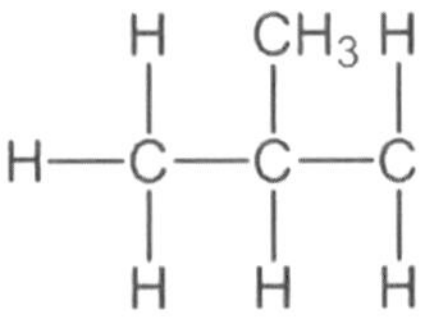

Solution

The structures of the esters (RCOOR') are:

A

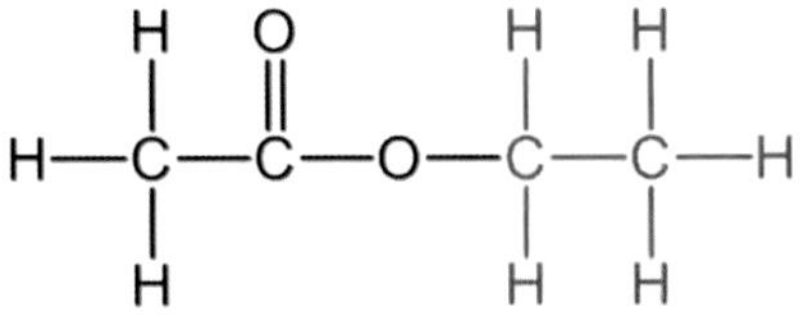

B

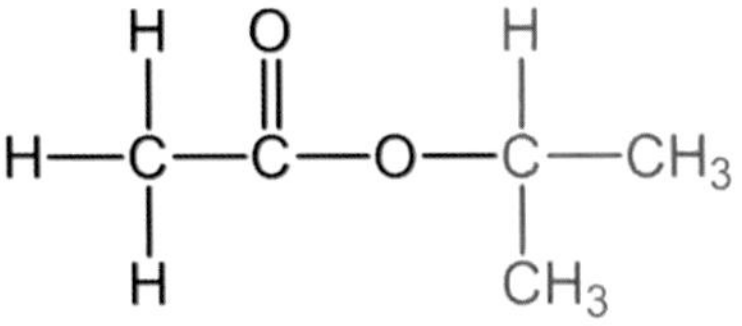

C

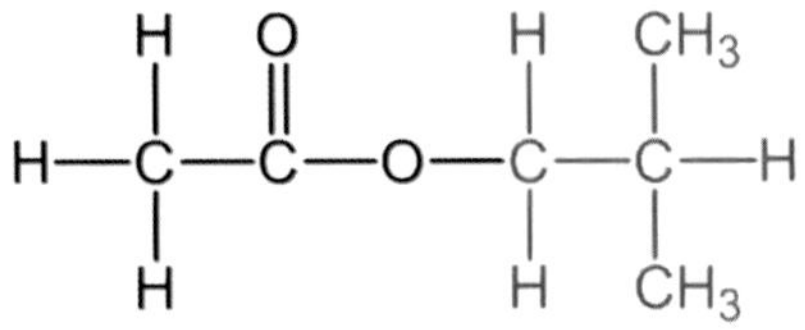

The esterification reaction is carried out by adding a few drops of concentrated sulfuric acid to the reaction mixture in a round-bottom flask. Anti-bumping granules are then added and the mixture refluxed for an extended period. The reaction does not go to completion and contains significant amounts of reactants and products after refluxing is complete. The incomplete nature of the reaction is indicated by using a double arrow ($\leftrightarrows$) when writing the equation for the reaction.

$$RCOOH + R'OH \leftrightarrows RCOOR' + H_2O$$

The concentrated acid acts as a catalyst as it speeds-up the reaction but is not consumed by the reaction. The concentrated acid also increases the amount of ester formed by absorbing water from the reaction mixture. As water is absorbed by the acid more of the reactants are converted into products to replace the water removed by the acid.

With the reflux complete, the ester is obtained from the reaction mixture by distillation. Many esters are non-toxic sweet smelling liquids with characteristic tastes that make them suitable for use as artificial flavours in food. Esters are also used as solvents in glues and resins.

Worked Example 2.6iv

Ester A is one of several compounds responsible for the flavour of beer. In contrast, the presence of ester B in beer indicates that the beer may not have been brewed in sterile conditions. (a) State the reagents needed to form each ester from a carboxylic acid and an alcohol. (b) Write the systematic name for each ester. (c) Write the equation for the formation of each ester from a carboxylic acid and an alcohol.

$$CH_3CH_2CH_2-\overset{\overset{\displaystyle O}{\|}}{C}-O-CH_2CH_3$$
A

$$CH_3CH_2CH_2CH_2CH_2-\overset{\overset{\displaystyle O}{\|}}{C}-O-CH_2CH_3$$
B

Solution

(a) Ester A is formed by reacting ethanol ($HOCH_2CH_3$) with butanoic acid ($CH_3CH_2CH_2COOH$). Ester B is formed by reacting ethanol ($HOCH_2CH_3$) with hexanoic acid ($CH_3CH_2CH_2CH_2CH_2COOH$).

(b) Ester A is ethyl butanoate and ester B is ethyl hexanoate.

(c) Ester A: $C_3H_7COOH + C_2H_5OH \leftrightarrows$
$$C_3H_7COOC_2H_5 + H_2O$$

Ester B: $C_5H_{11}COOH + C_2H_5OH \leftrightarrows$
$$C_5H_{11}COOC_2H_5 + H_2O$$

Exercise 2.60

1. The ester responsible for the characteristic smell of bananas is formed by the reaction between ethanoic acid and isoamyl alcohol, $C_5H_{11}OH$. Write the equation for the reaction.

   (CCEA June 2003)

2. Ethanol undergoes an esterification reaction when refluxed with ethanoic acid in the presence of concentrated sulfuric acid. (a) State two roles of the concentrated sulfuric acid. (b) Draw the structure of the ester formed. (c) Name the ester formed in the reaction.

   (Adapted from CCEA June 2007)

3. Which one of the following combinations react to form an ester with the structure shown below?

$$H-\overset{\overset{\displaystyle CH_3}{|}}{\underset{\underset{\displaystyle CH_3}{|}}{C}}-O-\overset{\overset{\displaystyle O}{\|}}{C}-CH_2CH_3$$

   A   ethanoic acid and propan-1-ol
   B   ethanoic acid and propan-2-ol
   C   propanoic acid and propan-1-ol
   D   propanoic acid and propan-2-ol

   (CCEA January 2006)

4. Which one of the following is not an isomer of the ester $CH_3CO_2CH(CH_3)_2$?

   A   propyl ethanoate
   B   butyl methanoate
   C   pentanoic acid
   D   ethyl ethanoate

   (CCEA January 2009)

Esters from Acyl Chlorides

Esters can also be made by reacting an alcohol with an **acyl chloride** ($RCOCl$).

acyl chloride
$RCOCl$

alcohol
$R'OH$

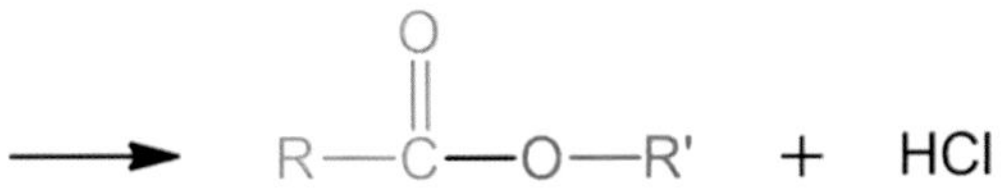

ester
$RCOOR'$

The reaction produces hydrogen chloride gas and is generally preferred over other methods of making esters as the reaction goes to completion.

The condensed formulas and systematic names for acyl chlorides with up to six carbon atoms are summarised in Table 5. Acyl chlorides are volatile liquids and are much more reactive than carboxylic acids. Reactions involving acyl chlorides must be carried out in a fume cupboard as acyl chlorides react with water vapour in the air to produce pungent fumes of HCl.

$$RCOCl_{(l)} + H_2O_{(g)} \rightarrow RCOOH_{(aq)} + HCl_{(g)}$$

The following examples illustrate the synthesis of an ester by the reaction between an alcohol and an acyl chloride.

Parent alkane	Acyl chloride (Suffix: -oyl chloride)
methane, CH_4 (Naming prefix: methan)	HCOCl **methan**oyl chloride
ethane, CH_3CH_3 (Naming prefix: ethan)	CH_3COCl **ethan**oyl chloride
propane, $CH_3CH_2CH_3$ (Naming prefix: propan)	CH_3CH_2COCl **propan**oyl chloride
butane, $CH_3CH_2CH_2CH_3$ (Naming prefix: butan)	$CH_3CH_2CH_2COCl$ **butan**oyl chloride
pentane, $CH_3CH_2CH_2CH_2CH_3$ (Naming prefix: pentan)	$CH_3CH_2CH_2CH_2COCl$ **pentan**oyl chloride
hexane, $CH_3CH_2CH_2CH_2CH_2CH_3$ (Naming prefix: hexan)	$CH_3CH_2CH_2CH_2CH_2COCl$ **hexan**oyl chloride

Table 5: Systematic names for acyl chlorides (RCOCl) with up to six carbon atoms.

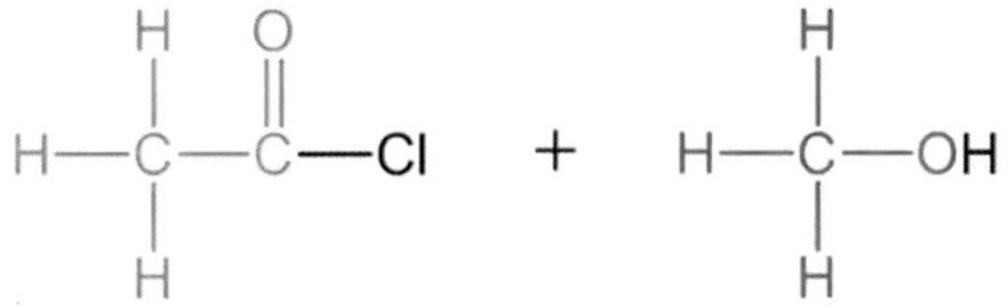

ethanoyl chloride
CH_3COCl

methanol
CH_3OH

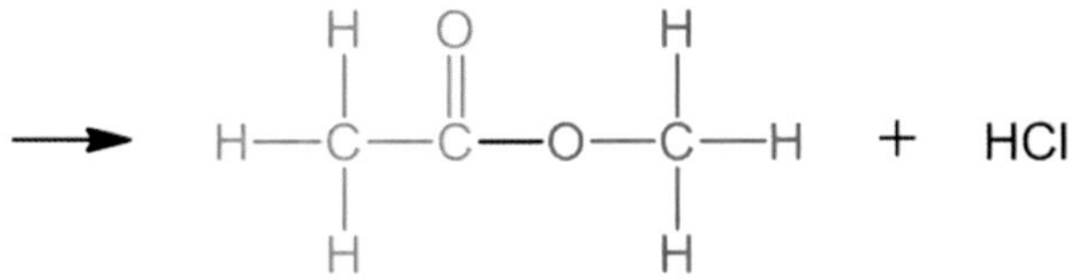

methyl ethanoate
CH_3COOCH_3

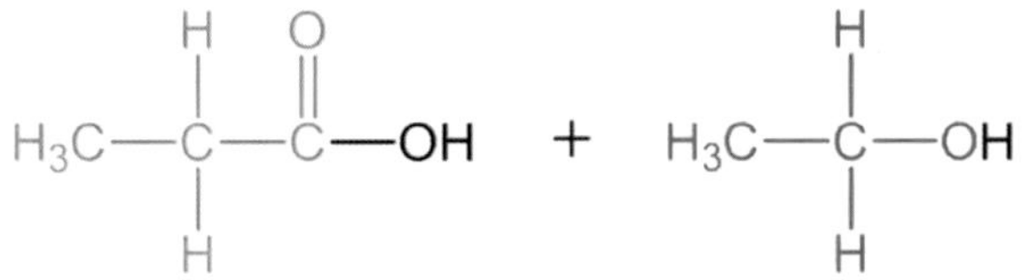

propanoyl chloride
CH_3CH_2COCl

ethanol
CH_3CH_2OH

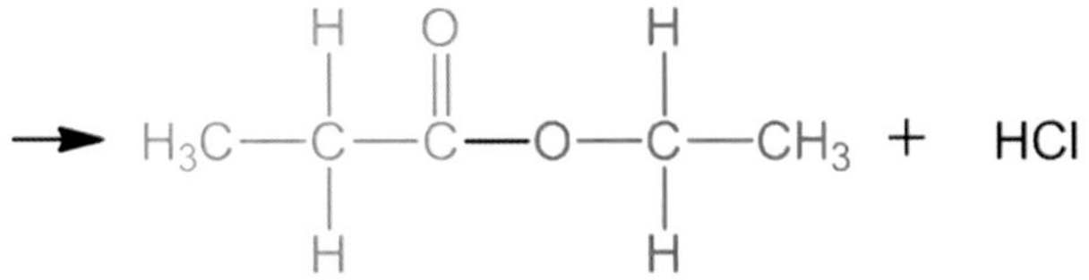

ethyl propanoate
$CH_3CH_2COOCH_2CH_3$

Worked Example 2.6v

The ester ethyl valerate is used as an artificial flavour and is formed by reacting ethanol with valeric acid. (a) Write the systematic name for valeric acid. (b) Write the systematic name for the ester ethyl valerate. (c) Name another combination of reagents that could be used to form ethyl valerate. (d) Write an equation for the formation of the ester using the reagents identified in part (c).

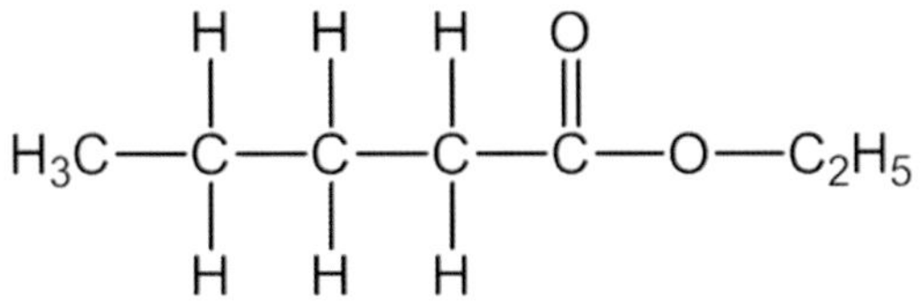

ethyl valerate

Solution

(a) The systematic name for valeric acid, $CH_3CH_2CH_2CH_2COOH$ is pentanoic acid.

(b) The systematic name of the ester is ethyl pentanoate.

(c) The ester can also be made from ethanol (C_2H_5OH) and pentanoyl chloride ($CH_3CH_2CH_2CH_2COCl$).

(d) $C_2H_5OH + C_4H_9COCl \rightarrow$
$$C_4H_9COOC_2H_5 + HCl$$

....

Exercise 2.6P

1. (a) Name the type of reaction that occurs when ethanoic acid reacts with ethanol to form ethyl ethanoate. (b) Name another reagent which reacts with ethanol to form ethyl ethanoate.

(CCEA June 2010)

2. The compound CH_3CH_2OH reacts with CH_3COOH to form $CH_3COOCH_2CH_3$. (a) Name another compound that will react with CH_3CH_2OH to form the product. (b) Write the equation for the reaction involving the named compound.

(Adapted from CCEA June 2006)

3. What is formed when propanol reacts with ethanoyl chloride?

A   chloropropane
B   ethyl propanoate
C   propanoyl chloride
D   propyl ethanoate

(CCEA June 2005)

4. Which one of the following combinations can be used to produce methyl ethanoate?

A   ethanoyl chloride and methanoic acid
B   ethanoyl chloride and methanol
C   methane and ethanoic acid
D   methanoic acid and ethanol

(CCEA January 2008)

5. The ester ethyl butanoate is largely responsible for the taste and smell of pineapples. Which two reagents would combine to form this ester?

A   butan-1-ol and ethanoic acid
B   butanoyl chloride and ethanoic acid
C   ethanol and butanoic acid
D   ethanoyl chloride and butanoic acid

(CCEA January 2002)

Before moving to the next section, check that you are able to:

- Use the structure of an ester to deduce the reagents used to make the ester.
- Write equations for the esterification of alcohols and deduce the structure of the ester formed.
- Describe the role of concentrated sulfuric acid when forming an ester from a carboxylic acid.
- Recall why esterification using an acyl chloride is the generally preferred method for making esters.
- Deduce systematic names for esters.

Exercise 2.6Q

Additional Problems

1. Complete the flow scheme by writing the formula for each product. *(CCEA June 2008)*

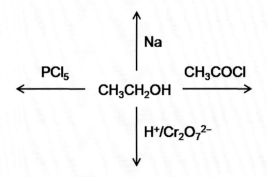

2. The -OH group in glycolic acid, $HOCH_2COOH$ acts in the same way as a primary alcohol. Complete the flow scheme by drawing the structure of each product.

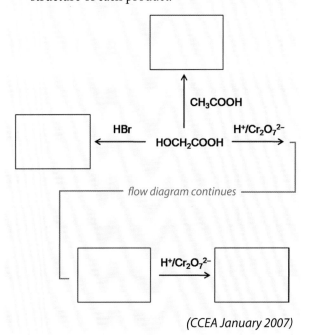

(CCEA January 2007)

The Iodoform Reaction

In this section we are learning to:

- Describe the preparation of a pure, dry sample of iodoform, CHI_3.
- Use the iodoform test to identify alcohols with the structure $RCH(OH)CH_3$.

A pale yellow precipitate of iodoform, CHI_3 is formed when alcohols with the structure $RCH(OH)CH_3$ are oxidised by iodine in alkaline solution. The reaction occurs in several steps.

$$R-\underset{\underset{H}{|}}{\overset{\overset{OH}{|}}{C}}-CH_3 \xrightarrow{\text{Oxidation}} \xrightarrow{\text{Substitution}}$$

$$R-\overset{\overset{O}{\|}}{C}-Cl_3 \xrightarrow{\text{Hydrolysis}} RCOO^- + CHI_3$$

Preparation of Iodoform

The first step in the preparation of iodoform involves dissolving solid iodine in an excess of alcohol to form a dark brown solution. On adding aqueous sodium hydroxide the dark brown solution is replaced by a solution containing a cloudy yellow suspension of solid iodoform. The crude iodoform is then separated from the reaction mixture by **vacuum filtration**. The Buchner apparatus used to vacuum filter the reaction mixture is shown in Figure 9. Vacuum filtration speeds up the process of filtering the reaction mixture by using a water pump to lower the pressure inside the Buchner flask. The higher pressure outside the flask then pushes the reaction mixture through the filter in the bottom of the Buchner funnel. The crude iodoform collects in the filter where it is washed with distilled water to remove iodine and other water soluble impurities. The iodoform is then removed from the Buchner funnel and dried between two pieces of filter paper.

Having been separated from the reaction mixture, the crude iodoform is then purified by **recrystallisation**. The first step in the recrystallisation process is to dissolve the crude iodoform in the minimum amount of hot ethanol. The resulting solution is then filtered. Any insoluble impurities present in the crude iodoform are retained by the filter. As the filtrate cools soluble impurities remain in solution as iodoform crystallises from the solution. The recrystallised iodoform is then collected by vacuum filtration, washed with a small amount of cold ethanol, and left to dry in air.

The recrystallised iodoform is expected to be pure as the recrystallisation process removes both soluble and insoluble impurities from the crude iodoform. The purity of the recrystallised iodoform can be confirmed by determining the temperature range over which it melts. The **melting point determination** is carried out by placing a small sample of the recrystallised iodoform in a capillary tube sealed at one end. The

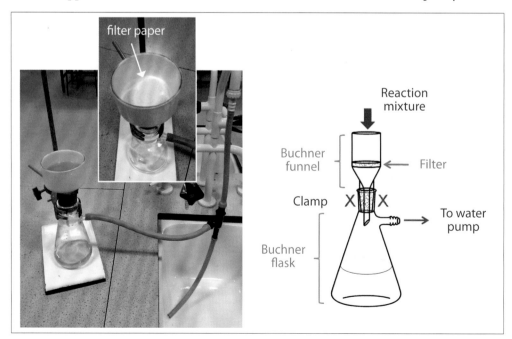

Figure 9: The Buchner apparatus used to vacuum filter the reaction mixture.

sample is then heated slowly. The melting range is determined by recording the temperature at which the sample starts to melt and the temperature at which the sample finishes melting. If the recrystallised iodoform is pure it will melt within a narrow range of 1–2 °C. In contrast, if the recrystallised iodoform contains impurities it will melt over a broader range of temperature. In this way a 'sharp' melting point obtained over a range of 1–2 °C can be used to confirm that the sample is pure.

Worked Example 2.6vi

Iodoform, CHI_3 is used as an antiseptic. It is a yellow solid with a melting point of 119 °C. The preparation of a pure sample of iodoform is carried out as follows:

> Add 4 cm^3 of ethanol to 0.85 g of iodine in a test tube. Then add 4 cm^3 of 10% aqueous sodium hydroxide. Shake the test tube vigorously until the colour of the iodine has been completely replaced by a yellow precipitate of iodoform. Filter off the iodoform using vacuum filtration, wash with water, drain thoroughly and dry.

(a) What colour is the dissolved iodine?

Iodine dissolves to form a dark brown solution.

(b) Draw a labelled diagram to show how the filtration may be carried out.

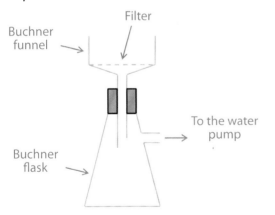

(c) Suggest why the yellow precipitate is washed with water.

The precipitate is washed to remove iodine and other water soluble impurities such as ethanol and sodium hydroxide.

(d) How may the iodoform be dried?

The iodoform can be dried between two pieces of filter paper or in a low temperature oven.

(e) How could you show that the sample of iodoform was pure?

Determine the melting point of the sample. A sharp melting point (narrow range) indicates that the sample is pure.

(CCEA June 2002)

Exercise 2.6R

0.48 g of iodoform, CHI_3 is obtained when 0.85 g of iodine reacts with an excess of ethanol. Calculate (a) the moles of iodine reacted, (b) the theoretical yield, (c) the actual yield, and (d) the percentage yield of iodoform.

(CCEA June 2002)

The Iodoform Test

The formation of iodoform can be used to test for alcohols with the structure $RCH(OH)CH_3$. If an alcohol with the structure $RCH(OH)CH_3$ is shaken with an alkaline solution of iodine, the brown colour of the iodine is replaced by a cloudy yellow suspension of iodoform. In contrast, if the alcohol does not have the structure $RCH(OH)CH_3$ the brown colour of the solution remains on shaking.

Worked Example 2.6vii

A mixture of ethanol and gasoline is known as Gasohol. Explain how you would carry out a chemical test to show that ethanol was present in a sample of Gasohol.

(CCEA January 2010)

Strategy

Ethanol will give a positive iodoform test as it has the structure $RCH(OH)CH_3$. The structure of ethanol CH_3CH_2OH is obtained by setting R = H.

Solution

Dissolve solid iodine in a sample of Gasohol. The brown colour of the mixture will be replaced by a cloudy yellow suspension of iodoform when the mixture is shaken with sodium hydroxide solution.

Exercise 2.6S

1. Describe, giving practical details, how the iodoform reaction could be used to distinguish between the alcohols A and B.

A $\qquad$ B

$$CH_3CH_2CHCH_3$$
$$CH_3CH_2CH_2CH_2OH \qquad\qquad |$$
$$OH$$

(CCEA June 2005)

2. Which one of the following will not give a yellow precipitate with a solution of iodine in sodium hydroxide?

   A butan-2-ol

   B ethanol

   C butan-1-ol

   D propan-2-ol

(CCEA January 2010)

3. (a) What structural feature must an alcohol contain to give a positive iodoform test? (b) Describe how you would carry out the iodoform test and state the result for a positive test.

(CCEA January 2008)

4. Which one of the following alcohols will give a positive result in the iodoform test?

   A $CH_3C(CH_3)(OH)CH_3$

   B $CH_3CH_2CH_2CH_2OH$

   C $CH_3CH(OH)CH_2CH_3$

   D $CH_3CH(CH_3)CH_2OH$

(CCEA June 2007)

5. Which one of the following alcohols will give a positive result in the iodoform test?

   A $CH_3CH_2CH_2CH_2CH_2OH$

   B $CH_3CH_2CH_2CH(OH)CH_3$

   C $CH_3CH_2CH(OH)CH_2CH_3$

   D $CH_3C(CH_3)_2CH_2OH$

(CCEA January 2011)

Before moving to the next section, check that you are able to:

- Describe the reaction used to prepare crude iodoform and the procedure used to obtain a pure, dry sample of iodoform from the reaction mixture.
- Explain how recrystallisation removes impurities from crude iodoform.
- Draw a labelled diagram of the apparatus used for vacuum filtration.
- Describe how the melting point of iodoform is determined, and how the melting range is used to verify that the iodoform is pure.
- Explain how the iodoform test can be used to identify alcohols with the structure $RCH(OH)CH_3$.
- Identify alcohols that give a positive iodoform test.

2.7 Infra-Red Spectroscopy

In this section we are learning to:

- Explain why molecules absorb infra-red radiation and why the frequencies absorbed depend on the structure of the molecule.
- Use infra-red spectroscopy to detect functional groups within molecules.
- Describe how infra-red spectroscopy can be used to check for the presence of impurities in a mixture.

When a beam of infra-red (IR) radiation is passed through a substance the bonds in the substance absorb IR radiation from the beam causing them to vibrate. The frequencies absorbed by the substance match the frequencies at which the individual bonds in the substance vibrate. As a result, the absorption of IR radiation with a particular frequency can be used to detect bonds that vibrate at that frequency within the substance.

Infra-red analysis of a substance involves passing a beam of IR radiation containing a range of frequencies through a specially prepared sample of the substance. The amount of radiation absorbed at each frequency is reported as *percent transmission* where 100 % transmission describes the intensity of a beam that passes through the sample without being absorbed. The percent transmission at each frequency is then used to generate the **infra-red (IR) spectrum** for the substance by plotting percent transmission (%T) against frequency, where frequency is given in units of wavenumber (Units: cm^{-1}). The process of obtaining the IR spectrum of a substance is illustrated in Figure 1 and is known as **infra-red (IR) spectroscopy**.

Exercise 2.7A

Which one of the following occurs when a molecule absorbs infra-red radiation?

- A electrons in the bonds are excited
- B the bonds bend and eventually break
- C the bonds rotate
- D the bonds vibrate

(CCEA January 2010)

Before moving to the next section, check that you are able to:

- Explain why molecules absorb IR radiation.
- Describe how the infra-red (IR) spectrum of a compound is determined.

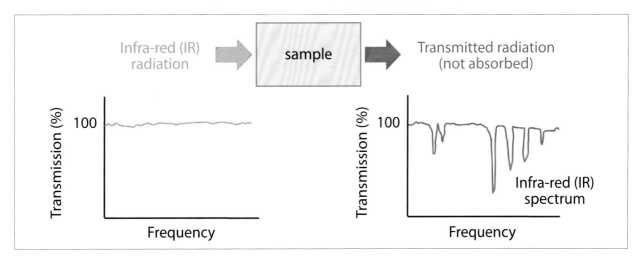

Figure 1: Generating the infra-red (IR) spectrum for a substance by measuring the absorption of infra-red radiation.

Identifying Functional Groups

The IR spectrum of a compound can be used to detect individual bonds, and in some cases, entire functional groups within the compound. For example, the IR spectrum for butan-2-ol in Figure 2 reveals strong absorption (low %T) over the range 3500–3200 cm^{-1}. The absorption is attributed to the hydroxyl (-OH) group in butan-2-ol as the hydroxyl groups in other compounds also absorb strongly over this range. Similarly, strong absorption over the range 3000–2850 cm^{-1} is attributed to the C-H bonds in butan-2-ol as the C-H bonds in other compounds also absorb over this range.

....

Worked Example 2.7i

The infra-red spectrum for an alcohol with molecular formula C_2H_6O is shown below.

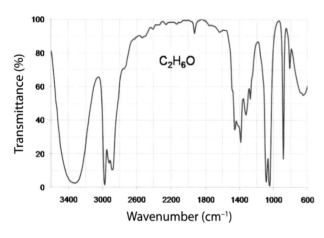

(a) Draw the structural formula for the alcohol showing all bonds present. (b) Explain, using information obtained from the spectrum, how the infra-red spectrum can be used to identify the compound as an alcohol.

Solution

(a)

H—C—C—O—H (with H atoms shown)

(b) Absorption over the range 3500–3100 cm^{-1} is due to the O-H bond within a hydroxyl (-OH) group. The presence of a hydroxyl group identifies the compound as an alcohol.

....

The IR spectrum for butanone in Figure 3a reveals that the C-H bonds in butanone also absorb over the range 3000–2850 cm^{-1}. The IR spectrum for butanone also reveals strong adsorption due to the C=O bond within the range 1750–1650 cm^{-1}. As would be expected, both features are present in the IR spectrum for ethyl ethanoate, $CH_3COOCH_2CH_3$ shown in Figure 3b. The consistency with which C-H bonds absorb in the range 3000–2850 cm^{-1} and C=O bonds absorb in the range 1750–1650 cm^{-1} demonstrates that absorption within a well-defined wavenumber range can be used to reliably determine the presence of specific types of bond in a compound. The

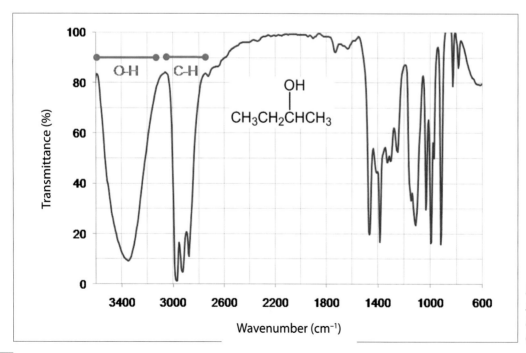

Figure 2: The IR spectrum for butan-2-ol, $CH_3CH_2CH(OH)CH_3$.

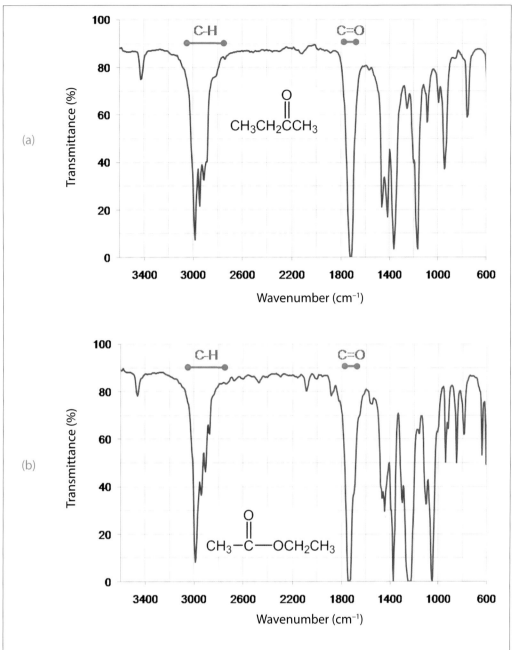

Figure 3: The IR spectrum of (a) butanone, $CH_3CH_2COCH_3$ and (b) ethyl ethanoate, $CH_3COOCH_2CH_3$.

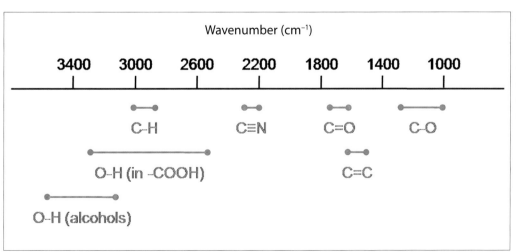

Figure 4: The approximate wavenumber range over which several common bond types absorb IR radiation.

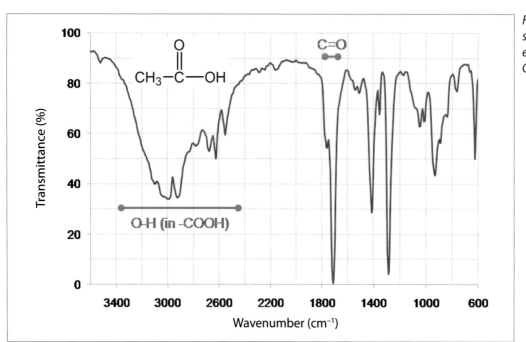

Figure 5: The IR spectrum for ethanoic acid, CH₃COOH.

approximate wavenumber ranges over which several common bond types absorb IR radiation are summarised in Figure 4.

The IR spectrum for ethanoic acid, CH_3COOH is shown in Figure 5. As in butanone (Figure 3a) and ethyl ethanoate (Figure 3b), strong absorption within the range 1750–1650 cm⁻¹ signals the presence of the C=O bond within the carboxyl (-COOH) group. Strong absorption over the range 3300–2500 cm⁻¹ is due to the O-H bond in the carboxyl group, and is easily distinguished from absorption by a hydroxyl (-OH) group over the range 3500–3100 cm⁻¹. In this way absorption within the range 1750–1650 cm⁻¹ (C=O) can be combined with broad absorption over the range 3300–2500 cm⁻¹ (O-H in -COOH) to detect the presence of a carboxyl (-COOH) group.

Exercise 2.7B

1. Parts of three infra-red spectra A, B and C are given opposite. The spectra are those of ethanol, ethanoic acid and ethyl ethanoate but not necessarily in that order. Use the following information to help identify each compound.

   - O-H bonds produce broad absorptions in the range 2500–3500 cm⁻¹

   - C=O bonds produce sharp absorptions in the range 1650–1750 cm⁻¹

   (CCEA June 2010)

A

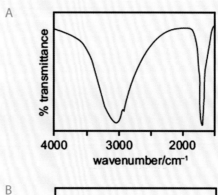

B

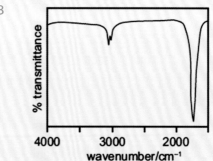

C

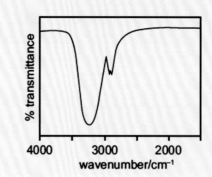

2. The infra-red spectra for ethanol, ethanal and ethanoic acid are shown below, but not necessarily in that order. (a) Explain how the absorption of infra-red radiation arises in molecules. (b) Use the data in the table to identify the absorptions at 3000 cm^{-1} and 3400 cm^{-1} in Spectrum A and 1700 cm^{-1} in Spectrum B. (c) Identify which molecules give rise to Spectrum B and Spectrum C.

(Adapted from CCEA January 2011)

Bond	Wavenumber /cm^{-1}
C-H	2850–3300
C=C	1620–1680
C=O	1680–1750
C-O	1000–1300
O-H (alcohols)	3230–3550
O-H (acids)	2500–3000

Spectrum A

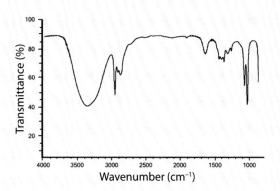

Spectrum B

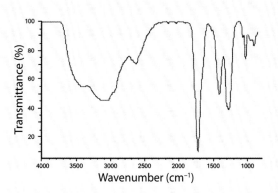

Spectrum C

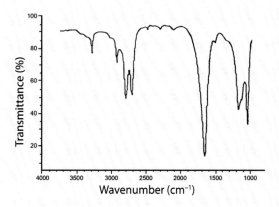

Detecting Impurities

The pattern of absorption in an IR spectrum is unique to the substance that generated the spectrum. As a result, the identity of a substance can be verified by comparing its IR spectrum with the IR spectrum of a pure sample of the same substance. If the substance is pure its IR spectrum will exactly match the IR spectrum of the pure sample. In contrast, if the substance contains impurities the IR spectra will not match as the impurities may absorb in different wavenumber ranges, or may further reduce the percent transmission in regions of the spectrum where the substance absorbs.

Worked Example 2.7ii

Propenonitrile, CH_2=CHCN can be polymerised to form a fibre known as Orlon that is used to make clothes. Propenonitrile is manufactured from propene, ammonia and oxygen. Suggest how you could use infra-red spectroscopy to show that no propene was present in the product from the reaction.

(CCEA June 2009)

Solution

The IR spectrum of a compound is unique. If the product is pure and no propene is present, the IR spectrum of the product will exactly match the IR spectrum for propenonitrile.

Before moving to the next section, check that you are able to:

- Use IR spectra to identify bonds and functional groups within molecules.
- Describe how IR spectroscopy can be used to check for impurities in a mixture.

2.8 Energetics

Enthalpy

In this section we are learning to:

- Use the terms exothermic and endothermic to explain the relationship between the enthalpy of the reactants and products in a chemical reaction.
- Construct and use enthalpy diagrams to explain the nature of the enthalpy change for a chemical reaction.

All substances contain energy. The total energy contained within a substance is known as the **enthalpy** of the substance (Symbol: H). If the enthalpy of the products formed in a chemical reaction is less than the enthalpy of the reactants, energy (enthalpy) is released from the reaction mixture and the reaction is described as exothermic. The energy released by an **exothermic** reaction increases the temperature of the reaction mixture.

The relationship between the enthalpy of the reactants ($H_{reactants}$), the enthalpy of the products ($H_{products}$), and the amount of energy released from the reaction mixture is best shown by constructing an enthalpy diagram. The enthalpy diagram for an exothermic reaction is shown in Figure 1a. The energy released by the reaction is referred to as the **enthalpy of reaction** (Symbol: ΔH). The enthalpy of reaction for an exothermic reaction is negative.

$$\Delta H = H_{products} - H_{reactants} < 0 \quad \text{Exothermic reaction (generates heat)}$$

In contrast, if the enthalpy of the reactants is less than the enthalpy of the products, energy is needed for the reaction to occur and the reaction is described as **endothermic**. The enthalpy diagram for an endothermic reaction is shown in Figure 1b. The enthalpy of reaction (ΔH) for an endothermic reaction is positive.

$$\Delta H = H_{products} - H_{reactants} > 0 \quad \text{Endothermic reaction (absorbs heat)}$$

The energy needed for an endothermic reaction to occur is taken from the reaction mixture. As a result the temperature of the reaction mixture decreases as the reaction proceeds.

Worked Example 2.8i

The partial oxidation of ammonia is an exothermic reaction and is used in the manufacture of nitric acid. Draw a labelled enthalpy diagram for the reaction.

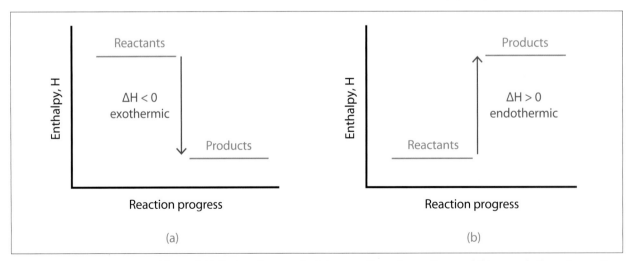

Figure 1: Enthalpy diagram for (a) an exothermic reaction and (b) an endothermic reaction.

$$4NH_3 + 5O_2 \rightarrow 4NO + 6H_2O$$

(CCEA January 2007)

Strategy

Use an arrow labelled ΔH to describe the relationship between the enthalpy of the reactants and products.

Solution

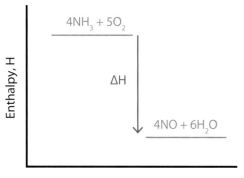

Exercise 2.8A

1. The formation of ice crystals from water is an exothermic reaction. Draw an enthalpy diagram for the freezing of water. Mark the enthalpy change as ΔH. *(CCEA January 2005)*

2. Photosynthesis is an endothermic process used by plants to produce carbohydrates. (a) Explain what is meant by the term endothermic. (b) Draw a fully labelled enthalpy diagram for the reaction. *(CCEA June 2003)*

$$6CO_2\,_{(g)} + 6H_2O\,_{(l)} \rightarrow C_6H_{12}O_6\,_{(s)} + 6O_2\,_{(g)}$$

3. Some reusable hand warmers contain concentrated sodium thiosulfate solution, $Na_2S_2O_3\,_{(aq)}$. Squeezing the packet releases a seed crystal which causes sodium thiosulfate crystals, $Na_2S_2O_3.5H_2O\,_{(s)}$ to be produced. The process of forming sodium thiosulfate crystals is exothermic. (a) Explain what is meant by the term exothermic. (b) Draw an enthalpy diagram for the reaction. *(CCEA January 2003)*

> **Before moving to the next section, check that you are able to:**
>
> • Use the terms exothermic and endothermic to describe the relationship between the enthalpy of the reactants and products in a chemical reaction.
> • Construct labelled enthalpy diagrams to describe enthalpy changes.

Measuring Enthalpy Changes

> **In this section we are learning to:**
>
> • Use the idea of standard conditions to define the standard enthalpy change for a reaction and the standard state of a substance.
> • Use the temperature change that occurs when a reaction takes place to calculate the enthalpy change for a reaction.
> • Explain how to use a simple calorimeter to determine the standard enthalpy change for a reaction.
> • Define the standard enthalpy of neutralisation for an acid.

Standard Conditions

The enthalpy change for a chemical reaction depends on the conditions under which the reaction is carried out. As a result it is difficult to know how to compare enthalpy changes measured at different temperatures and it becomes necessary to determine all enthalpy changes under the same set of 'standard' conditions. By convention the term **standard conditions** is used to refer to a temperature of 25 °C and a pressure of 1 atmosphere. An enthalpy change that occurs under standard conditions is known as a **standard enthalpy change** and is denoted by the symbol ΔH°. The standard temperature is often reported as 298 K where we are using the following conversion between degrees Celcius (°C) and Kelvin (K):

$$\text{Temperature (K)} = \text{Temperature (°C)} + 273$$

Having defined standard conditions, the term **standard state** can then be used to refer to the physical state of a substance under standard conditions. For example, metals such as iron are solids under standard conditions. This is equivalent to stating that the standard state of iron is solid. Similarly, water is a liquid under standard conditions and we can describe the standard state of water as liquid.

Worked Example 2.8ii

Which formula does not represent a substance in its standard state? Explain your answer and write the correct formula.

$$CH_4\,_{(g)} \qquad CO_2\,_{(g)} \qquad C_4H_{10}\,_{(g)} \qquad C_2H_5OH\,_{(aq)}$$

Solution

The standard state of ethanol, C_2H_5OH is liquid. The formula C_2H_5OH (aq) represents a solution of ethanol in water. The correct formula for the standard state of ethanol is C_2H_5OH (l).

Exercise 2.8B

1. Which one of the following formulas does not represent a substance in its standard state? Explain your answer and write the correct formula.

   Cl_2 (g) Br_2 (g) I_2 (s) S_8 (s)

2. Which one of the following formulas does not represent a substance in its standard state? Explain your answer and write the correct formula.

   N_2 (g) Cu (s) H (g) CH_3OH (l)

Burning Fuels

The amount of heat produced when a fuel burns can be calculated by measuring the rise in temperature when the heat produced by burning the fuel is used to heat a known quantity of liquid. Liquid fuels such as ethanol can be burnt in a controlled way using a 'spirit burner' of the type shown in Figure 2. The heat produced (ΔH) is related to the rise in temperature (ΔT) and the mass of liquid heated (m) by the equation:

$$\Delta H = - m c \Delta T$$

The **specific heat capacity** of the liquid (c) is defined as the amount of energy needed to raise the temperature of 1 g of the liquid by 1 °C and has units of $J\,g^{-1}\,°C^{-1}$. If we recall that a change in temperature of one Kelvin (1 K) is the same size as one degree centigrade (1 K = 1 °C) the units for specific heat capacity can also be written as $J\,g^{-1}\,K^{-1}$. The accuracy of the enthalpy change (ΔH) calculated by this method can be improved by maximising the amount of heat transferred to the liquid being heated, and stirring the liquid as it is heated to ensure that the liquid is heated uniformly.

Worked Example 2.8iii

Burning 0.05 moles of a liquid fuel increased the temperature of 200 g of water by 10 K. Calculate the molar enthalpy of combustion of the fuel. The heat capacity of water is $4.2\,J\,g^{-1}\,K^{-1}$. *(CCEA June 2010)*

Figure 2: Use of a 'spirit burner' to control the burning of a liquid fuel such as ethanol.

Strategy

- Calculate the enthalpy change for burning 0.05 mol of liquid fuel.
- Calculate the enthalpy change for burning 1 mol of liquid fuel.

Solution

Mass of water heated, m = 200 g

Specific heat capacity of water, $c = 4.2\,J\,g^{-1}\,K^{-1}$
  $= 4.2\,J\,g^{-1}\,°C^{-1}$

Temperature change, $\Delta T = + 10\,K = + 10\,°C$

$\Delta H = - m c \Delta T = - 200\,g \times 4.2\,J\,g^{-1}\,°C^{-1} \times 10\,°C$

  $= - 8.4 \times 10^3\,J = -8.4\,kJ$

Molar enthalpy change =

$$\frac{\Delta H}{\text{Moles of fuel}} = \frac{-8.4\,kJ}{0.05\,mol} = - 168\,kJ\,mol^{-1}$$

Reactions in Solution

The enthalpy change for a reaction that occurs in solution can also be obtained by measuring the change in the temperature of the solution that occurs when the reaction takes place. The process of measuring enthalpy changes is known as calorimetry and the apparatus used to measure the temperature change when a reaction occurs is known as a calorimeter. A simple 'coffee cup calorimeter' of the type shown in Figure 3 can be used to measure many enthalpy changes that occur in solution. The accuracy of the enthalpy changes measured using a calorimeter can be improved by reducing the amount of heat lost or gained by the reaction mixture in the course of the reaction. The enthalpy change for the reaction (ΔH) is again related to the temperature change in the solution (ΔT) and the mass of the solution (m) by the equation $\Delta H = - m c \Delta T$.

If the reaction is exothermic ($\Delta H < 0$) the enthalpy change is calculated by measuring the increase in the temperature of the solution ($\Delta T > 0$) produced by the reaction. Conversely, if the reaction is endothermic ($\Delta H > 0$), the energy needed for the reaction is taken from the solution and the enthalpy change calculated by measuring the decrease in the temperature ($\Delta T < 0$) of the solution. If the reaction occurs in aqueous solution it is reasonable to assume that the density of the solution is similar to the density of water. It is also reasonable to assume that the specific heat capacity of an aqueous solution is similar to the specific heat capacity for water. Pure water has a density of 1 g cm^{-3} and a specific heat capacity of 4.2 J g^{-1} °C^{-1}.

....

Worked Example 2.8iv

A solution of zinc sulfate is formed when zinc powder is added to a solution of copper sulfate. When 6.00 g of zinc powder (in excess) was added to 50.0 cm^3 of a 0.5 mol dm^{-3} solution of copper sulfate in a polystyrene cup, the temperature of the solution increased by 25.3 K. Calculate the energy change for the reaction in units of kJ mol^{-1} (of copper sulfate). The heat capacity and density of the solution is 4.2 J g^{-1} K^{-1} and 1.0 g cm^{-3} respectively. *(Adapted from CCEA June 2009)*

Strategy

- Calculate the enthalpy change for the reaction (in kJ).
- Calculate the molar enthalpy change (in kJ mol^{-1}).

Solution

Mass of solution, m = Volume × Density
= 50.0 cm^3 × 1.0 g cm^{-3} = 50 g

Specific heat capacity of solution, c = 4.2 J g^{-1} K^{-1}
= 4.2 J g^{-1} °C^{-1}

Temperature change, $\Delta T = + 25.3$ K = + 25.3 °C

$\Delta H = - m c \Delta T = - 50$ g × 4.2 J g^{-1} °C^{-1} × 25.3 °C
= − 5.313 kJ

Molar enthalpy change =
$$\frac{\Delta H}{\text{Moles of CuSO}_4} = \frac{-5.313 \text{ kJ}}{0.025 \text{ mol}} = -212.5 \text{ kJ mol}^{-1}$$

....

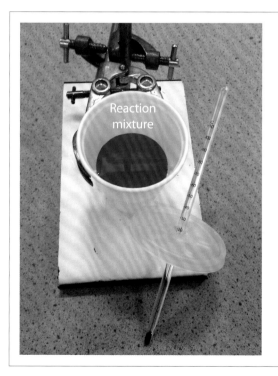

Start reaction

Figure 3: A simple 'coffee cup calorimeter' made from a polystyrene cup.

Enthalpy of Neutralisation

The term **standard enthalpy of neutralisation**, $\Delta H_n^{\ominus}$ refers to the enthalpy change that occurs when one mole of water is produced by a neutralisation reaction carried out under standard conditions. The enthalpy of neutralisation is easily determined using a simple calorimeter of the type shown in Figure 2. For example, the enthalpy of neutralisation for hydrochloric acid by sodium hydroxide refers to the enthalpy change that occurs when one mole of water is produced by the reaction between hydrochloric acid and sodium hydroxide.

$$HCl_{(aq)} + NaOH_{(aq)} \rightarrow NaCl_{(aq)} + H_2O_{(l)}$$

$$\Delta H^{\ominus} = \Delta H_n^{\ominus}$$

Ionic equation: $H^+_{(aq)} + OH^-_{(aq)} \rightarrow H_2O_{(l)}$

Similarly, the enthalpy of neutralisation for nitric acid by sodium hydroxide refers to the enthalpy change that occurs when one mole of water is formed by the reaction between nitric acid and sodium hydroxide.

$$HNO_{3\,(aq)} + NaOH_{(aq)} \rightarrow NaNO_{3\,(aq)} + H_2O_{(l)}$$

$$\Delta H^{\ominus} = \Delta H_n^{\ominus}$$

Ionic equation: $H^+_{(aq)} + OH^-_{(aq)} \rightarrow H_2O_{(l)}$

The ionic equations remind us that the overall chemical change is the same in both neutralisation reactions. The nature of the other (spectator) ions in the reaction mixture does not significantly affect the enthalpy change with the result that the enthalpy of neutralisation for strong acids such as hydrochloric acid, $HCl_{(aq)}$ and nitric acid, $HNO_{3\,(aq)}$ is approximately the same.

Hydrochloric acid, $HCl_{(aq)}$ and nitric acid, $HNO_{3\,(aq)}$ are examples of acids that produce one mole of water for every mole of acid neutralised. If the formula of an acid contains more than one hydrogen ion (H^+), one mole of water will be produced for every hydrogen ion in the formula when one mole of the acid is neutralised. For example sulfuric acid, $H_2SO_{4\,(aq)}$ contains two hydrogen ions per formula and, as a result, produces two moles of water when one mole of the acid is neutralised. In this way the enthalpy change that occurs when one mole of sulfuric acid is neutralised corresponds to twice the enthalpy of neutralisation for sulfuric acid.

$$H_2SO_{4\,(aq)} + 2NaOH_{(aq)} \rightarrow Na_2SO_{4\,(aq)} + 2H_2O_{(l)}$$

$$\Delta H^{\ominus} = 2\,\Delta H_n^{\ominus}$$

Ionic equation: $2H^+_{(aq)} + 2OH^-_{(aq)} \rightarrow 2H_2O_{(l)}$

Worked Example 2.8v

Describe, giving practical details, how the molar enthalpy change for the neutralisation of sulfuric acid with sodium hydroxide could be determined in the laboratory. Measurements and calculations should be described. *(CCEA June 2004)*

Solution

Place a known amount of sulfuric acid in an insulated flask and measure the temperature of the acid using a thermometer. Slowly add an excess of sodium hydroxide to the acid while stirring to mix the solutions.

Record the temperature of the solution after mixing using a thermometer. Calculate the temperature change (ΔT) and use it to calculate the enthalpy change for the reaction (ΔH) using the equation: $\Delta H = -\,m\,c\,\Delta T$.

Calculate the moles of acid neutralised and use the moles of acid to calculate the enthalpy change per mole of acid neutralised. Divide the enthalpy change per mole by two to obtain the enthalpy change per mole of water formed.

Exercise 2.8C

1. The temperature of the water dropped from 25.0 °C to 24.1 °C when 5.0 g of ammonium nitrate was added to 100 g of water. Calculate (a) the enthalpy change taking place, (b) the molar enthalpy change for dissolving ammonium nitrate in 100 g of water, and (c) the mass of ammonium nitrate needed to decrease the temperature of 120 g of water by 25 °C. The specific heat capacity of water is 4.2 J K^{-1} g^{-1}.

   (Adapted from CCEA January 2011)

2. Explain how you would carry out an experiment to determine the enthalpy change for the hydration of magnesium sulfate, stating the equipment used, the measurements made, and the possible sources of error. Explain how these errors can be minimised.

$$MgSO_4 \text{ (s)} + 7 H_2O \text{ (l)} \rightarrow MgSO_4.7H_2O \text{ (s)}$$

(CCEA June 2009)

3. (a) Write the equation for the reaction between potassium hydroxide and hydrochloric acid. (b) Describe how the enthalpy of neutralisation for this reaction is determined. Include experimental details, including one potential source of error, and one safety precaution. Details of calculations are not required. *(CCEA June 2007)*

Before moving to the next section, check that you are able to:

- Use the concept of standard conditions to define the standard enthalpy change for a reaction and the standard state of a substance.
- Explain how to use a basic calorimeter to calculate enthalpy changes.
- Define the standard enthalpy of neutralisation for acids with one or more hydrogen ions per formula.

Calculating Enthalpy Changes

In this section we are learning to:

- Describe how the energy involved in making and breaking bonds is related to the enthalpy change for a reaction.
- Explain the term average bond enthalpy and use average bond enthalpies to estimate the enthalpy change for a reaction.
- Define the standard enthalpy of formation for a substance and use standard enthalpies of formation to calculate the enthalpy change for a reaction.

Bond Enthalpy Calculations

The enthalpy change for a chemical reaction by calculating the difference between the energy needed to break bonds in the reactants, and the energy released when bonds are formed in the products. The relationship between the energy involved in making and breaking bonds, and the enthalpy change for a reaction, is illustrated in Figure 4. As shown in Figure 4a, if the energy released by making bonds (E_{making}) is greater than the energy needed to break bonds ($E_{breaking}$) the reaction is exothermic ($\Delta H < 0$). Conversely, if the energy needed to break bonds is greater than the energy released by making bonds the reaction is endothermic as shown in Figure 4b.

$$\Delta H = E_{breaking} - E_{making}$$

The energy needed to break a bond can be estimated by the **average bond enthalpy** for the particular type of bond. The term average bond enthalpy refers to the energy needed to break one mole of a particular type of bond averaged over many compounds. The use of average bond enthalpies to estimate the enthalpy change for a reaction is illustrated by the following example.

Worked Example 2.8vi

Use the following bond enthalpies to calculate the enthalpy change when one mole of propane is completely burnt:

$$C_3H_8 + 5O_2 \rightarrow 3CO_2 + 4H_2O$$

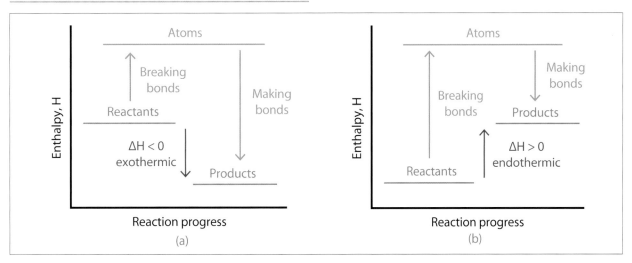

Figure 4: The energy changes associated with making and breaking bonds in (a) an exothermic reaction and (b) an endothermic reaction.

Bond:	C-C	C-H	O=O	C=O	O-H
Bond Enthalpy (kJ mol^{-1}):	347	413	498	805	464

Strategy

- Calculate the moles of bonds broken and the moles of bonds formed when one mole of propane is burnt.

- Use the bond enthalpies to calculate the total energy needed to break bonds and the total energy released by making bonds.

Solution

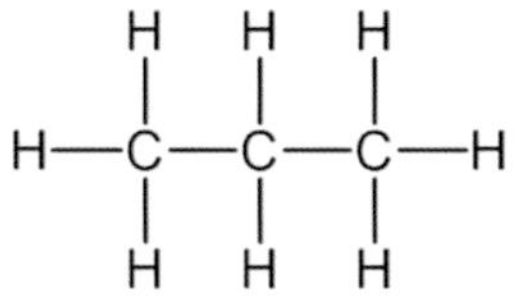

$$3O=C=O + 4H-O-H$$

Bonds broken (in reactants) =

  2 mol of C-C + 8 mol of C-H + 5 mol of O=O

Total energy needed to break bonds ($E_{breaking}$):

  2 E(C-C) + 8 E(C-H) + 5 E(O=O) =

    $2(347) + 8(413) + 5(498) = 6488$ kJ

Bonds made (in products) =

  6 mol of C=O + 8 mol of O-H

Total energy released by making bonds (E_{making}):

  6 E(C=O) + 8 E(O-H) = 6(805) + 8(464) = 8542 kJ

Enthalpy change, ΔH =

  $E_{breaking} - E_{making} = 6488 - 8542 = -2044$ kJ mol^{-1}

....

Exercise 2.8D

1. (a) Explain what is meant by the term bond enthalpy. (b) Use the bond enthalpy values given below to calculate i) the total bond enthalpy for the products, and ii) the enthalpy change for the following reaction, given that the total bond enthalpy of the reactants is 16548 kJ.

$$C_8H_{18\,(l)} + \frac{25}{2} O_{2\,(g)} \rightarrow 8CO_{2\,(g)} + 9H_2O_{(l)}$$

Bond:	C=O	O-H
Bond Enthalpy (kJ mol^{-1}):	750	463

(CCEA January 2008)

2. Chloromethane, CH_3Cl is formed in an exothermic reaction between methane and chlorine. (a) Use the following bond enthalpies to calculate the enthalpy change for the reaction. (b) Draw an enthalpy diagram for the reaction. (c) Explain why the measured enthalpy of reaction is slightly different from the value calculated in part (a).

$$CH_{4\,(g)} + Cl_{2\,(g)} \rightarrow CH_3Cl_{(g)} + HCl_{(g)}$$

Bond:	C-H	Cl-Cl	C-Cl	H-Cl
Bond Enthalpy (kJ mol^{-1}):	413	243	346	432

(CCEA January 2006)

3. (a) Explain what is meant by the term average bond enthalpy. (b) Use the following information to calculate the bond enthalpy for a C-H bond in methane, CH_4.

$$CH_4 + 2O_2 \rightarrow CO_2 + 2H_2O \quad \Delta H = -698 \text{ kJ mol}^{-1}$$

Bond:	C=O	O=O	O-H
Bond Enthalpy (kJ mol^{-1}):	743	496	463

(CCEA June 2010)

4. Use the following bond energies to calculate the enthalpy change for the reaction:

$$C_2H_4 + 3O_2 \rightarrow 2CO_2 + 2H_2O$$

Bond:	C=C	C-H	O-H	O=O	C=O
Bond Enthalpy (kJ mol^{-1}):	612	412	464	497	803

(CCEA June 2005)

5. Use the following bond energies to calculate the enthalpy change for the reaction:

$$CH_3CH_2OH + 3O_2 \rightarrow 2CO_2 + 3H_2O$$

Bond:	C-O	C-H	O-H	C=O	O=O	C-C
Bond Enthalpy (kJ mol^{-1}):	360	413	464	805	498	347

(CCEA January 2010)

6. (a) Use the following bond enthalpies to calculate the enthalpy change for the combustion of one mole of ammonia. (b) Explain why the reaction is exothermic.

$$4NH_3 + 3O_2 \rightarrow 2N_2 + 6H_2O$$

Bond:	N-H	O=O	N≡N	O-H
Bond Enthalpy (kJ mol^{-1}):	391	498	945	464

(CCEA January 2007)

7. The reaction between fluorine and diborane, a hydride of boron, produces a large amount of energy. Use the following bond enthalpies to calculate the enthalpy change when one mole of diborane reacts completely with fluorine.

diborane

$$B_2H_6 + 6F_2 \rightarrow 6HF + 2BF_3$$

Bond:	F-F	B-H	B-B	H-F	B-F
Bond Enthalpy (kJ mol^{-1}):	158	389	293	566	627

(CCEA June 2006)

Before moving to the next section, check that you are able to:

- Describe the relationship between the energy involved in making and breaking bonds in exothermic and endothermic reactions.
- Explain what is meant by the term average bond enthalpy.
- Use average bond enthalpies to estimate the enthalpy change for a reaction.

Enthalpy of Formation

The **standard enthalpy of formation**, $\Delta H_f^\ominus$ refers to the enthalpy change when one mole of a substance is formed from its elements under standard conditions. For example, the standard enthalpy of formation for propane, $\Delta H_f^\ominus(C_3H_8)$ is the standard enthalpy change when one mole of propane is formed from carbon (graphite) and hydrogen gas under standard conditions.

$$3C_{(s)} + 4H_{2\,(g)} \rightarrow C_3H_{8\,(g)} \qquad \Delta H^\ominus = \Delta H_f^\ominus(C_3H_8)$$

Similarly, the standard enthalpy of formation for sodium chloride, $\Delta H_f^\ominus(NaCl)$ is the standard enthalpy change when 1 mole of sodium chloride is formed

from sodium metal and chlorine gas under standard conditions.

$$Na_{(s)} + \frac{1}{2}Cl_{2\,(g)} \rightarrow NaCl_{(s)} \qquad \Delta H^\ominus = \Delta H_f^\ominus(NaCl)$$

Worked Example 2.8vii

Which one of the following defines the standard enthalpy of formation for water?

A $H_{2\,(g)} + \frac{1}{2}O_{2\,(g)} \rightarrow H_2O_{(g)}$

B $2H_{(g)} + O_{(g)} \rightarrow H_2O_{(l)}$

C $2H_{2\,(g)} + O_{2\,(g)} \rightarrow 2H_2O_{(l)}$

D $H_{2\,(g)} + \frac{1}{2}O_{2\,(g)} \rightarrow H_2O_{(l)}$

Strategy

Look for reactions:
- that form one mole of product in its standard state
- in which the reactants are elements in their standard states

Solution

Reactions B and D form one mole of water in its standard state.
However, the reactants in reaction B are NOT in their standard state.
The answer is D.

Exercise 2.8E

1. Which one of the following defines the standard enthalpy of formation for ammonia?

   A $N_{2\,(g)} + 3H_{2\,(g)} \rightarrow 2NH_{3\,(g)}$

   B $N_{2\,(g)} + 3H_{2\,(g)} \rightarrow 2NH_{3\,(l)}$

   C $\frac{1}{2}N_{2\,(g)} + \frac{3}{2}H_{2\,(g)} \rightarrow NH_{3\,(l)}$

   D $\frac{1}{2}N_{2\,(g)} + \frac{3}{2}H_{2\,(g)} \rightarrow NH_{3\,(g)}$

2. Which one of the following represents the standard enthalpy of formation for potassium bromide?

   A $2K_{(s)} + Br_{2\,(g)} \rightarrow 2KBr_{(s)}$

   B $2K_{(s)} + Br_{2\,(l)} \rightarrow 2KBr_{(s)}$

C $K_{(s)} + \dfrac{1}{2} Br_{2\,(g)} \rightarrow KBr_{(s)}$

D $K_{(s)} + \dfrac{1}{2} Br_{2\,(l)} \rightarrow KBr_{(s)}$

3. Which one of the following represents the standard enthalpy change for the formation of ethanol?

A $2C_{(g)} + 6H_{(g)} + O_{(g)} \rightarrow C_2H_5OH_{(g)}$

B $2C_{(s)} + 3H_{2\,(g)} + O_{(g)} \rightarrow C_2H_5OH_{(l)}$

C $2C_{(s)} + 3H_{2\,(g)} + \dfrac{1}{2}O_{2\,(g)} \rightarrow C_2H_5OH_{(g)}$

D $2C_{(s)} + 3H_{2\,(g)} + \dfrac{1}{2}O_{2\,(g)} \rightarrow C_2H_5OH_{(l)}$

(CCEA January 2011)

4. Which one of the following equations corresponds to a standard enthalpy of formation?

A $2NO_{(g)} \rightarrow N_{2\,(g)} + O_{2\,(g)}$

B $2H_{2\,(g)} + O_{2\,(g)} \rightarrow 2H_2O_{(g)}$

C $Na_{(s)} + Cl_{(g)} \rightarrow NaCl_{(s)}$

D $Mg_{(s)} + Br_{2\,(l)} \rightarrow MgBr_{2\,(s)}$

(CCEA June 2009)

Having defined the standard enthalpy of formation to be the enthalpy change when one mole of the substance is formed from its elements under standard conditions, it follows that the standard enthalpy of formation for an element must be zero.

$$\Delta H_f^\oplus \text{ (element)} = 0$$

Defining standard enthalpies of formation in this way allows us to calculate the standard enthalpy change for a reaction by subtracting the total enthalpy of formation for the reactants from the total enthalpy of formation for the products.

$$\Delta H^\oplus = \Delta H_f^\oplus \text{ (products)} - \Delta H_f^\oplus \text{ (reactants)}$$

- -

Worked Example 2.8viii

A highly explosive mixture of hydrazine, N_2H_4 and hydrogen peroxide, H_2O_2 was used to power the first jet aircraft. Use the following enthalpies of formation to calculate the enthalpy change for the reaction between hydrazine and hydrogen peroxide.

$$N_2H_4 + 2H_2O_2 \rightarrow N_2 + 4H_2O$$

	N_2H_4	H_2O_2	H_2O
Standard enthalpy of formation (kJ mol⁻¹):	+50	−191	−286

(CCEA January 2005)

Solution

$\Delta H_f^\oplus$ (products) = $\Delta H_f^\oplus$ (N_2) + 4 $\Delta H_f^\oplus$ (H_2O)

   = 0 + 4(−286) = −1144 kJ

$\Delta H_f^\oplus$ (reactants) = $\Delta H_f^\oplus$ (N_2H_4) + 2 $\Delta H_f^\oplus$ (H_2O_2)

   = 50 + 2(−191) = −332 kJ

Enthalpy change per mole of hydrazine reacted:

$\Delta H^\oplus = \Delta H_f^\oplus$ (products) − $\Delta H_f^\oplus$ (reactants)

   = −1144 − (−332) = −812 kJ mol⁻¹

- -

Exercise 2.8F

1. (a) Use the following bond enthalpies to calculate the standard enthalpy of formation for hydrogen fluoride, HF. (b) Draw an enthalpy diagram for the reaction.

Bond:	H-H	F-F	H-F
Bond Enthalpy (kJ mol⁻¹):	436	158	568

(CCEA January 2004)

2. The enthalpy change for the formation of ammonia is −46.2 kJ mol⁻¹. What is the enthalpy change (in kJ) for the reaction:

$$2NH_{3\,(g)} \rightarrow N_{2\,(g)} + 3H_{2\,(g)}$$

(CCEA January 2007)

Before moving to the next section, check that you are able to:

- Define the standard enthalpy of formation for a substance.

- Use standard enthalpies of formation to calculate the standard enthalpy change for a reaction.

Enthalpy of Combustion

The term **standard enthalpy of combustion**, $\Delta H_c^\ominus$ refers to the enthalpy change when one mole of a substance is completely burnt in oxygen under standard conditions. For example, the standard enthalpy of combustion for butane is the enthalpy change that occurs when 1 mole of butane, C_4H_{10} burns to form carbon dioxide and water under standard conditions.

$$C_4H_{10\ (g)} + \frac{13}{2}O_{2\ (g)} \rightarrow 4CO_{2\ (g)} + 5H_2O_{\ (l)}$$

$$\Delta H^\ominus = \Delta H_c^\ominus(C_4H_{10})$$

When hydrocarbons such as butane are burnt, the carbon and hydrogen in the compound are converted to carbon dioxide and water. Carbon dioxide and water are very stable compounds and a great deal of energy is released when they are formed. As a result, the combustion of hydrocarbons is highly exothermic and they are very good fuels.

. . . .

Worked Example 2.8ix

Burning glucose releases energy:

$$C_6H_{12}O_{6\ (s)} + 6O_{2\ (g)} \rightarrow 6CO_{2\ (g)} + 6H_2O_{\ (l)}$$

The standard enthalpy of combustion for glucose may be measured directly, or calculated using standard enthalpies of formation. Use the following standard enthalpies of formation to calculate the standard enthalpy of combustion for glucose.

Substance:	$CO_{2\ (g)}$	$H_2O_{\ (l)}$	$C_6H_{12}O_{6\ (s)}$
$\Delta H_f^\ominus$ (kJ mol^{-1}):	–394	–286	–1273

(CCEA June 2005)

Solution

$\Delta H_f^\ominus$ (products) = 6 $\Delta H_f^\ominus$ (CO_2) + 6 $\Delta H_f^\ominus$ (H_2O)
= 6(–394) + 6(–286) = – 4080 kJ

$\Delta H_f^\ominus$ (reactants) = $\Delta H_f^\ominus$ ($C_6H_{12}O_6$) + 6 $\Delta H_f^\ominus$ (O_2)
= –1273 + 6(0) = –1273 kJ

Enthalpy change per mole of glucose burnt:

$\Delta H_c^\ominus = \Delta H_f^\ominus$ (products) – $\Delta H_f^\ominus$ (reactants)
= –4080 –(–1273) = –2807 kJ mol^{-1}

. . . .

Exercise 2.8G

1. (a) Define the term standard enthalpy of combustion. (b) Use the following standard enthalpies of formation to calculate the enthalpy change for the complete combustion of methane: $CH_4 + 2O_2 \rightarrow CO_2 + 2H_2O$.

Substance:	$CO_{2\ (g)}$	$H_2O_{\ (l)}$	$CH_{4\ (g)}$
$\Delta H_f^\ominus$ (kJ mol^{-1}):	–394	–286	–75

(CCEA June 2010)

2. Kerosine is a mixture that contains the compound dodecane, $C_{12}H_{26}$. (a) Write an equation for the complete combustion of dodecane. (b) Draw an enthalpy diagram for the combustion of dodecane. (c) Explain, in terms of enthalpy, why the combustion of dodecane is exothermic. *(CCEA January 2008)*

3. (a) Define the term standard enthalpy of formation. (b) Use the following standard enthalpies of formation to calculate the standard enthalpy change for photosynthesis:

$$6CO_{2\ (g)} + 6H_2O_{\ (l)} \rightarrow C_6H_{12}O_{6\ (s)} + 6O_{2\ (g)}$$

Substance:	$CO_{2\ (g)}$	$H_2O_{\ (l)}$	$C_6H_{12}O_{6\ (s)}$
Standard enthalpy of formation (kJ mol^{-1}):	–394	–286	–1273

(CCEA June 2003)

Hess's Law

In this section we are learning to:

- Use Hess's law to calculate enthalpy changes that are difficult to measure directly in the laboratory.

Many of the enthalpy changes that accompany chemical reactions can be measured in the laboratory by calorimetry. Enthalpy changes that are too difficult to measure under normal laboratory conditions must instead be calculated using Hess's Law. For example, the enthalpy change when anhydrous copper(II) sulfate dissolves in water (ΔH_1) can be accurately measured in the laboratory. The enthalpy change that occurs when the hydrate $CuSO_4.5H_2O_{\ (s)}$ dissolves in water (ΔH_2) can also be accurately measured in the laboratory. In contrast, the enthalpy change that occurs when anhydrous copper(II) sulfate, $CuSO_{4\ (s)}$

reacts with water to form the hydrate $CuSO_4.5H_2O$ (s) is difficult to measure accurately and is instead calculated from ΔH_1 and ΔH_2 using Hess's Law.

$$CuSO_4 \text{ (s)} \rightarrow CuSO_4 \text{ (aq)} \qquad \Delta H = \Delta H_1$$

$$CuSO_4.5H_2O \text{ (s)} \rightarrow CuSO_4 \text{ (aq)} \qquad \Delta H = \Delta H_2$$

The enthalpy cycle in Figure 5 demonstrates that the overall chemical change that occurs when anhydrous copper(II) sulfate dissolves (ΔH_1) is equivalent to the change that occurs when anhydrous copper(II) sulfate is hydrated to form the hydrate $CuSO_4.5H_2O$ (ΔH) and the hydrate dissolved to form a solution of copper(II) sulfate (ΔH_2). If the overall chemical change is the same it follows that the total enthalpy change must be same and we can write:

$$\Delta H_1 = \Delta H + \Delta H_2$$

This equation is the result of applying **Hess's Law** which states that the enthalpy change for a chemical reaction depends on the state of the reactants and products and does not depend on the way in which the reaction is carried out.

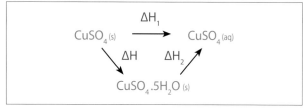

Figure 5: Enthalpy cycle to calculate the enthalpy change for the reaction of anhydrous copper(II) sulfate with water to form the hydrate $CuSO_4.5H_2O$.

Worked Example 2.8x

The following diagram shows the enthalpy changes that are used to determine the enthalpy change for the reaction between anhydrous copper(II) sulfate and water to form the hydrate $CuSO_4.5H_2O$ (s).

$CuSO_4$ (s) $\xrightarrow{\Delta H_1}$ $CuSO_4$ (aq)
ΔH ΔH_2
$CuSO_4.5H_2O$ (s)

(a) Dissolving 8.0 g of anhydrous copper(II) sulfate, $CuSO_4$ (s) in 100 g of water produces a rise in temperature of 1.2 °C. Calculate the enthalpy change ΔH_1. The specific heat capacity of water is 4.2 J °C^{-1} g^{-1}.

(b) When 12.5 g of hydrated copper(II) sulfate, $CuSO_4.5H_2O$ (s) dissolves in 100 g of water the temperature of the solution drops by 1.4 °C. Calculate the enthalpy change ΔH_2. The specific heat capacity of water is 4.2 J °C^{-1} g^{-1}.

(c) Use the values for ΔH_1 and ΔH_2 to calculate the molar enthalpy change ΔH.

(CCEA June 2011)

Solution

(a) Mass of solution, m = 100 g

$\Delta H_1 = - m\,c\,\Delta T = - 100\text{ g} \times 4.2\text{ J °C}^{-1}\text{ g}^{-1} \times 1.2\text{ °C}$
$= - 504\text{ J}$

(b) Mass of solution, m = 100 g

$\Delta H_2 = - m\,c\,\Delta T = - 100\text{ g} \times 4.2\text{ J °C}^{-1}\text{ g}^{-1} \times (-1.4\text{ °C})$
$= + 588\text{ J}$

(c) Applying Hess's Law gives: $\Delta H_1 = \Delta H + \Delta H_2$

$\Delta H = \Delta H_1 - \Delta H_2 = (-504) - 588 = -1092\text{ J}$

Molar enthalpy change =

$$\frac{\Delta H}{\text{Moles of } CuSO_4} = \frac{-1.092\text{ kJ}}{0.05\text{ mol}} = -21.84\text{ kJ mol}^{-1}$$

Exercise 2.8H

1. The enthalpy change for the combustion of graphite is –393.5 kJ mol^{-1} and the enthalpy change for the combustion of diamond is –395.4 kJ mol^{-1}. Calculate the enthalpy change for the reaction: C(graphite) $\rightarrow$ C(diamond).

(CCEA June 2011)

2. When 0.10 mol of anhydrous $MgSO_4$ was dissolved in 100 g of water the temperature rose by 9 °C. When 0.10 mol of $MgSO_4.7H_2O$ was dissolved in 100 g of water, the temperature dropped by 3 °C. The specific heat capacity for water is 4.2 J °C^{-1} g^{-1}. Use this information to calculate the enthalpy change for the hydration of magnesium sulfate:

$$MgSO_4 \text{ (s)} + 7H_2O \text{ (l)} \rightarrow MgSO_4.7H_2O \text{ (s)}$$

(CCEA June 2009)

3. (a) Explain what is meant by the term standard enthalpy of combustion. (b) State Hess's law. (c) Use the following enthalpy changes to calculate the enthalpy of combustion for octane, C_8H_{18}.

$$C_8H_{18} \text{ (l)} + \frac{25}{2}O_2 \text{ (g)} \rightarrow 8CO_2 \text{ (g)} + 9H_2O \text{ (l)}$$

$C_{(s)} + O_{2\,(g)} \rightarrow CO_{2\,(g)}$ $\Delta H^\circ = -393.5\ kJ\ mol^{-1}$

$8C_{(s)} + 9H_{2\,(g)} \rightarrow C_8H_{18\,(l)}$ $\Delta H^\circ = -250.0\ kJ\ mol^{-1}$

$H_{2\,(g)} + \frac{1}{2}O_{2\,(g)} \rightarrow H_2O_{(l)}$ $\Delta H^\circ = -286.0\ kJ\ mol^{-1}$

(CCEA January 2008)

4. The standard enthalpies of combustion for carbon, hydrogen and ethyne, C_2H_2 are given below. Use this data to calculate the standard enthalpy of formation for ethyne.

$C_{(s)} + O_{2\,(g)} \rightarrow CO_{2\,(g)}$ $\Delta H_c^\circ = -394\ kJ\ mol^{-1}$

$H_{2\,(g)} + \frac{1}{2}O_{2\,(g)} \rightarrow H_2O_{(l)}$ $\Delta H_c^\circ = -286\ kJ\ mol^{-1}$

$C_2H_{2\,(g)} + \frac{5}{2}O_{2\,(g)} \rightarrow 2CO_{2\,(g)} + H_2O_{(l)}$

$\Delta H_c^\circ = -1300\ kJ\ mol^{-1}$

(CCEA January 2011)

5. Use the following standard enthalpies of combustion to calculate the standard enthalpy of formation for ethanoic acid, $CH_3COOH_{(l)}$.

	$C_{(s)}$	$H_{2\,(g)}$	$CH_3COOH_{(l)}$
Standard enthalpy of combustion ($kJ\ mol^{-1}$):	–393	–286	–487

(CCEA June 2007)

6. The enthalpy change for the thermal decomposition of sodium hydrogencarbonate (ΔH_1) can be determined using Hess's Law. (a) State Hess's Law. (b) Use the following enthalpy changes and energy cycle to calculate the enthalpy change ΔH_1.

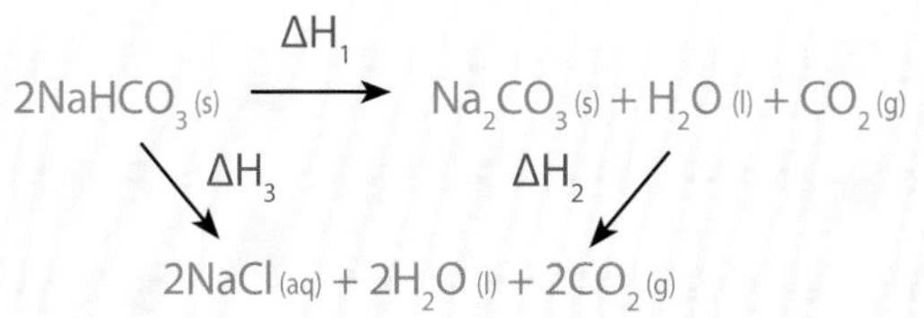

$NaHCO_{3\,(s)} + HCl_{(aq)} \rightarrow NaCl_{(aq)} + H_2O_{(l)} + CO_{2\,(g)}$

$\Delta H = +16\ kJ$

$Na_2CO_{3\,(s)} + 2HCl_{(aq)} \rightarrow 2NaCl_{(aq)} + H_2O_{(l)} + CO_{2\,(g)}$

$\Delta H = -21\ kJ$

(CCEA June 2004)

Before moving to the next section, check that you are able to:

- Recall Hess's Law and explain how it can be used to calculate enthalpy changes by constructing an enthalpy cycle.
- Use Hess's law to determine enthalpy changes by constructing an enthalpy cycle.

2.9 Equilibrium

CONNECTIONS

- The transport of oxygen around the human body depends on the ability of oxygen to bind reversibly to the protein haemoglobin in red blood cells.
- The pH of blood is maintained in the narrow range 7.35–7.45 by a chemical equilibrium involving dissolved carbon dioxide and hydrogencarbonate ions.

Chemical Equilibrium

In this section we are learning to:

- Describe how chemical equilibrium results from a state of dynamic equilibrium in a reaction mixture.
- Explain the conditions under which a dynamic equilibrium is established.

The term **reversible reaction** can be used to describe a reaction in which the products can be transformed back into the reactants. The melting of ice is an example of a reversible reaction. A block of ice melts if the temperature of the surroundings is above 0 °C. The process can be reversed by cooling the water formed to below 0 °C. If the temperature is exactly 0 °C the melting of ice and the freezing of water both occur with the result that mixtures of ice and water can coexist at 0 °C. If a mixture of ice and water is left at 0 °C for long enough, the amount of ice and water in the mixture remains constant. This is a state of matter known as a **dynamic equilibrium** in which the ice is converted to water at same rate as water is converted to ice. The dynamic equilibrium between ice and water at 0 °C is shown in Figure 1.

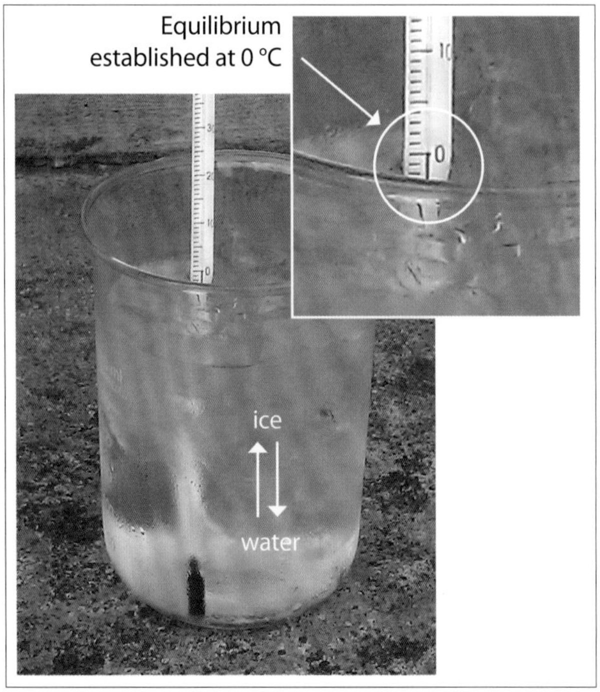

Figure 1: Dynamic equilibrium between ice and water at 0 °C.

A state of dynamic equilibrium is represented by a double-arrow ($\leftrightarrows$) when writing chemical equations. The dynamic equilibrium between ice and water at 0 °C is represented by the equation: $H_2O_{(s)} \leftrightarrows H_2O_{(l)}$.

Many chemical reactions produce a dynamic equilibrium in which the reactants are converted into products at the same rate as the products are converted back into reactants. For example, ammonia is produced on an industrial scale by reacting a mixture of nitrogen gas and hydrogen gas in the presence of a catalyst.

Formation of ammonia: $N_2 + 3H_2 \rightarrow 2NH_3$

The reaction between nitrogen and hydrogen is reversible with the result that the ammonia formed in the reaction immediately begins to decompose and reform nitrogen and hydrogen.

Decomposition of ammonia: $2NH_3 \rightarrow N_2 + 3H_2$

The rate at which ammonia decomposes increases as the amount of ammonia in the reaction mixture increases. Eventually the rate of formation of ammonia (the forward reaction) is equal to the rate at which ammonia decomposes (the reverse reaction). This corresponds to a state of dynamic equilibrium in which the composition of the reaction mixture remains constant, and is referred to as a **chemical equilibrium**. The changes in concentration that occur when nitrogen and hydrogen react and establish chemical equilibrium are illustrated in Figure 2.

$$\text{Chemical equilibrium: } N_2 + 3H_2 \rightleftharpoons 2NH_3$$

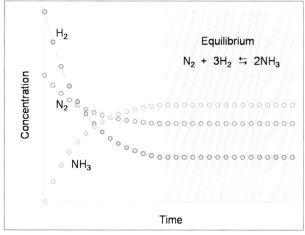

Figure 2: Changes in concentration when a mixture of nitrogen and hydrogen react to form ammonia and establish a chemical equilibrium.

Exercise 2.9A

Nitrogen dioxide, NO_2 exists in dynamic equilibrium with dinitrogen tetroxide, N_2O_4. Explain the term dynamic equilibrium.

$$N_2O_{4\,(g)} \rightleftharpoons 2NO_{2\,(g)} \qquad \Delta H = +56 \text{ kJ}$$

(CCEA January 2007)

Before moving to the next section, check that you are able to:

- Recall the meaning of the term reversible reaction.
- Explain how a reversible reaction can produce a dynamic equilibrium.
- Explain how chemical equilibrium results from a state of dynamic equilibrium.

Factors Affecting Equilibrium

In this section we are learning to:

- Explain the effect of changing the temperature, pressure and composition of a chemical equilibrium on the amount of product in the equilibrium.
- Recall the effect of a catalyst on the amount of product formed in a chemical equilibrium.

The composition of an equilibrium mixture depends on the nature of the substances in the equilibrium mixture, and the conditions under which the equilibrium is established. If the composition of an equilibrium mixture is changed, the mixture is no longer at equilibrium, and the composition of the mixture adjusts until a new equilibrium is established. Similarly, if the conditions under which equilibrium is established change, the reaction mixture is no longer at equilibrium and the composition of the reaction mixture adjusts until a new equilibrium is established.

In general, *when an equilibrium mixture is disturbed, the mixture responds in a way that minimises the effect of the disturbance.* Consider, for example, the reaction between hydrogen and nitrogen to form ammonia.

$$N_2 + 3H_2 \rightleftharpoons 2NH_3$$

If the reaction mixture is allowed to reach equilibrium, and a small amount of ammonia removed, the reaction mixture is no longer at equilibrium. The reaction mixture then attempts to re-establish equilibrium by using the forward reaction to increase the amount of ammonia in the mixture.

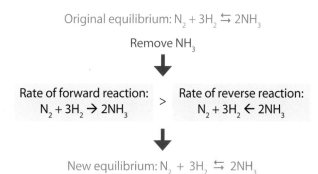

$$\text{New equilibrium: } N_2 + 3H_2 \rightleftharpoons 2NH_3$$

The effect of generating more ammonia on the composition of the reaction mixture is illustrated in Figure 3. Making more ammonia decreases the amount of nitrogen and hydrogen in the reaction mixture. As a result, the amount of nitrogen and hydrogen in the reaction mixture when equilibrium is re-established is lower than in the original equilibrium. In this way removing ammonia has the effect of shifting the **position of equilibrium** to the right in favour of ammonia. Adding nitrogen or hydrogen will also shift the position of equilibrium to the right in an attempt to minimise the effect of adding reactants to the equilibrium. Conversely, the position of the equilibrium can be shifted to the left by adding ammonia, or removing some of the reactants from the equilibrium.

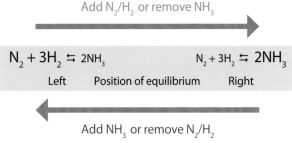

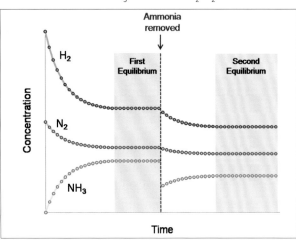

Figure 3: The effect of removing ammonia on the composition of the equilibrium $N_2 + 3H_2 \leftrightharpoons 2NH_3$.

Worked Example 2.9i

The reaction between bromine and water is represented by the following equation. Which one of the following reagents would move the equilibrium position to the right?

$$Br_2 + H_2O \leftrightharpoons Br^- + OBr^- + 2H^+$$

A   nitric acid
B   sodium carbonate
C   sodium bromide
D   sulfuric acid

(CCEA June 2011)

Solution

The solution is acidic (contains H^+). Adding sodium carbonate (an alkali) reduces the amount of H^+ ions in solution by reacting with the H^+ ions to form water: $H^+ + OH^- \rightarrow H_2O$. The equilibrium position shifts to the right in an attempt to replace the H^+ ions that reacted with the sodium carbonate.

Answer B.

In industry the reaction between nitrogen and hydrogen is carried out in the presence of a catalyst. The catalyst increases the rate of the forward and reverse reactions and allows equilibrium to be established more quickly. The catalyst does not affect the composition of the equilibrium mixture. The amount of ammonia at equilibrium is instead increased by reacting nitrogen and hydrogen at high pressure. When an equilibrium mixture of nitrogen and hydrogen is compressed, the increase in pressure can be reduced by using the forward reaction to shift the position of equilibrium to the right and decrease the number of molecules of gas in the equilibrium. The effect of increasing pressure on the composition of an equilibrium mixture of nitrogen, hydrogen and ammonia is illustrated in Figure 4. Conversely, reducing the pressure shifts the position of equilibrium to the left as the equilibrium attempts to maintain the pressure by using the reverse reaction to increase the number of molecules of gas in the equilibrium.

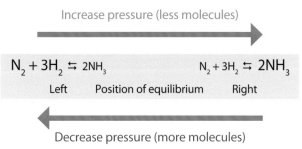

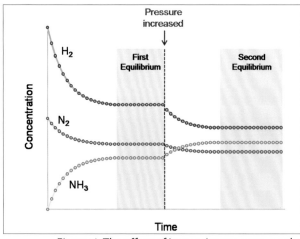

Figure 4: The effect of increasing pressure on the composition of the equilibrium $N_2 + 3H_2 \leftrightharpoons 2NH_3$

The amount of ammonia at equilibrium is also affected by the temperature of the equilibrium mixture. The reaction between nitrogen and hydrogen is exothermic. When the temperature is increased, the reaction is no longer at equilibrium and the reaction mixture responds by using the reverse reaction (endothermic) to absorb heat. This has the effect of shifting the position of the equilibrium to the left. Conversely, when the temperature is decreased, the reaction is no longer at equilibrium and responds by using the forward reaction (exothermic) to generate heat. As a result, the position of the equilibrium shifts to the right. The effect of increasing temperature on the position of equilibrium between nitrogen, hydrogen and ammonia is illustrated in Figure 5.

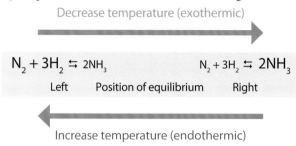

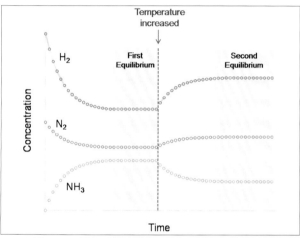

Figure 5: The effect of increasing temperature on the composition of the equilibrium $N_2 + 3H_2 \leftrightarrows 2NH_3$.

Worked Example 2.9ii

The Birkeland-Eyde process for the manufacture of nitric acid was developed in 1903. In the first step of the process, nitrogen and oxygen react to form nitrogen(II) oxide. Explain the effect, if any, of each of the following changes on the yield of nitrogen(II) oxide.

$$N_{2\,(g)} + O_{2\,(g)} \leftrightarrows 2NO_{(g)} \qquad \Delta H = +180 \text{ kJ mol}^{-1}$$

(a) increasing the temperature
(b) adding more nitrogen
(c) increasing the pressure
(d) adding a catalyst

(CCEA January 2011)

Solution

(a) The forward reaction is endothermic. As a result, the equilibrium shifts to the right and the amount of NO increases as the reaction mixture absorbs heat to reduce the effect of increasing the temperature.

(b) The yield of NO increases as the position of the equilibrium shifts to the right to reduce the amount of nitrogen.

(c) The yield of NO is not affected by pressure as changing the position of the equilibrium does not change the amount of gas in the reaction mixture.

(d) The amount of NO at equilibrium is not affected by adding a catalyst. Adding a catalyst does not affect the position of equilibrium.

Exercise 2.9B

1. Methanol, CH_3OH is produced by the reaction between carbon dioxide and hydrogen. If the reaction is carried out at a higher temperature the equilibrium yield of methanol decreases. Determine the sign of the enthalpy change for the forward reaction and explain your reasoning.

$$CO_{2\,(g)} + 3H_{2\,(g)} \leftrightarrows CH_3OH_{(g)} + H_2O_{(g)}$$

(CCEA January 2008)

2. Hydrogen is produced on an industrial scale by the reaction between methane and steam. The reaction is endothermic and is carried out at a pressure of 40 atmospheres in the presence of a nickel catalyst. Explain why the reaction is also carried out at 1023 K.

$$CH_{4\,(g)} + 2H_2O_{(g)} \leftrightarrows CO_{2\,(g)} + 4H_{2\,(g)}$$

(CCEA June 2009)

3. When solid ammonium chloride is heated, it dissociates to form a mixture of gases:
$NH_4Cl_{(s)} \leftrightarrows NH_{3\,(g)} + HCl_{(g)}$

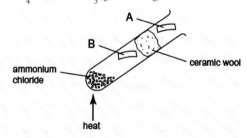

(a) Explain why the pH paper changes to a blue colour at A.

(b) Explain why the pH paper turns a red colour at B.

(c) Suggest the purpose of the ceramic wool.

(d) Determine if the forward reaction is exothermic or endothermic and explain your reasoning.

(CCEA June 2011)

4. Which one of the following statements regarding the following chemical equilibrium is correct?

$$2SO_{2\,(g)} + O_{2\,(g)} \rightleftharpoons 2SO_{3\,(g)} \qquad \Delta H = -192 \text{ kJ}$$

A Increasing the concentration of oxygen, O_2 increases the amount of sulfur dioxide, SO_2 at equilibrium.

B Decreasing the pressure increases the concentration of sulfur trioxide, SO_3 at equilibrium.

C Increasing the temperature increases the concentration of sulfur dioxide, SO_2 at equilibrium.

D Removing sulfur trioxide, SO_3 from the reaction increases the concentration of SO_2 at equilibrium.

(CCEA June 2006)

5. The second stage in the production of nitric acid involves the reaction of nitrogen monoxide with oxygen to form nitrogen dioxide:

$$2NO_{(g)} + O_{2\,(g)} \rightleftharpoons 2NO_{2\,(g)} \qquad \Delta H = -116 \text{ kJ mol}^{-1}$$

(a) Explain what is meant by the term dynamic equilibrium. State and explain how (b) increasing the pressure, (c) increasing the temperature and (d) adding a catalyst will affect the equilibrium yield of nitrogen dioxide.

(CCEA June 2010)

6. Ethylene glycol, CH_2OHCH_2OH is produced by passing a mixture of ethene and air over silver metal at high temperature. The reaction occurs in two steps.

Step 1 $\quad CH_2=CH_2 + \frac{1}{2}O_2 \rightleftharpoons CH_2OCH_2$

ethylene oxide

Step 2 $\quad CH_2OCH_2 + H_2O \rightarrow CH_2OHCH_2OH$

(a) Suggest the purpose of the silver. Using an equilibrium argument explain why (b) a high pressure and (c) a high temperature is used.

(CCEA January 2005)

7. The hydrogen needed for the production of ammonia is obtained from methane or naphtha. Previously hydrogen was obtained from coke and steam using a two stage process known as the water gas reaction.

Stage 1 $\quad C_{(s)} + H_2O_{(g)} \rightleftharpoons CO_{(g)} + H_{2\,(g)}$

$$\Delta H = +122 \text{ kJ}$$

Stage 2 $\quad CO_{(g)} + H_2O_{(g)} \rightleftharpoons CO_{2\,(g)} + H_{2\,(g)}$

$$\Delta H = -41 \text{ kJ}$$

Explain the effect, if any, of (a) increasing the temperature, (b) increasing the pressure and (c) adding a catalyst on the position of equilibrium in stage 2. *(CCEA January 2004)*

Before moving to the next section, check that you are able to:

- Recall Le Chatelier's Principle and use it to describe the effect of changing the temperature, pressure, and composition of an equilibrium mixture on the position of equilibrium.

- Recall that a catalyst increases the rate at which equilibrium is established but does not affect the position of equilibrium.

Applications of Equilibrium

In this section we are learning to:

- Recall the conditions used to produce ammonia by the Haber-Bosch process and the conditions used to make sulfuric acid by the Contact process.

- Use equilibrium arguments to account for the reaction conditions used in the Haber-Bosch process and the Contact process.

Production of Ammonia

In industry ammonia is produced by the Haber-Bosch process. A mixture of nitrogen and hydrogen react in the presence of a granulated iron catalyst at a temperature of 450 °C and a total pressure of 250 atmospheres.

$$N_{2\,(g)} + 3H_{2\,(g)} \rightleftharpoons 2NH_{3\,(g)} \qquad \Delta H = -92 \text{ kJ}$$

The reaction conditions are chosen to maximise profits by producing ammonia as quickly as possible. The rate at which ammonia is produced is increased by using a catalyst to increase the rate at which equilibrium is established. The rate of ammonia production can be further increased by removing ammonia from the reaction mixture as it forms. This shifts the position of equilibrium further to the right, producing more ammonia as the reaction proceeds. The effect of temperature and pressure on the yield of ammonia obtained from the equilibrium is shown in Figure 6. At higher pressures the yield of ammonia increases as the position of equilibrium moves to the right in order to reduce the number of molecules in the equilibrium. As a result we might expect the process to be more profitable at high pressure. However, the increased cost of maintaining equipment capable of operating at high pressure reduces profits to the extent that it becomes necessary to operate the process at a pressure of 250 atmospheres. In this way *an operating pressure of 250 atmospheres represents a compromise between increasing the yield of ammonia at equilibrium and the increased cost of operating the process at higher pressures.*

A similar compromise is involved in choosing to operate the process at a temperature of 450 °C. The relationship between the yield of ammonia and the reaction temperature in Figure 6 demonstrates that the yield of ammonia decreases as the temperature of the reaction mixture is increased. This is expected as the forward reaction is exothermic and, according to Le Chatelier's Principle, the position of equilibrium shifts to the left as the reverse reaction (endothermic) is used to absorb heat when the temperature is increased. A higher yield of ammonia at lower temperatures is not desirable. Reducing the temperature reduces the rate at which equilibrium is established and, as a result, the rate at which ammonia is produced. In this way *an operating temperature of 450 °C represents a compromise between maintaining a satisfactory rate of reaction and keeping the temperature low enough to obtain a reasonable yield of ammonia at equilibrium.*

Exercise 2.9C

1. (a) State the temperature and pressure used in the production of ammonia by the Haber process. (b) Why is the temperature used for the Haber process described as a compromise temperature? *(CCEA June 2010)*

2. The Haber process for the manufacture of ammonia involves the equilibrium reaction between nitrogen and hydrogen. (a) Write the equation for the reaction. (b) Name the catalyst used in the Haber process. (c) Explain why a combination of high pressure and low temperature would maximise the yield of ammonia. *(CCEA January 2009)*

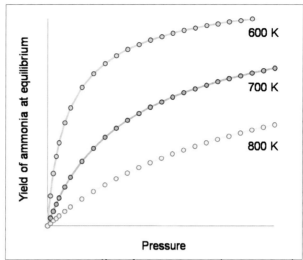

Figure 6: Effect of temperature and pressure on the equilibrium yield of ammonia obtained from the Haber-Bosch process.

3. The graph shows how the equilibrium yield of ammonia varies with temperature for the production of ammonia by the Haber-Bosch process. Use the graph to determine if the reaction is exothermic or endothermic.

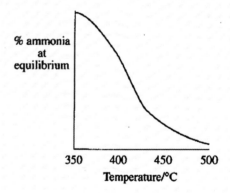

(CCEA June 2005)

Before moving to the next section, check that you are able to:

- Recall the conditions used for the Haber-Bosch process.
- Explain why the temperature and pressure used for the Haber-Bosch process represent a compromise.

Manufacture of Sulfuric Acid

Sulfuric acid is used to make a wide range of useful materials including fertiliser, paints, detergents and pharmaceuticals. It is produced on an industrial scale by a process known as the Contact process. In the first stage of the process sulfur dioxide, SO_2 is produced by burning sulfur in air.

Step 1 $S_{(s)} + O_{2\ (g)} \rightarrow SO_{2\ (g)}$

The sulfur dioxide is then mixed with more air and heated to 450 °C before being passed over a solid vanadium(V) oxide, V_2O_5 catalyst. In the presence of the catalyst sulfur dioxide reacts with oxygen to form sulfur trioxide, SO_3 and establish a chemical equilibrium.

Step 2 $2SO_2\ (g) + O_2\ (g) \rightleftharpoons 2SO_3\ (g)$ $\Delta H = -197\ kJ$

The reaction between sulfur dioxide and oxygen is exothermic. Increasing the temperature increases the rate at which equilibrium is established but decreases the yield of sulfur trioxide as the equilibrium shifts to the left in an effort to absorb heat. As a result it becomes necessary to find a temperature that is high enough to maintain the rate, and at the same time low enough to maintain a reasonable yield of sulfur trioxide. At temperatures below 450 °C the reaction is too slow to be sustained and, as a result, *operating the process at 450 °C represents a compromise between increasing the yield of sulfur trioxide and maintaining an acceptable rate of reaction.*

Increasing the operating pressure would be expected to further increase the yield of sulfur trioxide at equilibrium. The additional cost of operating the process at high pressure cannot however be justified as the yield of ammonia is already high when the process is operated at a slightly elevated pressure of 1-2 atmospheres.

In the final stage of the process sulfuric acid is produced by dissolving the sulfur trioxide in sulfuric acid and adding water.

Step 3 $SO_{3\ (g)} + H_2SO_{4\ (l)} + H_2O_{(l)} \rightarrow 2H_2SO_{4\ (l)}$

Exercise 2.9D

1. Which set of conditions are used in the Contact Process?

Conditions	Catalyst	Pressure (atm)	Temperature (°C)
A	iron	1–2	250
B	iron	200–1000	450
C	vanadium(V) oxide	1–2	450
D	vanadium(V) oxide	200–1000	250

(CCEA June 2008)

2. The Contact Process for the production of sulfuric acid involves the following equilibrium.
    (a) State and explain the effect of increasing the total pressure on the yield of sulfur trioxide.
    (b) Explain why the reaction is carried out at a moderate temperature.

$2SO_2\ (g) + O_2\ (g) \rightleftharpoons 2SO_3\ (g)$ $\Delta H = -197\ kJ$

(Adapted from CCEA June 2001)

Before moving to the next section, check that you are able to:

- Recall the conditions used for the Contact process.
- Explain why the temperature used in the Contact process represents a compromise and why a pressure of 1–2 atmospheres is sufficient for the Contact process.

2.10 Kinetics

Rate of Reaction

In this section we are learning to:

- Define the term rate of reaction.
- Suggest techniques to measure the rate of a reaction.

The speed or 'rate' of a chemical reaction can be measured using a wide variety of techniques. The technique chosen to measure the rate of a particular reaction depends on the nature of the reactants and products. If the reaction produces a gas, the rate can be determined by using a gas syringe to collect and measure the volume of gas produced during the reaction. The use of a gas syringe to collect the hydrogen gas produced when magnesium reacts with dilute hydrochloric acid is shown in Figure 1.

$$Mg_{(s)} + 2HCl_{(aq)} \rightarrow MgCl_{2\ (aq)} + H_{2\ (g)}$$

If we define the rate of this reaction to be the volume of hydrogen produced per second (Units: $cm^3\ s^{-1}$), the rate can be calculated at any point during the reaction

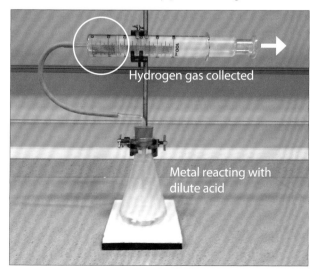
Hydrogen gas collected

Metal reacting with dilute acid

Figure 1: Use of a gas syringe to measure the volume of gas produced during the reaction between magnesium and dilute hydrochloric acid.

by measuring the volume of hydrogen produced in one second. In this way we see that the **rate of reaction** refers to the change in the amount of a reactant or product per unit of time. In any chemical reaction the rate of the reaction decreases as the reactants are used up. In the reaction between magnesium and hydrochloric acid, the rate at which hydrogen is produced decreases until no more gas is produced and the rate becomes zero.

In the case of a reaction that produces a colour change, the rate of reaction can be calculated by measuring the time needed for the colour change to occur. In the reaction between sodium thiosulfate solution and dilute hydrochloric acid, the rate is calculated by measuring the time needed for the reaction mixture to produce enough sulfur to make the solution too cloudy to see through.

$$Na_2S_2O_{3\ (aq)} + 2HCl_{(aq)} \rightarrow$$

$$2NaCl_{(aq)} + H_2O_{(l)} + SO_{2\ (g)} + S_{(s)}$$

A rate of reaction measured in this way is known as the **average rate of reaction** as it does not take into account the steady decrease in rate that occurs as the reaction proceeds.

$$\text{Average rate} = \frac{1}{\text{Time for reaction}}$$

Before moving to the next section, check that you are able to:

- Define the term rate of reaction and recall examples of techniques to measure the rate of a chemical reaction.
- Explain how the average rate of reaction differs from the rate of reaction.

Factors Affecting Rate

In this section we are learning to:

- Use collision theory to describe chemical reactions.
- Explain how the reaction conditions affect the rate of a chemical reaction.

Collision Theory

The particles in liquids and gases are constantly moving and colliding with each other. The particles gain or lose energy when they collide and, as a result, are constantly changing speed and direction. If the particles collide with sufficient energy and the correct orientation they will react and form the products of the reaction. The role of orientation in determining if a collision is successful is illustrated in Figure 2. A collision that results in a chemical reaction is referred to as a 'reactive' or **successful collision**. The rate of reaction is a measure of the number of successful collisions per second in the reaction mixture. If changes to the reaction conditions increase the number of successful collisions per second, the rate of reaction will increase. Conversely, if changing the reaction conditions reduces the number of successful collisions per second, the rate of reaction will decrease.

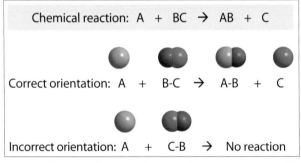

Chemical reaction: A + BC → AB + C

Correct orientation: A + B-C → A-B + C

Incorrect orientation: A + C-B → No reaction

Figure 2: The role of orientation in determining if a collision is successful.

Effect of Concentration

The number of collisions per second in a mixture of gases can be increased by increasing the concentration of the gas particles in the reaction mixture. This can be achieved by reducing the volume of the mixture, or equivalently, increasing the pressure of the mixture by adding more gas. The effect of decreasing the volume on the concentration of particles in the mixture is illustrated in Figure 3. Increasing the concentration by decreasing the volume or increasing the pressure does not affect the energy of the particles. As a result, when the concentration of particles is increased, the particles have the same average speed and a smaller average separation (d_{avg}). This results in more collisions per second and, if the particles in the mixture react, more successful collisions per second. In this way we can use collision theory to explain why increasing the concentration of particles in a mixture of gases increases the rate of reaction.

If a reaction occurs in solution the reaction mixture is difficult to compress and the volume of the solution remains approximately constant as the pressure changes. As a result, the rate of reaction is not affected by pressure and the concentration of the reactants must instead be changed by adding or removing reactants.

Effect of Temperature

The particles in a mixture of liquids or gases have a range of energies. The distribution of energy amongst the particles is described by the Maxwell-Boltzmann distribution shown in Figure 4. The Maxwell-Boltzmann distribution is a function that describes the number of particles in the mixture with a particular energy. As a result, the total area under the distribution curve represents the total number of particles in the mixture. The distribution curve reveals that all of the particles in

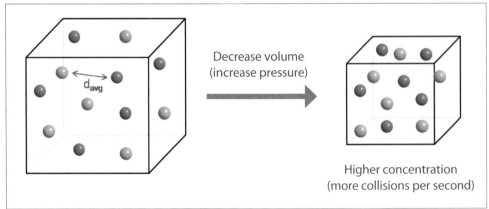

Figure 3: Increasing the concentration of particles in a mixture of gases by reducing the volume of the mixture. The average separation of the particles, d_{avg} becomes smaller as the concentration is increased.

d_{avg}

Decrease volume (increase pressure)

Higher concentration (more collisions per second)

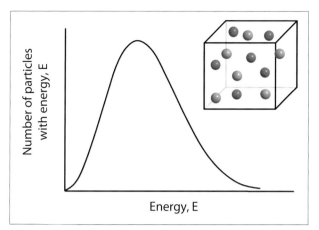

Figure 4: The Maxwell-Boltzmann distribution of energy amongst the particles in a mixture of liquids or gases.

the mixture have energy and are moving. The distribution also reveals that while a few particles have lots of energy and are moving very fast, most have a moderate amount of energy and move relatively slowly.

If the rate of a reaction is slow enough to be measured only a small fraction of the collisions in the reaction mixture involve particles with enough energy to react. If we define the **activation energy**, E_a to be the minimum amount of energy needed to transform the reactants into products, *the number of particles with energy greater than E_a becomes a measure of how many collisions will involve particles with enough energy to react.* The number of particles with energy greater than E_a corresponds to the area under the Maxwell-Boltzmann distribution above E_a. The Maxwell-Boltzmann distributions for a mixture of liquids or gases at a temperature T_{hot}, and the same mixture at a temperature T_{cold} where $T_{hot} > T_{cold}$ are compared in

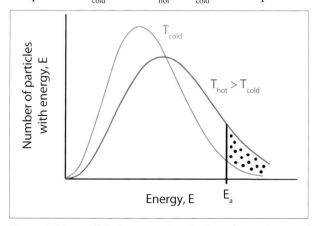

Figure 5: Maxwell-Boltzmann distributions for a mixture of liquids or gases at a temperature T_{cold} and the same mixture at a temperature T_{hot} where $T_{hot} > T_{cold}$. The shaded area represents the additional number of particles with energy greater than E_a as the temperature increases from T_{cold} to T_{hot}.

Figure 5. The total area under each distribution is the same as the number of particles represented by the distribution is the same at both temperatures. The comparison in Figure 5 reveals that as temperature increases the distribution spreads out and shifts towards higher energy. The shaded area between the distributions in Figure 5 represents the additional number of particles with energy greater than E_a as the temperature increases from T_{cold} to T_{hot}.

Exercise 2.10A

1. Which one of the following graphs most accurately represents the distribution of molecular energies in a gas at 500 K if the dotted curve represents the distribution for the same gas at 300 K? *(CCEA January 2010)*

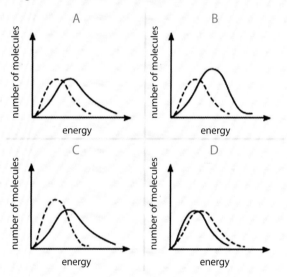

2. The energy distribution for the molecules in a mixture of nitrogen and oxygen at 298 K is shown below. (a) Label the axes and state the significance of the area under the curve. (b) Sketch the distribution of molecular energies for the mixture at a higher temperature on the same axes.

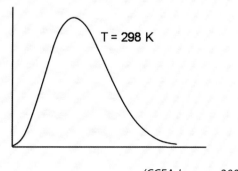

(CCEA January 2003)

3. The Maxwell-Boltzmann distribution for a mixture of SO_2 and O_2 at 450 K is shown below. (a) Label the axes on the diagram and suggest why the curve starts at the origin. (b) Draw a second curve on the same axes to describe the mixture at 440 K. (c) With reference to the two curves state and explain the effect of reducing the temperature on the rate of reaction between SO_2 and O_2 to form SO_3.

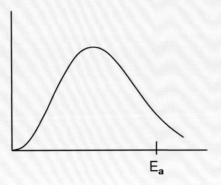

(CCEA June 2010)

4. The distribution of energy amongst the molecules in a mixture of SO_2 and O_2 is shown below. Which one of the following changes increases the proportion of molecules with enough energy to react and form SO_3?

$$2SO_2 + O_2 \leftrightarrows 2SO_3 \qquad \Delta H = -92 \text{ kJ}$$

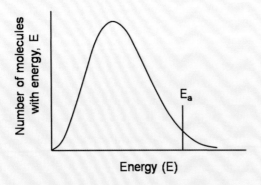

A Decreasing the pressure of the mixture.
B Decreasing the temperature of the mixture.
C Increasing the pressure of the mixture.
D Increasing the temperature of the mixture.

(CCEA January 2009)

5. The graph shows the effect of thiosulfate concentration on the rate of reaction between sodium thiosulfate solution and hydrochloric acid at 25 °C. Sketch the graph of rate against concentration for a similar series of experiments carried out at 35 °C. Use collision theory to explain the difference in the graphs.

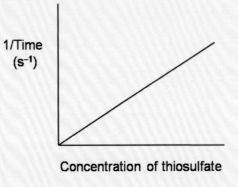

(CCEA June 2003)

> **Before moving to the next section, check that you are able to:**
>
> • Use collision theory to explain why increasing the concentration of the reactants in a reaction mixture increases the rate of reaction.
>
> • Use the Maxwell-Boltzmann distribution to explain the effect of temperature on the rate of chemical reactions.

Catalysis

> **In this section we are learning to:**
>
> • Recall the characteristics of a catalyst and explain how a catalyst affects the energy profile for a reaction.
>
> • Use collision theory to explain how a catalyst increases the rate of reaction.

The term catalysis is used to describe the speeding-up of a chemical reaction that results from adding a catalyst to the reaction mixture. The term 'catalyst' is used to describe a substance that speeds up a chemical reaction without being consumed by the reaction. For example, adding a small amount of solid manganese dioxide, MnO_2 to an aqueous solution of hydrogen peroxide, H_2O_2 (aq) greatly increases the rate at which the hydrogen peroxide decomposes to form water and oxygen.

$$2H_2O_2 \text{ (aq)} \rightarrow 2H_2O \text{ (l)} + O_2 \text{ (g)}$$

The manganese dioxide reacts with the hydrogen peroxide. It is then regenerated in the course of the reaction and, as a result, is not used up by the reaction. A catalyst works by lowering the activation energy for

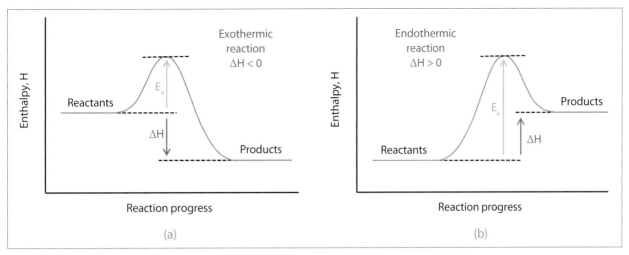

Figure 6: The relationship between the enthalpy change, ΔH and activation energy, E_a for (a) an exothermic reaction and (b) an endothermic reaction.

the reaction. The relationship between the activation energy (E_a) and the enthalpy change for a reaction (ΔH) can be seen by drawing the **reaction pathway**. The pathway for a reaction is often referred to as the reaction profile and shows how the total enthalpy of the reactants changes as they are transformed into products. The reaction pathways in Figure 6 illustrate the relationship between the enthalpy change (ΔH) and activation energy (E_a) for exothermic and endothermic reactions.

Adding a catalyst changes the reaction pathway. In this way a catalyst can be defined as *a substance that combines with one or more of the reactants to produce a new reaction pathway with a smaller activation energy, E_{cat} where $E_{cat} < E_a$.* The effect of a catalyst on the progress of a reaction is illustrated by the reaction profiles in Figure 7. Reducing the activation energy increases the number of collisions involving particles with enough energy to react. This, in turn, increases the number of successful collisions per second in the reaction mixture and explains why adding a catalyst increases the rate of reaction.

Exercise 2.10B

1. Manganese(IV) oxide catalyses the decomposition of hydrogen peroxide solutions. Explain, in terms of activation energy and reaction pathway, how a catalyst works.

$$2H_2O_{2\ (aq)} \rightarrow 2H_2O_{\ (l)} + O_{2\ (g)}$$

(CCEA June 2010)

2. Hydrogen reacts quietly with chlorine in the presence of a platinum catalyst. Explain this catalysis in terms of reaction pathway and activation energy.

$$H_2 + Cl_2 \rightarrow 2HCl$$

(CCEA January 2006)

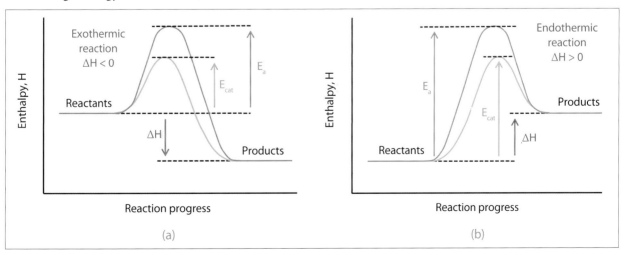

Figure 7: The effect of a catalyst on the reaction pathway for (a) an exothermic reaction and (b) an endothermic reaction.

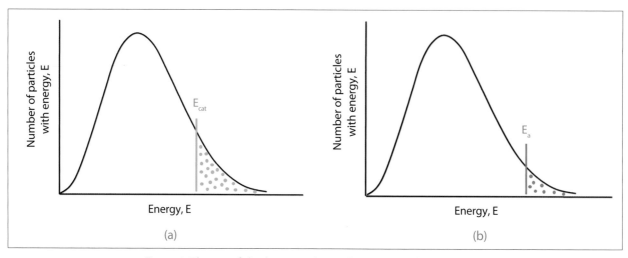

Figure 8: The use of shading to indicate the number of particles with enough energy to react in (a) the presence of a catalyst and (b) the absence of a catalyst.

The effect of a catalyst on the rate of reaction can also be explained by considering the Maxwell-Boltzmann distribution for the particles in the reaction mixture. The number of particles with enough energy to react in the presence of a catalyst ($E > E_{cat}$) is represented by the shaded area under the distribution curve in Figure 8a. The relatively small number of particles with enough energy to react in the absence of a catalyst is represented by the shaded area under the distribution curve in Figure 8b. Increasing the number of particles with energy greater than the activation energy (shaded) increases the number of collisions involving particles with enough energy to react. In this way we can use the Maxwell-Boltzmann distribution to explain why adding a catalyst increases the rate of reaction.

Exercise 2.10C

1. The distribution of molecular kinetic energies in a mixture of CO and NO with a temperature T_1 is shown in the diagram. The activation energy, E_a is indicated on the diagram. (a) Explain the term *activation energy*. (b) Explain why most collisions between molecules of CO and NO do not result in a reaction. (c) On the diagram draw the distribution of molecular kinetic energies at a higher temperature and label it T_2. (d) Using the distribution curves explain why the reaction between CO and NO is faster at the higher temperature.

(CCEA January 2008)

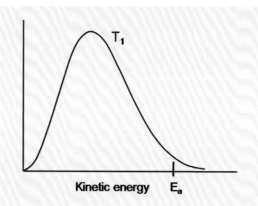

2. The diagram shows the distribution curve for the energies of the gas molecules in a reaction mixture. E_a is the activation energy for a particular reaction. (a) Explain why the curve starts at the origin. (b) Why does the curve not meet the horizontal axis at high energies? (c) What does the shaded area represent? (d) With reference to the distribution curve explain the effect of a catalyst on the rate of a chemical reaction. *(Adapted from CCEA June 2009)*

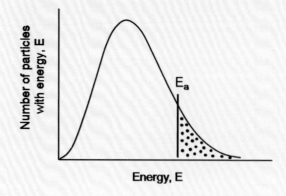

3. Chloroethane, CH_3CH_2Cl reacts with nucleophiles such as ammonia. The distribution of molecular energies in a gaseous mixture of chloroethane and ammonia at 20 °C is shown below. (a) Explain the significance of the shaded area. (b) Sketch the distribution for the same mixture at 30 °C and use the distributions to explain the difference between the rate of reaction at 20 °C and 30 °C. *(CCEA June 2003)*

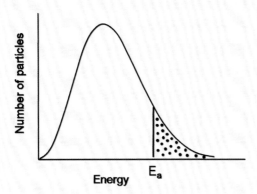

4. Sketch the distribution of molecular kinetic energies for the gas molecules in a reaction mixture. Mark the activation energy, E_a for the uncatalysed reaction and the activation energy, E_{cat} for the catalysed reaction on the distribution.

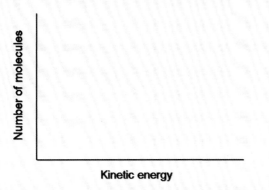

(Adapted from CCEA June 2008)

Before moving to the next section, check that you are able to:

- Recall that a catalyst speeds up a reaction by providing an alternative pathway for the reaction with lower activation energy.

- Recall that a catalyst is not consumed by a reaction as it is regenerated in its original form by the reaction.

- Use a Maxwell-Boltzmann distribution to explain why adding a catalyst increases the rate of reaction.

Applications of Catalysts

In this section we are learning to:

- Explain the effect of a catalyst on the composition of a chemical equilibrium and the rate at which equilibrium is established.

- Explain why catalysts are more effective when the size of the catalyst particles is reduced.

Catalysts are widely used in the chemical industry to speed up the production of valuable chemicals such as sulfuric acid and ammonia. Many of the reactions catalysed reach a state of chemical equilibrium. In industry ammonia is produced by reacting a mixture of nitrogen and hydrogen at elevated temperature and pressure in the presence of a granulated iron catalyst. In the presence of the catalyst the reaction mixture quickly reaches a state of equilibrium. The catalyst increases the rate at which equilibrium is established by lowering the activation energy for the forward and reverse reactions. The reaction profile in Figure 9 demonstrates that adding a catalyst reduces the activation energy for the forward reaction, E_a and the activation energy for the reverse reaction, E'_a by the same amount.

The composition of an equilibrium mixture is determined by the enthalpy change for the reaction and is not affected by the size of the activation energy for the reaction. As a result, adding a catalyst increases the rate at which equilibrium is established but does not affect the composition of the equilibrium mixture.

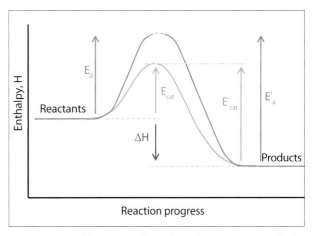

Figure 9: Adding a catalyst alters the reaction profile for an equilibrium reaction by lowering the activation energy for the forward reaction (E_a) and the reverse reaction (E_a') by the same amount.

219

Exercise 2.10D

1. Which letter (A–D) represents the activation energy for the back reaction?

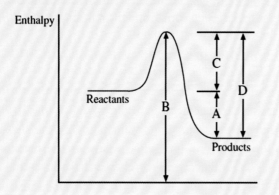

(CCEA June 2006)

2. The energy level diagram for a reversible reaction is shown below. Which one of the following statements is correct?

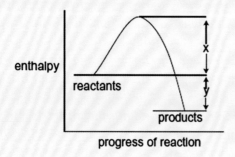

A The activation energy for the forward reaction is x.

B The activation energy for the reverse reaction is y.

C The forward reaction is endothermic.

D The enthalpy change for the reverse reaction is y–x.

(CCEA June 2011)

Catalysts also play an important role in reducing the amount of toxic gases in exhaust emissions from motor vehicles. When the exhaust gases are passed through a catalytic converter, toxic gases such as carbon monoxide and nitrogen oxides are converted into less toxic gases such as carbon dioxide and nitrogen. The catalytic converter contains small metal particles supported on an inert material with a honeycomb structure. The large surface created by the

honeycomb structure greatly increases the number of metal particles that come into contact with the exhaust gases. The small size of the metal particles also greatly increases the area on which the exhaust gases can bind to the metal and react. In this way decreasing the size of the catalyst particles increases the rate of reaction by increasing the surface area on which the reaction occurs. Catalysts containing small particles are said to be finely divided. The use of a finely divided nickel catalyst to hydrogenate vegetable fats and oils when making margarine (C=C → C-C) is another example of improving the efficiency of the catalyst by making the catalyst particles smaller.

Exercise 2.10E

1. A mixture of ethanol and gasoline (petrol) is known as gasohol. The gases produced by the combustion of gasohol can be passed through a catalytic converter. Explain the role of the catalyst using a simple labelled enthalpy diagram. Assume the reactions catalysed are exothermic. *(CCEA January 2010)*

2. The inside surfaces of a catalytic converter are coated with finely divided metal particles. Suggest why the particles are finely divided.

(CCEA January 2009)

Before moving to the next section, check that you are able to:

- Explain why adding a catalyst increases the rate at which equilibrium is established but does not affect the composition of the equilibrium mixture.
- Draw and label reaction pathways to illustrate the effect of adding a catalyst to an equilibrium mixture.
- Explain why finely divided catalysts are more effective than catalysts made of larger particles.

2.11 Group II: The Alkaline Earth Metals

CONNECTIONS
- Group II metals and their salts are used in emergency flares and fireworks.
- Magnesium is used as a reducing agent in the industrial scale production of less reactive metals such as titanium and uranium.
- A 'barium meal' containing barium sulfate is used to improve the quality of CT scans showing the interior of the human body.

Properties

In this section we are learning to:

- Recall the appearance and physical properties of Group II metals.
- Explain trends in the properties of the Group II elements within the group.
- Account for differences in the properties of the Group I and II elements.

The elements in Group II are hard, silvery metals known as the **Alkaline Earth Metals**. They are less reactive than the corresponding Group I metal but too reactive to be found in nature. Most Group II metals are found in the form of carbonates and are described as **s-block elements** as their outermost electrons are in an s-type subshell. The electron configurations in Table 1 reveal that each Group II metal has a pair of electrons in its outermost shell that determines many of its properties. For example, when Group II metals form an ionic compound, they satisfy the Octet rule by losing the pair of electrons in the outermost s-subshell to form the corresponding 2+ ion (M^{2+}).

Element	Ground State	Atomic Radius (pm)	Density (g cm^{-3})
Be	$[He](2s)^2$	112	1.85
Mg	$[Ne](3s)^2$	145	1.74
Ca	$[Ar](4s)^2$	194	1.55
Sr	$[Kr](5s)^2$	219	2.63
Ba	$[Xe](6s)^2$	253	3.51

Notes:
- The shorthand [He], [Ne], ... is used to represent the ground state electron configurations of the Noble gases.
- 1 pm = 1×10^{-12} m

Table 1: Properties of the Group II metals.

Density

The Group II metal atoms get bigger as the number of filled shells in the atom increases down the group. The corresponding M^{2+} ions also get bigger down the group, and the density of the metals is expected to decrease down the group as fewer metal atoms are able to fit in every 1 cm^3 of the metal. However, the increasing size of the metal atoms is offset by an increase in atomic mass to the extent that the density of the Group II metals increases down the group. The densities of the Group II metals in Table 1 reveal that even lighter Group II metals such as calcium and magnesium have a greater density than 1 g cm^{-3} and will sink in water.

Atomic Properties

The electron configuration for a Group II element is obtained by adding an electron to the electron configuration for the adjacent Group I element. The electron forms a pair of electrons in the outermost s-type subshell and is shielded by the same amount as the outermost electron in the adjacent Group I element. As a result, the electrons in the outermost s-type subshell of a Group II metal experience a greater nuclear charge and are held more tightly than the outermost electron in the adjacent Group I element. This explains why a Group II metal is smaller, and has a higher first ionisation energy than the adjacent Group I metal. The atomic radii for the Group I and Group II metals are compared in Figure 1. The first ionisation energies for the Group I and Group II metals are compared in Figure 2.

The ionisation energies in Figure 2 reveal that the first ionisation energies of the Group I and Group II elements become smaller down the group. This can be explained by noting that the electrons in the outermost s-type subshell are further from the nucleus and are better shielded as the number of filled shells increases

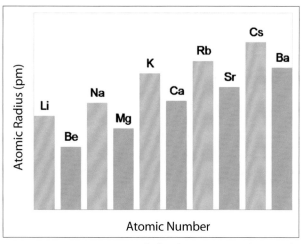

Figure1: Atomic radii for the Group I and II metals.

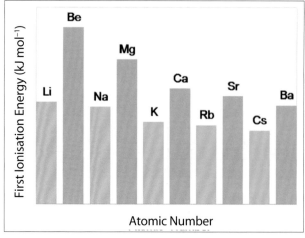

Figure 2: First ionisation energies for the Group I and II metals.

down the group. As a result, the electrons in the outermost s-subshell become easier to remove and the first ionisation energy becomes smaller as the atoms become bigger down the group.

The Group II metal ions also get bigger as the number of filled shells increases down the group. The ions formed by a Group II metal (M^{2+}) and the adjacent Group I metal (M^+) have the same electron configuration. As a result, the outermost electrons in the M^{2+} and M^+ ions are shielded by the same amount, and the M^{2+} ion is smaller as the outermost electrons are more strongly attracted to the nucleus. The radii for the Group I and II metal ions are compared in Figure 3.

Melting Point

In a Group II metal, the pair of electrons in the outermost s-type subshell is delocalised and can move

freely throughout the metal. The metallic bonds resulting from the sharing of two electrons per atom in a Group II metal are significantly stronger than those resulting from the sharing of one electron per atom in a Group I metal. In this way we can explain why the melting points of the Group II metals are much higher than those of the Group I metals. The melting points of the Group I and II metals are compared in Figure 4 and reveal that, with the exception of magnesium (Mg), the melting points of the Group II metals decrease down the group from beryllium (Be) to barium (Ba). The general decrease in melting point down Groups I and II results from a decrease in the attraction between the delocalised electrons and the positive metal ions in the metal as the ions get bigger down the group.

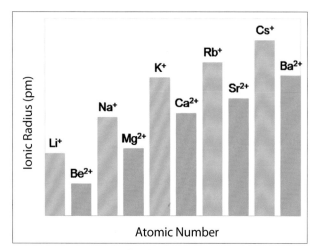

Figure 3: Ionic radii for the Group II metal ions (M^{2+}) and the adjacent Group I metal ions (M^+).

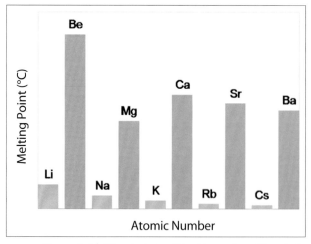

Figure 4: Melting points of the Group I and II metals.

Exercise 2.11A

1. (a) Explain why the Group II elements are regarded as s-block elements.

    (b) Write an equation, including state symbols, for the first ionisation energy of magnesium.

    (c) State and explain the change in the value of the first ionisation energy from magnesium to barium.

    (CCEA January 2011)

2. The table contains information about the Group II elements.

	magnesium	calcium	strontium	barium
Atomic number	12	20	38	56
Atomic radius (nm)	0.160	0.197	0.215	
Density (g cm^{-3})	1.74	1.54	2.6	3.5

(a) Explain why none of the Group II elements are found as free elements.

(b) Write the electronic configuration for calcium.

(c) Explain why the atomic radius of the elements increases down the group.

(d) Suggest a relationship between the atomic radius of the Group II elements and the corresponding elements in Group I.

(e) Predict the atomic radius of barium.

(f) Use the information in the table to explain why barium has the highest density of all the Group II elements. *(CCEA June 2011)*

3. Which statement best describes the trend in the melting points of the Group II elements?

A They decrease as the atomic number increases.

B They increase as the atomic number increases.

C They decrease from magnesium to calcium and then increase.

D They increase from magnesium to calcium and then decrease.

(CCEA June 2008)

Before moving to the next section, check that you are able to:

- Recall the appearance of the Group II metals and explain why they are found in nature as carbonates and other compounds.
- Explain why the Group II metals are s-block elements and why the Group II metals and their ions get larger as atomic number increases down the group.
- Explain why the density of the Group II metals increases down the group.
- Explain why the melting point and first ionisation energy of the Group II metals decreases down the group.
- Explain why the Group II metals have a higher melting point and first ionisation energy than the adjacent Group I metal.

Reactions

In this section we are learning to:

- Account for the nature of the reactions of Group II metals with oxygen, water and dilute acids in terms of the relative reactivity of the Group II metals.

Reaction with Oxygen

The Group II metals form the corresponding metal oxide when heated in air. The reaction is exothermic and the metal emits visible light with a colour characteristic of the metal.

$$2Mg_{(s)} + O_{2\,(g)} \rightarrow 2MgO_{(s)}$$

Observations: white powder formed, white flame.

The oxides of the Group II metals are white powders. Calcium burns with a brick red flame, strontium produces a crimson flame and barium produces a green flame when it burns in air to form barium oxide, BaO.

Heating the heavier Group II metals in an oxygen rich atmosphere also produces the corresponding metal peroxide, MO_2.

$$Ba_{(s)} + O_{2\,(g)} \rightarrow BaO_{2\,(s)}$$

Observations: white powder formed, green flame.

Before moving to the next section, check that you are able to:

- Recall what is observed when a Group II metal reacts with air and oxygen.
- Write equations to describe reactions of Group II metals with air and oxygen.

Reaction with Water

Group II metals react with water to form a solution of the corresponding metal hydroxide and hydrogen gas. Granules of calcium metal react vigorously with cold water to form a solution of calcium hydroxide. The reaction also produces hydrogen gas.

$$Ca_{(s)} + 2H_2O_{(l)} \rightarrow Ca(OH)_{2\ (aq)} + H_{2\ (g)}$$

The solution becomes increasingly alkaline as the reaction proceeds and is strongly alkaline within a few seconds. Calcium hydroxide is only sparingly soluble in water and the solution quickly becomes saturated. Once saturated a suspension of solid calcium hydroxide forms giving the solution a cloudy white appearance as shown in Figure 5.

The reaction between magnesium turnings and cold water again produces a solution of the corresponding metal hydroxide and hydrogen gas.

$$Mg_{(s)} + 2H_2O_{(l)} \rightarrow Mg(OH)_{2\ (aq)} + H_{2\ (g)}$$

The reaction occurs very slowly and the formation of magnesium hydroxide can be monitored over several minutes by placing a few drops of universal indicator in the solution. The gradual increase in pH as magnesium hydroxide is formed is accompanied by a colour change from green to blue as shown in Figure 6. The relative rate at which calcium and magnesium react with cold water demonstrates that the reaction between Group II metals and water becomes much more vigorous as the metals become more reactive towards the bottom of the group.

Less reactive Group II metals such as magnesium react much more vigorously when heated in the presence of steam. The reaction between magnesium and steam is very exothermic and produces intense white light as shown in Figure 7.

$$Mg_{(s)} + H_2O_{(g)} \rightarrow MgO_{(s)} + H_{2\ (g)}$$

Figure 6: Using universal indicator to monitor the increase in pH as magnesium reacts with cold water.

(a)

(b)

Figure 5: (a) The reaction between calcium metal and cold water. (b) A suspension of calcium hydroxide forming as the solution becomes saturated.

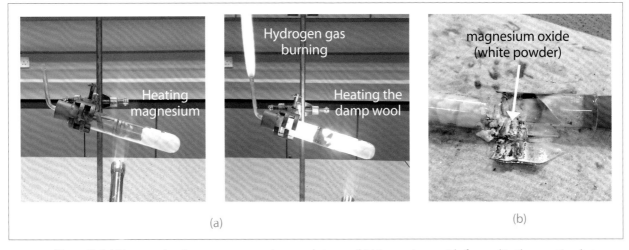

Figure 7: (a) The reaction between magnesium and steam. (b) Magnesium oxide formed in the reaction between magnesium and steam.

Before moving to the next section, check that you are able to:

- Recall what is observed when calcium and magnesium react with water.
- Write equations to describe the reaction of calcium and magnesium with water.
- Relate what is observed when calcium and magnesium react with water to the reactivity of the metal.
- Describe the collection of hydrogen by the downward displacement of water.

Reaction with Dilute Acids

The Group II metals react with dilute acids to form hydrogen gas and an aqueous solution of the corresponding metal salt. The reaction becomes much more vigorous as the reactivity of the metal increases down the group. Only the lighter Group II elements (Be, Mg and Ca) react safely with dilute acids.

$$Mg_{(s)} + 2HCl_{(aq)} \rightarrow MgCl_{2\,(aq)} + H_{2\,(g)}$$

$$Mg_{(s)} + H_2SO_{4\,(aq)} \rightarrow MgSO_{4\,(aq)} + H_{2\,(g)}$$

$$Ca_{(s)} + 2HNO_{3\,(aq)} \rightarrow Ca(NO_3)_{2\,(aq)} + H_{2\,(g)}$$

Exercise 2.11B

1. (a) Does calcium float or sink in water? Explain your answer. (b) State two further observations when calcium reacts with water. (c) Write the equation for the reaction of calcium with water. (d) Draw a labelled diagram to show how the gas given off when calcium reacts with water can be collected using a test tube and a beaker.

(CCEA June 2011)

2. Compare the chemistry of calcium with that of magnesium using the headings: (a) Combustion, (b) Reaction with water and (c) Reaction with dilute hydrochloric acid. Include observations.

(CCEA January 2005)

Before moving to the next section, check that you are able to:

- Write equations to describe the reaction of Group II metals with dilute acids.
- Recall that the reaction of Group II metals with dilute acids becomes more vigorous as the metals become more reactive down the group.

Compounds of Group II Metals

In this section we are learning to:

- Recall the properties of Group II metal compounds.
- Write equations to describe the reactions of Group II metal oxides, hydroxides and carbonates.

Properties

Group II metal compounds such as MgO, $CaCO_3$, $SrCl_2$ and $BaSO_4$ are ionic compounds. When a Group II metal forms a compound, the Group II metal loses two electrons to form the corresponding M^{2+} cation. The M^{2+} ions form part of an ionic lattice held together by strong attractive forces between oppositely charged ions. The M^{2+} ions have a full outer shell and do not absorb visible light. As a result, Group II metal compounds are not coloured; they are white crystalline solids with a high melting point that results from strong ionic bonding in the lattice.

Group II metal halides such as MgF_2, $CaBr_2$ and $BaCl_2$ are soluble in water at room temperature. Magnesium sulfate, $MgSO_4$ is also soluble in water at room temperature. However, the Group II sulfates become less soluble down the group to the extent that calcium sulfate, $CaSO_4$ is only sparingly soluble, and the sulfates of heavier Group II metals such as barium sulfate, $BaSO_4$ are insoluble in water at room temperature. The Group II metal carbonates also become less soluble down the group. They are less soluble than the corresponding sulfates to the extent that magnesium carbonate, $MgCO_3$ is only sparingly soluble, and calcium carbonate, $CaCO_3$ is insoluble in water at room temperature. In contrast, Group II metal hydroxides become more soluble down the group. The hydroxides of heavier Group II metals such as $Ba(OH)_2$ are soluble in water, while $Ca(OH)_2$ is only sparingly soluble and $Mg(OH)_2$ is insoluble in water at room temperature.

Solutions of Group II metal compounds are colourless and conduct electricity on account of the ions formed when the compound dissolves. Group II halides and sulfates dissolve to give neutral solutions.

$$CaBr_2 \text{ (s)} \rightarrow Ca^{2+} \text{ (aq)} + 2Br^- \text{ (aq)} \qquad pH \approx 7$$

$$MgSO_4 \text{ (s)} \rightarrow Mg^{2+} \text{ (aq)} + SO_4^{2-} \text{ (aq)} \qquad pH \approx 7$$

In contrast, Group II oxides, hydroxides and carbonates are bases, and may dissolve or react with water to form an alkali.

$$Ca(OH)_2 \text{ (s)} \rightarrow Ca^{2+} \text{ (aq)} + 2OH^- \text{ (aq)} \qquad pH > 7$$

$$BaO \text{ (s)} + H_2O \text{ (l)} \rightarrow Ba(OH)_2 \text{ (aq)} \qquad pH > 7$$

Exercise 2.11C

Which one of the following chlorides with the formula MCl_2 is the chloride of a Group II element?

A White solid. Melting point 280 °C. Boiling point 304 °C. Fairly soluble in water to give a colourless neutral solution with poor electrical conductivity.

B White solid. Melting point 815 °C. Readily soluble in water to give a green-blue solution with good electrical conductivity.

C White solid. Melting point 875 °C. Readily soluble in water to give a colourless neutral solution with good electrical conductivity.

D White solid. Melting point 672 °C. Dissolves to give a pale green solution with good electrical conductivity.

(CCEA January 2010)

Before moving to the next section, check that you are able to:

- Recall the appearance and solubility of Group II metal compounds.
- Describe the appearance and properties of aqueous solutions of Group II metal compounds.

Reactions of Group II Oxides, Hydroxides and Carbonates

Group II metal oxides react with water to form the corresponding metal hydroxide. The reaction is very exothermic and must be carried out by the controlled addition of water to the solid oxide.

$$CaO \text{ (s)} + H_2O \text{ (l)} \rightarrow Ca(OH)_2 \text{ (aq)}$$

A solution of calcium hydroxide, $Ca(OH)_2$ (aq) is known as limewater. Observing the formation of a cloudy white suspension when carbon dioxide is bubbled through limewater is a positive test for carbon dioxide.

$$Ca(OH)_2 \text{ (aq)} + CO_2 \text{ (aq)} \rightarrow CaCO_3 \text{ (s)} + H_2O \text{ (l)}$$

Observations: colourless solution turns cloudy white.

Group II metal oxides and hydroxides are bases and react with acids to form an aqueous solution of the corresponding Group II metal salt and water. Group II metal carbonates are also bases and react with acids to form an aqueous solution of the corresponding Group II metal salt, water and carbon dioxide.

$$CaO \text{ (s)} + 2HCl \text{ (aq)} \rightarrow CaCl_2 \text{ (aq)} + H_2O \text{ (l)}$$

$$Ca(OH)_2 \text{ (s)} + 2HCl \text{ (aq)} \rightarrow CaCl_2 \text{ (aq)} + 2H_2O \text{ (l)}$$

$$CaCO_3 \text{ (s)} + 2HCl \text{ (aq)} \rightarrow CaCl_2 \text{ (aq)} + H_2O \text{ (l)} + CO_2 \text{ (g)}$$

If we also consider a **base** to be any substance that

accepts a proton (an H^+ ion) from another substance, the basic character of the Group II oxides, hydroxides and carbonates can be seen by writing ionic equations for their reaction with acids. The ionic equations for the reaction of CaO, $Ca(OH)_2$ and $CaCO_3$ with dilute acid clearly show that, in each case, the calcium salt accepts protons (H^+) from the acid to form the products of the reaction.

$$CaO_{(s)} + 2H^+_{(aq)} \rightarrow Ca^{2+}_{(aq)} + H_2O_{(l)}$$

$$Ca(OH)_{2\,(s)} + 2H^+_{(aq)} \rightarrow Ca^{2+}_{(aq)} + 2H_2O_{(l)}$$

$$CaCO_{3\,(s)} + 2H^+_{(aq)} \rightarrow Ca^{2+}_{(aq)} + H_2O_{(l)} + CO_{2\,(g)}$$

When heated, Group II metal carbonates and hydroxides decompose to form the corresponding metal oxide.

$$CaCO_{3\,(s)} \rightarrow CaO_{(s)} + CO_{2\,(g)}$$

$$Ca(OH)_{2\,(s)} \rightarrow CaO_{(s)} + H_2O_{(l)}$$

The decomposition of a Group II metal carbonate or hydroxide on heating is an example of a **thermal decomposition** reaction in which a substance is broken down into simpler substances by the application of heat.

Exercise 2.11D

1. Calcium oxide is basic and reacts with water to form calcium hydroxide. (a) Explain the term basic. (b) Write the equation for the reaction of calcium oxide with water. (c) If the solubility of calcium hydroxide is 0.021 mol dm^{-3} at 20 ºC, calculate the mass of calcium hydroxide that could dissolve in 250 cm^3 of water at 20 ºC. (d) Write the equation for the reaction of calcium hydroxide with hydrochloric acid.

   (CCEA June 2003)

2. (a) Write an equation for the reaction of barium carbonate with hydrochloric acid. (b) Describe what is observed when the gas produced is bubbled through limewater. (c) Calculate the volume of carbon dioxide produced at 20 ºC and 1 atmosphere when 0.66 g of barium carbonate is reacted with an excess of acid.

   (CCEA January 2005)

3. (a) A saturated solution of calcium hydroxide is known as limewater. Describe how you would

prepare limewater and use it to test for carbon dioxide. State the result of a positive test. (b) Write the equation for the reaction of aqueous calcium hydroxide with carbon dioxide. Include state symbols. (c) When 5 dm^3 of polluted air containing an excess of carbon dioxide was passed through limewater 0.05 g of calcium carbonate was precipitated. Calculate the % carbon dioxide in the air sample. All measurements were carried out at 20 ºC and 1 atmosphere pressure.

(CCEA January 2010)

4. (a) Write the equation for the formation of strontium chloride from strontium oxide and hydrochloric acid. (b) Describe how a pure, dry sample of strontium chloride could be obtained from the reaction mixture.

(CCEA January 2003)

5. (a) Write the equation for the reaction of calcium carbonate with hydrochloric acid. (b) An impure sample of limestone is 95% calcium carbonate. Calculate the volume of carbon dioxide produced at 20 ºC and 1 atmosphere pressure when 15.00 g of impure limestone is added to excess hydrochloric acid.

(CCEA June 2005)

6. The mineral Dolomite has the formula $CaCO_3$.$MgCO_3$. (a) State one observation when dolomite is treated with dilute hydrochloric acid. (b) Write an equation for the reaction. (c) State the flame colour expected when a sample of dolomite is used in a flame test.

(CCEA June 2007)

Before moving to the next section, check that you are able to:

- Write equations to describe the reactions of Group II metal oxides, hydroxides and carbonates with water and dilute acids.

- Recall the effect of heat on Group II metal carbonates and hydroxides.

- Explain the use of limewater to produce a positive test for the presence of carbon dioxide.

Thermal Stability of Group II Compounds

In this section we are learning to:

- Recall trends in the thermal stability of Group II carbonates and hydroxides.
- Explain how the thermal stability of Group II metal compounds is affected by the size of the Group II metal ion.

The carbonates of the heavier Group II metals decompose at much higher temperatures than the carbonates of the lighter Group II metals.

$$MgCO_{3\ (s)} \rightarrow MgO_{\ (s)} + CO_{2\ (g)}$$

Decomposes above 540 °C

$$BaCO_{3\ (s)} \rightarrow BaO_{\ (s)} + CO_{2\ (g)}$$

Decomposes above 1360 °C

The increase in decomposition temperature reflects an increase in the **thermal stability** of the Group II carbonates down the group. The Group II metal carbonates are ionic compounds and the decomposition temperature reflects an increase in the strength of the ionic bonding between the metal ions and carbonate ions in the compound. In general, the bonding between the ions in an ionic compound becomes stronger as the ions become smaller and the distance between neighbouring ions decreases. As shown in Figure 8, the distance between neighbouring ions in magnesium carbonate, $MgCO_3$ is less than in barium carbonate, $BaCO_3$. As a result we would expect

the ionic bonding in $MgCO_3$ to be stronger than in $BaCO_3$ and the temperature at which $MgCO_3$ decomposes to be higher. Clearly this is not the case and the thermal stability of the Group II carbonates must instead be explained by considering the effect of the metal ions on the surrounding carbonate ions.

As the Group II metal ions (M^{2+}) get smaller towards the top of the group, the positive charge becomes more concentrated, and the density of positive charge within the ion increases. As the **charge density** within the metal ion increases, more of the positive charge is close to the neighbouring carbonate ions, and the electrons in the carbonate ions are more strongly attracted to the metal ions. The attraction between the electrons in the carbonate ions and the metal ion increases the polarity of C-O bonds adjacent to the metal as shown in Figure 9a. Polarising a C-O bond reduces the extent to which electrons are shared in the bond, and by so doing reduces the strength of the C-O bond. As a result, less energy is needed to break the polarised C-O bond and the carbonate ion becomes less resistant to the effects of heating. This explains why the thermal stability of the Group II carbonates increases down the group as the charge density on the metal decreases, and the metal ion becomes less able to polarise C-O bonds within neighbouring carbonate ions. The thermal decomposition of a carbonate ion to form an oxide ion (O^{2-}) and carbon dioxide (CO_2) is illustrated in Figure 9b.

The Group II hydroxides also become more thermally stable down the group as the charge density

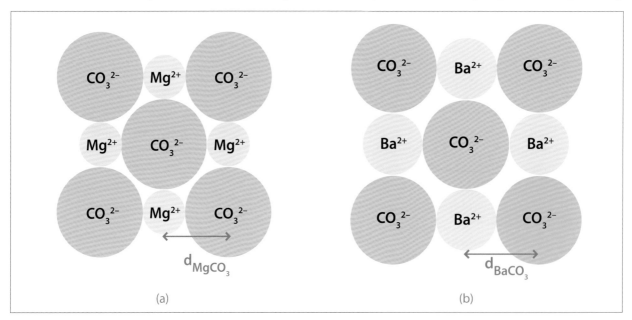

(a)   (b)

Figure 8: The ionic lattice in (a) $MgCO_3$ and (b) $BaCO_3$. The distance between neighbouring ions, d is greater in $BaCO_3$.

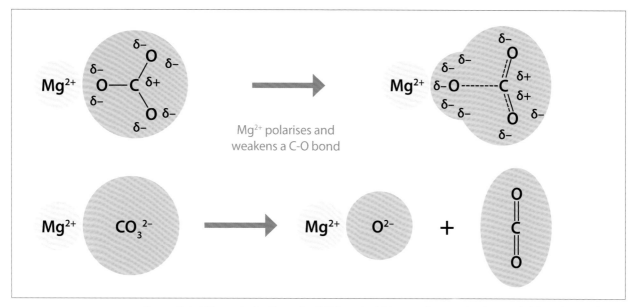

Figure 9: (a) The polarisation of a C-O bond within a carbonate ion by a neighbouring Mg^{2+} ion. (b) Decomposition of a carbonate ion in $MgCO_3$ to form magnesium oxide, MgO and carbon dioxide, CO_2.

on the metal decreases, and the metal ions become less able to polarise O-H bonds within neighbouring hydroxide ions.

Worked Example 2.11i

Currently 280 million tonnes of calcium oxide is produced annually by heating limestone (calcium carbonate) to a temperature of 1200 °C. The heat needed to sustain the reaction is provided by the combustion of fossil fuels.

$$CaCO_3 \rightarrow CaO + CO_2$$

(a) Compare the thermal stability of calcium carbonate with other Group II metal carbonates. (b) Explain how the thermal stability of a Group II carbonate is related to the charge and size of the cation. (c) Explain how the manufacture of calcium oxide contributes to global warming. *(CCEA January 2010)*

Solution

(a) Calcium carbonate is more stable than $BeCO_3$ and $MgCO_3$ and less stable than $SrCO_3$ and $BaCO_3$.

(b) The Group II carbonates become more resistant to heating as the charge density within the metal ion decreases down the group.

(c) The decomposition process produces carbon dioxide. Burning fossil fuels also produces carbon dioxide. Carbon dioxide is a greenhouse gas and contributes to global warming.

Exercise 2.11E

1. Which one of the following (A–D) lists the Group II carbonates and hydroxides in order of increasing thermal stability?

	Carbonates	Hydroxides
A	$MgCO_3$ $CaCO_3$ $SrCO_3$ $BaCO_3$	$Ba(OH)_2$ $Sr(OH)_2$ $Ca(OH)_2$ $Mg(OH)_2$
B	$BaCO_3$ $SrCO_3$ $CaCO_3$ $MgCO_3$	$Mg(OH)_2$ $Ca(OH)_2$ $Sr(OH)_2$ $Ba(OH)_2$
C	$MgCO_3$ $CaCO_3$ $SrCO_3$ $BaCO_3$	$Mg(OH)_2$ $Ca(OH)_2$ $Sr(OH)_2$ $Ba(OH)_2$
D	$BaCO_3$ $SrCO_3$ $CaCO_3$ $MgCO_3$	$Ba(OH)_2$ $Sr(OH)_2$ $Ca(OH)_2$ $Mg(OH)_2$

(CCEA January 2008)

2. (a) Write the equation for the thermal decomposition of calcium carbonate. (b) Explain why the decomposition temperature for magnesium carbonate would be expected to be greater than or less than the decomposition temperature for calcium carbonate.

(CCEA June 2005)

3. (a) Write an equation for the decomposition of calcium hydroxide. (b) Compare and explain the thermal stability of magnesium hydroxide with barium hydroxide. *(CCEA January 2011)*

4. (a) Calcium sulfate occurs as gypsum, $CaSO_4.2H_2O$. Calculate the percentage yield of $CaSO_4$ when 34.4 g of gypsum is heated to form 26.0 g of anhydrous calcium sulfate. (b) Heating an anhydrous Group II sulfate produces the corresponding Group II oxide and sulfur trioxide. Write the equation for the decomposition of anhydrous calcium sulfate. (c) The thermal stability of Group II sulfates can be explained in a similar way as the stability of the Group II carbonates. Explain the relative stability of the Group II sulfates with reference to the cations involved. *(CCEA June 2009)*

5. (a) Write the equation for the decomposition of barium carbonate. (b) Suggest why the thermal stability of barium carbonate is higher than that of beryllium carbonate. (c) The decomposition of barium carbonate occurs at a much lower temperature if it is heated with carbon to form barium oxide and carbon monoxide. Write the equation for the reaction. *(CCEA January 2009)*

Before moving to the next section, check that you are able to:

- Explain the term thermal stability and recall the trend in thermal stability for the Group II metal carbonates and hydroxides.

- Explain how the size of the Group II metal ion affects the thermal stability of Group II compounds.

Solubility of Group II Compounds

In this section we are learning to:

- Recall trends in the solubility of Group II metal compounds.
- Explain trends in the solubility of Group II metal compounds by considering the enthalpy changes that occur when a compound dissolves.
- Describe how the size of the Group II metal ion determines the size of the enthalpy changes that occur when a Group II metal compound dissolves.

We have already seen that the Group II hydroxides become more soluble towards the bottom of the group while the Group II sulfates become less soluble down the group. We can understand this contrasting behaviour if we consider the enthalpy changes that occur when a solid dissolves to form a solution. The Group II sulfates and hydroxides are ionic compounds. When an ionic solid dissolves, ions break from the solid lattice and form bonds with molecules in the solvent. When magnesium sulfate, $MgSO_4$ dissolves in water the magnesium ions, Mg^{2+} and sulfate ions, SO_4^{2-} break from the solid, and bond with water molecules to form **solvated ions**. The attractive **ion-dipole forces** between the ions and the permanent dipoles on the surrounding water molecules are illustrated in Figure 10. The solvated ions are represented by the formulas Mg^{2+} (aq) and SO_4^{2-} (aq).

Dissolving magnesium sulfate:

$$MgSO_4 \text{ (s)} \rightarrow Mg^{2+} \text{ (aq)} + SO_4^{2-} \text{ (aq)}$$

A Model for Dissolving

The enthalpy change that occurs when an ionic solid dissolves is determined by the amount of energy

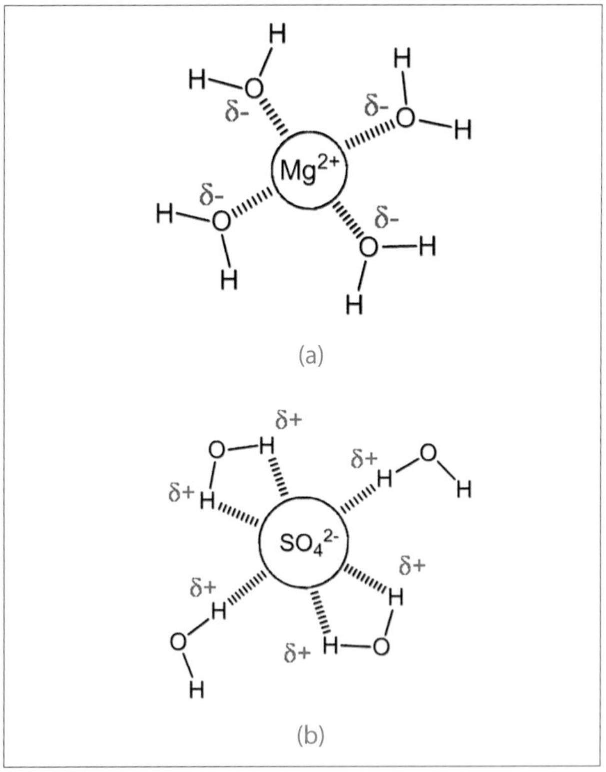

Figure 10: (a) A solvated magnesium ion, Mg^{2+} (aq) and (b) a solvated sulfate ion, SO_4^{2-} (aq) in an aqueous solution of magnesium sulfate. The arrangement of the water molecules around each ion can vary.

needed to break the ionic lattice into ions, and the energy released when the ions bind to solvent molecules to form solvated ions. If we define the **lattice enthalpy**, ΔH_{latt} to be the energy required to convert one mole of an ionic compound into ions in the gas phase, and the **hydration enthalpy**, ΔH_{hyd} to be the enthalpy change when the gaseous ions formed from one mole of an ionic compound are solvated in water, we can construct an enthalpy cycle for the dissolving process. Applying the definitions of lattice enthalpy and hydration enthalpy to magnesium sulfate, $MgSO_4$ gives:

$$MgSO_{4\ (s)} \rightarrow Mg^{2+}_{\ (g)} + SO_4^{\ 2-}_{\ (g)} \qquad \Delta H = \Delta H_{latt}$$

$$Mg^{2+}_{\ (g)} + SO_4^{\ 2-}_{\ (g)} \rightarrow Mg^{2+}_{\ (aq)} + SO_4^{\ 2-}_{\ (aq)} \quad \Delta H = \Delta H_{hyd}$$

If we now also define the **enthalpy of solution**, ΔH_{soln} to be the enthalpy change when 1 mole of an ionic compound dissolves to form solvated ions, the enthalpy of solution for magnesium sulfate is defined by the change:

$$MgSO_{4\ (s)} \rightarrow Mg^{2+}_{\ (aq)} + SO_4^{\ 2-}_{\ (aq)} \qquad \Delta H = \Delta H_{soln}$$

The definitions of lattice enthalpy, hydration enthalpy and enthalpy of solution for magnesium sulfate demonstrate that the enthalpy of solution for an ionic compound is related to its lattice enthalpy and hydration enthalpy by the equation:

$$\Delta H_{soln} = \Delta H_{latt} + \Delta H_{hyd}$$

This relationship between ΔH_{latt}, ΔH_{hyd} and ΔH_{soln}

for an ionic compound is illustrated by the enthalpy cycle in Figure 11a. The corresponding cycle for magnesium sulfate is shown in Figure 11b.

The enthalpy of solution can be exothermic or endothermic. However, a solid is more likely to be soluble if the enthalpy of solution is negative. As a result, an ionic compound is more likely to be soluble ($\Delta H_{soln} < 0$) if the energy released when the ions are hydrated (ΔH_{hyd}) is greater than the energy needed to break the lattice into ions (ΔH_{latt}). The balance between the size of the lattice enthalpy and the size of the hydration enthalpy can be used to explain trends in the solubility of the Group II sulfates, hydroxides and carbonates.

Enthalpy Changes when Group II Compounds Dissolve

The ionic bonds between the ions in an ionic compound become stronger as the ions become smaller, and the distance between neighbouring ions decreases. The lattice enthalpy of an ionic compound is determined by the strength of the ionic bonding in the compound and increases as the ionic bonds within the compound become stronger. As a result, the lattice enthalpies of the Group II sulfates, carbonates and hydroxides decrease as the Group II metal ions get bigger, and the ionic bonding within the compounds gets weaker, towards the bottom of the group.

The strength of the ion-dipole forces between the Group II metal ions (M^{2+}) and the surrounding water molecules also decreases as the charge density on the

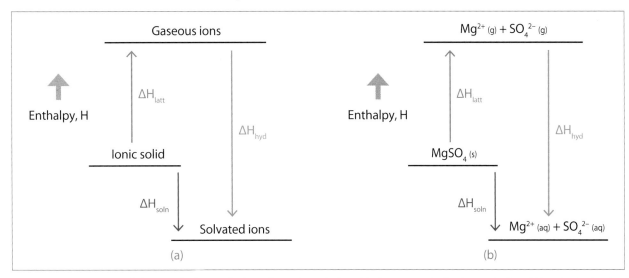

Figure 11: (a) An enthalpy cycle describing the relationship between the lattice enthalpy, ΔH_{latt} the hydration enthalpy, ΔH_{hyd} and the enthalpy of solution, ΔH_{soln} for an ionic compound. (b) The corresponding enthalpy cycle for magnesium sulfate, $MgSO_4$.

metal ions decreases down the group. As a result, the hydration enthalpy for the Group II metal sulfates, carbonates and hydroxides becomes less exothermic as the metal ions become bigger down the group.

Trends in the solubility of the Group II sulfates, carbonates and hydroxides result from the balance between the size of the decrease in ΔH_{latt} and the size of the decrease in ΔH_{hyd} as the metal ions become bigger down the group.

The Solubility of Group II Sulfates and Carbonates

In the case of the Group II sulfates, the lattice enthalpy decreases by less than the hydration enthalpy as the metal ions get bigger down the group. This results in the enthalpy of solution becoming less exothermic, and a decrease in the solubility of the Group II sulfates, as the metal ions become bigger down the group. The effect of the balance between lattice enthalpy and hydration enthalpy on the solubility of the Group II sulfates is illustrated in Figure 12.

The Group II carbonates also become less soluble down the group. Carbonate ion, CO_3^{2-} and sulfate ion, SO_4^{2-} both have a 2– charge and are of similar size. As a result, the enthalpy changes that occur when a Group II carbonate dissolves are similar to those that occur when a Group II sulfate dissolves, and the decreasing solubility of the Group II carbonates can again be attributed to an increase in the size of the metal ion.

The Solubility of Group II Hydroxides

Sulfate, SO_4^{2-} and carbonate, CO_3^{2-} are much bigger than even the largest Group II metal ions. In contrast, hydroxide ion, OH^- is only slightly larger than Group II metal ions such as Ba^{2+}. As a result, the size of the metal ion affects the distance between neighbouring ions in a Group II hydroxide to a greater extent and results in the lattice enthalpy decreasing more rapidly than the hydration enthalpy as the metal ions get bigger down the group. This effect causes the enthalpy of solution to become less endothermic, and the solubility of the Group II hydroxides to increase, as the metal ions get bigger down the group.

....

Worked Example 2.11ii

The hydroxides of the Group II metals, magnesium to barium, are white ionic solids. They are sparingly soluble in water, the solubility rising with atomic number. (a) Suggest how you could determine the solubility of strontium hydroxide at 25 °C. Give full practical details. (b) Explain the solubility trend of the hydroxides using enthalpy considerations.

Compound:	$Mg(OH)_2$	$Ca(OH)_2$	$Sr(OH)_2$	$Ba(OH)_2$
Solubility: (g/100 g at 25 °C)	0.01	0.15	0.89	3.32

(CCEA January 2007)

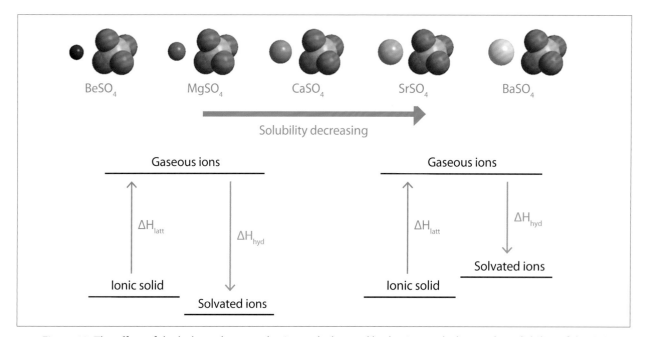

Figure 12: The effect of the balance between lattice enthalpy and hydration enthalpy on the solubility of the Group II metal sulfates.

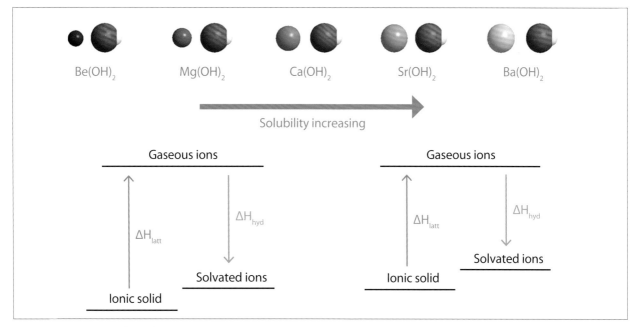

Figure 13: The effect of the balance between lattice enthalpy and hydration enthalpy on the solubility of the Group II metal hydroxides.

Solution

(a) Place a measured volume of water in a boiling tube. Place the boiling tube in a water bath set at 25 °C. Add a small amount of solid strontium hydroxide to the water and stir to dissolve. Repeat until no more dissolves. Filter the solution to remove undissolved solid then determine the amount of strontium hydroxide dissolved by titrating the solution with an acid.

(b) The Group II hydroxides become more soluble down the group as the lattice enthalpy decreases more rapidly than the hydration enthalpy, making the enthalpy of solution less endothermic.

Exercise 2.11F

1. Which one of the following (A–D) lists both sets of compounds in order of increasing solubility (least soluble first)?

	Sulfates	Hydroxides
A	$MgSO_4$ $CaSO_4$ $SrSO_4$ $BaSO_4$	$Ba(OH)_2$ $Sr(OH)_2$ $Ca(OH)_2$ $Mg(OH)_2$
B	$MgSO_4$ $CaSO_4$ $SrSO_4$ $BaSO_4$	$Mg(OH)_2$ $Ca(OH)_2$ $Sr(OH)_2$ $Ba(OH)_2$
C	$BaSO_4$ $SrSO_4$ $CaSO_4$ $MgSO_4$	$Mg(OH)_2$ $Ca(OH)_2$ $Sr(OH)_2$ $Ba(OH)_2$
D	$BaSO_4$ $SrSO_4$ $CaSO_4$ $MgSO_4$	$Ba(OH)_2$ $Sr(OH)_2$ $Ca(OH)_2$ $Mg(OH)_2$

(CCEA June 2010)

2. Explain the difference in pH when 0.1 mole of magnesium hydroxide and 0.1 mole of barium hydroxide are stirred with separate 100 cm³ portions of water. *(CCEA January 2011)*

3. Barium hydroxide reacts with dilute nitric acid to form a solution of barium nitrate. (a) Write an equation for the reaction and (b) explain why barium hydroxide does not dissolve in dilute sulfuric acid. *(CCEA January 2007)*

4. Dissolved calcium or magnesium sulfates contribute to the hardness of water. (a) State which sulfate is more soluble in water and explain your answer in terms of enthalpy considerations. (b) When a solution of sodium carbonate is added to a sample of hard water a precipitate of calcium carbonate is formed. Write an ionic equation, including state symbols, for the formation of the precipitate.

(CCEA June 2005)

5. Which one of the following describes a trend down Group II from beryllium to barium?

    A   The reactivity of the metal decreases.

    B   The solubility of the hydroxide decreases.

    C   The thermal stability of the carbonates increases.

    D   The solubility of the sulfate increases.

    (CCEA June 2004)

6. Which one of the following increases down Group II from calcium to barium?

    A   first ionisation energy

    B   melting point

    C   solubility of the sulfates

    D   thermal stability of the hydroxides

    (CCEA June 2007)

> **Before moving to the next section, check that you are able to:**
>
> - Recall trends in the solubility of the Group II metal sulfates, carbonates and hydroxides.
> - Construct enthalpy cycles to relate the lattice enthalpy, hydration enthalpy and enthalpy of solution for an ionic compound.
> - Explain how the lattice enthalpy and hydration enthalpy for an ionic compound is affected by the size of the metal ion.
> - Explain trends in the solubility of Group II metal compounds in terms of the balance between lattice enthalpy and hydration enthalpy.

2.12 Qualitative Analysis

Qualitative analysis is the science of identifying chemical compounds within mixtures. In this section the procedures used to identify the ions and gases in Table 1 are described, and key observations noted. A number of the terms used to describe procedures and record observations are defined in Table 2.

Table 1: The ions and gases to be detected by qualitative analysis.

Cations	Anions
Group I and II:	*Halides:*
Lithium, Li^+	Chloride, Cl^-
Sodium, Na^+	Bromide, Br^-
Potassium, K^+	Iodide, I^-
Magnesium, Mg^{2+}	
Calcium, Ca^{2+}	*Polyatomic ions:*
Barium, Ba^{2+}	Sulfate, SO_4^{2-}
	Carbonate, CO_3^{2-}
Other metals:	Hydrogencarbonate, HCO_3^-
Aluminium, Al^{3+}	
Copper(II), Cu^{2+}	**Gases**
Iron(II), Fe^{2+}	Hydrogen, H_2
Iron(III), Fe^{3+}	Oxygen, O_2
Zinc, Zn^{2+}	Chlorine, Cl_2
	Carbon dioxide, CO_2
Polyatomic ions:	Sulfur dioxide, SO_2
Ammonium, NH_4^+	Hydrogen chloride, HCl
	Ammonia, NH_3

Testing for Gases

In this section we are learning to:
- Recall the procedure to test for the presence of: H_2, O_2, Cl_2, CO_2, SO_2, HCl, NH_3 and the observations required to identify each gas.

The presence of a gas can be confirmed by observing its physical properties and performing chemical tests to demonstrate that the gas has the required chemical

Table 2: Glossary of terms for qualitative analysis.

- A **reagent** is a substance added to a reaction mixture to bring about a chemical reaction.
- A **precipitate** is an insoluble solid formed in solution as the result of a chemical reaction in the solution.
- A **suspension** is a cloudy mixture containing small particles of an insoluble solid distributed throughout a liquid.
- The term **miscible** is used to describe liquids that mix in all proportions.
- The term **effervescence** describes the release of gas from a reaction mixture.
- The term **evolved** is used to describe the release of energy or matter from a reaction mixture.
- The term **pungent** describes sharp 'acidic' odours.

properties. Physical properties such as colour, odour, and density frequently provide evidence for the presence of a gas. The chemical properties and tests used to confirm the presence of a gas are detailed below.

Hydrogen, H_2

Properties	Chemical Test	Observations
Colourless. Odourless. Flammable. Less dense than air.	Place a burning splint in an inverted test tube filled with the gas.	The gas produces a 'pop' sound when it burns.

Oxygen, O_2

Properties	Chemical Test	Observations
Colourless. Odourless.	Place a glowing splint in an inverted test tube filled with the gas.	The gas relights a glowing splint.

Chlorine, Cl_2

Properties	Chemical Test	Observations
Green gas. Pungent odour of 'bleach'. Denser than air.	Bring the gas into contact with a piece of damp blue litmus paper or damp Universal Indicator paper.	Turns the damp indicator paper red then bleaches the paper.

Carbon Dioxide, CO_2

Properties	Chemical Test	Observations
Colourless. Odourless. Denser than air. Soluble in water.	Bubble the gas through limewater.	A cloudy white suspension is formed in the limewater.

Sulfur Dioxide, SO_2

Properties	Chemical Test	Observations
Colourless. Pungent odour. Denser than air. Soluble in water.	Bubble the gas through acidified potassium dichromate solution.	The solution turns from orange to green.
	-OR-	-OR-
	Bubble the gas through acidified potassium permanganate solution.	The solution turns from purple to colourless.

Hydrogen Chloride, HCl

Properties	Chemical Test	Observations
Colourless. Pungent odour. Denser than air. Soluble in water.	Bring the gas into contact with a glass rod dipped in concentrated ammonia solution.	White fumes of solid ammonium chloride are formed.

Ammonia, NH_3

Properties	Chemical Test	Observations
Colourless. Pungent odour. Less dense than air. Soluble in water.	Bring the gas into contact with a glass rod dipped in concentrated hydrochloric acid.	White fumes of solid ammonium chloride are formed.

Exercise 2.12A

1. Describe a test for oxygen gas.

2. Describe a chemical test for ammonia. State the reagent used and the observation for a positive result. *(CCEA January 2009)*

3. Complete the table below by describing an appropriate test and the observation expected to identify each gas. *(CCEA June 2008)*

Gas	Test	Observation
Hydrogen		
Sulfur dioxide		
Hydrogen chloride		

Before moving to the next section, check that you are able to:

- Describe the procedure used to confirm the presence of each gas.
- Recall the observations required to confirm the presence of each gas.

Testing for Cations

In this section we are learning to:

- Recall the procedure to test for the presence of: Ba^{2+}, NH_4^+, Cu^{2+}, Fe^{2+}, Fe^{3+}, Mg^{2+}, Zn^{2+}, Al^{3+} and the observations required to identify each ion.
- Recall the procedure to conduct a flame test and the characteristic flame colours for the ions: Li^+, Na^+, K^+, Ca^{2+}, Ba^{2+} and Cu^{2+}.

Testing for Barium

Salts containing Group I or Group II metal ions are white solids and dissolve to give colourless solutions. The presence of barium (Ba^{2+}) ions in a salt is detected by adding a few drops of potassium chromate solution, K_2CrO_4 (aq) to an aqueous solution of the salt. If barium ion is present in the solution it will combine with chromate ion to form a yellow precipitate of barium chromate, $BaCrO_4$ (s). The presence of barium ion is confirmed when the precipitate dissolves in excess dilute hydrochloric acid to form a yellow solution.

$$Ba^{2+} _{(aq)} + CrO_4^{2-} _{(aq)} \rightarrow BaCrO_4 _{(s)}$$

yellow solid

Confirming the presence of barium ion, Ba^{2+}:

Method	Observations
1. Add a spatula of the solid to a test tube containing 2–3 cm³ of water.	Solid dissolves to give a colourless solution.
2. Add 3–4 drops of potassium chromate solution.	Yellow precipitate formed.
3. Add 3–4 cm³ of dilute hydrochloric acid and shake to mix.	Precipitate dissolves. Yellow solution formed.

Testing for Ammonium

Ammonium (NH_4^+) salts are also white solids and dissolve to give colourless solutions. The presence of ammonium ion can be detected by adding the salt to dilute sodium hydroxide and heating the mixture to form ammonia. The presence of ammonia is then detected by observing an alkaline gas with the characteristic smell of ammonia.

$$NH_4^+{}_{(aq)} + OH^-{}_{(aq)} \rightarrow NH_3{}_{(g)} + H_2O{}_{(l)}$$

pungent smell

Confirming the presence of ammonium ion, NH_4^+:

Method	Observations
1. Add a spatula of the solid to a test tube containing 4–5 cm³ of dilute sodium hydroxide.	Solid dissolves to give a colourless solution.
2. Warm the mixture gently and test any gas evolved with damp Universal Indicator paper.	Pungent smell. Universal Indicator paper turns blue.

Exercise 2.12B

Ammonium chloride dissolves in water to form aqueous ammonium ions and chloride ions. Describe how you would test for aqueous ammonium ions. *(CCEA June 2011)*

Testing for Copper

Salts containing d-block metals such as copper are often coloured and dissolve in water to give solutions with colours characteristic of the metal. Hydrated copper(II) sulfate, $CuSO_4.5H_2O$ is a blue crystalline solid and dissolves in water to give a blue solution. The blue colour of the solid and the solution results from

the presence of hydrated copper(II) ions. As a result, the presence of copper(II) ions, Cu^{2+} may be suspected if a salt is blue, or dissolves in water to form a blue solution.

The presence of copper(II) ions in a salt can be detected by adding a few drops of dilute ammonia solution to an aqueous solution of the salt. If copper(II) ion, Cu^{2+} is present in the solution it will combine with hydroxide ions from the ammonia solution to form a blue precipitate of copper(II) hydroxide, $Cu(OH)_2{}_{(s)}$. The presence of copper(II) ions can then be confirmed by observing that the precipitate dissolves to form a dark blue solution on adding ammonia solution to excess. The dark blue colour of the solution is due to the presence of copper(II) ion in the form of the complex ion $[Cu(NH_3)_4(H_2O)_2]^{2+}$.

Confirming the presence of copper(II) ions, Cu^{2+}:

Method	Observations
1. Add a spatula of the solid to a test tube containing 2–3 cm³ of water.	Solid dissolves to give a blue solution.
2. Add 3–4 drops of dilute ammonia to the solution.	Blue precipitate formed.
3. Add 3–4 cm³ of dilute ammonia solution and shake to mix.	Precipitate dissolves. Dark blue solution formed.

Exercise 2.12C

(a) Name the reagent which can be used to confirm the presence of Cu^{2+} ions in solution. (b) What would be observed when the reagent is added slowly, until present in excess, to a solution containing Cu^{2+}? *(CCEA June 2009)*

Testing for Iron

The presence of iron(II), Fe^{2+} or iron(III), Fe^{3+} in a salt can be detected by adding a few drops of dilute sodium hydroxide to an aqueous solution of the salt. If iron(II) is present it will combine with hydroxide ions to form a green precipitate of iron(II) hydroxide, $Fe(OH)_2{}_{(s)}$. If iron(III) is present it will instead form a brown precipitate of iron(III) hydroxide, $Fe(OH)_3{}_{(s)}$. Iron(II) hydroxide and iron(III) hydroxide do not dissolve on adding dilute sodium hydroxide.

$$Fe^{2+}{}_{(aq)} + 2OH^-{}_{(aq)} \rightarrow Fe(OH)_2{}_{(s)}$$

green solid

237

$$Fe^{3+}{}_{(aq)} + 3OH^-{}_{(aq)} \rightarrow Fe(OH)_{3\,(s)}$$

brown solid

The presence of iron(III) in a solution can be confirmed by adding a few drops of aqueous potassium thiocyanate, KSCN $_{(aq)}$. If iron(III) ions are present in the solution they will combine with thiocyanate (SCN$^-$) ions from the potassium thiocyanate solution to form the complex ion $[Fe(SCN)(H_2O)_5]^{2+}$. The complex turns the solution a characteristic blood red colour.

$$Fe^{3+}{}_{(aq)} + SCN^-{}_{(aq)} \rightarrow [Fe(SCN)(H_2O)_5]^{2+}{}_{(aq)}$$

blood red

Exercise 2.12D

(a) Name the reagent used to distinguish between $Fe^{2+}{}_{(aq)}$ and $Fe^{3+}{}_{(aq)}$. (b) Name another reagent which can be used to detect low concentrations of $Fe^{3+}{}_{(aq)}$. (c) What would be observed in a positive test? *(CCEA June 2009)*

Testing for Magnesium, Zinc and Aluminium

The presence of Mg^{2+}, Zn^{2+} or Al^{3+} ions in a salt can be detected by adding a few drops of dilute sodium hydroxide to an aqueous solution of the salt. If magnesium ion (Mg^{2+}) is present in the solution it will combine with the hydroxide ions from the sodium hydroxide to form a white precipitate of magnesium hydroxide, $Mg(OH)_2$. Similarly, if zinc ion (Zn^{2+}) is present it will combine with hydroxide ions to form zinc hydroxide, $Zn(OH)_2$, and if aluminium ion (Al^{3+}) is present it will combine with hydroxide ions to form aluminium hydroxide, $Al(OH)_3$. All three hydroxides are white solids and cannot be used to distinguish between the presence of Mg^{2+}, Zn^{2+} and Al^{3+} ions in solution. In order to distinguish between the ions we must also observe what happens to the metal hydroxides when dilute sodium hydroxide is added to excess.

A precipitate of magnesium hydroxide will remain on adding dilute sodium hydroxide to excess. In contrast, zinc hydroxide and aluminium hydroxide will dissolve in an excess of dilute sodium hydroxide to form colourless solutions. The use of dilute sodium hydroxide to distinguish between a solution containing Mg^{2+} and a solution containing Zn^{2+} or Al^{3+} ions is summarised by the flow scheme in Figure 1.

$$Zn(OH)_{2\,(s)} + 2OH^-{}_{(aq)} \rightarrow [Zn(OH)_4]^{2-}{}_{(aq)}$$

white solid   *colourless solution*

$$Al(OH)_{3\,(s)} + OH^-{}_{(aq)} \rightarrow [Al(OH)_4]^-{}_{(aq)}$$

white solid   *colourless solution*

Exercise 2.12E

1. Explain by including observations how you would use aqueous sodium hydroxide to distinguish between aqueous solutions of aluminium nitrate and magnesium nitrate.

(CCEA June 2011)

2. In which one of the following pairs will *neither* of the hydroxides dissolve in an excess of aqueous sodium hydroxide?

A $Al(OH)_3$ and $Fe(OH)_2$

B $Al(OH)_3$ and $Zn(OH)_2$

C $Fe(OH)_2$ and $Mg(OH)_2$

D $Mg(OH)_2$ and $Zn(OH)_2$

(CCEA June 2009)

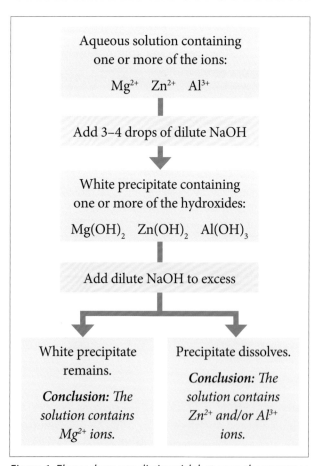

Figure 1: Flow scheme to distinguish between the presence of Mg^{2+} ions and either Zn^{2+} or Al^{3+} ions in solution by the addition of dilute sodium hydroxide.

In the absence of magnesium (Mg^{2+}) ions dilute ammonia, $NH_{3\,(aq)}$ can be used to distinguish between the presence of Zn^{2+} and Al^{3+} ions in a solution. Dilute ammonia is an alkali. If zinc (Zn^{2+}) ions are present they will combine with hydroxide ions from the ammonia solution to form a white precipitate of zinc hydroxide, $Zn(OH)_2$. Similarly, if aluminium (Al^{3+}) ions are present they will combine with hydroxide ions from the ammonia solution to form a white precipitate of aluminium hydroxide, $Al(OH)_3$. On adding dilute ammonia to excess zinc hydroxide dissolves to form a colourless solution. In contrast, aluminium hydroxide does not dissolve in excess ammonia and it becomes possible to distinguish between Zn^{2+} and Al^{3+} ions in solution by adding dilute ammonia solution to excess. The use of dilute ammonia solution to distinguish between Zn^{2+} and Al^{3+} ions in solution is summarised by the flow scheme in Figure 2.

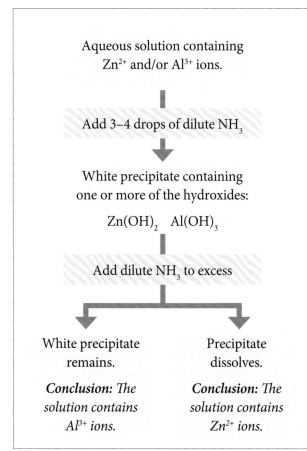

Figure 2: Flow scheme to distinguish between the presence of Zn^{2+} ions and Al^{3+} ions in solution by the addition of dilute ammonia solution.

Exercise 2.12F

1. Explain by including observations how you would use aqueous ammonia to distinguish between aqueous solutions of aluminium nitrate and zinc nitrate.

   (CCEA June 2011)

2. A solution of a metal sulfate gave a white precipitate when sodium hydroxide and ammonia solutions were added to it. The white precipitate was soluble in an excess of sodium hydroxide and in an excess of ammonia. Identify the sulfate.

   A $Al_2(SO_4)_3$ B $MgSO_4$

   C Na_2SO_4 D $ZnSO_4$

   (CCEA January 2011)

3. An aqueous solution produced a precipitate on adding a few drops of aqueous sodium hydroxide. The precipitate dissolved on adding excess sodium hydroxide but not on adding excess ammonia. Identify the ion in the solution.

   A $Al^{3+}_{(aq)}$ B $Fe^{3+}_{(aq)}$

   C $Mg^{2+}_{(aq)}$ D $Zn^{2+}_{(aq)}$

   (CCEA June 2010)

Flame Tests

A number of metal ions can be detected by performing a flame test. A flame test is conducted by suspending a small amount of solid on a nichrome wire and placing it in a blue Bunsen flame. The flame colour produced by the solid can then be used to confirm the presence of a metal ion in the solid. The origin of the flame colour produced by the metal has been discussed previously in the context of atomic structure.

Cation	Observations (Flame colour)
Lithium, Li^+	Crimson
Sodium, Na^+	Yellow (or Orange)
Potassium, K^+	Lilac (or Pink through blue glass)
Calcium, Ca^{2+}	Brick red
Barium, Ba^{2+}	Green
Copper, Cu^{2+}	Green-blue

Worked Example 2.12i

Describe how you would carry out a flame test to show the presence of sodium ions in a white solid. State the flame colour expected. *(CCEA June 2010)*

Solution

Wash the end of a piece of nichrome wire in concentrated hydrochloric acid. Transfer a small amount of the solid onto the wire by dipping the end of the wire in the solid. Place the solid sample in a blue Bunsen flame and record the flame colour. If the sample contains sodium ions the flame will turn a yellow colour.

Before moving to the next section, check that you are able to:

- Recall the procedures used to test for the presence of: Ba^{2+}, NH_4^+, Cu^{2+}, Fe^{2+}, Fe^{3+} and the observations required to identify each ion.
- Recall the use of thiocyanate to confirm the presence of Fe^{3+} ion.
- Describe the use of dilute sodium hydroxide and dilute ammonia to distinguish between Mg^{2+}, Zn^{2+} and Al^{3+} ions in solution.
- Recall the procedure to conduct a flame test and the characteristic flame colours for the ions: Li^+, Na^+, K^+, Ca^{2+}, Ba^{2+} and Cu^{2+}.

Testing for Anions

In this section we are learning to:

- Recall the procedure to test for the presence of: SO_4^{2-}, CO_3^{2-}, HCO_3^-, Cl^-, Br^-, I^- and the observations required to identify each ion.

Test for Sulfate

The presence of sulfate ions, SO_4^{2-} in a solid can be detected by adding a few drops of barium chloride solution to a slightly acidic solution of the solid. Barium ions from the barium chloride solution combine with sulfate ions from the solid to form a white precipitate of barium sulfate, $BaSO_4$.

$$Ba^{2+}_{(aq)} + SO_4^{2-}_{(aq)} \rightarrow BaSO_{4(s)}$$

white solid

Confirming the presence of sulfate, SO_4^{2-} ions:

Method	Observations
1. Add a spatula of the solid to a test tube containing 2–3 cm³ of water and shake to dissolve.	Solid dissolves.
2. Add 1 cm³ of dilute nitric acid followed by 3–4 drops of barium chloride solution and shake to mix.	White precipitate formed.

Exercise 2.12G

The table shows the results of analysing aqueous solutions of compounds A, B, C and D. Identify the compounds A, B, C and D.

Compound	Colour of aqueous solution	Addition of aqueous barium chloride	Other information
A	blue	white precipitate	blue-green flame test
B	colourless	white precipitate	pH = 1
C	yellow	yellow precipitate	yellow/orange flame test
D	colourless	white precipitate	lilac flame test

(CCEA June 2009)

Test for Carbonate and Hydrogencarbonate

Solid carbonates and hydrogencarbonates such as $BaCO_3$ and $NaHCO_3$ are bases and will react with dilute acid to form a salt, water and carbon dioxide. The formation of carbon dioxide when a solid reacts with dilute acid is used as a test to detect the presence of carbonate ion or hydrogencarbonate ion in the solid.

Confirming the presence of carbonate, CO_3^{2-} or hydrogencarbonate, HCO_3^- ions:

Method	Observations
1. Add a spatula of the solid to a test tube containing 2–3 cm³ of water.	Solid dissolves.
2. Add 1 cm³ of dilute nitric acid to the solution and collect any gas evolved with a pipette.	Colourless gas produced.

3. Bubble the contents of the pipette through 2–3 cm³ of limewater in a separate test tube.	The limewater turns cloudy white.

Adding a few drops of a solution containing magnesium ions to an aqueous solution of a solid can be used as a test to distinguish between the presence of carbonate ions and hydrogencarbonate ions in the solid. If carbonate ions are present they will combine with the magnesium ions to form a white precipitate of magnesium carbonate.

$$Mg^{2+}_{\ (aq)} \ + \ CO_3^{2-}_{\ (aq)} \ \rightarrow \ MgCO_{3\ (s)}$$

white solid

If a precipitate does not form the solution contains hydrogencarbonate ions. The presence of hydrogencarbonate ions can then be confirmed by gently heating the solution. When a solution containing hydrogencarbonate ions is heated, the hydrogencarbonate ions decompose to form carbonate ions. Once formed, the carbonate ions combine with the magnesium ions to form a white precipitate of magnesium carbonate. The procedure to distinguish between carbonate ions and hydrogencarbonate ions in solution is summarised by the flow scheme in Figure 3.

Confirming the presence of carbonate, CO_3^{2-} ions:

Method	Observations
1. Add a spatula of the solid to a test tube containing 2–3 cm³ of water and shake to dissolve.	Solid dissolves.
2. Add 1 cm³ of magnesium nitrate solution.	White precipitate formed.

Confirming the presence of hydrogencarbonate, HCO_3^- ions:

Method	Observations
1. Add a spatula of the solid to a test tube containing 2–3 cm³ of water and shake to dissolve.	Solid dissolves.
2. Add 1 cm³ of magnesium nitrate solution.	Solution remains clear. No precipitate formed.
3. Gently heat the solution.	White precipitate formed.

Worked Example 2.12ii

A white precipitate is formed when solutions of magnesium chloride and sodium hydrogencarbonate are mixed and boiled. Identify the precipitate and write an ionic equation for the precipitation reaction. Include state symbols.

(Adapted from CCEA January 2010)

Solution

The hydrogencarbonate ions decompose to form carbonate ions when the mixture is boiled. The carbonate ions then combine with magnesium ions to form a precipitate of magnesium carbonate.

Ionic equation: $Mg^{2+}_{\ (aq)} + CO_3^{2-}_{\ (aq)} \rightarrow MgCO_{3\ (s)}$

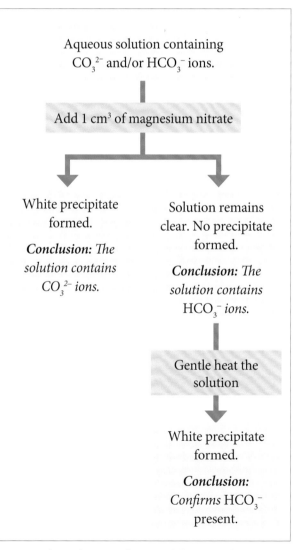

Figure 3: Flow scheme to distinguish between the presence of carbonate, CO_3^{2-} ions and hydrogencarbonate, HCO_3^- ions in aqueous solution.

Exercise 2.12H

1. Describe how you would confirm the presence of carbonate or hydrogencarbonate ions using dilute hydrochloric acid and confirm the identity of the gas produced. State any observations expected. *(CCEA June 2010)*

2. Describe how you would distinguish between the presence of carbonate and hydrogen carbonate ions. State any observations expected. *(CCEA June 2010)*

3. Limestone is mainly calcium carbonate, $CaCO_3$. Describe how you would confirm the presence of (a) calcium ions and (b) carbonate ions in a sample of limestone. *(CCEA June 2008)*

Testing for Halide Ions

The presence of chloride, Cl^- bromide, Br^- or iodide, I^- ions in a solid can be detected by adding dilute nitric acid, followed by a few drops of silver nitrate solution, to an aqueous solution of the solid. If chloride ion is present in the solution a white precipitate of silver chloride, AgCl forms.

$$Ag^+_{(aq)} + Cl^-_{(aq)} \rightarrow AgCl_{(s)}$$

white solid

If bromide ion is present, the acidified silver nitrate solution produces a cream precipitate of silver bromide, AgBr. Similarly, if the solution contains iodide ions, the acidified silver nitrate solution produces a yellow precipitate of silver iodide, AgI.

$$Ag^+_{(aq)} + Br^-_{(aq)} \rightarrow AgBr_{(s)}$$

cream solid

$$Ag^+_{(aq)} + I^-_{(aq)} \rightarrow AgI_{(s)}$$

yellow solid

The presence of chloride, bromide or iodide can be confirmed by examining the solubility of the silver halide precipitate in dilute and concentrated ammonia solutions. A precipitate of silver chloride, AgCl will dissolve when shaken with an excess of dilute ammonia solution. Silver chloride also dissolves when shaken with an excess of concentrated ammonia solution. In contrast, a precipitate of silver bromide, AgBr does not dissolve in dilute ammonia and will only dissolve when shaken with an excess of concentrated ammonia solution. A precipitate of silver iodide, AgI is insoluble in dilute and concentrated ammonia solutions.

Confirming the presence of chloride, Cl^- ion:

Method	Observations
1. Add a spatula of the solid to a test tube containing 2–3 cm³ of water and shake to mix.	Solid dissolves.
2. Add 1 cm³ of dilute nitric acid followed by 3–4 drops of silver nitrate solution.	White precipitate formed.
3. Add 4–5 cm³ of dilute ammonia solution and shake to mix.	Precipitate dissolves.

Confirming the presence of bromide, Br^- ion:

Method	Observations
1. Add a spatula of the solid to a test tube containing 2–3 cm³ of water and shake to mix.	Solid dissolves.
2. Add 1 cm³ of dilute nitric acid followed by 3–4 drops of silver nitrate solution.	Cream precipitate formed.
3. Add 4–5 cm³ of dilute ammonia solution and shake to mix.	Precipitate does not dissolve.
4. Repeat step 2 then add 4–5 cm³ of concentrated ammonia solution and shake to mix.	Precipitate dissolves.

Confirming the presence of iodide, I^- ion:

Method	Observations
1. Add a spatula of the solid to a test tube containing 2–3 cm³ of water and shake to mix.	Solid dissolves.
2. Add 1 cm³ of dilute nitric acid followed by 3–4 drops of silver nitrate solution.	Yellow precipitate formed.
3. Add 4–5 cm³ of dilute ammonia solution and shake to mix.	Precipitate does not dissolve.
4. Repeat step 2 then add 4–5 cm³ of concentrated ammonia solution and shake to mix.	Precipitate does not dissolve.

Exercise 2.12I

1. Describe how you would confirm the presence of chloride or iodide ions using dilute nitric acid and silver nitrate solution. State any observations expected. *(CCEA June 2010)*

2. Describe how silver chloride and silver iodide react with dilute and concentrated ammonia solutions. State any observations expected.

   (CCEA June 2010)

Before moving to the next section, check that you are able to:

- Describe the use of barium chloride solution to detect SO_4^{2-} ions in solution.
- Recall the use of dilute acid to detect CO_3^{2-} and HCO_3^- ions in solution.
- Describe the use of Mg^{2+} ions to distinguish CO_3^{2-} and HCO_3^- ions in solution.
- Describe the use of silver nitrate and ammonia solution to detect and distinguish between Cl^-, Br^- and I^- ions in solution.

Unit AS 3:
Practical Assessment

Practical Assessment

The practical assessment consists of two practical exercises: an acid-base titration and an observation-deduction exercise. The practical exercises are followed by a planning exercise, and a number of structured questions to test the candidate's knowledge of practical chemistry.

Acid-Base Titration

Candidates will be required to perform an acid-base titration based on the reaction between: a strong acid and a strong base (SASB), a weak acid and a strong base (WASB), or a weak base and a strong acid (WBSA). Candidates should be able to select phenolphthalein or methyl orange as a suitable indicator and recall the colour change when the indicator is used to detect the end point of the titration.

In addition to carrying out a titration and analysing the results, candidates may also be required to:

* provide a detailed method for the titration,
* describe the procedures used to prepare and transfer solutions, or
* detail any steps required to ensure that the results are accurate and reliable.

It is expected that candidates would be familiar with the techniques introduced in Section 9: Volumetric analysis, and the level of detail required when answering the associated problems. Worked Example 3i illustrates the level of response expected from candidates when completing the titration exercise.

....

Worked Example 3i

You are provided with:

* sodium hydroxide solution of concentration 0.10 mol dm⁻³.
* vinegar (ethanoic acid) of unknown concentration.
* phenolphthalein indicator.

You are required to carry out a titration and use your results to calculate the concentration of ethanoic acid in the vinegar.

(a) Give details of the procedure you intend to use.

Rinse the pipette with the vinegar solution. Use the pipette to transfer 25 cm³ of vinegar solution to a conical flask. Add 2–3 drops of phenolphthalein to the conical flask. Rinse the burette with sodium hydroxide solution before filling the burette with sodium hydroxide solution. Titrate the vinegar solution adding sodium hydroxide dropwise near the end-point. Repeat the titration to improve accuracy.

(b) Carry out your procedure. Present your results in a suitable table and calculate the average titre.

	Initial Burette Reading (cm³)	Final Burette Reading (cm³)	Titre (cm³)
Rough	0.0	22.0	22.0
First Accurate	21.7	43.1	21.4
Second Accurate	0.0	21.3	21.3

$$\text{Average titre} = \frac{21.4 + 21.3}{2} = 21.35 \text{ cm}^3$$

(c) State the colour change at the end point of your titration.

Colourless to pink.

(d) Write the equation, including state symbols, for the reaction of sodium hydroxide with the ethanoic acid present in vinegar.

$CH_3COOH_{(aq)} + NaOH_{(aq)} \rightarrow CH_3COONa_{(aq)} + H_2O_{(l)}$

(e) Calculate the number of moles of sodium hydroxide used in the titration.

Moles of NaOH used = 0.10 mol dm⁻³ × 2.135 × 10⁻² dm⁻³ = 2.135 × 10⁻³ mol

Calculate the number of moles of ethanoic acid neutralised in the titration.

Moles of ethanoic acid = moles of NaOH used = 2.135 × 10⁻³ mol

245

Calculate the concentration (in mol dm^{-3}) of the ethanoic acid in the vinegar.

$$\text{Molarity of ethanoic acid} = \frac{2.135 \times 10^{-3} \text{ mol}}{0.025 \text{ dm}^3}$$
$$= 0.0854 \text{ mol dm}^{-3}$$

Calculate the concentration (in g dm^{-3}) of the ethanoic acid in the vinegar.

$$0.0854 \text{ mol dm}^{-3} \times 60 \text{ g mol}^{-1} = 5.124 \text{ g}$$

(CCEA June 2009)

Observation-Deduction

The observation-deduction exercise assesses the candidate's ability to: make observations, construct a record of the observations, and make appropriate deductions based on the observation record. The observation-deduction exercise consists of two tasks: the identification of ions in a mixture of salts, and the identification of functional groups in an organic compound.

Identifying Salts in a Mixture

In this task the candidate must identify the individual compounds in a mixture of salts. Recent examples of mixtures to be identified include: $MgCl_2/MgSO_4$ and $NH_4Cl/(NH_4)_2SO_4$. The identity of the individual salts in the mixture is determined by conducting a series of tests to identify individual ions present in the mixture. It is expected that candidates would be able to conduct tests for the ions and gases in Section 21: Quantitative Analysis, and be familiar with reactions involving these ions and gases introduced in other sections of the course.

The first step in the exercise usually involves examining the mixture and making an appropriate deduction based on its appearance. If the mixture is coloured it is likely that it contains one or more salts that contain a transition metal. In this context a metal is considered a transition metal if it belongs to one of the groups spanned by the elements Ti–Cu. Conversely, if the mixture is a white solid it is unlikely to contain the salt of a transition metal, and is more likely to contain ammonium salts, or the salts of Group I and II metals.

Examples of observation-deduction based on appearance:

Experiment	Observations	Deductions
Describe the mixture.	Blue solid.	The mixture contains the salt of a transition metal.

Experiment	Observations	Deductions
Describe the mixture.	White solid.	The mixture probably contains Group I, II or ammonium salts.

The presence of individual ions in the mixture is then confirmed by performing chemical tests for specific ions. In an observation-deduction exercise the presence of an ion can only be **confirmed** if the observations indicate a **positive test** for the ion.

Observation-deduction record to confirm the presence of magnesium ion, Mg^{2+}:

Experiment	Observations	Deductions
Make a solution of A by dissolving a spatula measure of A in a test tube half-full of water. Transfer 1 cm^3 of the solution into each of two separate test tubes.	Colourless solution formed.	
(a) Add a few drops of sodium hydroxide solution to the first test tube then add a further 3 cm^3 of sodium hydroxide solution.	White precipitate formed. Precipitate is insoluble in excess sodium hydroxide.	Possibly magnesium, zinc or aluminium ion present. Magnesium ion present.
(b) Add a few drops of ammonia solution to the second test tube then add a further 3 cm^3 of ammonia solution.	White precipitate formed. Precipitate is insoluble in excess ammonia.	Confirms the presence of magnesium ion.

(CCEA June 2010)

Exercise 3A

1. Complete the following observation-deduction exercise to confirm the presence of zinc ion.

Experiment	Observations	Deductions
Make a solution of X by dissolving half a spatula measure of X in a test tube half-full of water. Transfer 1 cm³ of the solution into each of two separate test tubes.		
(a) Add a few drops of sodium hydroxide solution to the first test tube then add a further 10 cm³ of sodium hydroxide solution.		
(b) Add a few drops of ammonia solution to the second test tube then add a further 5 cm³ of ammonia solution.		

(CCEA June 2010)

2. Complete the following observation-deduction exercise to confirm the presence of copper(II) ions.

Experiment	Observations	Deductions
Make a solution of A by dissolving half a spatula measure of A in a test tube one-third full of water.		
(a) Add a few drops of dilute ammonia to the test tube.		
(b) Add an excess of dilute ammonia to the same test tube.		

(CCEA June 2011)

Often a positive test for an ion can only be obtained after it has been determined that other ions are not present in the mixture. For example, the observation-deduction sequence for Experiment 3 in Worked Example 3ii demonstrates that the presence of chloride ion can only be confirmed once dilute acid has been used to confirm that the mixture does not contain carbonate ions or hydrogencarbonate ions.

Worked Example 3.ii

You are provided with a mixture of two salts, labelled X, which have a common cation. Carry out the following experiments on the mixture. Record your observations and deductions in the spaces below and identify the two salts.

Experiment	Observations	Deductions
1. Describe X.	White solid.	Possibly Group I, II or ammonium salt.
2. (a) Fill a test tube one quarter full of water and record the temperature.	20 °C	
(b) Add three spatula measures of X to the test tube, stir and record the temperature.	18 °C	
(c) Record the temperature change. Keep the contents of this test tube for experiments 3 and 4.	–2 °C	Reaction is endothermic.
3. (a) Add 1–2 cm³ of the solution formed in experiment 2 to another test tube.		
(b) Acidify with 1 cm³ of dilute nitric acid and then add 1 cm³ of silver nitrate solution.	No effervescence. White precipitate formed.	Not a carbonate or hydrogen-carbonate. Possibly chloride ion.
(c) Add 5 cm³ of dilute ammonia solution to the test tube.	Precipitate dissolves to form a colourless solution.	Confirms the presence of chloride ion.

Experiment	Observations	Deductions
4. (a) Add 1–2 cm³ of the solution formed in experiment 2 to another test tube.		
(b) Acidify with 3 drops of dilute nitric acid and then add 3 drops of barium chloride solution.	White precipitate formed.	Sulfate ion present.
5. Add a spatula measure of X to a test tube one third full of dilute sodium hydroxide and warm gently, testing any gas evolved with moist Universal Indicator paper.	Pungent smell. Gas turns Universal Indicator paper blue.	Ammonia gas. Gas is alkaline. Confirms the presence of ammonia. Mixture contains an ammonium salt.

Name the two salts present in X:

Ammonium chloride and ammonium sulfate. **[2]**

(CCEA June 2011)

....

In Worked Example 3ii the observations and deductions confirm the absence of carbonate ion and hydrogencarbonate ion. The observations and deductions needed to suggest and then confirm the presence of carbonate or hydrogencarbonate ion are illustrated by the following examples.

Observation-deduction record confirming the presence of carbonate ion or hydrogencarbonate ion in a mixture of salts:

Experiment	Observations	Deductions
(a) Place a half spatula measure of A in a test tube and add about 1 cm³ of dilute nitric acid.	Effervescence. The solid dissolves to give a colourless solution.	Carbonate or hydrogen-carbonate present.
(b) Identify the gas evolved using a suitable reagent.	The gas turns limewater cloudy white.	The gas is carbon dioxide. Confirms carbonate or hydrogen-carbonate present.

(CCEA June 2006)

Additional tests to confirm the presence of hydrogencarbonate ion, HCO_3^- :

Experiment	Observations	Deductions
(a) Dissolve half a spatula measure of A in a test tube one-third full of water.	Solid dissolves to form a colourless solution.	
(b) Add 1cm³ of magnesium nitrate solution to the test tube.	No precipitate. Solution remains colourless.	Carbonate ion is not present. Hydrogen-carbonate ion is present.
(c) Gently heat the mixture using a Bunsen burner.	White precipitate formed on heating.	Confirms the presence of hydrogen-carbonate ion.

(Adapted from CCEA June 2006)

In Worked Example 3iii a mixture of potassium iodide and potassium sulfate is identified by testing for the presence of potassium ions, halide ions and sulfate ions. The presence of each ion is confirmed from observations that indicate a positive test for the ion. The reaction between potassium iodide and concentrated sulfuric acid (see Unit 1.8: The Halogens) is also included in the scheme and is used to provide initial evidence for the presence of iodide ions in the mixture.

....

Worked Example 3iii

You are provided with a mixture of two salts, labelled B, which have a common cation. Carry out the following experiments on the mixture. Record your observations and deductions in the spaces below and identify the two salts.

Experiment	Observations	Deductions
1. Describe the appearance of B.	White solid.	Does not contain the salt of a d-block metal.
2. Dip a wire loop in concentrated hydrochloric acid; touch sample B with the wire, then hold it in a blue Bunsen flame.	Lilac flame. -OR- Pink flame (viewed through blue glass).	Potassium ion present.

In a fume cupboard: 3. Add about 1 cm³ of concentrated sulfuric acid to a half spatula measure of B in a test tube. Heat the test tube gently.	Grey-black solid formed. Steam evolved. Purple fumes evolved.	Iodine formed. Iodide ion present.
4. Make up a solution of B by dissolving a half spatula measure of B in a test tube half-full of water. Put 1 cm³ of the solution into each of two separate test tubes.	Colourless solution formed.	
(a) (i) Add a few drops of silver nitrate solution to the first test tube.	Yellow precipitate formed.	Suggests iodide ion present.
(ii) Add about 2 cm³ of concentrated ammonia to the first test tube.	Yellow precipitate remains.	Confirms iodide ion present.
(b) Add a few drops of barium chloride solution to the second test tube and then add 2 cm³ of dilute nitric acid.	White precipitate formed. No effervescence on adding acid.	Sulfate ion present. Not a carbonate or hydrogen-carbonate.

Name the two salts present in X:

Potassium iodide and potassium sulfate. **[2]**

(CCEA June 2009)

Identifying Functional Groups

In this task a series of chemical tests are used to identify the functional groups present in an unknown organic compound. Candidates would be expected to recall the properties and reactions of: alkanes, alkenes, halogenoalkanes, and alcohols. On this basis it is reasonable to assume that candidates could be asked to confirm the presence of: a C=C bond in an alkene, a carbon-halogen bond in a halogenoalkane, a hydroxyl

(-OH) group in an alcohol, a carboxyl group (-COOH) in a carboxylic acid, and alcohols with the structure $RC(OH)CH_3$ through use of the iodoform reaction. Worked example 3iv illustrates a sequence of tests to detect and then confirm the presence of a C=C functional group.

Worked Example 3iv

You are provided with an organic liquid labelled Y. Carry out the following experiments on the liquid. Record your observations and deductions in the spaces below.

Experiment	Observations	Deductions
1. Place 10 drops of Y in a test tube and add 1 cm³ of water.	The liquids are immiscible and form two layers. Liquid Y floats on water.	Liquid Y cannot form hydrogen bonds. Liquid Y does not contain an -OH group or a -COOH group. Liquid Y is less dense than water.
2. Place 10 drops of Y on a watch glass placed on a heat proof mat and ignite it using a splint.	Liquid Y burns with a smoky yellow flame.	Liquid Y has a high carbon content.
3. Add approximately 10 drops of Y to a test tube one quarter full of bromine water and mix well.	The orange colour of the bromine disappears. A colourless solution is formed.	Liquid Y contains one or more C=C bonds.
4. Add 10 drops of Y to 2 cm³ of acidified potassium dichromate solution in a test tube. Warm the mixture gently.	The orange colour of dichromate remains.	Liquid Y is not oxidised. Confirms Y is not a primary or secondary alcohol.

Based on the above tests suggest a functional group which is present in Y:

The C=C functional group is present. **[2]**

(CCEA June 2010)

Exercise 3B

1. Complete the observations and deductions for the following sequence of experiments carried out on an organic liquid B.

Experiment	Observations	Deductions
1. Place 10 drops of B in a test tube and add 1 cm³ of water.	Liquid B mixes completely with water to form a colourless solution.	
2. Place 10 drops of B on a watch glass placed on a heat proof mat and ignite it using a splint.	Liquid B burns with a clean blue flame.	
3. Add approximately 10 drops of B to a test tube one quarter full of bromine water and mix well.	The orange colour of bromine remains when the liquids mix.	
4. Add 10 drops of B to 2 cm³ of acidified potassium dichromate solution in a test tube. Warm the mixture gently.	The colour of the mixture changes from orange to green during heating. The mixture has a different smell after heating.	

(CCEA June 2010)

2. Complete the observations and deductions for the following sequence of experiments carried out on an aqueous solution of an organic liquid B.

Experiment	Observations	Deductions
1. Describe the solution and place a few drops on a piece of Universal Indicator paper.		
In a fume cupboard: 2. Shake a small volume of the solution with bromine water.		
3. Gently heat 2 cm³ of the solution with 2 cm³ of acidified potassium dichromate solution.		

(CCEA June 2009)

In Worked Example 3v an aqueous solution of ethanoic acid (vinegar) is quickly identified by its characteristic smell. Subsequent tests are then conducted to confirm the presence of a carboxyl group (-COOH) by demonstrating that the organic compound behaves as an acid when mixed with bases and metals.

Worked Example 3v

You are provided with an aqueous solution of an organic liquid labelled Y. Carry out the following experiments on the solution. Record your observations and deductions in the spaces below.

Experiment	Observations	Deductions
1. Describe the smell of solution Y.	Smell of vinegar.	The solution is an aqueous solution of ethanoic acid.
2. Using a glass rod place a drop of Y onto Universal Indicator paper.	The Universal Indicator paper turns orange.	Liquid Y is a weak acid. Confirms that Y is a carboxylic acid.
3. Add a spatula measure of anhydrous sodium carbonate to a test tube one quarter full of solution Y and identify the gas evolved using a suitable reagent.	Sodium carbonate reacts to form a colourless solution. Effervescence. The gas produced turns limewater cloudy white.	Confirms that Y is acidic. Carbon dioxide is produced.
4. Add 1 cm³ of Y to a test tube and then add a 2 cm length of magnesium ribbon.	Effervescence. The solution gets warm. Magnesium reacts to form a colourless solution.	The reaction is exothermic. Confirms that Y is acidic.

Based on the above tests suggest a functional group which is present in Y:

The carboxyl (-COOH) functional group is present. [2]

Liquid Y contains one functional group and two carbon atoms. Write an equation for the reaction occurring in experiment 4.

$$2CH_3COOH + Mg \rightarrow (CH_3COO)_2Mg + H_2 \text{ [2]}$$

(CCEA June 2011)

Exercise 3C

The halogenoalkanes 1-chlorobutane, 1-bromobutane and 1-iodobutane are colourless liquids. A sample of each liquid is provided in containers labelled X, Y and Z. Identify the samples by completing the following observation-deduction exercise.

Experiment	Observations	Deductions
Place 1 cm³ of X, Y and Z separately into three test tubes. Label the test tubes with their contents.	X	X
Add 1 cm³ of ethanol and 1 cm³ of silver nitrate solution to each test tube. Place the three test tubes in a beaker of water heated to 50–60 °C. Leave for 5 minutes and note the relative rate of reaction.	Y	Y
	Z	Z

(CCEA June 2011)

Planning and Structured Questions

The practical exercises are followed by an exercise to test the candidate's ability to plan an investigation and analyse the results that would be obtained. It is expected that candidates will be able to demonstrate familiarity with standard laboratory equipment and standard ways of working that would arise as a result of having conducted practical work to accompany the various aspects of the course.

Worked Example 3vi

You are required to plan an experiment to determine the degree of hydration in a sample of sodium carbonate. If the sample of hydrated sodium carbonate is heated in a crucible to constant mass and appropriate masses measured, the value of x in the formula $Na_2CO_3.xH_2O$ can be found.

(a) Explain the meaning of the term hydrated sodium carbonate.

Solid sodium carbonate that contains water of crystallisation.

Draw a labelled diagram to show the apparatus which could be used to heat the hydrated sodium carbonate.

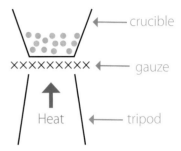

(b) What masses should be recorded before heating the hydrated carbonate?

The mass of the empty crucible and the mass of the crucible when it contains the sample of hydrated sodium carbonate.

The hydrated sodium carbonate is heated to remove all the water. What steps would you take to ensure that it had all been removed?

Heat then weigh the sample. Repeat until the mass does not decrease further.

State one safety precaution which should be followed after the sample is heated and before weighing.

Use tongs or gloves to lift the crucible after heating.

(c) When 11.44 g of hydrated sodium carbonate was heated 4.24 g of anhydrous sodium carbonate was formed. What is the mass of water lost?

$$11.44 - 4.24 = 7.20 \text{ g}$$

What is the number of moles of water lost?

$$\frac{7.20 \text{ g}}{18 \text{ g mol}^{-1}} = 0.4 \text{ mol}$$

What is the number of moles of anhydrous sodium carbonate formed?

$$\frac{4.24 \text{ g}}{106 \text{ g mol}^{-1}} = 0.04 \text{ mol}$$

Calculate the value of x in $Na_2CO_3.xH_2O$.

$$\frac{0.4 \text{ mol of water}}{0.04 \text{ mol of hydrate}} = 10$$

(CCEA June 2009)

Exercise 3D

The formula of hydrated zinc sulfate is $ZnSO_4.xH_2O$. The value of x can be found by heating a sample of hydrated zinc sulfate to constant mass. (a) Explain the meaning of the term hydrated zinc sulfate. (b) Draw a labelled diagram to show the apparatus which could be used to heat the hydrated zinc sulfate. (c) What masses should be recorded before heating the hydrated zinc sulfate? (d) The hydrated zinc sulfate is heated to remove all the water. What steps would you take to ensure that it had all been removed? (e) State one safety precaution which should be followed after heating and before weighing. (f) Heating 8.63 g of hydrated zinc sulfate produced 4.85 g of anhydrous zinc sulfate. Calculate i) the mass of water lost, ii) the moles of water lost, iii) the moles of anhydrous salt formed, and iv) the formula of hydrated zinc sulfate.

(CCEA June 2009)

Worked Example 3vii

(a) The empirical formula of an oxide of copper can be found by reducing the oxide in the following apparatus.

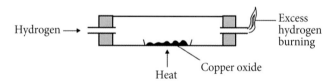

What weighings should be taken before heating?

The mass of the container and the mass of the container when filled with copper oxide.

In addition to wearing safety glasses, suggest and explain one other safety precaution which should be taken.

Flush the apparatus with hydrogen gas to remove air before heating. A mixture of hydrogen and oxygen is explosive and should not be heated.

What steps would you take to ensure that all of the oxygen has been removed from the copper?

Heat then weigh the sample in its container. Repeat until the mass of the sample and container does not change.

Explain why the hydrogen continues to be passed through the apparatus after all the copper oxide has been reduced.

To prevent the copper reacting with oxygen in the air to reform copper oxide.

(b) When 2.16 g of the copper oxide was reduced, 1.92 g of copper was formed.

What mass of oxygen was present in the copper oxide?

$2.16 - 1.92 = 0.24$ g

How many moles of oxygen were present in the copper oxide?

$$\frac{0.24 \text{ g}}{16 \text{ g mol}^{-1}} = 0.015 \text{ mol}$$

How many moles of copper were formed?

$$\frac{1.92 \text{ g}}{64 \text{ g mol}^{-1}} = 0.030 \text{ mol}$$

Calculate the empirical formula of the copper oxide.

$$1 \text{ mol of O reacts with } \frac{0.030 \text{ mol}}{0.015 \text{ mol}} = 2 \text{ mol of Cu.}$$

The formula of the copper oxide is Cu_2O.

(CCEA June 2010)

The practical assessment concludes with a number of structured questions to further test the candidate's knowledge of practical chemistry. Questions may involve the use of standard laboratory equipment to carry out a routine task such as:

• determining the formula of a compound by heating to constant mass.

• measuring the enthalpy change for a reaction by calorimetry.

• calculating the purity of a solid sample by back-titration.

• determining the rate of a reaction.

• testing for the presence of ions in solution.

• obtaining a pure, dry product from a reaction mixture.

The following examples illustrate the level of response expected from candidates when explaining the use of standard laboratory apparatus, and analysing data from an experiment.

. . . .

Worked Example 3viii

A separating funnel can be used to remove impurities from crude organic liquids by shaking the organic liquid with an aqueous solution before separating the layers.

(a) How would you decide which layer was the aqueous layer?

Add water to the separating funnel. The water will increase the volume of the aqueous layer.

(b) Why would anhydrous calcium chloride be added to the organic liquid after separation?

Anhydrous calcium chloride is a drying agent and will absorb small amounts of water from the organic layer.

(Adapted from CCEA June 2009)

Worked Example 3ix

Heating a reacting mixture under reflux is an important practical technique in organic chemistry.

(a) Draw a labelled diagram of the apparatus used to reflux a reaction mixture.

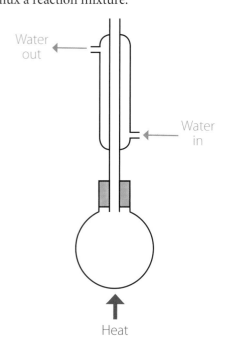

Water out

Water in

Heat

(b) Why are anti-bumping granules added to a mixture being refluxed?

To ensure that the reaction mixture boils smoothly.

(CCEA June 2009)

Worked Example 3x

A student used 13.7 cm³ of butan-1-ol (density = 0.81 g cm^{-3} and RFM = 74) to produce 10.28 g of 1-bromobutane (RFM = 137).

(a) Calculate the mass of butan-1-ol used.

$$\text{Mass} = \text{Density} \times \text{Volume} = 0.81 \text{ g cm}^{-3} \times 13.7 \text{ cm}^3$$
$$= 11.10 \text{ g}$$

(b) Calculate the number of moles of butan-1-ol used.

$$\text{Moles} = \frac{11.10 \text{ g}}{74 \text{ g mol}^{-1}} = 0.150 \text{ mol}$$

(c) What is the theoretical yield of 1-bromobutane in moles?

Theoretical yield of 1-bromobutane = moles of butan-1-ol used = 0.150 mol

(d) Calculate the actual yield of 1-bromobutane in moles.

$$\text{Actual yield} = \frac{10.28 \text{ g}}{137 \text{ g mol}^{-1}} = 0.075 \text{ mol}$$

(e) State the equation used to calculate the percentage yield of a product.

$$\% \text{ yield} = \frac{\text{Actual yield}}{\text{Theoretical yield}} \times 100 \%$$

(f) Calculate the percentage yield of product.

$$\% \text{ yield} = \frac{0.075 \text{ mol}}{0.150 \text{ mol}} \times 100 = 50 \%$$

(CCEA June 2009)

Answers

Exercise 1.1A

a) Nitrogen, bromine and iodine are diatomic.
b) Nitrogen is a gas.
c) Iodine, sulfur and silver are solids.

Exercise 1.1B

1. a) $NaNO_3$ and $MgBr_2$ are ionic compounds.
   b) NO_2 and CCl_4 are molecular.
   c) SiO_2 has a giant structure.
2. Calcium chloride is an ionic compound. Ionic compounds do not contain molecules. Answer: B

Exercise 1.1C

a) LiF b) KCl c) $MgBr_2$ d) MgS e) Al_2O_3

Exercise 1.1D

1. a) PBr_3 b) NO_2 c) SF_4 d) $HgCl_2$
2. a) SO_2 b) PCl_5 c) MnO_2 d) XeF_2

Exercise 1.1E

1. a) calcium chloride, b) aluminium oxide, c) silver bromide, d) lithium hydride, e) zinc sulfide
2. a) zinc carbonate, b) zinc sulfate, c) magnesium nitrate, d) magnesium nitride, e) potassium permanganate
3. a) silver nitrate, b) ammonium nitrate, c) sodium nitrite, d) aluminium sulfate, e) sodium sulfite
4. a) sodium oxide, b) sodium peroxide, c) calcium hydrogen carbonate, d) sodium hypochlorite, e) potassium chromate

Exercise 1.1F

a) sulfur tetrafluoride, b) sulfur trioxide, c) silicon tetrachloride, d) phosphorus tribromide, e) xenon tetrafluoride

Exercise 1.1G

a) copper(II) oxide, b) copper(II) sulfate, c) copper(I) oxide, d) copper(II) chloride, e) mercury(II) chloride, f) mercury(I) chloride

Exercise 1.1H

a) sulfur(IV) fluoride, b) tin(II) chloride, c) silicon(IV) chloride, d) phosphorus(III) bromide, e) xenon(IV) fluoride, f) lead(IV) oxide

Exercise 1.1I

1. a) $C + O_2 \rightarrow CO_2$, b) $2C + O_2 \rightarrow 2CO$
2. $3Mg + N_2 \rightarrow Mg_3N_2$
3. a) $P_4 + 10Cl_2 \rightarrow 4PCl_5$, b) $P_4 + 6Cl_2 \rightarrow 4PCl_3$

Exercise 1.1J

1. a) $2Na_{(s)} + Cl_{2\,(g)} \rightarrow 2NaCl_{(s)}$
   b) $H_{2\,(g)} + Cl_{2\,(g)} \rightarrow 2HCl_{(g)}$
   c) $2Ca_{(s)} + O_{2\,(g)} \rightarrow 2CaO_{(s)}$
   d) $Mg_{(s)} + Br_{2\,(l)} \rightarrow MgBr_{2\,(s)}$
2. a) $Fe_{(s)} + S_{(s)} \rightarrow FeS_{(s)}$
   b) $CaCO_{3\,(s)} \rightarrow CaO_{(s)} + CO_{2\,(g)}$
   c) $2Fe_{(s)} + 3Br_{2\,(l)} \rightarrow 2FeBr_{3\,(s)}$
   d) $2Al_{(s)} + 3I_{2\,(s)} \rightarrow 2AlI_{3\,(s)}$

Exercise 1.1K

1. a) and c), 2. They are all soluble,
3. b) and d), 4. c) and d)

Exercise 1.1L

1. Ethanoic acid dissociates to produce hydrogen ions: $C_2H_4O_2 \rightarrow H^+ + C_2H_3O_2^-$
2. a) Phosphoric acid dissociates to produce hydrogen ions: $H_3PO_4 \rightarrow H^+ + H_2PO_4^-$, b) Some of the H_3PO_4 molecules do not dissociate.
3. The reaction shows zinc oxide reacting with an acid to form a salt and water.
4. Carbonate ions in the solution react with water to form hydroxide ions: $CO_3^{2-}{}_{(aq)} + H_2O_{(l)} \rightarrow HCO_3^-{}_{(aq)} + OH^-{}_{(aq)}$

Exercise 1.1M

1. $Ag^+{}_{(aq)} + I^-{}_{(aq)} \rightarrow AgI_{(s)}$
2. $Ca^{2+}{}_{(aq)} + CO_3^{2-}{}_{(aq)} \rightarrow CaCO_{3\,(s)}$

Exercise 1.1N

1. a) $CuO + 2HCl \rightarrow CuCl_2 + H_2O$
   b) $CuO + 2H^+ \rightarrow Cu^{2+} + H_2O$
2. a) $Na_2CO_3 + 2HCl \rightarrow 2NaCl + H_2O + CO_2$
   b) $CO_3^{2-} + 2H^+ \rightarrow H_2O + CO_2$

Exercise 1.1O

1. 1×10^{22} atoms, 2. 3.29 g, 3. a) 182   b) 182 g
c) 3.02×10^{-22} g   d) 1.81×10^{-20} g

Exercise 1.1P

1. a) 369 g b) 652 g, 2. 301 g, 3. a) 9.2 g, b) 217 g,
4. 40.8 g, 5. 218 kg, 6. 118 kg

Exercise 1.1Q

£52

Exercise 1.1R

1. 0.48 g, 2. 2.24 kg, 3. 250 tonnes, 4. 37 kg, 5. 4.8 kg

Exercise 1.1S

62.9 %

Exercise 1.1T

1. $CoCl_2.7H_2O$, 2. x = 2

Exercise 1.2A

Mg^{2+} and Ne both have 10 electrons.

Exercise 1.2B

1. 11 protons, 11 electrons and 12 neutrons.
2. They have the same number of protons but a different number of neutrons.

Exercise 1.2C

3. 23.02

Exercise 1.2D

1. 127.1, 2. 131.6

Exercise 1.2E

Answer C

Exercise 1.2F

1. Ca atom: $(1s)^2(2s)^2(2p)^6(3s)^2(3p)^6(4s)^2$

   O atom: $(1s)^2(2s)^2(2p)^4$

   Ca^{2+} ion: $(1s)^2(2s)^2(2p)^6(3s)^2(3p)^6$

   O^{2-} ion: $(1s)^2(2s)^2(2p)^6$

2. (a) $(1s)^2(2s)^2(2p)^6$, (b) $(1s)^2(2s)^2(2p)^6(3s)^2(3p)^6$,
   (c) Al^{3+} and F^- , (d) Cl^- and K^+

Exercise 1.2G

1. (a) Mn $(1s)^2(2s)^2(2p)^6(3s)^2(3p)^6(4s)^2(3d)^5$
   (b) Mn^{2+} $(1s)^2(2s)^2(2p)^6(3s)^2(3p)^6(3d)^5$
   (c) Zn^{2+} $(1s)^2(2s)^2(2p)^6(3s)^2(3p)^6(3d)^{10}$
   (d) Ni $(1s)^2(2s)^2(2p)^6(3s)^2(3p)^6(4s)^2(3d)^8$

2. (a) Sc $(1s)^2(2s)^2(2p)^6(3s)^2(3p)^6(4s)^2(3d)^1$
   (b) V $(1s)^2(2s)^2(2p)^6(3s)^2(3p)^6(4s)^2(3d)^3$
   (c) V^{3+} $(1s)^2(2s)^2(2p)^6(3s)^2(3p)^6(3d)^2$
   (d) Ca $(1s)^2(2s)^2(2p)^6(3s)^2(3p)^6(4s)^2$

Exercise 1.2H

1. Answer C, 2. fluorine and potassium

Exercise 1.2I

IE1(Ca) < IE1(Mg) because the outermost electron in calcium is further from the nucleus and is better shielded.

Exercise 1.2J

1. (a) The electron configuration in which the electrons occupy the lowest available energy levels.

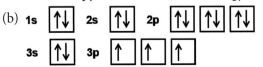

(c) Phosphorus has a half-filled subshell.
2. Answer C
3. (a) The charge on the nucleus increases while the shielding of the outermost electrons remains constant.
   (b) IE1 decreases from 12 to 13 (Mg to Al) because the outermost 3p electron in Al is further from the nucleus and better shielded than the outermost 2s electrons in Mg.
   (c) The paired 3p electrons in S repel and are easier to remove than the unpaired 3p electrons in P.
   Alternative answer: The 3p electrons in P are harder to remove as the 3p subshell is half-filled.

Exercise 1.2K

1. (a) IE1(K) < IE1(Na) because the outermost electron in potassium is further from the nucleus and better shielded by the inner shells of electrons.
   (b) IE2 >> IE1 because removing a second electron from the atom involves taking an electron from a full shell.
2. Answer B
3. Answer D

4.

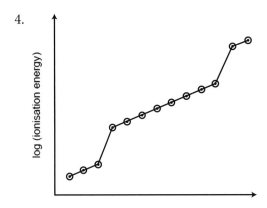

Exercise 1.2L

1. Answer B, 2. Answer D, 3. Answer D, 4. Answer A

Exercise 1.2M

1. 3.287×10^{15} Hz (1 Hz = 1 s^{-1})
2. (a) $Na_{(g)} \rightarrow Na^+_{(g)} + e^-_{(g)}$ (b) 499 kJ mol^{-1}
3. Answer B
4. Multiply the frequency at the convergence limit by Planck's constant.

Exercise 1.2N

2.29 Make a small loop at the end of a piece of nichrome wire. Dip the loop in concentrated hydrochloric acid and then in the sample. Place the loop in a blue Bunsen flame and record the flame colour. The presence of lithium ions in the sample produces a crimson flame.

Exercise 1.3A

1. (a) $2Na_{(s)} + F_{2\,(g)} \rightarrow 2NaF_{(s)}$

(b)

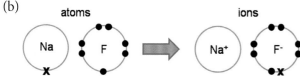

atoms   ions

2. (a)

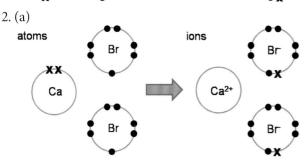

atoms   ions

(b) Ca^{2+} $(1s)^2(2s)^2(2p)^6(3s)^2(3p)^6$

Br^- $(1s)^2(2s)^2(2p)^6(3s)^2(3p)^6(4s)^2(3d)^{10}(4p)^6$

Exercise 1.3B

(a) $P_4 + 6\,F_2 \rightarrow 4PF_3$

(b)

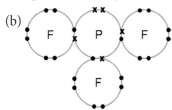

(c) The atoms in PF_3 have satisfied the octet rule by sharing electrons to obtain a full outer-shell containing eight electrons.

Exercise 1.3C

1. Carbon dioxide, O=C=O.

Exercise 1.3D

$$H-\overset{H}{\underset{H}{C}}-\overset{H}{\underset{H}{C}}-H \qquad \overset{H}{\underset{H}{C}}=\overset{H}{\underset{H}{C}} \qquad H-C\equiv C-H$$

ethane, C_2H_6 ethene, C_2H_4 ethyne, C_2H_2

Exercise 1.3E

1. (a) A coordinate bond. (b) A pair of electrons on the nitrogen atom is shared with the boron atom.

Exercise 1.3F

1. (a) $BeCl_2$ and H_2O. (b) All except $BeCl_2$.

2. (a)

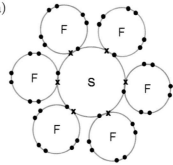

(b) Each fluorine atom has eight electrons in its outer shell and satisfies the octet rule. The sulfur atom has twelve electrons in its outer shell and does not satisfy the octet rule. In this way the compound SF_6 does not satisfy the octet rule.

Exercise 1.3G

1. (a) Electronegativity is the ability of an element to attract the shared electrons in a covalent bond to itself. (b) The electronegativity values for beryllium and chlorine are more similar than the electronegativity values for barium and chlorine.

2. HF.

Exercise 1.3H

1. *Use as lubricant*: Graphite contains layers of carbon atoms. The bonding between the layers is weak allowing the layers to slide over each other. *Electrical conductor*: The electrons involved in bonding the layers together are free to move and carry a charge through the solid.

2. (a) The term covalent refers to the sharing (of pairs) of electrons between atoms. (b) The atoms in diamond form a covalent bond with each of four neighbouring atoms to form a giant structure. The bonds about each carbon atom have a tetrahedral arrangement. The atoms in graphite form a covalent bond with each of three neighbouring atoms to form layers of atoms. The layers of atoms are held together by weak bonds between the layers. (c) The layers in graphite are held together by electrons that are free to move between the layers. (d) The network of strong covalent bonds in diamond forms a rigid structure.

3. (a) Diamond. (b) Diamond is hard because the bonds are strong and are arranged to form a rigid structure. (c) Diamond does not conduct electricity because the outer-shell electrons are all held tightly in the bonds and are not able to move through the material.

4. Answer D.

Exercise 1.3I

1. (a) The layers of ions can move past each other.
(b) The outermost electrons are delocalised and free to move.

2. The bonding in a metal results from the attraction between the positively charged metal ions and the delocalised electrons in the metal. Metals are ductile because the metal ions can move past each other without disturbing the bonding in the metal. Metals conduct electricity because the delocalised electrons are able to move and carry a charge through the metal.

3. Strontium metal is a good conductor because the delocalised electrons in the metal are free to move and carry a charge through the metal. Strontium fluoride is a poor conductor because the ions in the solid are not free to move.

4. (a) Metallic bonding refers to the attraction between the array of positive metal ions and the delocalised electrons in a metal.

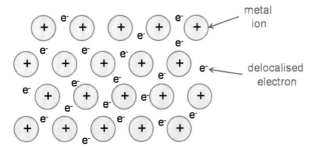

(b) The attraction between the ions and the delocalised electrons decreases as the metal ions get bigger. (c) Calcium has two delocalised electrons for every metal ion. Potassium has only one delocalised electron for every metal ion.

....

Exercise 1.4A

1.   The four pairs of electrons in the outer shell of the nitrogen atom repel to give ammonia a trigonal pyramidal shape.

2. (a) 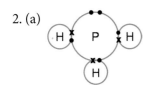 (b)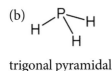

trigonal pyramidal

3. 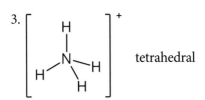 tetrahedral

4. (a) 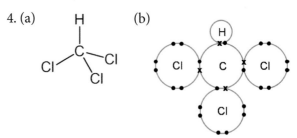 (b)

(c) The four pairs of electrons in the outer shell of the carbon atom repel to give chloroform a tetrahedral shape.

5. (a)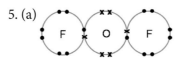

(b) The four pairs of electrons in the outer shell of the oxygen atom repel to give the molecule a bent shape similar to water.

6. (a)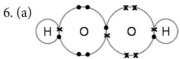

(b) The four pairs of electrons in the outer shell of each oxygen atom repel to give the molecule a bent shape with an H-O-O angle of around 105° (similar angle to water).

Exercise 1.4B

1. (a)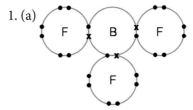

(b) Each fluorine atom has eight electrons in its outer shell and obeys the octet rule. The boron atom has six electrons in its outer shell and does not obey the octet rule.

(c)   The three pairs of electrons in the outer shell of the boron atom repel to give the molecule a trigonal planar shape.

2. (a) $Be + 2HCl \rightarrow BeCl_2 + H_2$

(b)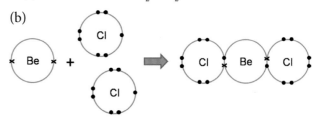

(c) The chlorine atoms have eight electrons in their outer shell and obey the octet rule. The beryllium atom has only four electrons in its outer shell and does not obey the octet rule.

(d) Cl-Be-Cl linear.

(e) The two pairs of electrons in the outer shell of the beryllium atom repel and move as far from each other as possible.

Exercise 1.4C

1. The silicon atom in $SiCl_4$ has four pairs of electrons in its outer shell that repel to give $SiCl_4$ a tetrahedral shape. The sulfur atom in SF_4 has five pairs of electrons in its outer shell that repel to give SF_4 a see-saw shape.

2. Boron has three pairs of electrons in its outer shell that repel to give BF_3 a trigonal planar shape. Phosphorus has four pairs of electrons in its outer shell that repel to give PF_3 a trigonal pyramidal shape. Chlorine has five pairs of electrons that repel to make ClF_3 T-shaped.

Exercise 1.4D

1. The CCl_4 molecule is very symmetric. It has a tetrahedral shape which allows the C-Cl bond dipoles to cancel. Answer B.

2. (a)

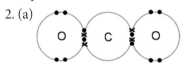

(b) Carbon dioxide is linear O=C=O.

(c) The electrons in the double bonds repel and push the double bonds as far apart as possible.

(d) The CO_2 molecule is very symmetric. The linear shape allows the C=O bond dipoles to cancel each other.

3. (a) The H-F bond is a polar covalent bond. (b) BF_3 is very symmetric and the B-F bond dipoles cancel each other.

4. The B-F and C-F bond dipoles in BF_3 and CF_4 cancel. OF_2 has a bent shape and the O-F bond dipoles do not cancel. Answer C.

5. (a)

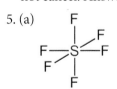

The six pairs of electrons in the outer shell of sulfur repel to give SF_6 an octahedral shape.

(b) The SF_6 molecule is very symmetric. The S-F bond dipoles cancel each other.

Exercise 1.5A

1. Answer A

2.

liquid	van der Waals	permanent dipole	hydrogen bonding
water	✓	✗	✓
ammonia	✓	✗	✓
xenon	✓	✗	✗
hydrogen chloride	✓	✓	✗

3. (a) Hydrogen bonding. (b) Dipole forces. (c) Van der Waals forces.

4. (a) Ammonia forms hydrogen bonds. Phosphine is not able to form hydrogen bonds. (b) The van der Waals attraction between SbH_3 molecules is stronger because antimony has more electrons than arsenic.

5. (a) Dipole forces and van der Waals forces. (b) A hydrogen bond is formed when a lone pair of electrons on oxygen interacts with a hydrogen atom on a neighbouring water molecule. (c) Hydrogen bonding in ice allows the water molecules to form a more open structure with greater distances between the water molecules.

6. The H-F bond is more polar than the O-H bonds in water. As a result the hydrogen bonding in HF is stronger than in water and is harder to break.

7. (a)

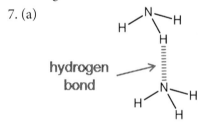

(b) Ammonia reacts with a hydrogen ion to form an ammonium ion, NH_4^+. The nitrogen atom in an ammonium ion does not have a lone pair.

8. Boron trifluoride is not able to form hydrogen bonds. Molecules of boron trifluoride are held together by much weaker van der Waals forces.

Exercise 1.5B

1. The hydrogen atoms in ammonia molecules can hydrogen bond with the oxygen atoms in water molecules. The hydrogen atoms in water molecules can also form hydrogen bonds with the nitrogen atoms in ammonia molecules.

2. The solubility of carbon dioxide is due to dipole forces between carbon ($\delta+$) and the oxygen atoms in water ($\delta-$), and hydrogen bonding between the oxygen atoms in carbon dioxide and the hydrogen atoms in water.

Exercise 1.6A

1. (a) Oxidation is the loss of electrons. (b) Reduction corresponds to a decrease in

oxidation state.

2. The oxidation number of hydrogen increases from 0 in H_2 to +1 in HCl. The oxidation number of chlorine decreases from 0 in Cl_2 to –1 in HCl. Hydrogen is oxidised and chlorine is reduced.

3. Copper has an oxidation number of +2 in CuO and 0 in Cu. Hydrogen has an oxidation number of 0 in H_2 and +1 in H_2O. Hydrogen is oxidised and copper is reduced.

Exercise 1.6B

Uranium has an oxidation number of +4 in UF_4 and +6 in UF_6. ClF_3 acts as an oxidising agent.

Exercise 1.6C

Nitrogen has an oxidation number of –3 in NH_3 and 0 in N_2. Copper has an oxidation number of +2 in CuO and 0 in Cu. Nitrogen is oxidised and copper is reduced.

Exercise 1.6D

1. (a) +5 (b) +2.
2. Silver has an oxidation number of 0 in Ag and +1 in $AgNO_3$. Nitrogen has an oxidation number of +5 in HNO_3 and +2 in NO. Silver is oxidised and nitrogen is reduced.
3. Potassium has an oxidation number of +1. Manganese has an oxidation number of +7.
4. Answer (a). Silver is reduced by hydrogen peroxide.
5. Chlorine has an oxidation number of 0 in Cl_2, –1 in NaCl and +1 in NaOCl. Chlorine is oxidised to form OCl^- and reduced to form Cl^-.
6. Answer (a). Nitrogen is oxidised and hydrogen is reduced.
7. Answer (a). Bromine is oxidised and sulfur is reduced.

Exercise 1.6E

1. Oxidation of iodide: $2I^- \rightarrow I_2 + 2e^-$

   $2HNO_3 + 6H^+ + 6I^- \rightarrow 2NO + 4H_2O + 3I_2$

2. $2HOCl_{(aq)} + 2H^+_{(aq)} + 2Fe^{2+}_{(aq)} \rightarrow$

   $Cl_{2\,(aq)} + 2H_2O_{(l)} + 2Fe^{3+}_{(aq)}$

3. $2MnO_4^- + 16H^+ + 5C_2O_4^{2-} \rightarrow$

   $2Mn^{2+} + 8H_2O + 10CO_2$

4. (a) $N_2H_4 + 2H_2O_2 \rightarrow N_2 + 4H_2O$

   (b) The oxidation number of nitrogen increases from –2 in N_2H_4 to 0 in N_2. The oxidation number of oxygen decreases from –1 in H_2O_2 to –2 in H_2O. Nitrogen is oxidised and oxygen is reduced.

Exercise 1.6F

$2BrO_3^-_{(aq)} + 12H^+_{(aq)} + 10e^- \rightarrow Br_{2\,(aq)} + 6H_2O_{(l)}$

Exercise 1.6G

1. (a) The oxidation number of xenon is +6 in $HXeO_4^-$, 0 in Xe and +8 in XeO_6^{4-}. (b) Xenon is oxidised to form XeO_6^{4-} and reduced to Xe.

2. (a) The oxidation number of chlorine is +5 in $NaClO_3$ and –1 in NaCl. (b) Chlorine is oxidised to form ClO_3^- and reduced to form Cl^-.

3. (a) $3I_{2\,(aq)} + 6NaOH_{(aq)} \rightarrow$

   $5NaI_{(aq)} + NaIO_{3\,(aq)} + 3H_2O_{(l)}$

   (b) The oxidation number of iodine is +1 in NaIO, –1 in NaI and +5 in $NaIO_3$. Iodine is oxidised to form IO_3^- and reduced to form I^-.

Exercise 1.7A

1. MgF_2 (QR_2)
2. (a) Atomic number. (b) The outermost electrons are in a d-subshell.
3. (a) The outermost electrons are in an s-subshell. (b) The number of filled shells increases.
4. X (= vanadium, V) belongs to the d-block. Y (= sulfur, S) belongs to the p-block. Z (= argon, Ar) belongs to the p-block.
5. M_2O_3
6. (a)

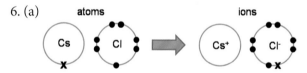

   (b) Cs^+
   $(1s)^2(2s)^2(2p)^6(3s)^2(3p)^6(4s)^2(3d)^{10}(4p)^6(5s)^2(4d)^{10}(5p)^6$
   Cl^-
   $(1s)^2(2s)^2(2p)^6(3s)^2(3p)^6$

7. X_2Y_3
8. EuH_2

Exercise 1.7B

Answer C

Exercise 1.7C

(a) The melting point increases to silicon and then decreases to argon.
(b) Atomic radius decreases from left to right across the period because the amount of shielding remains the same as the nuclear charge increases.

(c)

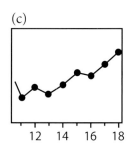

The graph should show an overall increase from left to right and a slight decrease from atomic number 12 to 13 and 15 to 16.

Exercise 1.8A

1. Answer D
2. Solid iodine has a molecular covalent structure. A crystal of iodine contains diatomic molecules held together by van der Waals attractions. Water is a polar liquid. Iodine is more soluble in hexane since iodine and hexane are nonpolar and like-dissolves-like.
3. The van der Waals attraction between molecules increases as the number of electrons in the halogen atom increases down the group.
4.

Property	Result for Astatine
molecular formula	At_2
physical state at room temperature	solid
colour at room temperature	grey-black
colour of vapour	purple
solubility in water (answer yes or no)	no
solubility in hexane (answer yes or no)	yes

Exercise 1.8B

1. (a) The outermost electrons are in a p-subshell. (b) Atomic radius increases down the group as the halogen atoms have more filled shells.
2. (a) The ability of an atom to attract bonding electrons when forming covalent bonds. (b) The halogens become less electronegative down the group as the electrons involved in covalent bonding are further from the nucleus and better shielded.

Exercise 1.8C

1. (a) $Br_2 + 2I^- \rightarrow 2Br^- + I_2$ (b) The solution formed should be darker as the orange colour of bromine is replaced with the brown colour of iodine.
2. (a) $Cl_2 + 2NaBr \rightarrow 2NaCl + Br_2$ (b) Both solutions are colourless. Mixing the solutions produces a solution with the orange colour of bromine.
3. $I_2 + 2NaAt \rightarrow 2NaI + At_2$

Exercise 1.8D

1. (a) A cream precipitate forms.
   (b) $Ag^+_{(aq)} + Br^-_{(aq)} \rightarrow AgBr_{(s)}$
   (c) The cream precipitate dissolves.
2. Add acidified silver nitrate to a few drops of A, B and C. Sodium chloride solution produces a white precipitate, sodium bromide solution produces a cream precipitate, and sodium iodide solution produces a yellow precipitate. The white precipitate dissolves on adding dilute ammonia. The cream precipitate is insoluble in dilute ammonia and only dissolves on adding concentrated ammonia. The yellow precipitate is insoluble in dilute and concentrated ammonia.
3. Answer D
4. Fluoride is added to water to reduce tooth decay. The fluoridation of water is opposed on the grounds that individuals do not have the right to choose.

Exercise 1.8E

1. (a) $Cl_2 + 2NaOH \rightarrow NaCl + NaOCl + H_2O$
   (b) Disproportionation refers to the simultaneous oxidation and reduction of an element in a reaction.
2. Answer D

Exercise 1.8F

1. (a) HI < HBr < HCl < HF (b) HF
2. (a) HF < HCl < HBr (b) A strong acid is an acid in which most of the molecules dissociate to form hydrogen ions. (c) H^+ and Br^-.
3. Answer C
4. The H-Cl bond is stronger than the H-I bond and does not break as easily when the compound is heated.

Exercise 1.8G

1. Answer B
2. Answer D
3. The reaction produces a grey-black solid that, in turn, produces: purple fumes, a yellow solid, the smell of rotten eggs, and a choking colourless gas (any 2).

Exercise 1.9A

Rinse the pipette with oven cleaner. Use the pipette to transfer 25 cm^3 of oven cleaner into the 500 cm^3 volumetric flask and make-up to the fill line using distilled water. Stopper and invert the flask to mix the solution. Rinse the pipette with the diluted solution and transfer 25 cm^3 to the conical flask.

Exercise 1.9B

1. 0.100 mol dm^{-3}
2. 0.20 mol dm^{-3}

Exercise 1.9C

1. 100 cm^3
2. Mg

Exercise 1.9D

0.75 mol dm^{-3}

Exercise 1.9E

1. (a) A stable solution of known concentration.
   (b) Phenolphthalein OR methyl orange.
   (c) Colourless to pink (phenolphthalein) OR red to yellow (methyl orange).
2. (a) $Na_2CO_3 + 2HCl \rightarrow 2NaCl + H_2O + CO_2$
   (b) Methyl orange: yellow to red.

Exercise 1.9F

(a) Rinse the pipette with the vinegar solution. Use the pipette to transfer 25 cm^3 of vinegar solution to a conical flask. Add 2–3 drops of phenolphthalein to the conical flask. Rinse the burette with sodium hydroxide solution before filling the burette with sodium hydroxide solution. Titrate the vinegar solution adding sodium hydroxide dropwise near the end point. Repeat the titration to improve accuracy.
(b) Colour change: colourless to pink.
$NaOH_{(aq)} + CH_3COOH_{(aq)} \rightarrow CH_3COONa_{(aq)} + H_2O_{(l)}$

Exercise 1.9G

(a) Phenolphthalein: colourless to pink.
(b) 1) 21.35 cm^3 2) 2.135×10^{-3} mol
   3) 0.0854 mol dm^{-3} 4) 0.854 mol dm^{-3}

Exercise 1.9H

1. $x = 7$
2. (a) $BaCl_2 + 2AgNO_3 \rightarrow 2AgCl + Ba(NO_3)_2$
   (b) $Ag^+ + Cl^- \rightarrow AgCl$ (c) $x = 2$

Exercise 1.9I

1) 0.0400 mol 2) 0.00186 mol 3) 0.0186 mol
4) 0.0214 mol 5) 1.07 g 6) 95.5%

Exercise 2.1A

1. 60%
2. 88%
3. K_2PtCl_4 is limiting; 84%

Exercise 2.1B

1. 5.40 tonnes
2. The alcohol is limiting; 3.16 g

Exercise 2.1C

1. 78%
2. 80%
3. (a) 38% (b) 60%

Exercise 2.1D

1. 16.7 dm^3
2. 8 dm^3
3. 90.3 g
4. 1.2 dm^3
5. 1.2 dm^3
6. 15 dm^3

Exercise 2.1E

1. (a) 8.3×10^{-5} g cm^{-3} (b) 1.3×10^{-3} g cm^{-3}
   (c) 1.8×10^{-3} g cm^{-3}
2. Weigh the flasks. The flask containing nitrogen is heavier because the flasks contain the same number of moles and nitrogen has a greater molar mass.

Exercise 2.1F

1. (a) 82% C, 18% H (b) 84% 16% H
2. 40.0% C, 6.7% H, 53.3% O

Exercise 2.1G

1. $x = 6$
2. Molybdenum, Mo
3. CF_2Cl
4. $C_4H_8Br_2$
5. $C_8H_{20}Pb$
6. CH_2Cl

Exercise 2.3A

1. Answer B.
2. Answer D.

Exercise 2.3B

1. (a) C_nH_{2n+2} (b) Structural isomers have the same molecular formula but different structural formulas. (c) Isopentane is 2-methylbutane. Neopentane is 2,2-dimethylpropane. (d) The van der Waals attraction between molecules is greatest between straight-chain alkanes. More branched isomers have lower boiling points due to weaker van der Waals attraction between molecules.
2. Two.

3. Three.

Exercise 2.3C

Answer A.

Exercise 2.3D

(a) Fractional distillation. (b) A hydrocarbon contains only carbon and hydrogen and is saturated if it contains only single bonds between carbon atoms. (c) 2,2,3,3-tetramethylbutane.

Exercise 2.3E

An oil spill has a negative impact on wildlife and the landscape. Animals in direct contact with oil may suffer organ damage as a result of ingesting the oil. They may also be less able to feed or defend against predators as a result of exposure to oil. An oil spill at sea damages plant life by forming a barrier on the surface of the water that prevents the sunlight needed for photosynthesis reaching plant life below the surface.

Exercise 2.3F

1. $C_{20}H_{42} \rightarrow C_5H_{12} + C_{15}H_{30}$

2. The decomposition of a hydrocarbon into smaller hydrocarbons by heating in the presence of a catalyst.

Exercise 2.3G

1. C_3H_6

2. (a)

(b) $C_8H_{18} + \dfrac{25}{2}O_2 \rightarrow 8CO_2 + 9H_2O$

Exercise 2.3H

1. (a) $C_5H_{12} + 8O_2 \rightarrow 5CO_2 + 6H_2O$

   (b) $2C_5H_{12} + 11O_2 \rightarrow 10CO + 12H_2O$

   or $C_5H_{12} + \dfrac{11}{2}O_2 \rightarrow 5CO + 6H_2O$

2. $2C_{17}H_{36} + 35O_2 \rightarrow 34CO + 36H_2O$

   or $C_{17}H_{36} + \dfrac{35}{2}O_2 \rightarrow 17CO + 18H_2O$

3. (a) Carbon monoxide and water. (b) A limited supply of oxygen during combustion.

4. (a) 2,5-dimethylhexane

(b) Structural isomers are compounds with the same molecular formula but different structural formulas.

(c) $C_8H_{18} + \dfrac{17}{2}O_2 \rightarrow 8CO + 9H_2O$.

(d) There is insufficient oxygen to react with the carbon.

Exercise 2.3I

The combustion of hydrocarbon-based fuels produces large quantities of carbon dioxide that contribute to global warming. Repeated exposure to nitrogen oxides, hydrocarbons and particulates (mostly soot) from the combustion of gasoline causes respiratory problems. Carbon monoxide is toxic and is also produced by the combustion of hydrocarbons. Brief exposure to carbon monoxide produces acute breathing difficulties.

Exercise 2.3J

1. (a) Carbon dioxide. (b) Carbon dioxide and water. (c) Nitrogen.

2. (a) Chemisorption refers to the formation of a chemical bond when a substance adsorbs on a surface and the weakening of bonds within the substance when it forms a bond with the surface. (b) To increase the efficiency of the catalyst by increasing the surface area on which the reactants can react with the catalyst.

3. (a) To increase the efficiency of the catalyst by increasing the surface area on which chemisorption can occur. (b) Molecules in the exhaust gases chemisorb on the metal by forming a bond with the metal surface. The bonds within the molecules weaken as the molecules chemisorb making it easier for the molecules to react. Chemisorption also brings the reacting molecules closer together making it easier for them to react. (c) Lead produced by the combustion of 'leaded' petrol reduces the efficiency of the catalyst by bonding to its surface and preventing the chemisorption of exhaust gases.

4. (a) $2CO + 2NO \rightarrow N_2 + 2CO_2$ (b) Any one of: platinum, rhodium or palladium. (c) To increase the efficiency of the catalyst by increasing the surface area on which molecules can chemisorb. (d) The exhaust gases and the metal catalyst are in different physical states.

Exercise 2.3K

1. (a) A free radical is an atom, molecule or ion that contains one or more unpaired electrons.

(b) $CH_4 + Cl_2 \rightarrow CH_3Cl + HCl$

(c) i) Initiation: $Cl_2 \rightarrow 2Cl\bullet$

    ii) Propagation: $CH_4 + Cl\bullet \rightarrow \bullet CH_3 + HCl$

       $\bullet CH_3 + Cl_2 \rightarrow CH_3Cl + Cl\bullet$

    iii) Termination: $Cl\bullet + \bullet CH_3 \rightarrow CH_3Cl$

      or $\bullet CH_3 + \bullet CH_3 \rightarrow C_2H_6$

2. (a) Ultraviolet radiation provides the energy for homolytic fission of the Cl-Cl bond in chlorine. (b) Methyl radical is formed when methane reacts with chlorine radical to form hydrogen chloride.

methyl radical

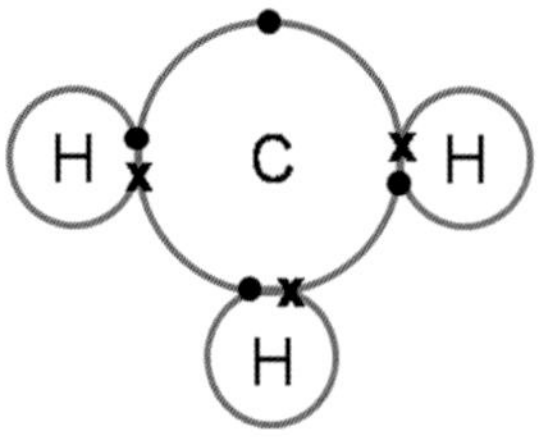

3. Answer C.

4. A catalyst speeds up a reaction but is not consumed by the reaction. Light cannot be considered a catalyst as it is consumed by the reaction.

....

Exercise 2.4A

Answer C.

Exercise 2.4B

1. (a) Cracking. (b) High temperature.

   (c) $C_8H_{18} \rightarrow C_3H_6 + C_5H_{12}$

2. $C_{12}H_{26} \rightarrow C_2H_4 + C_{10}H_{22}$

3. $C_{16}H_{34} \rightarrow 2C_2H_4 + C_3H_6 + C_9H_{20}$

Exercise 2.4C

1. Answer B

2. Answer C

Exercise 2.4D

Answer B

Exercise 2.4E

(a) The C=C bond in ethene consists of σ- and π-bonds, and is stronger than the C-C σ-bond in ethane. The C=C bond in ethene is shorter as the bond is stronger and the carbon atoms are held together more tightly.

(b) The C-C π-bond in ethene is weaker than the C-C σ-bond in ethane and is exposed making it vulnerable to attack by molecules or ions seeking electrons to bond with.

Exercise 2.4F

1. Answer C

2. Answer B

3. Either:

(a)

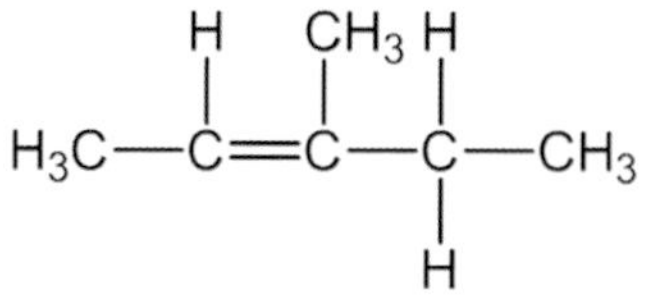

(b) 3-methylpent-2-ene

(c)

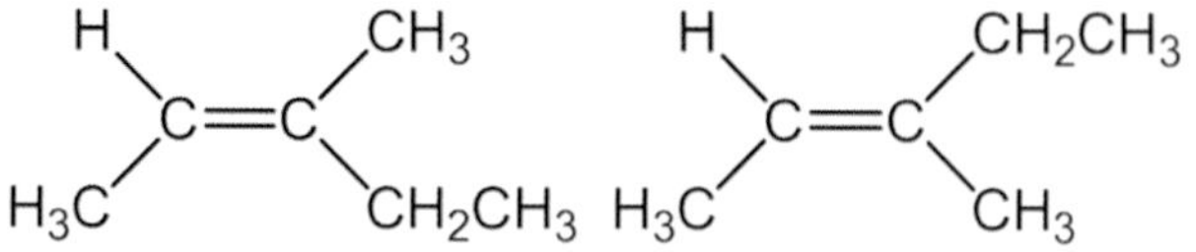

Or:

(a)

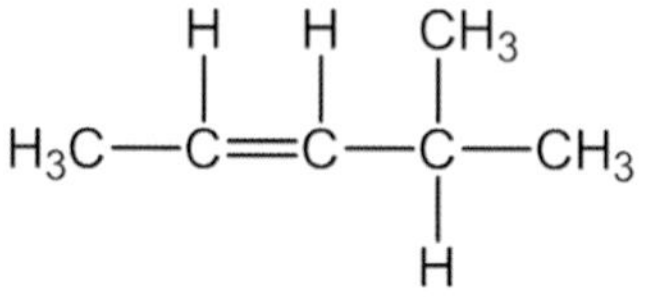

(b) 4-methylpent-2-ene

(c)

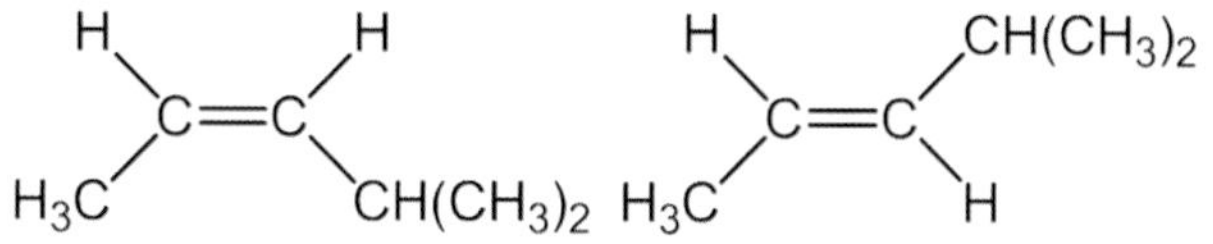

Exercise 2.4G

1.

E isomer: Z isomer:

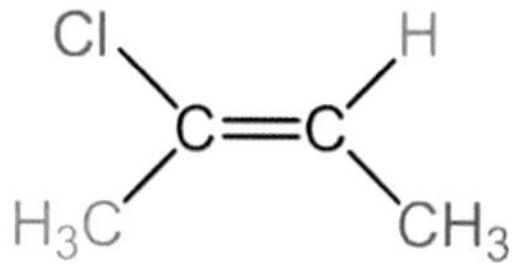

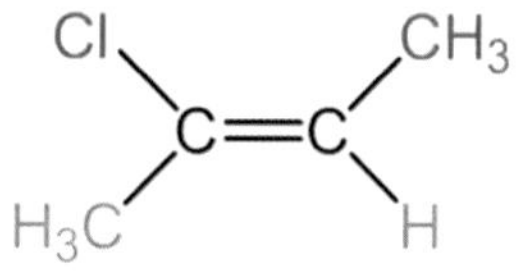

2.

E isomer: Z isomer:

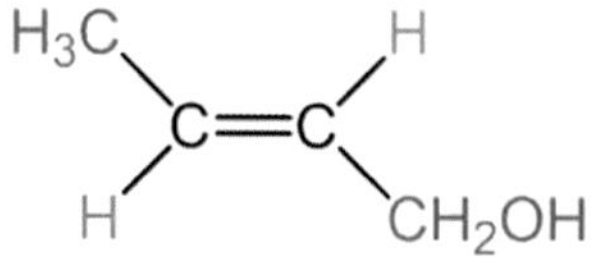

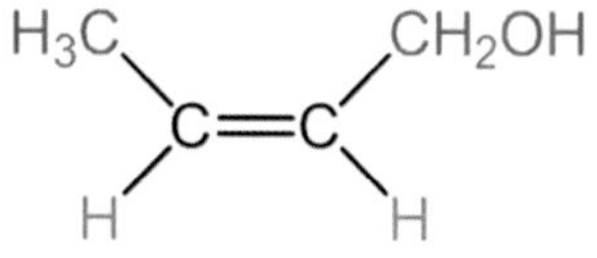

3.

E isomer: Z isomer:

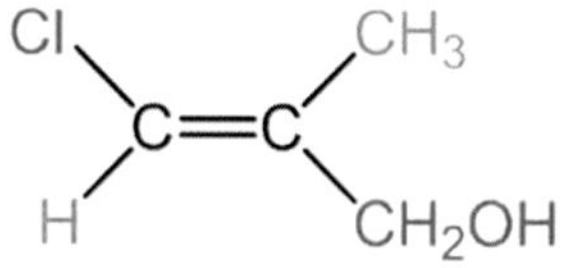

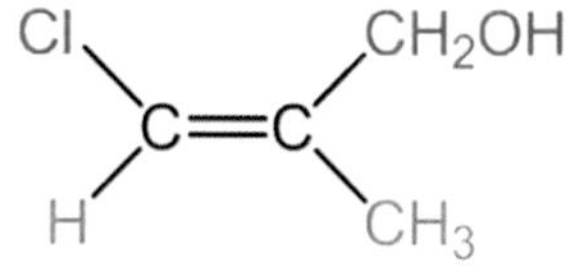

Exercise 2.4H

1. (a)

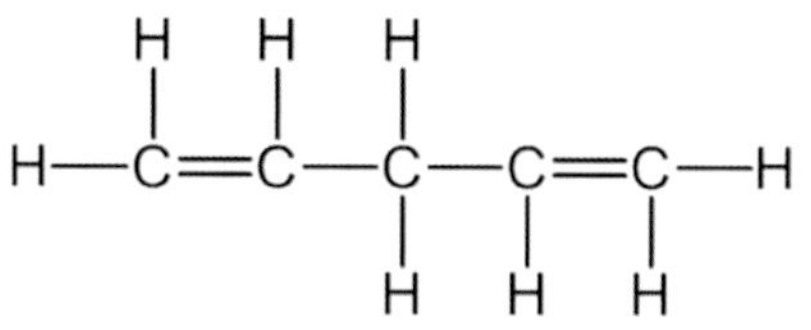

   (b) $C_5H_8 + 2H_2 \rightarrow C_5H_{12}$

(c) (Finely divided) nickel.

2. (a) $C_6H_5CH=CHCH_2OH + H_2 \rightarrow$
$\quad\quad C_6H_5CH_2CH_2CH_2OH$

(b) (Finely divided) nickel.

Exercise 2.4I

1. (a) $CH_2=CHCH_2CH_3 + Cl_2 \rightarrow$
$\quad\quad CH_2ClCHClCH_2CH_3$

(b)

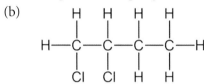

2. (a) $CH_2=CHCH_2CH=CH_2 + 2Br_2 \rightarrow$
$\quad\quad CH_2BrCHBrCH_2CHBrCH_2Br$

(b)

3. (a) Molecular
formula: $C_{10}H_{16}$
Empirical formula:
C_5H_8

(b) The bromine
water is
decolourised and
forms a colourless
solution.

(c)

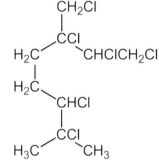

4. C_3H_6

5. C_3H_6

6. 0.25 cm^3

Exercise 2.4J

1. The addition of a molecule or ion seeking electrons across a C=C bond.

2. Answer B

3. (a) The C=C π-bond in an alkene has a high electron density and is weaker than the C-C (σ) bonds in alkanes.

(b) Electrophilic addition.

(c)

4.

Exercise 2.4K

1. (a)

(b) Propenonitrile does not form cis-trans isomers as two hydrogen atoms are bonded to the same end of the C=C bond.

(c)

(d) Addition polymerisation.

2. (a)

(b) Tetrafluoroethene contains a C=C bond.
(c) Addition polymerisation.

3. (a) Addition polymerisation.
(b)

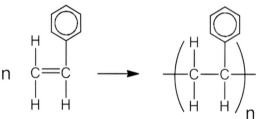

Exercise 2.5A

1. (a)

(b) The C-Br bond is polar because carbon and bromine have different electronegativity values.

2. Boiling point increases in the order: 2-chloropropane, 1-bromopropane, 1-iodopropane as the number of electrons in the molecule increases,

increasing the van der Waals attraction between molecules. The boiling point of 1,1-dichloropropane is greater than the boiling point of 2-chloropropane as the second chlorine atom increases the van der Waals attraction between molecules.

3. The boiling point of 1,2-dichloropropane is greater than the boiling point of 1-chloropropane as the second chlorine atom increases the van der Waals attraction between molecules. The remaining boiling points increase in the order: 1-chloro-2-fluoropropane, 1,2-dichloropropane, 2-bromo-1-chloropropane as the number of electrons in the molecule increases, increasing the van der Waals attraction between molecules.

Exercise 2.5B

1. (a)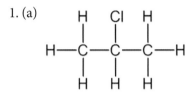

(b) The carbon bonded to chlorine is bonded to two other carbon atoms.

2. (a) primary / secondary

(b) Isomers have the same molecular formula but a different arrangement of atoms.

3. (a)

(b) The carbon bonded to fluorine is bonded to one other carbon atom.

Exercise 2.5C

1. CFC-12 (CCl_2F_2) is dichlorodifluoromethane and CFC-13 ($CClF_3$) is chlorotrifluoromethane.

2. (a) 1,1,1-trichloroethane   (b) 1,1,2-trichloroethane

3. (a) 1-bromo-1,1-dichloroethane

(b) 2-bromo-1,1-dichloroethane

1-bromo-1,2-dichloroethane

4.

Structure	Name	Classification
	1-bromobutane	primary
	2-bromo-2-methylpropane	tertiary
	1-bromo-2-methylpropane	primary
	2-bromobutane	secondary

5. (a) C_4H_9Cl (b) $C_nH_{2n+1}Cl$ (c) 2-chloro-2-methylpropane (d) Secondary. (e) The van der Waals attraction between molecules is weaker in t-butyl chloride as it has a more branched structure.

Exercise 2.5D

1. See Worked Example 2.5iv
2. (a) To remove acidic impurities from the product.
   (b) To remove salts and other water soluble

impurities from the product. (c) To dry the product. (d) To ensure smooth boiling during the distillation process. (e) To release carbon dioxide formed during shaking. (f) 88 %

3. 65 %

Exercise 2.5E

Ammonia, NH_3 has a lone pair of electrons and can form a coordinate bond with an atom seeking electrons. An ammonium ion, NH_4^+ has a positive charge and does not have a lone pair of electrons. It is not attracted to regions of low electron density and cannot form a coordinate bond.

Exercise 2.5F

1.

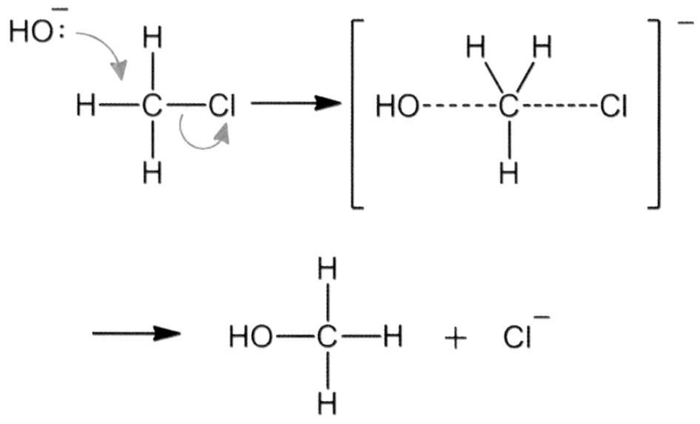

2. Answer C

3. (a) The compounds are isomers as they have the same chemical formula but a different arrangement of atoms.

(b)

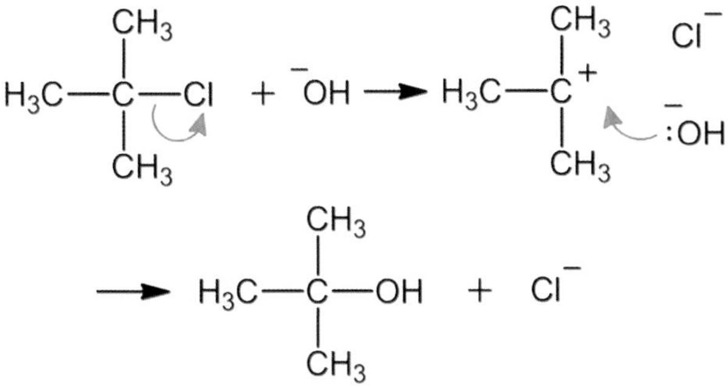

Exercise 2.5G

1. $CH_3CH_2Cl + 2NH_3 \rightarrow CH_3CH_2NH_2 + NH_4Cl$

2.

(a)   (b)

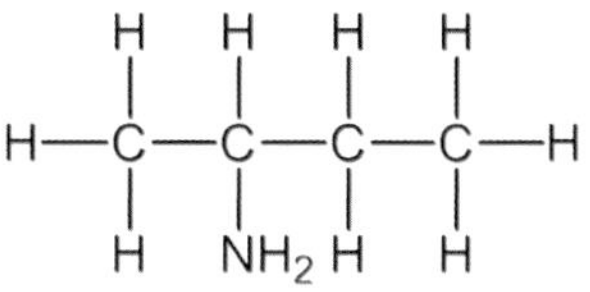

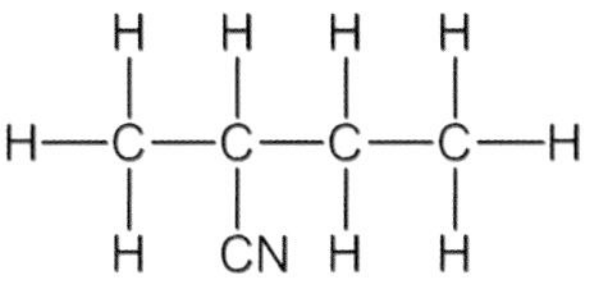

3. (a) $Cl(CH_2)_5Cl + 4NH_3$
$\rightarrow H_2N(CH_2)_5NH_2 + 2NH_4Cl$

(b) Cadaverine is a base.

Exercise 2.5H

$CH_3Cl + D_2O \rightarrow CH_3OD + DCl$

Exercise 2.5I

1. (a) A yellow precipitate forms on heating.

(b) See Worked Example 2.5v

(c) $CH_3CH_2CH_2CH_2Br + H_2O$
$\rightarrow CH_3CH_2CH_2CH_2OH + HBr$
$AgNO_3 + HBr \rightarrow AgBr + HNO_3$

2. The C-Br bond is the weakest carbon-halogen bond and the most likely to be broken when the compound is hydrolysed.

3. The compound t-butyl chloride is a tertiary halogenoalkane. In contrast, n-butyl chloride is a primary halogenoalkane. The hydrolysis of n-butyl chloride is slower as the attraction between water and the primary carbon in n-butyl chloride is weaker than the attraction between water and the carbocation formed when t-butyl chloride undergoes hydrolysis.

Exercise 2.5J

1. (a) $CH_3CH_2CH_2CH_2Br + NaOH$
$\rightarrow CH_3CH_2CH=CH_2 + NaBr + H_2O$

(b) But-1-ene.

(c) Elimination.

2. $CH_3CH_2Br + KOH \rightarrow CH_2=CH_2 + KBr + H_2O$

Bromoethane is refluxed with a solution of potassium hydroxide in ethanol.

Exercise 2.5K

1. (a)   (b)

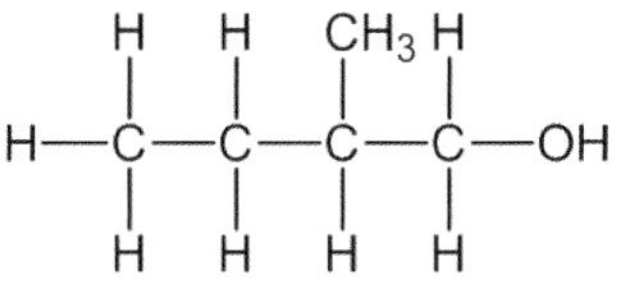

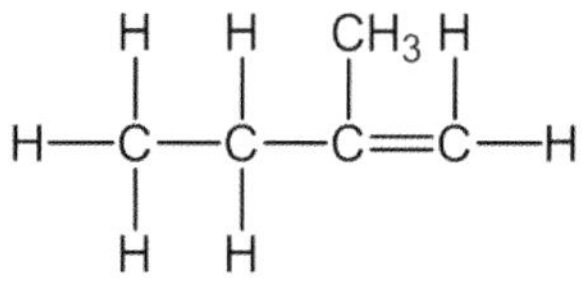

2. Elimination.

Exercise 2.6A

1. (a)

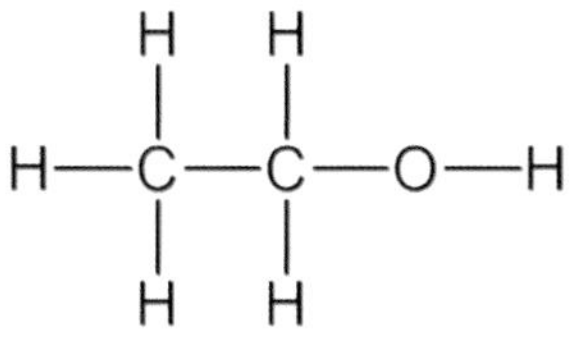

(b) Ethanol can form hydrogen bonds with water.

2. Answer C

3. Ethanol can form hydrogen bonds with water. Ethene does not have a permanent dipole and cannot form hydrogen bonds with water.

4. (a) Ethanol, methanol and water can hydrogen bond with each other. (b) Fractional distillation.

Exercise 2.6B

1. (a) Molecule A is methanol and molecule B is water. (b) A hydrogen bond. (c) Any one of: solubility, melting point, boiling point.

2. Answer B

3. Answer B

Exercise 2.6C

1. (a) The carbon bonded to the hydroxyl group is bonded to one other carbon atom. (b) The hydroxyl groups are able to form hydrogen bonds with water.

2. Answer D

3. (a) Primary (b) Secondary (c) Primary (d) Tertiary

Exercise 2.6D

1.

Structure	Name	Classification
butan-1-ol structure	butan-1-ol	primary
2-methylpropan-2-ol structure	2-methyl propan-2-ol	tertiary
2-methylpropan-1-ol structure	2-methyl propan-1-ol	primary
butan-2-ol structure	butan-2-ol	secondary

2. Answer B

Exercise 2.6E

1. (a) Reacting ethene with steam at high temperature and pressure in the presence of a phosphoric acid catalyst: $C_2H_4 + H_2O \rightarrow C_2H_5OH$. (b) The fermentation of sugars.

2. (a) The respiration of sugars in the absence of oxygen to form ethanol.

(b) $C_6H_{12}O_6 \rightarrow 2C_2H_5OH + 2CO_2$.

3. Answer D

Exercise 2.6F

1. Beneficial effects (any one of): aids relaxation, helps socialisation, prevents heart disease in moderate amounts. Harmful effects (any one of): damage to organs, eg: liver, brain and nervous system, neurological disorders, eg: depression.

2. (a) 0.0196 mol dm^{-3} (b) Any one of: liver, brain.

3. (a) 0.252 mol (b) Harmful effects (any one of): damage to organs eg: liver, brain and nervous system, neurological disorders eg: depression.

Exercise 2.6G

(a) $2CH_3OH + 3O_2 \rightarrow 2CO_2 + 4H_2O$

(b) $CH_3OH + O_2 \rightarrow CO + 2H_2O$

(c) See Worked Example 2.6i

Exercise 2.6H

1. (a) $CH_3CHClCH_3 + KOH \rightarrow$
$CH_3CH(OH)CH_3 + KCl$

(b) propan-2-ol

2. (a) Nucleophilic substitution. (b) The mixture is refluxed in order to increase the yield of product by allowing the reactants to react at a high temperature for an extended period of time.

3. (a) $CH_2ClCH_2Cl + 2NaOH \rightarrow$
$CH_2(OH)CH_2(OH) + 2NaCl$

(b) ethane-1,2-diol

Exercise 2.6I

1. Sodium reacts to form a colourless solution. The reaction produces heat. Bubbles of gas are evolved.

2. (a) $2CH_3CH_2CH_2OH + 2Na \rightarrow$
$2CH_3CH_2CH_2ONa + H_2$ (b) Sodium propoxide.

3. (a) $2C_4H_9OH + 2Na \rightarrow 2C_4H_9ONa + H_2$
(b) 2-methylpropan-2-ol (c) Tertiary.

Exercise 2.6J

1. CH_3CH_2Cl (with PCl_5 and $SOCl_2$)

CH_3CH_2ONa (with Na)

CH_3CH_2Br (with HBr)

2. (a) $CH_3CH_2CH(OH)CH_3 + HBr \rightarrow$

$CH_3CH_2CHBrCH_3 + H_2O$

(b) 20.55 g (c) 17.47 g

3. (a) Butan-1-ol (b) $CH_3CH_2CH_2CH_2OH + PCl_5 \rightarrow$

$CH_3CH_2CH_2CH_2Cl + HCl + POCl_3$

(c) Any two of: pungent gas evolved, heat produced, white solid reacts to form a liquid mixture.

4. $CH_3CH_2OH + SOCl_2 \rightarrow CH_3CH_2Cl + HCl + SO_2$

5. Answer C

6. Answer C

Exercise 2.6K

1. $CH_3CH_2OH + 2[O] \rightarrow CH_3COOH + H_2O$

2. Answer D

Exercise 2.6L

1. (a)   (b)

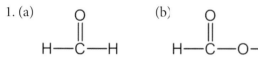

2. (a) Acidified potassium dichromate. (b) Cr^{3+}
   (c) Distillation (d) Reflux

Exercise 2.6M

1. Answer C

2. Answer D

Exercise 2.6N

1. Answer D

2. Propan-1-ol is a primary alcohol and propan-2-ol is a secondary alcohol. They cannot be distinguished as both isomers will be oxidised and will turn dichromate from orange to green.

3. Place samples of the alcohols in separate test tubes. Add acidified permanganate to each alcohol and warm gently. The mixture containing pentan-3-ol will turn from purple to colourless when heated. The mixture containing 2-methylbutan-2-ol will remain purple when heated.

4. Place a sample of Gasohol in a test tube. Add acidified dichromate and gently warm the mixture. The ethanol in the mixture will be oxidised and will turn the mixture from orange to green.

Exercise 2.6O

1. $CH_3COOH + C_5H_{11}OH \rightleftharpoons CH_3COOC_5H_{11} + H_2O$

2. (a) The concentrated acid acts as a catalyst and

increases the yield by absorbing water formed in the reaction.

(b)

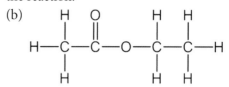

(c) The ester is ethyl ethanoate.

3. Answer D

4. Answer D

Exercise 2.6P

1. (a) Esterification. (b) Ethanoyl chloride.

2. (a) Ethanoyl chloride. (b) $CH_3COCl + CH_3CH_2OH$
   $\rightarrow CH_3COOCH_2CH_3 + HCl$

3. Answer D

4. Answer B

5. Answer C

Exercise 2.6Q

1. CH_3CH_2Cl (with PCl_5)

   CH_3CH_2ONa (with Na)

   $CH_3COOCH_2CH_3$ (with CH_3COCl)

   CH_3COOH (with $H^+/Cr_2O_7^{2-}$)

2. $CH_2BrCOOH$ (with HBr)

   CH_3COOCH_2COOH (with CH_3COOH)

   $OHCCOOH$ (with $H^+/Cr_2O_7^{2-}$)

   and then $HOOCCOOH$ (with $H^+/Cr_2O_7^{2-}$)

Exercise 2.6R

(a) 0.0034 mol (b) 0.0022 mol (c) 0.0012 mol (d) 55 %

Exercise 2.6S

1. Dissolve solid iodine in a sample of each alcohol. The brown colour of the iodine solution is replaced by a yellow suspension of iodoform on adding sodium hydroxide solution to the mixture containing B. The mixture containing A remains brown on adding sodium hydroxide solution.

2. Answer C

3. (a) $-CH(OH)CH_3$ (b) Dissolve solid iodine in an excess of the alcohol before adding sodium hydroxide solution. If the alcohol gives a positive result the brown colour of the iodine solution will be replaced by a yellow suspension of iodoform.

4. Answer C

5. Answer B

Exercise 2.7A

Answer D.

Exercise 2.7B

1. Compound A is ethanoic acid, B is ethyl ethanoate and C is ethanol.

2. (a) Molecules absorb infra-red radiation by using the energy from the radiation to vibrate. (b) Compound A: C-H absorbs at 3000 cm^{-1} and O-H (alcohol) absorbs at 3400 cm^{-1}. Compound B: C=O absorbs at 1700 cm^{-1}. (c) Compound B is ethanoic acid and compound C is ethanal.

Exercise 2.8A

1.

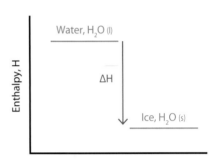

Reaction progress

2. (a) The term endothermic refers to a reaction in which the enthalpy of the products is greater than the enthalpy of the reactants.

(b)

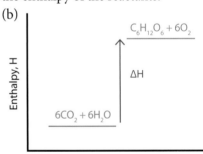

Reaction progress

3. (a) The term exothermic refers to a reaction in which the enthalpy of the products is less than the enthalpy of the reactants.

(b)

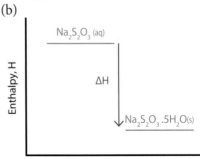

Reaction progress

Exercise 2.8B

1. Bromine is a liquid under standard conditions. The formula for the standard state of bromine is $Br_{2\ (l)}$.

2. Hydrogen is a diatomic gas under standard conditions. The formula for the standard state of hydrogen is $H_{2\ (g)}$.

Exercise 2.8C

1. (a) $\Delta H = -m\ c\ \Delta T = -100 \times 4.2 \times (-0.9) = 378$ J

(b) Molar enthalpy change $= \dfrac{0.378\ kJ}{0.0625\ mol} = 6.05$ kJ mol^{-1}

(c) Mass needed $= 5\ g \times \dfrac{25\ ^\circ C}{0.9\ ^\circ C} \times \dfrac{120\ g}{100\ g} = 166.7$ g

2. Add a known amount of water to an insulated container such as a polystyrene cup and measure the temperature of the water with a thermometer. Add a known amount of magnesium sulfate to the water and stir with a glass rod to dissolve. Measure the temperature of the solution with a thermometer after the salt has completely dissolved. A major source of error is heat loss. Heat loss can be minimised by putting a lid on the cup and reducing drafts around the cup.

3. (a) $KOH + HCl \rightarrow KCl + H_2O$

(b) Wear eye protection. Add a known amount of potassium hydroxide solution to an insulated container and measure the temperature of the solution with a thermometer. Add an excess of hydrochloric acid to the potassium hydroxide and stir briefly with a glass rod to mix. Measure the temperature of the solution with a thermometer. A major source of error is heat loss. Heat loss can be minimised by putting a lid on the cup and reducing drafts.

Exercise 2.8D

1. (a) The energy required to break one mole of bonds of a specified type.
(b) i) Bond enthalpy for products =
        16(750) + 18(463) = 20334 kJ
    ii) ΔH = 16548 – 20334 = –3786 kJ

2. (a) Bond enthalpy of reactants =
        4(413) + 243 = 1895 kJ
    Bond enthalpy of products =
        3(413) + 346 + 432 = 2017 kJ
    ΔH = 1895 - 2017 = –122 kJ

(b)

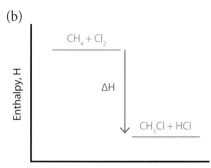

Reaction progress

(c) The bond enthalpies used to calculate ΔH are averaged over many compounds and are not specific to the compounds in the reaction.

3. (a) The energy needed to break one mole of bonds of a specified type averaged over many compounds.

(b) Bond enthalpy of reactants = 4 E(C-H) + 2(496) kJ
   Bond enthalpy of products =
      2(743) + 4(463) = 3338 kJ
      ΔH = 4E(C-H) + 992 – 3338 = –698
      E(C-H) = 412 kJ

4. Bond enthalpy of reactants =
      612 + 4(412) + 3(497) = 3751 kJ
   Bond enthalpy of products =
      4(803) + 4(464) = 5068 kJ
      ΔH = 3751 – 5068 = –1317 kJ

5. Bond enthalpy of reactants =
      347 + 5(413) + 360 + 464 + 3(498) = 4730 kJ
   Bond enthalpy of products =
      4(805) + 6(464) = 6004 kJ
      ΔH = 4730 – 6004 = –1274 kJ

6. (a) Bond enthalpy of reactants =
      12(391) + 3(498) = 6186 kJ
   Bond enthalpy of products =
      2(945) + 12(464) = 7458 kJ
      ΔH = 6186 – 7458 = –1272 kJ
   Enthalpy change per mole of ammonia =
      –1272 ÷ 4 = –318 kJ mol^{-1}

(b) The reaction is exothermic because the energy needed to break bonds is less than the energy produced by making bonds.

7. Bond enthalpy of reactants =
      293 + 6(389) + 6(158) = 3575 kJ
   Bond enthalpy of products =
      6(566) + 6(627) = 7158 kJ
      ΔH = 3575 – 7158 = –3583 kJ

Exercise 2.8E

1. Answer D

2. Answer D
3. Answer D
4. Answer D

Exercise 2.8F

1. (a) $H_2 + F_2 \rightarrow 2HF$ $\Delta H = 2 \Delta H_f^\circ(HF)$
      ΔH = 594 - 1136 = –542 kJ
      $\Delta H_f^\circ(HF)$ = –271 kJ

(b)

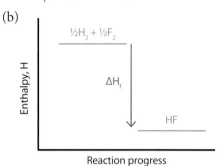

Reaction progress

2. ΔH = 2 × 46.2 = 92.4 kJ

Exercise 2.8G

1. (a) The enthalpy change when one mole of a substance is completely burnt in oxygen under standard conditions.

(b) ΔH_f° (products) = (–394) + 2(– 286) = –966 kJ
   ΔH_f° (reactants) = –75 + 2(0) = –75 kJ
   $\Delta H_c^\circ = \Delta H_f^\circ$ (products) – ΔH_f° (reactants) = –891 kJ mol^{-1}

2. (a) $C_{12}H_{26} + \dfrac{37}{2}O_2 \rightarrow 12CO_2 + 13H_2O$

(b)

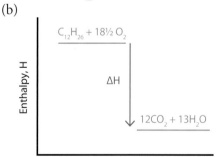

Reaction progress

(c) The enthalpy of the products is less than the enthalpy of the reactants. The enthalpy difference is released as heat.

3. (a) The enthalpy change when one mole of substance is formed from its elements under standard conditions.

(b) ΔH_f° (products) = –1273 + 6(0) = –1273 kJ
   ΔH_f° (reactants) = 6(–394) + 6(–286) = –4080 kJ
   $\Delta H_c^\circ = \Delta H_f^\circ$ (products) – ΔH_f° (reactants) = 2807 kJ mol^{-1}

Exercise 2.8H

1.

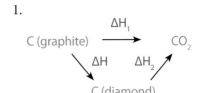

$$\Delta H = \Delta H_1 - \Delta H_2 = -393.5 - (-395.4) = +1.9 \text{ kJ mol}^{-1}$$

2.

$$MgSO_{4\,(s)} \xrightarrow{\Delta H_1} MgSO_{4\,(aq)}$$
$$\searrow^{\Delta H} \quad \nearrow^{\Delta H_2}$$
$$MgSO_4.7H_2O_{(s)}$$

$$\Delta H_1 = -m\,c\,\Delta T = -100 \times 4.2 \times 9 = -3780 \text{ J}$$

$$\Delta H_1 = -3.78 \text{ kJ} \times \frac{1}{0.10 \text{ mol}} = -37.8 \text{ kJ mol}^{-1}$$

$$\Delta H_2 = -m\,c\,\Delta T = -100 \times 4.2 \times (-3) = 1260 \text{ J}$$

$$\Delta H_2 = 1.26 \text{ kJ} \times \frac{1}{0.10 \text{ mol}} = 12.6 \text{ kJ mol}^{-1}$$

$$\Delta H = \Delta H_1 - \Delta H_2 = -37.8 - 12.6 = -50.4 \text{ kJ mol}^{-1}$$

3. (a) The enthalpy change when one mole of a substance is completely burnt in oxygen under standard conditions.

(b) The enthalpy change for a reaction depends on the state of the reactants and products and does not depend on how the reaction was carried out.

(c)

$$C_8H_{18\,(l)} + 12\tfrac{1}{2}O_{2\,(g)} \xrightarrow{\Delta H^\ominus_c} 8CO_{2\,(g)} + 9H_2O_{(l)}$$
$$\nwarrow^{\Delta H^\ominus_1} \quad \nearrow^{\Delta H^\ominus_2}$$
Elements in standard state: C $_{(s)}$ H$_2$ $_{(g)}$ O$_2$ $_{(g)}$

Hess' law: $\Delta H^\ominus_1 + \Delta H^\ominus_c = \Delta H^\ominus_2$

$\Delta H^\ominus_1 = -250.0 \text{ kJ}$ and $\Delta H^\ominus_2 = 8(-393.5) + 9(-286.0) = -5722 \text{ kJ}$

$\Delta H^\ominus_c = \Delta H^\ominus_2 - \Delta H^\ominus_1 = -5472 \text{ kJ mol}^{-1}$

4.

$$C_2H_{2\,(g)} + 2\tfrac{1}{2}O_{2\,(g)} \xrightarrow{\Delta H^\ominus_2} 2CO_{2\,(g)} + H_2O_{(l)}$$
$$\nwarrow^{\Delta H^\ominus_1} \quad \nearrow^{\Delta H^\ominus_3}$$
Elements in standard state: C $_{(s)}$ H$_2$ $_{(g)}$ O$_2$ $_{(g)}$

Hess's Law: $\Delta H^\ominus_1 + \Delta H^\ominus_2 = \Delta H^\ominus_3$

where $\Delta H^\ominus_1 = \Delta H^\ominus_f(C_2H_2)$, $\Delta H^\ominus_2 = -1300 \text{ kJ}$

and $\Delta H^\ominus_3 = 2(-394) + (-286) = -1074 \text{ kJ}$

$\Delta H^\ominus_f(C_2H_2) = \Delta H^\ominus_3 - \Delta H^\ominus_2 = +226 \text{ kJ mol}^{-1}$

5.

$$CH_3COOH_{(l)} + 2O_{2\,(g)} \xrightarrow{\Delta H^\ominus_2} 2CO_{2\,(g)} + 2H_2O_{(l)}$$
$$\nwarrow^{\Delta H^\ominus_1} \quad \nearrow^{\Delta H^\ominus_3}$$
Elements in standard state: C $_{(s)}$ H$_2$ $_{(g)}$ O$_2$ $_{(g)}$

Hess's Law: $\Delta H^\ominus_1 + \Delta H^\ominus_2 = \Delta H^\ominus_3$

where $\Delta H^\ominus_1 = \Delta H^\ominus_f(CH_3COOH)$, $\Delta H^\ominus_2 = -487 \text{ kJ}$

and $\Delta H^\ominus_3 = 2(-393) + 2(-286) = -1358 \text{ kJ}$

$\Delta H^\ominus_f(C_2H_2) = \Delta H^\ominus_3 - \Delta H^\ominus_2 = -871 \text{ kJ mol}^{-1}$

6. (a) The enthalpy change for a reaction depends on the state of the reactants and products and does not depend on how the reaction was carried out.

(b)

$$2NaHCO_{3\,(s)} \xrightarrow{\Delta H_1} Na_2CO_{3\,(s)} + H_2O_{(l)} + CO_{2\,(g)}$$
$$\searrow^{\Delta H_3} \quad \swarrow^{\Delta H_2}$$
$$2NaCl_{(aq)} + 2H_2O_{(l)} + 2CO_{2\,(g)}$$

Hess's Law: $\Delta H_3 = \Delta H_1 + \Delta H_2$

$\Delta H_1 = \Delta H_3 - \Delta H_2 = (2 \times 16) - (-21) = +53 \text{ kJ}$

Exercise 2.9A

The rate at which NO_2 forms N_2O_4 is the same as the rate at which N_2O_4 forms NO_2. The composition of the reaction mixture remains constant.

Exercise 2.9B

1. The forward reaction is exothermic ($\Delta H < 0$). Increasing the temperature shifts the position of equilibrium to the left by using the reverse reaction (endothermic) to reduce the amount of methanol.

2. The position of equilibrium shifts to the right by using the forward reaction to absorb heat (endothermic) when the temperature is increased.

3. (a) Ammonia is present at A. (b) Hydrogen chloride is present at B. (c) To separate the gases. (d) The forward reaction is endothermic. The position of equilibrium shifts to the right as the equilibrium uses the forward reaction (endothermic) to absorb heat.

4. Answer C.

5. (a) The rate of the forward and reverse reactions are the same. As a result the composition of the reaction mixture does not change. (b) The yield of NO_2 increases as the equilibrium uses the forward reaction to reduce the molecules of gas at equilibrium. (c) The yield of NO_2 decreases as the equilibrium uses the reverse reaction (endothermic) to absorb heat. (d) Adding a catalyst speeds up the forward and reverse reactions but has no effect on the composition of the equilibrium.

6. (a) The silver acts as a catalyst. (b) Increasing the pressure shifts the position of the equilibrium to the right increasing the yield of ethylene oxide. (c) The (forward) reaction must be endothermic. The yield of ethylene oxide would increase as the forward reaction (endothermic) is used to absorb heat.

7. (a) The position of equilibrium shifts to the left as the reverse reaction is used to absorb heat. (b) Increasing pressure has no effect as changing the position of equilibrium has no effect on the amount of gas in the mixture. (c) Adding a catalyst speeds up the rate of the forward and reverse reactions but has no effect on the position of equilibrium.

Exercise 2.9C

1. (a) 450 °C, 250 atm (b) The temperature is a compromise between increasing the yield at lower temperatures and increasing the rate at higher temperatures.

2. (a) $N_2 + 3H_2 \rightleftharpoons 2NH_3$ (b) Iron (c) The equilibrium uses the forward reaction (exothermic) to produce heat as the temperature decreases and reduce the molecules of gas at equilibrium as the pressure increases.

3. The (forward) reaction is exothermic. The reverse reaction (endothermic) shifts the position of equilibrium to the left as the temperature is increased.

Exercise 2.9D

1. Answer C.

2. (a) Increasing the pressure increases the yield of sulfur trioxide as the position of equilibrium shifts to the right to reduce the amount of gas in the equilibrium. (b) A moderate temperature is used to maintain a reasonable rate and avoid lower yields at high temperatures.

Exercise 2.10A

1. Answer C

2. (a) See (b) for labels. The area under the curve represents the number of molecules in the mixture.

(b)

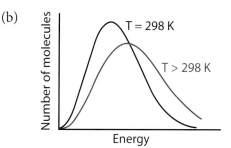

3. (a) See (b) for labels. The curve starts at the origin because all of the molecules have energy and are moving.

(b)

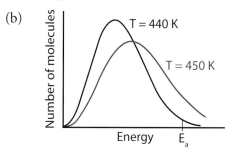

(c) The number of molecules with energy greater than the activation energy, E_a decreases as the temperature is decreased.

4. Answer D.

5.

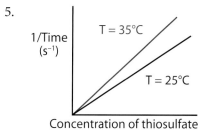

The rate is greater at a higher temperature because the particles have more energy and there are more successful collisions per second.

Exercise 2.10B

1. A catalyst increases the rate of reaction by providing an alternative reaction pathway with lower activation energy.

2. The platinum catalyst increases the rate of reaction by providing an alternative reaction pathway with lower activation energy.

Exercise 2.10C

1. (a) The activation energy is the minimum amount of energy needed for the reaction to occur.
(b) Most collisions involve molecules whose energy is less than the activation energy.

273

(c)

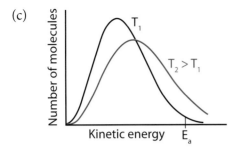

(d) A greater number of collisions involve molecules with at least the activation energy at a higher temperature.

2. (a) All of the molecules are moving. (b) There is no limit to the amount of energy a molecule can have. (c) The number of molecules with at least the activation energy. (d) A catalyst lowers the activation energy with the result that more molecules have at least the activation energy.

3. (a) The number of particles with at least the activation energy.

(b)

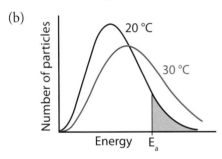

The rate is faster at 30 °C because more particles have an energy of at least the activation energy.

4.

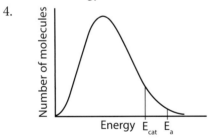

Exercise 2.10D

1. Answer D.

2. Answer A.

Exercise 2.10E

1. The catalyst alters the reaction pathway by lowering the activation energy from E_a to E_{cat}.

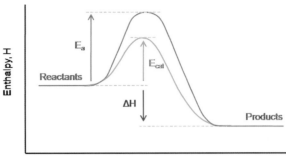

Reaction progress

2. Reducing the size of the metal particles increases the size of the metal surface, increasing the area on which the reaction occurs.

....

Exercise 2.11A

1. (a) Outermost electrons in s-type subshell. (b) $Mg_{(g)} \rightarrow Mg^+_{(g)} + e^-$ (c) IE1 decreases down the group as the outermost electrons are further from the nucleus and better shielded.

2. (a) The Group II metals are very reactive. (b) $(1s)^2(2s)^2(2p)^6(3s)^2(3p)^6(4s)^2$ (c) The number of filled shells increases down the group. (d) The Group II metals are smaller due to a greater nuclear charge. (e) 0.224 nm (f) Barium atoms have a greater atomic mass than strontium atoms and occupy a similar volume.

3. Answer D.

Exercise 2.11B

1. (a) Calcium sinks because it has a greater density than water. (b) Any 2 of: the amount of metal decreases, bubbles of gas are produced, the reaction produces heat, a white solid is formed in the solution.

(c) $Ca_{(s)} + 2H_2O_{(l)} \rightarrow Ca(OH)_{2\ (aq)} + H_{2\ (g)}$

(d)

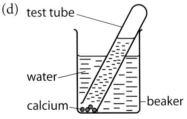

2. (a) Both metals form a white solid when they burn in air. Burning magnesium produces intense white light. Calcium turns the flame a brick red colour when it burns. (b) Calcium reacts quickly. Heat and bubbles of gas are produced as the amount of metal decreases. A white solid forms in the solution. Magnesium reacts very slowly. (c) Both metals react

quickly. Heat and bubbles of gas are produced as the amount of metal decreases.

Exercise 2.11C

Answer C.

Exercise 2.11D

1. (a) A compound is basic if it can neutralise an acid/accept a proton (H^+ ion). (b) $CaO + H_2O \rightarrow Ca(OH)_2$ (c) 0.39 g (d) $Ca(OH)_2 + 2HCl \rightarrow CaCl_2 + 2H_2O$

2. (a) $BaCO_3 + 2HCl \rightarrow BaCl_2 + H_2O + CO_2$ (b) A cloudy white suspension is formed. (c) 80.4 cm^3

3. (a) Add solid calcium hydroxide to water with stirring until no more dissolves then filter the solution. Bubble carbon dioxide through the limewater. Formation of a cloudy white suspension indicates that the gas was carbon dioxide. (b) $Ca(OH)_{2\,(aq)} + CO_{2\,(g)} \rightarrow CaCO_{3\,(s)} + H_2O_{(l)}$ (c) 0.24%

4. (a) $SrO + 2HCl \rightarrow SrCl_2 + H_2O$ (b) Boil the solution to remove most of the water. Leave the solution for crystals to form. Filter to remove the crystals then dry the crystals between two pieces of filter paper.

5. (a) $CaCO_3 + 2HCl \rightarrow CaCl_2 + H_2O + CO_2$ (b) 3.42 dm^3

6. (a) Any one of: amount of solid decreases, bubbles of colourless gas produced. (b) $CaCO_3.MgCO_3 + 4HCl \rightarrow CaCl_2 + MgCl_2 + 2H_2O + 2CO_2$ (c) Brick red.

Exercise 2.11E

1. Answer C.

2. (a) $CaCO_3 \rightarrow CaO + CO_2$ (b) The decomposition temperature would be less for $MgCO_3$ because the Mg^{2+} ion is smaller, has a greater charge density, and is more able to destabilise the carbonate ions by polarising the bonds within the carbonate ions.

3. (a) $Ca(OH)_2 \rightarrow CaO + H_2O$ (b) Magnesium hydroxide is less thermally stable because the Mg^{2+} ion is smaller, has a greater charge density, and is more able to destabilise the carbonate ions by polarising the bonds within the carbonate ions.

4. (a) 95.6 % (b) $CaSO_4 \rightarrow CaO + SO_3$ (c) The Group II sulfates become more thermally stable as the metal ion gets bigger down the group. The larger metal ions towards the bottom of the group have a lower charge density and are less able to destabilise the carbonate ions by polarising the bonds within the carbonate ions.

5. (a) $BaCO_3 \rightarrow BaO + CO_2$ (b) Barium carbonate is more thermally stable because the Ba^{2+} ion is larger, has a smaller charge density, and is less able to destabilise carbonate ions by polarising the bonds within the carbonate ions. (c) $BaCO_3 + C \rightarrow BaO + 2CO$.

Exercise 2.11F

1. Answer C.

2. The Group II hydroxides become more soluble down the group. Barium hydroxide is more soluble and gives a higher pH.

3. (a) $Ba(OH)_2 + 2HNO_3 \rightarrow Ba(NO_3)_2 + 2H_2O$ (b) The barium sulfate formed is insoluble.

4. (a) Magnesium sulfate is more soluble. The decrease in hydration enthalpy on going from magnesium to calcium is greater than the decrease in lattice enthalpy making the enthalpy of solution for calcium sulfate less exothermic. (b) $Ca^{2+}_{(aq)} + CO_3^{2-}_{(aq)} \rightarrow CaCO_{3\,(s)}$

5. Answer C.

6. Answer D.

Exercise 2.12A

1. A glowing splint will relight when it comes into contact with oxygen gas.

2. Bring the gas into contact with a glass rod dipped in concentrated hydrochloric acid. White fumes of solid ammonium chloride are formed when fumes from the acid come into contact with ammonia.

3.

Gas	Test	Observation
Hydrogen	*Burning splint*	*Burns with a 'pop'*
Sulfur dioxide	*Acidified potassium permanganate solution*	*Purple solution is decolourised*
Hydrogen chloride	*Glass rod dipped in concentrated ammonia*	*White fumes of ammonium chloride*

Exercise 2.12B

Add dilute sodium hydroxide solution and gently heat the mixture. White fumes form when the ammonia produced by the reaction contacts the fumes from a glass rod dipped in concentrated hydrochloric acid.

Exercise 2.12C

(a) Ammonia solution. (b) Adding a few drops of ammonia solution produces a blue precipitate. The precipitate dissolves to form a dark blue solution on adding ammonia solution.

Exercise 2.12D

(a) Dilute sodium hydroxide solution. (b) Aqueous potassium thiocyanate. (c) If iron(III) is present the solution turns a blood red colour.

Exercise 2.12E

1. Both solutions give a white precipitate on adding a few drops of aqueous sodium hydroxide solution. The precipitate formed by aluminium dissolves to form a colourless solution on adding sodium hydroxide solution. The precipitate formed by magnesium remains on adding sodium hydroxide solution.
2. Answer C.

Exercise 2.12F

1. Both solutions give a white precipitate on adding a few drops of aqueous ammonia. The precipitate formed by zinc dissolves to form a colourless solution on adding ammonia solution. The precipitate formed by aluminium remains on adding ammonia solution.
2. Answer D.
3. Answer A.

Exercise 2.12G

A is copper sulfate, B is sulfuric acid, C is sodium chromate and D is potassium sulfate.

Exercise 2.12H

1. Add dilute hydrochloric acid to the solid. Collect the gas evolved using a pipette and bubble the gas through limewater. If the limewater turns cloudy white the gas is carbon dioxide and the solid contains carbonate or hydrogencarbonate ions.
2. Dissolve the solid in water. Adding a solution containing magnesium ions will produce a white precipitate if the solution contains carbonate. The solution will remain colourless if hydrogencarbonate ions are present.
3. (a) Calcium ion is confirmed by performing a flame test. Calcium produces a brick red flame. (b) Carbonate ion is confirmed by the production of a gas that turns limewater a cloudy white colour when the solid reacts with dilute acid.

Exercise 2.12I

1. Dissolve the solid in water. Add dilute nitric acid followed by several drops of silver nitrate solution. Formation of a white precipitate confirms that chloride is present. A yellow precipitate confirms that iodide is present.
2. Silver chloride will dissolve in dilute or concentrated ammonia solution to form a colourless solution. Silver iodide is insoluble in dilute and concentrated ammonia solution.

Exercise 3A

1.

Experiment	Observations	Deductions
Make a solution of X by dissolving half a spatula measure of X in a test tube half-full of water. Transfer 1 cm³ of the solution into each of two separate test tubes.	Colourless solution formed.	
(a) Add a few drops of sodium hydroxide solution to the first test tube then add a further 10 cm³ of sodium hydroxide solution.	White precipitate formed. Precipitate dissolves in excess sodium hydroxide.	Possibly magnesium, zinc or aluminium ion present. Possibly zinc or aluminium ion present.

(b) Add a few drops of ammonia solution to the second test tube then add a further 5 cm³ of ammonia solution.	White precipitate formed. Precipitate dissolves in excess ammonia.	 Confirms the presence of zinc ion.

2.

Experiment	Observations	Deductions
(a) Make a solution of A by dissolving half a spatula measure of A in a test tube one-third full of water.	Blue solution formed.	
(b) Add a few drops of dilute ammonia to the test tube.	Blue precipitate formed.	Copper(II) ions present.
(c) Add an excess of dilute ammonia to the same test tube.	Precipitate dissolves in excess ammonia. Dark blue solution formed.	 Confirms the presence of copper(II) ions.

Exercise 3B

1.

Experiment	Observations	Deductions
1. Place 10 drops of B in a test tube and add 1 cm³ of water.	Liquid B mixes completely with water to form a colourless solution.	Liquid B is miscible with water. Liquid B is able to form hydrogen bonds with water. Liquid B contains an -OH group or a -COOH group.
2. Place 10 drops of B on a watch glass placed on a heat proof mat and ignite it using a splint.	Liquid B burns with a clean blue flame.	Liquid B has a low carbon content. Liquid B is saturated and does not contain a C=C bond.
3. Add approximately 10 drops of B to a test tube one quarter full of bromine water and mix well.	The orange colour of bromine remains when the liquids mix.	Confirms that B does not contain a C=C bond and is not an alkene.
4. Add 10 drops of B to 2 cm³ of acidified potassium dichromate solution in a test tube. Warm the mixture gently.	The colour of the mixture changes from orange to green during heating. The mixture has a different smell after heating.	Liquid B is a primary or secondary alcohol. Liquid B is oxidised to form the corresponding aldehyde or ketone.

2.

Experiment	Observations	Deductions
1. Describe the solution and place a few drops on a piece of Universal Indicator paper.	Colourless solution. Turns Universal Indicator paper green.	Neutral solution. Liquid B is not a carboxylic acid.
In a fume cupboard: 2. Shake a small volume of the solution with bromine water.	The orange colour of bromine remains when the liquids mix.	Liquid B does not contain a C=C bond. Liquid B is not an alkene.
3. Gently heat 2 cm³ of the solution with 2 cm³ of acidified potassium dichromate solution.	The colour of the mixture changes from orange to green during heating. The mixture has a different smell after heating.	Liquid B is a primary or secondary alcohol. Liquid B is oxidised to form the corresponding aldehyde or ketone.

Exercise 3C

Experiment	Observations	Deductions
Place 1 cm3 of X, Y and Z separately into three test tubes. Label the test tubes with their contents. Add 1 cm³ of ethanol and 1 cm³ of silver nitrate solution to each test tube. Place the three test tubes in a beaker of water heated to 50–60 °C. Leave for 5 minutes and note the relative rate of reaction.	X Yellow precipitate formed. Fastest reaction.	X Iodide ion is formed in the reaction. The compound contains the weakest carbon-halogen bond. The sample is 1-iodobutane.
	Y White precipitate formed. Very slow reaction. Last precipitate to form.	Y Chloride ion is formed in the reaction. The compound contains the strongest carbon-halogen bond. The sample is 1-chlorobutane.
	Z Cream precipitate formed. Slow reaction. Second precipitate formed.	Z Bromide ion is formed in the reaction. The compound contains the second strongest carbon-halogen bond. The sample is 1-bromobutane.

Exercise 3D

See Worked Example 3vi for answers to (a)–(e)

(f) (i) 3.78 g (ii) 0.21 mol

(iii) 0.030 mol (iv) $ZnSO_4.7H_2O$

Glossary

Important note: Definitions that are not included in the CCEA specification are indicated by grey text. Definitions in black text were consistent with the specification at the time of going to press. However, as the specification can change with time, candidates should always refer to the most recent set of definitions from CCEA and give them precedence in the event of of any discrepancies.

1.1 Formulas, Equations and Amounts of Substance

Elements and Compounds

- An **atom** is the smallest amount of an element.
- An **element** is a pure substance that contains one type of atom.
- A **molecule** contains two or more atoms bonded together to form a single uncharged particle.
- A **molecular material** is an element, compound or mixture composed of molecules.
- A **diatomic element** is an element made up of diatomic molecules.
- A **diatomic molecule** is a molecule that contains two atoms.
- An **allotrope** is one physical form of an element.
- A **monatomic element** is an element made up of particles that each contain a single atom.
- A **compound** is a pure substance that contains two or more elements bonded together.
- An **ionic compound** is made of ions held together by attractive forces between oppositely charged ions.

Chemical Formulas

- The **chemical formula** of a substance defines the relative amount of each element in the substance and is the smallest amount of substance that can participate in a chemical reaction.
- The **valency** of an element represents the ability of the element to combine with other elements when forming compounds.

Naming Compounds

- A **cation** is an ion with a positive charge.
- An **anion** is an ion with a negative charge.
- A **polyatomic ion** is an ion containing two or more atoms bonded together.

Chemical Equations

- A **chemical equation** relates the amounts of substance that react and the amounts of products formed in a chemical change.
- A **state symbol** represents the physical state of a substance under the specified conditions.

Aqueous Solutions

- An **aqueous solution** is a solution containing one or more substances dissolved in water.
- An **acid** is a substance that produces hydrogen ions in solution.
- An **alkali** is a soluble base that produces hydroxide ions in solution.
- A **base** is a substance that reacts with an acid to form a salt, water and possibly carbon dioxide.

Ionic Equations

- An **ionic equation** contains only those compounds and ions needed to describe the change that occurs during a chemical reaction.
- The term **precipitate** refers to an insoluble solid formed in solution by a chemical reaction.
- The term **precipitation** refers to any chemical reaction in which a precipitate is formed.
- The term **spectator ion** refers to an ion that is present in a reaction mixture but does not participate in the reaction.
- The term **neutralisation** refers to any chemical reaction in which an acid reacts with a base to form a salt, water and possibly carbon dioxide.

Amounts of Substances

- One **mole** of a substance contains Avogadro's number of formulas of the substance.
- The **molar mass** of a substance is the mass of one mole of the substance in grams.
- The **relative formula mass (RFM)** of a substance is the sum of the relative atomic masses for the atoms in one formula of the substance.

Calculating Reacting Masses

- A reactant **is limiting** (a **limiting reactant**) if the amount of product formed is determined by how much of the reactant is present.
- A reactant is **in excess** if some of the reactant remains after the reaction is complete.

Salts Containing Water

- **Water of crystallisation** refers to water molecules that are chemically bonded within a substance.

- A **hydrated salt** is a salt that contains water of crystallisation.
- An **anhydrous salt** is a salt that does not contain water of crystallisation.
- The technique of **heating to constant mass** is used to remove water from a substance by a process of repeated heating and weighing until the mass of substance remains constant.

1.2 Atomic Structure

Atoms Ions and Isotopes

- The **atomic number** is the number of protons in the nucleus of an atom.
- An **ion** is a charged particle containing one or more atoms.
- An **isotope** is an atom with the same number of protons and a different number of neutrons.
- The **mass number** of an isotope is the total number of protons and neutrons in one atom of the isotope.
- The **relative isotopic mass (RIM)** of an isotope is the mass of one atom of the isotope relative to one-twelfth of the mass of one atom of carbon-12.
- **Avogadro's number** is the number of atoms in exactly 12 g of carbon-12.
- The **relative atomic mass (RAM)** of an element is the average mass of one atom of the element relative to one-twelfth of the mass of an atom of carbon-12.
- The **mass spectrum** of a substance is the relative abundance of each fragment obtained by ionising the substance.
- The **relative molecular mass (RMM)** of a molecule is the mass of the molecule relative to one-twelfth of the mass of an atom of carbon-12.
- A **molecular ion** is an ion formed by removing electrons from a molecule.

Atomic Structure

- An **atomic orbital** is a region of space within an atom that can be occupied by up to two electrons.
- A **shell** consists of atomic orbitals grouped to form one or more subshells.
- A **subshell** is a set of atomic orbitals with the same properties.
- A **multielectron atom** is an atom containing two or more electrons.

- The **electron configuration** of an atom or ion describes the distribution of the electrons amongst the subshells in the atom or ion.
- The **Aufbau principle** asserts that the electron configuration with the lowest energy is obtained by filling the atomic orbitals in order of increasing energy.
- The **ground state** of an atom or ion is the electron configuration in which the electrons occupy the lowest available energy levels.
- The **spin** of an electron describes the arrangement of an electron within an atomic orbital.
- The **first ionisation energy** of an atom is the energy needed to remove one mole of electrons from one mole of gaseous atoms to form one mole of gaseous ions with a single positive charge.
- The **shielding** experienced by an electron is the reduction in attraction to the nucleus due to repulsion by electrons in shells closer to the nucleus.

Atomic Spectroscopy

- The **wavelength** of electromagnetic radiation is the distance between adjacent crests/troughs of the wave.
- The **frequency** of electromagnetic radiation is the number of waves passing a point every second.
- The **Balmer series** is a series of wavelengths resulting from electron transitions to the n=2 shell in the hydrogen emission spectrum.
- The **Lyman series** is a series of wavelengths resulting from electron transitions to the n=1 shell in the hydrogen emission spectrum
- The **convergence limit** is the point in an emission series at which the energy spacing between the electron shells becomes zero.
- A **flame test** is a procedure to identify the presence of a metal ion in a compound by observing the colour of light emitted when the compound is placed in a blue flame.

1.3 Bonding and Structure

Ionic Compounds

- The term **ionic lattice** refers to the regular structure resulting from the packing together of ions in an ionic compound.

- The term **ionic bond** refers to the attractive forces between oppositely charged ions in an ionic compound.

Covalent Bonding

- The **octet rule** states that atoms will attempt to gain, lose or share electrons when forming compounds in order to achieve a full outer shell containing eight electrons.
- The term **covalent bond** refers to the bond formed when two atoms each use one electron to form a shared pair of electrons.
- The term **double bond** refers to the covalent bonds formed when two atoms each use two electrons to share two pairs of electrons.
- The term **triple bond** refers to the covalent bonds formed when two atoms each use three electrons to share three pairs of electrons.
- The term **multiple bonding** refers to the formation of two or more covalent bonds between a pair of atoms.
- A **structural formula** describes the bonding in a molecule or ion by using a line between atoms to represent a shared pair of electrons.
- A **polyatomic ion** is an ion containing two or more atoms held together by covalent bonds.
- The term **coordinate bond** refers to the covalent bond formed when two atoms share a pair of electrons donated by one of the atoms.
- A **polar covalent bond** is a covalent bond in which the electrons forming the bond are not shared equally by the atoms forming the bond.
- The **electronegativity** of an element is the ability of the element to attract the shared electrons in a covalent bond to itself.
- The term **bond dipole** refers to the partial charges on the atoms that result from the unequal sharing of electrons in the bond.
- The **permanent (molecular) dipole** refers to the extent to which positive and negative charge is separated to produce oppositely charged ends in a molecule.
- A **polar molecule** is a molecule with a permanent dipole.

Covalent Materials

- A substance has a **molecular covalent structure** if it is composed of molecules held together by weak attractive forces.

- A substance has a **giant covalent structure** if it contains a network of atoms held together by covalent bonds.
- A **delocalised electron** is an outer shell electron that is not associated with an atom or ion and is able to move freely.

Metals

- The term **metallic bond** refers to the attractive force between the metal ions and the delocalised outer shell electrons in a metal.
- A substance is **malleable** if it can be worked into different shapes.
- A substance is **ductile** if it can be drawn into wires.
- A substance is an **electrical conductor** if it allows an electric current to flow within it.

1.4 Shapes of Molecules and Ions

VSEPR Theory

- A **bonding pair** is a pair of electrons used to form a covalent bond between two atoms.
- A **lone pair** is an unshared pair of electrons in the outer shell of an atom.
- **VSEPR theory** asserts that a molecule or ion will always try to minimise the repulsion between outer shell electrons by arranging the outer shell electrons as far away from each other as possible.
- The term **bond angle** refers to the angle between three bonded atoms.
- The term **molecular shape** refers to the shape formed by the positions of the atoms in a molecule.

Nonpolar Molecules

- A **nonpolar molecule** does not have a permanent dipole.

1.5 Intermolecular Forces

- The term **intermolecular force** refers to any type of bonding interaction between molecules.

Van der Waals Forces

- The term **van der Waals** force refers to the attraction between induced dipoles on neighbouring atoms/molecules/ions.

Dipole Forces

- The term **dipole force** refers to the attraction

between permanent dipoles on neighbouring molecules.

Hydrogen Bonding

- A **hydrogen bond** is a strong dipole-like force of attraction between a lone pair on a very electronegative atom (N, O or F) and a hydrogen atom attached to a very electronegative atom (N, O or F) on a neighbouring molecule.

Properties of Liquids

- The **principle of like-dissolves-like** asserts that liquids with similar types of intermolecular forces are more likely to be miscible.
- The term **miscible** describes liquids that mix in all proportions.
- The term **immiscible** describes liquids that do not mix.

1.6 Oxidation and Reduction

Redox Reactions

- The term **redox reaction** refers to a chemical reaction in which oxidation and reduction occur.
- An **oxidising agent** is a substance that oxidises another substance and is itself reduced in the process.
- A **reducing agent** is a substance that reduces another substance and is itself oxidised in the process.
- **Oxidation** occurs when an element loses electrons.
- **Reduction** occurs when an element gains electrons.
- A **half-equation** describes the chemical change that occurs when an element is oxidised or reduced.

Oxidation States

- The **oxidation state** of an element indicates the extent to which an element has been oxidised.
- The **oxidation number** of an element indicates the number of electrons lost or gained by an element.

Disproportionation

- **Disproportionation** refers to a redox reaction in which the same element is oxidised and reduced.

1.7 The Periodic Table

Organisation and Structure

- The term **group** refers to a column of elements in the Periodic Table.
- The term **period** refers to a row of elements in the Periodic Table.
- A **periodic trend** describes variation in the properties or behaviour of the elements within a group or period.
- A **semimetal** is an element with properties in common with both metals and nonmetals.
- The **metallic character** of an element refers to the extent to which the properties and behaviour of the element resemble those of a metal.

Trends Across a Period

- The **atomic radius** of an atom is the distance between the electrons in the outermost subshell and the nucleus.

1.8 Group VII: The Halogens

Reactions

- The **oxidising ability** of a substance refers to its ability to act as an oxidising agent.

Halide Ions in Solution

- **Fluoridation** is the process of adding fluoride ion.

The Hydrogen Halides

- A **strong acid** is an acid in which most of the molecules dissociate to form hydrogen ions.
- A **weak acid** is an acid in which only a small fraction of the molecules dissociate to form hydrogen ions.
- The **thermal stability** of a substance refers to its ability to resist the effects of heating.

1.9 Volumetric Analysis

Working with Solutions

- A **volumetric pipette** is used to accurately measure a fixed volume of solution.
- A **burette** is used to accurately dispense measured volumes of solution.
- A **volumetric flask** is used to accurately prepare a fixed volume of solution.
- The term **meniscus** refers to the surface of a liquid.

Calculations with Solutions

- The term **concentration** refers to the amount of substance dissolved per unit volume of solution.
- The term **molarity (M)** refers to the concentration of a solution expressed in units of mol dm^{-3}.

Titration Experiments

- A **titration** is conducted to accurately determine the concentration of a substance in solution based on the volume of a standard solution needed to completely react with it.
- A **standard** is a stable solution whose concentration has been accurately determined.
- An **acid-base titration** is a titration experiment based on the neutralisation of an acid by an alkali or vice versa.
- The **equivalence point** in a titration is the point at which the sample has completely reacted with the standard solution.
- The **titre** is the volume of solution needed to reach the equivalence point in a titration.
- An **indicator** is a substance that changes colour over a range of pH values.
- The **end point** is the point in the titration at which the indicator changes colour.
- A **back-titration** is a procedure used to determine the amount of substance in a sample that cannot be analysed directly by titration.

2.1 Further Calculations

Percentage Yield

- The **percentage yield** for a chemical reaction is the actual yield expressed as a percentage of the expected yield.
- The **expected yield** of a chemical reaction is the yield assuming complete reaction and no loss of product during recovery.
- The **actual yield** of a chemical reaction is the yield obtained after recovery of the product.

Atom Economy

- The **atom economy** of a chemical process is the yield of useful products expressed as a percentage of the total yield of all products.
- **Green chemistry** refers to a chemical process that has been designed to generate less waste, use renewable resources and sustainable energy sources.

- A **renewable resource** is a natural resource that can be replaced in time to ensure a continuous supply of the resource.
- **Sustainable energy** refers to energy that satisfies current demand without compromising the ability of future generations to meet their energy needs.

Calculating Gas Volumes

- The **molar (gas) volume** at a given temperature and pressure refers to the volume occupied by one mole of gas under the specified conditions.
- **Avogadro's Law** states that the volume of one mole of any gas is exactly 24 dm^3 if measured at 20 °C and 1 atmosphere pressure.

Percent Composition Calculations

- The **mass percent** of an element in a substance is the mass of the element in 100 g of the substance expressed as a percentage.
- The **percent composition** of a substance is the composition of the substance expressed in terms of mass percents.
- The **empirical formula** of a compound describes the simplest whole number ratio of atoms of each element in the compound.

2.2 Organic Chemistry

- An **organic compound** is a compound whose structure is based on the element carbon.
- **Isomers** are compounds with the same chemical formula but a different arrangement of atoms.
- A **hydrocarbon** is a compound that contains only carbon and hydrogen.
- A **space-filling model** represents the size of the atoms in a molecule.
- A **homologous series** is a family of compounds with similar chemical properties whose formulas are related by a general formula and differ by CH_2.
- A **condensed formula** is obtained from a structural formula by using formulas to represent groups of atoms within the structure.
- The term **functional group** refers to a group of atoms within a compound that together determine the reactions of the compound.

2.3 Hydrocarbons: Alkanes

Structure and Properties

- A **saturated hydrocarbon** is a hydrocarbon that does not contain any C=C or C≡C bonds.
- The term **parent alkane** refers to the straight-chain alkane on which the structure of a molecule is based.
- A **structural isomer** is a molecule with the same molecular formula but a different structural formula.
- An **alkyl group** is a functional group that consists of carbon and hydrogen atoms held together by single bonds.

Sources of Alkanes

- The term **volatile** describes a substance that can be easily transformed into vapour.
- A **fraction** is a liquid mixture containing compounds with a specified range of boiling points.
- **Thermal cracking** is the decomposition of larger molecules into smaller molecules using heat.
- **Catalytic cracking** is the decomposition of larger molecules into smaller molecules using heat in the presence of a catalyst.

Combustion of Alkanes

- **Complete combustion** refers to the reaction of a compound with an excess of oxygen.
- **Incomplete combustion** refers to the reaction of a compound with a limited supply of oxygen.
- A **catalyst** is a substance that speeds up a chemical reaction without being consumed by the reaction.
- **Chemisorption** refers to the formation of a chemical bond between a molecule and a surface after the molecule has adsorbed on the surface.
- **Heterogeneous catalysis** refers to a reaction in which the reactants are in a different physical state than the catalyst.
- The term **finely divided** is used to describe a solid that consists of small particles with a large surface area.

Halogenation of Alkanes

- A **free radical** is an atom, molecule or ion with one or more unpaired electrons.
- **Homolytic fission** refers to the breaking of a bond in a way that each atom forming the bond gains one of the electrons shared in the bond.
- A **photochemical reaction** is a reaction that occurs when one or more of the reactants absorb radiation.
- A **chain reaction** is a reaction that can sustain itself by generating reactants as the reaction proceeds.
- A **reaction mechanism** details the individual steps that describe the changes occurring during a chemical reaction.
- A **substitution reaction** involves replacing one atom or group of atoms with a different atom or group of atoms.
- The term **free radical substitution** describes a substitution reaction which is propagated by free radicals.

2.4 Hydrocarbons: Alkenes

Structure and Properties

- An **unsaturated hydrocarbon** is a hydrocarbon that contains one or more C=C or C≡C bonds.
- A **diene** is an unsaturated hydrocarbon that contains two C=C bonds.

The C=C Functional Group

- A **sigma (σ) bond** is a covalent bond formed by the head-on overlap of atomic orbitals that does not restrict rotation about the bond between the atoms.
- A **pi (π) bond** is a covalent bond formed by the side-on overlap of atomic orbitals that restricts rotation about the bond between the atoms.
- **Bond length** refers to the distance between the nuclei of two covalently bonded atoms.
- **Bond energy** refers to the energy needed to break one mole of a specified type of bonds.
- **Geometric isomers** have the same structural formula but a different arrangement of atoms in space as a result of the structure being unable to rotate about one or more C=C bonds.

Reactions of Alkenes

- **Hydrogenation** refers to the addition of a hydrogen molecule across a C=C bond.
- The term **addition reaction** describes a reaction in which a molecule adds across a C=C bond.
- The term **electrophile** describes an atom or ion that attacks regions of high electron density in a molecule.

- **Heterolytic fission** describes the breaking of a covalent bond in a way that both of the shared electrons are given to one of the atoms forming the bond.
- A **carbocation** is a cation that contains an electron deficient carbon atom (C^+).
- **Electrophilic addition** describes the addition of an electrophile across a C=C bond.
- A **polymer** is a large molecule formed from many small molecules known as monomers.
- The term **polymerisation** refers to a reaction in which a large polymer molecule is formed from its monomers.
- **Addition polymerisation** refers to the formation of a polymer as a result of addition reactions between monomers.

2.5 Halogenoalkanes

Structure and Properties

- A **halogenoalkane** is a saturated hydrocarbon containing one or more halogen atoms.
- The term **immiscible** describes liquids that do not mix.
- In a **primary halogenoalkane** the halogen atom is bonded to a carbon atom that has one carbon atom attached.
- In a **secondary halogenoalkane** the halogen atom is bonded to a carbon atom that has two carbon atoms attached.
- In a **tertiary halogenoalkane** the halogen atom is bonded to a carbon atom that has three carbon atoms attached.

Preparation

- **Organic synthesis** is the process of making an organic compound.
- The term *in situ* is used to describe the formation of a reactant within the reaction mixture.
- **Reflux** refers to the continuous boiling and condensing of a reaction mixture in a round-bottom flask fitted with a Liebig condenser in the vertical position.
- **Boiling chips (anti-bumping granules)** are small pieces of an inert material that are added to a reaction mixture to ensure smooth boiling.
- **Distillation** refers to the process of separating compounds by heating a mixture in a round-bottom flask fitted with a Liebig condenser in the horizontal position.
- The term **distillate** refers to a liquid extracted by distillation.
- A **separating funnel** is used to separate immiscible liquids.
- A **drying agent** is a substance that absorbs water.

Reactions

- **Nucleophilic substitution** describes a reaction in which substitution occurs as the result of a reactant behaving as a nucleophile.
- A **nucleophile** is a molecule or ion that attacks regions of low electron density, and has a lone pair that can form a coordinate bond with an electron-deficient atom.
- The term **transition state** describes a structure formed during a reaction that cannot be isolated from the reaction mixture.
- An **amine** is a compound containing an amino ($-NH_2$) functional group.
- A **nitrile** is a compound containing a cyano (-CN) functional group.
- The term **hydrolysis** describes a reaction in which bonds are broken as the result of a compound reacting with water.
- The term **alkaline hydrolysis** refers to the hydrolysis of a compound using dilute alkali.
- The term **ethanolic** is used to describe a solution in which the solvent is ethanol.
- An **elimination reaction** involves the loss of a small molecule from a larger molecule or ion.

2.6 Alcohols

Structure and Properties

- An **alcohol** is a saturated hydrocarbon containing one or more hydroxyl groups.
- The term **miscible** describes liquids that mix in all proportions to form a single layer.
- In a **primary alcohol** the hydroxyl group is bonded to a carbon atom that has one carbon atom attached.
- In a **secondary alcohol** the hydroxyl group is bonded to a carbon atom that has two carbon atoms attached.
- In a **tertiary alcohol** the hydroxyl group is bonded to a carbon atom that has three carbon atoms attached.

Production and Uses of Ethanol

- A **hydration reaction** involves the addition of water to a compound to form a new substance.
- The term **fermentation** refers to the respiration of sugars under anaerobic conditions to form ethanol.
- A **unit of alcohol** is an amount of ethanol used to describe the ethanol content of alcoholic drinks.

Reactions of Primary Alcohols

- A **halogenation reaction** is a reaction in which one or more halogen atoms add to a compound or replace atoms in the compound.

Oxidation of Alcohols

- A **carboxylic acid** is a compound with the structure RCOOH whose reactions are determined by the carboxyl (COOH) functional group.
- An **aldehyde** is a compound with the structure RCHO whose reactions are determined by the -CHO functional group.
- A **ketone** is a compound with the structure RCOR' whose reactions are determined by the carbonyl (C=O) functional group.

Esterification of Alcohols

- An **ester** is a compound with the structure RCOOR' whose reactions are determined by the ester linkage (-COO-).
- An **esterification reaction** is a reaction in which an ester is formed by reacting an alcohol with a carboxylic acid or acyl chloride.
- A **condensation reaction** is a reaction in which a small molecule such as water or ammonia is formed when the reactants combine to form the product.
- An **acyl chloride** is a compound with the structure RCOCl whose reactions are determined by the -COCl functional group.

The Iodoform Reaction

- **Vacuum filtration** is the process of filtering a mixture into a flask that is maintained at a reduced pressure.
- **Recrystallisation** is the process of removing impurities from a substance by filtering a hot saturated solution of the substance before allowing the substance to recrystallise as it cools.

- **Melting point determination** is the process of determining the temperature range over which a substance melts.

2.7 Infra-Red Spectroscopy

- The **infra-red (IR) spectrum** of a substance is the plot of percent transmission against frequency obtained by passing infra-red radiation through the substance.
- **Infra-red (IR) spectroscopy** is the procedure by which the IR spectrum of a substance is obtained.

2.8 Energetics

Enthalpy

- The **enthalpy** of a substance refers to the total amount of energy contained within the substance.
- A chemical reaction is **exothermic** if the total enthalpy of the products is less than the total enthalpy of the reactants.
- The **enthalpy of reaction** is the enthalpy change when the amounts specified in the chemical equation for the reaction react.
- A chemical reaction is **endothermic** if the total enthalpy of the products is greater than the total enthalpy of the reactants.

Measuring Enthalpy Changes

- The term **standard conditions** refers to a temperature of 25 °C (298 K) and 1 atmosphere pressure.
- The term **standard enthalpy change** refers to an enthalpy change measured under standard conditions.
- The **standard state** of a substance refers to the physical state of the substance under standard conditions.
- The **specific heat capacity** of a substance is the energy needed to raise the temperature of 1 g of the substance by 1 °C (1 K).
- The **standard enthalpy of neutralisation** of a substance is the enthalpy change when one mole of water is formed by neutralising the substance under standard conditions.

Calculating Enthalpy Changes

- The term **average bond enthalpy** refers to the energy needed to break one mole of bonds of a specified type averaged over many compounds.

- The **standard enthalpy of formation** of a substance refers to the enthalpy change when one mole of the substance is formed from its constituent elements under standard conditions.
- The **standard enthalpy of combustion** of a substance refers to the enthalpy change when one mole of the substance is completely burnt in oxygen under standard conditions.

Hess's Law

- **Hess's law** states that the enthalpy change for a reaction is independent of the route taken, provided the initial and final conditions are the same.

2.9 Equilibrium

Chemical Equilibrium

- A chemical reaction is **reversible** if the products can be transformed back into the reactants.
- The term **dynamic equilibrium** refers to a reversible process in which the forward and reverse processes occur at the same rate.
- The term **chemical equilibrium** refers to a reaction mixture whose composition does not change as the result of a dynamic equilibrium between the reactants and products.

Factors Affecting Equilibrium

- The **position of equilibrium** describes the extent to which a chemical equilibrium favours the reactants (on the left) or products (on the right).

2.10 Kinetics

Rate of Reaction

- The **rate of reaction** refers to the change in the amount of a reactant or product per unit time during a chemical reaction.
- The **average rate (of reaction)** refers to the average change in the amount of a reactant or product per unit time during a chemical reaction.

Factors Affecting Rate

- A **successful collision** occurs when particles collide with enough energy to react and the correct orientation to react.
- The **activation energy** for a chemical reaction is the minimum amount of energy needed for the reaction to occur.

Catalysis

- A **catalyst** is a substance that combines with one or more reactants to produce a new reaction pathway with lower activation energy.
- The **reaction pathway** shows how the enthalpy of the reactants changes as they are transformed into products.

2.11 Group II: The Alkaline Earth Metals

Properties and Reactions

- The atoms in an **s-block element** have their outermost electron in an s-type subshell.

Salts of Group II Metals

- A **base** is a molecule or ion that accepts protons (H^+ ions) from another substance.
- **Thermal decomposition** is the decomposition of a substance into simpler substances by the action of heat.

Thermal Stability of Group II Salts

- **Thermal stability** refers to the ability of a substance to resist the effects of heating.
- The **charge density** within an ion is the net charge per unit volume within the ion.

Solubility of Group II Salts

- A **solvated ion** is an ion that has dissolved in a solvent and bonded with the surrounding solvent molecules.
- An **ion-dipole bond** results from the attraction between an ion and the oppositely charged ends of neighbouring dipoles.
- The **lattice enthalpy** of an ionic compound is the enthalpy change when one mole of an ionic compound is converted into gaseous ions.
- The **hydration enthalpy** of an ionic compound is the enthalpy change when the gaseous ions formed from one mole of the compound dissolve in water to form solvated ions.
- The **enthalpy of solution** is the enthalpy change when one mole of an ionic compound dissolves to form solvated ions.